The Iatrogenics Handbook

A Critical Look at Research and Practice in the Helping Professions

Dr. Robert F. Morgan, Editor
California School of Professional Psychology,
Fresno Campus
Fresno, California

IPI Publishing Limited
Toronto, Ontario

This book is dedicated to those who dare to criticize their own, with caring and with data, nor lacking a sense of humility or humor, but they dare.

CANADIAN CATALOGUING IN PUBLICATION DATA

Main Entry under title:
The Iatrogenics handbook

Bibliography: p.
Includes index.
ISBN 0-920702-20-1

1. Iatrogenic diseases—Addresses, essays, lectures.
2. Medicine—Practice—Addresses, essays, lectures.
I. Morgan, Robert F.

RC90I2   610   C83-098734-7

Manufactured in Canada by Webcom Limited
COVER DESIGN: Brant Cowie/Artplus Limited
PROJECT EDITOR: Sara Jane Kennerley

Acknowledgements

Many belong here; in addition to those already appearing in this handbook, the following stand out: the late Stanley C. Ratner for his critical eye, satirical wisdom and infinite integrity; the late Dr. Martin Luther King Jr. for his moral courage and social wisdom; the still enduring J.R. Kantor (Ratner's mentor and a founder of behaviorism); psychologist Robert L. Green (Dr. King's education chief), and present day data-based critics of iatrogenesis from George Albee, Julian Rappaport, David Bakan, to Ralph Nader, Albert Szent-Gyorgyi, Jane Fonda and Thomas Hanrahan.

I am especially grateful for the early editorial work and typing done by Lynn Walker and Susan D'Ambrosio with support from Regina Robertson and her crew. Indexing and proofreading by Frank Hoshino, renaissance psychologist, was also a great help. Further, the manuscript review by students in my psychology classes plus further reviews by colleagues and compadres made the entire process more effective, more fun and less iatrogenic than it might have been. The superb editorial work by Sara Jane Kennerley and the courageous support by Dr. Daniel Baum, my publisher, was crucial to the materialization of the manuscript.

Finally, I would like to acknowledge Angel Kwan-Yin and Cinnamon Morgan, whose love and beauty characterize a generation of children deserving a much less iatrogenic world than presently exists. **R.F.M.**

Contents

Introduction

In 1981, Knight Steel, M.D. and his colleagues from Boston University tracked 815 Boston hospital patients over a period of five months. In 36 percent of the cases, patients suffered ill effects directly resulting from drugs, therapy or diagnostic procedures prescribed by their physicians; in 9 percent of the cases, major disability or risk of life resulted; and in 2 percent of the cases, patients died as a result of their treatment. The ill effects were attributed to drug reactions, falls and routine medical procedures (e.g., catheterization or intravenous). A second study published by Nathan Couch and Harvard University colleagues with Dr. Steel's work in the *New England Journal of Medicine* 304, n. 11 (1981) uncovered thirty-six mistakes in the treatment of 5,612 surgical patients at another Boston hospital. Eleven died and five went home with serious impairments. These surgical mistakes added an average of forty-two days to the patients' hospital stays at a total cost of $1.7 million. Iatrogenesis resulted from overoptimism, needless haste and "obsessive perfectionism."

Robert Mendelsohn, pediatrician and associate professor of community health and preventive medicine at the University of Illinois School of Medicine, has campaigned hard against doctor-caused illness and injury plus *nosocomial* or hospital-acquired diseases in his book *Confessions of a Medical Heretic* (New York: Warner Books, 1979) and subsequently in the public media. He cites two- to four-million unnecessary surgeries annually in the United States at a cost of four billion dollars and 12,000 lives. The American College of Surgeons is quoted as stating the present *excess* of U.S. surgeons exceeds 50,000. Dr. Mendelsohn's position is also that chauvinism by doctors puts women at great risk via needless procedures during pregnancy, delivery and general care. He estimates that 40 percent of the hysterectomies performed are unnecessary and states that Caesarian-section deliveries are becoming the norm, both for economic (profit) reasons. He recommends, barring known medical problems, that expectant mothers avoid doctors during pregnancy and use a midwife to have their babies at home (*Male Practice.* Chicago: Contemporary Books, 1981).

In Canada, Dr. Clarence Ekstrand, an economist with the Department of Community Health Science, University of Calgary, recently shared the results of two of his Manitoba studies with me over the telephone. In the first, reviewing twelve-million medical records over a period of four years from 1971 to 1975, he found that the 8,000 families of medical doctors received surgery less than one-third as often as the general population. In a second study on the medical records of native Canadian Indians, he found a surgery rate five times *higher* than the general population, particularly for women and particularly for tubal ligations. These studies have only been released recently by the Manitoba government and at this time were not available for formal publication in this handbook.

The silver lining in these tragedies and others like them is that physicians are increasingly willing to criticize their own in order to develop a more data-based effectiveness in service of the patient. It still takes courage to do so, not to mention the risk of much punishment in many cases.

Professional services to clients take more paths than medical ones. Just as medical doctors commit errors, so do psychologists, researchers, social workers, nurses and educators. If we enlarge the word *iatrogenic* to include any disorders caused by members of the *helping* professions in the process of helping, then we may hold accountable a more comprehensive range of disciplines and services actually affecting the consumer.

Therefore, it made sense to bring together the professionals from those disciplines, in and out of medicine, who might contribute to a handbook of constructive, data-based self-criticism, a handbook suited for the professional, the classroom or enlightened consumer use. Using my own article on iatrogenics as a frame of reference, I contacted all those who were leaders in their field (or in criticizing it) and also those who seemed to have fresh or important points to make on iatrogenesis.

Several hundred people responded, with sixty volunteering to do a chapter or contribute information. Ultimately, twenty-six professionals contributed twenty-nine chapters fitting the biases of this editor: work that informs, educates, stimulates, amuses or exposes that which we need to improve our services. An Afterthought includes excerpts from letters from additional distinguished professionals whose *regrets* seemed worth looking at as a sample of the larger group of well-wishing nonparticipants. The disciplines of the chapter authors include twelve psychologists (including epidemiology, clinical and social-community), eight physicians (including five psychiatrists), three sociologists, an economist, a philosopher and a journalist. Several of the chapters include material from consumers. In unprecedented cooperation between Canada and the United States in this area of inquiry, about half of the chapters are written by Canadians and half come from south of the border. Some reprinted material is included (e.g., Rosenthal and Jacobson) but the majority of the chapters represent original material, including important conceptual and informational statements from Alexander, Breggin, Buck, Clarke, Fevens, Frey, Gabbard, Helmer, Kamlet, Mason, Nelson, Shamsie, Tong, Twemlow, etc. The material chosen by Carl Rogers and his reason for choosing it, I found both characteristic and challenging. This first handbook is at least the kind of book likely to stir the waters, initiate some change and some controversy, and if I had not edited it, I would still want to buy it.

Following the article (Chapter 1) used as a frame of reference for contributors, is a section of a dozen chapters of conceptual or scientific impact. Philosopher Robert Alexander sets the conceptual stage with an example from the physical sciences. Epidemiologist David Frey picks up the theme as it applies to mental health, drawing on his work in the San

Francisco Bay area. Peter Breggin then paints a moving portrait of learned helplessness in authoritarian psychiatry, based in part on his research at the Center for the Study of Psychiatry, Washington, D.C. From Psychiatrist Breggin we go to Psychologists Epling and Woodward whose Saskatchewan Corn Soup Principle underlines our need for better practical success evaluation. Sociologist Michael Miller than shares his devastating critique of health systems in the *community over time,* a first rate example of data analysis with social significance. In a subsequent chapter, a collaboration between social scientists Jeffrey Buck and Mark Kamlet, key issues in cost-benefit decisions are added. The appropriately much honored leader of the self-criticism movement within psychiatry, Thomas Szasz, chooses then to share a recent statement as it applied to iatrogenesis. Psychiatrists Stuart Twemlow and Glen Gabbard of Menningers share some psychoanalytic cautions on interpretation, followed by sociologist Juanne Clarke's use of Canadian data to delineate the physician as a moral entrepreneur. Sociologist Richard Mason reviews selected methods for professional self defeat while Harvard's Robert Rosenthal reproduces his classic study with Los Angeles's Lenore Jacobson on the self-fulfilling prophecy in the classroom. Some final footnotes on efficiency percentages and gender genetics lead the way to the Part Three.

In the treatment context section on case histories, Carl Rogers has reintroduced his analysis of a *failure case* with a prefatory note of concern that we not rule out good intentions in our judgment of iatrogenesis within this handbook (and within this movement). There follows a short sample of perspective from an institutional consumer held in a maximum security setting, with a final chapter reprinting Berton Roeché's moving case history of a shock treatment victim.

The next treatment context section brings us to clinical applications. Stanley Fevens and Robert Morgan challenge conceptual defeatism and its practical implications for the retarded. Dr. Kenneth Walker shares some of his most relevant public journalism statements in *The Doctor Game,* a key weekly prevention activity. Following Walker's informed wit and wisdom, are three chapters tracing the research and professional resistance to electroconvulsive shock treatment over the decades: Robert Morgan in the 1960s, John Friedberg in the 1970s and Peter Breggin for the 1980s. Subsequently, a book review focuses on how reactionary discipline supremacy can masquerade as a reform of iatrogenesis: a warning not to let change be coopted by competetive self interests. Child Psychiatrist Jalal Shamsie contributes a very candid statement on his view of the state of the art in child treatment, material greeted with much uproar in this part of the world when voiced recently. Following some modest proposals on new and personalized therapies, a final chapter by hypnosis pioneer David B. Cheek rounds out the section. Obstetrician-Gynecologist Cheek shows how unintentional hypnosis (e.g., during general anaesthetic) can be iatrogenic and how the power of hypnosis, giving specific examples, can be used to reverse iatrogenesis.

The handbook section on social-community context includes a powerful original chapter by psychologist-sociologist-actor-writer-martial artist Benjamin Tong on the destructive power of *positive* racist stereotypes, using the Chinese-American community as focus. Community Psychologist D'Arcy Helmer follows organizational style within nursing to understand professional burnout. Following that is a brief chapter by the editor to raise some cautions about over-kill in the back-to-the-community movement, with suggestions for change. Lastly, Community Psychologist Geoffrey Nelson shares an original comprehensive statement on contemporary iatrogenics in the school system with some thoughts on prevention.

To edit a handbook of this size, I have tried to preserve the powerful and often classic material submitted without letting it ramble on for too long. For this editorial hubris, there is some modern precedent: a fifteen-year-old computer genius was recently caught using a telephone hook up to tap into a university computer. He was arrested for grand larceny for the fifty hours of unpaid computer time he'd used. With this as a legal and exemplar precedent, it would seem reasonable to determine how much our time is worth by the hour and, if someone wastes it, have them arrested for grand larceny. Therefore, with the editing of this handbook, I have tried to avoid arrest on those grounds.

One definition of an editor is "the person who, when the battle is over, shoots the wounded." May the wrong wounded not have been shot.

ROBERT F. MORGAN, Ph.D.
EDITOR, The Iatrogenics Handbook
Bob Morgan is the Dean for Academic and Professional Affairs at the California School of Professional Psychology, Fresno Campus. He has served full time on the faculties of Saint Bonaventure University, Nova Scotia's Acadia University, the San Francisco (now Berkeley) Campus of the California School of Professional Psychology, the University of Southern Colorado and, most recently as Chairman of the Department of Psychology, Wilfred Laurier University, Waterloo, Ontario.

He has provided clinical and supervisory services to numerous community mental health facilities. Professional consultation over the last two decades has included government agencies from the Peace Corps to the U.S. Office of Education, community organizational change groups such as Dr. M.L. King Jr.'s SCLC, evaluation and appraisal services and communication media including *Science Digest* **and the** *London Sunday Times*. **Dr. Morgan is the author of more than sixty published articles, chapters, books and papers.**

PART ONE

FRAME OF REFERENCE

ROBERT F. MORGAN

1

Iatrogenic Practitioner Defeatism and Other Null Assertions

The theme of iatrogenic behavior refers to those incidents where the cure is worse than the disease, where (often) well-intentioned *helpers* create substantial problems for themselves or others through *helping*. Therefore, mature professions must endure and even seek out data-based criticism of this iatrogenic dimension of their activity. The following reprint exemplifies this approach. It was used to define the objectives of this book. Consequently, the contributors improved on the theme and presentation without abandoning the frame of reference.

The article was originally written while the author was co-ordinating prevention, training, research and education for Nevada's state mental health and mental retardation division. At that time, organizational psychologist Chuck Dickson and a dedicated cadre of psychologists, social workers and educators had completed their eighth year evolving a delivery system responsive to the needs of the citizens they served and open to continual constructive criticism through evaluation and research. Some of these noniatrogenic models (e.g., Children's Behavioral Services, Summer Programs for Retarded, etc.) continue to survive.
R.F.M.

The Iatrogenic Psychology of Practitioners' Defeatism and Other Assertions of the Null Hypothesis

Summary—To illustrate iatrogenic defeatism, a series of surveys gave 370 psychiatrists, psychologists, and physicians (randomly selected from their national association biographical directories) the opportunity to submit examples of "incurable" disorders. Despite the scientific, logical, semantic, and practical absurdity of identifying anything as "incurable" (an assertion of the null hypothesis), the majority of the 139 respondents did exactly that, often listing disorders from their own specialization as hopeless. To the extent the respondents are representative of present clinical practice, a best guess is that scientifically grounded *non*-defeatist practitioners may be found in one of every two psychologists, one of every four psychiatrists, and one of every ten non-psychiatric physician-specialists. The null assertions of Bender, Bergman, Hayflick, and other distinguished iatrogens are examined in the topic contexts of mortality and aging, child development norms, cortical decay, human

Reprinted with permission from *Psychological Reports* 43 (1978):963-967.

genetics, senility, variable intelligence, and some new directions including biofeedback and hypnosis. The iatrogenic impact of prestigious defeatism may be hazardous to our health.

Clinicians, at times, make mistakes. When these mistakes are repeated systematically, categorized, and amenable to prediction, the study of such errors or 'iatrogenic' behavior may be called iatrogenic psychology. Where iatrogenic intervention has become ritualized or institutionalized, it deserves etiological credit as a pathological entity in its own right.

In 1971, I suggested this to the editors of the second *Diagnostic and Statistical Manual* (DSM-II, American Psychiatric Association, 1968), per their request for feedback. The third edition, it seemed to me, would be much improved if it contained a general category for iatrogenic disorders with specific numbers for subcategories labeled "institutionalization," "brain and behavioral damage from electroshock treatment" (Morgan 1976b), "prescription drug overdose or misapplication," "inadequate discharge planning," "addiction to treatment," etc. (I also suggested "celibacy" as an addition to the category of sexual deviations.) Four years went by; no response or acknowledgement of these constructive suggestions occurred. I therefore published them in an alternate but equally distinguished vehicle (Morgan 1975) and focused more on the iatrogenics of professional practice.

The Incurable Illness with Hopeless Prognosis

Dr. A is a medical specialist (proctology) with credentials in psychiatry and psychology. He has just completed a thorough examination of Georgia, age five. Dr. A states that Georgia suffers from a condition we will call "Blight" and adds: "I'm sorry to have to tell you this but Blight is an incurable illness with hopeless prognosis."

Certainly such candor is better than lying or misleading Georgia's parents. Nevertheless, Dr. A has erred on scientific, logical, and practical grounds. The very act of making such a pronouncement is a key iatrogenic intervention. Surveys presented later in this paper suggest it a common one, with the labels of 'incurable' disorder ranging from cancer to rabies, mental retardation to psoriasis, epilepsy to racism, heart disease to schizophrenia, autism to senility.

Asserting the Null Hypothesis

Deemer (1947) defined the power of a statistical test as the probability of rejecting the null hypothesis. Fisher (1947) felt experiments existed *only* to give the facts a chance to disprove the null hypothesis. The null hypothesis is one of no difference (e.g., Crest and Brand X produce about the same number of cavities). Failure to prove a difference does not prove there is none (Crest may not have performed well with this particular sample even if Brand X was Coca Cola).

Language is an imprecise dialect of mathematics; words communicate relationships. An assertion of the null hypothesis in daily language might be exemplified by the statement "There is no God" ("Then Who changes the water?" wondered the goldfish . . .). Such a statement infers omnipotent awareness of a universe already searched through and is, apparently, an act of faith. The more mathematically aware agnostic might choose "A personal God as presently described is unlikely," using a probabilistic best guess, a prediction based on his observation of the environment.

Psychologists know this from their earliest training as do many of their medical cousins. Yet translating this concept into daily conversation or professional discourse is not readily observed. Asserting the impossibility of a disorder's cure is asserting the null hypothesis, a scientific blunder of iatrogenic consequence.

The Logic of the Hopeless Disorder
Dr. A's generality infers that treatment success is impossible: past, present, and future. To infer success has never occurred suggests omnipotent awareness of the technological rise and fall of civilization. To infer success has not occurred in the present suggests omnipotent awareness of ongoing treatment across the globe (or, more modestly, total comprehension of the published literature). To infer success will never occur suggests precognition of a very high order within an infinity of possibilities. He guarantees no success will ever occur in Boston or Stockholm, nor has it already occurred in Cambridge or Auckland.

It could be that Dr. A only meant to say his best guess was that Georgia will not survive the Blight. If so, he intended prediction but communicated certainty. Logically, if Georgia's parents accept him at his word, failure is believed to be a sure thing. In our probabilistic universe, sure things are most elusive.

The Practical Reality of Asserted Hopelessness
Disabling human pathology is under assault throughout the modern world: no disorder stands unchallenged and most seem to have yielded ground to a variety of published interventions. As ever, there is a tremendous gap between published breakthroughs in the literature and seeing their widespread use in practice. Professional and public education at their best narrow this gap. Yet it is not unusual for successful treatment approaches to co-exist in close proximity with practitioners most vocal on the incurability of the disorder. Bureaucracies seize on such statements to withhold spending on expensive but effective innovations. It is much easier to say something cannot be done than to grapple honestly with the politically sensitive question of whether or not the expense is worth it. So goes the socially iatrogenic impact of the defeatist practitioners and researchers; some of the most prestigious gladly accept huge sums of research money to solve problems they've categorized as hopeless.

A Professionally Honest Response
Dr. A was wise not to downplay his concern about the seriousness of Georgia's condition so as to "protect" her or her parents. Often done with

terminally ill clients, this approach deprives the client of the right to crucial personal information and initiation of many contingent decisions. He was also correct to make no false guarantees of success.

To revise his original statement into a more accurate and helpful one, he might have said: "I don't know how to cure Georgia's Blight nor do I know of anyone who can. Based on the most recent statistics I can find, of every hundred children contracting the Blight only two have survived it. That means, without some treatment of which I'm not aware, her chances of survival are best guessed at 50:1."

This is a less devastating statement than the 'hopeless' one made earlier but, clearly, it is not head-in-the-clouds optimism either. The new statement is also noteworthy in that it admits to professional limitations and lack of information, an important but rarely contributed professional responsibility.

To complete his more thoughtful alternate response, Dr. A might say: "I will, however, immediately do some more reading, consult experts in this area, and get back to you as soon as I have anything new to suggest. In the meantime, I very much recommend that you get a second opinion."

Now Dr. A is being honest about his limited awareness of the current relevant research. He is open to changing his prognosis based on the efficiency (Morgan 1968b) of new research data. He has shown willingness to learn more in the interests of his client, and he undefensively recommends a second opinion to cross-validate his own. Dr. A now demonstrates both professionalism and realism, not defeatism or pseudo-omnipotence. A contemporary pragmatist, he no longer asserts the null, inferring "If I can't help you, no one can." Is such a practitioner too good to be true?

On to the surveys.

The Distinguished Scientist Surveys

American Psychologists

In late 1971 and throughout 1972, a randomly selected (from the current American Psychological Association's biographical directory) sample of one hundred American psychologists received a "Distinguished Scientist Survey Form" which gave them the opportunity to list up to three disorders that were, in their opinion, incurable. The form also specified the option to say "none" if indeed they felt that nothing, by definition, was incurable.[1]

One person so selected turned out to be deceased. Of the remaining 99, 51 responded. Of these respondents, 26 (51%) asserted incurable disorders. Of the 79 supposedly incurable disorder responses, 15 (19%) were commonly diagnosed mental disorders including "schizophrenia" (4), "mental retardation" (3), "autism" (2), "senile psychoses" (1), "trauma induced mental aberration" (1), "mental illness" (1). Other (presumably) nonorganic incurables were "stupidity" and "white racism." Of the 64 predominantly organic diagnoses labeled incurable, most (32) went to "cancer" and "heart disease" as might be expected. Other alleged organic incurable categories included "neurological diseases" (13), "arthritis" (5), "muscular dystrophy" (5), "physical disorders of aging" (4), and one vote each for "epilepsy," "crib deaths," "rabies," "diabetes," "psoriasis."

Using biographical information, there were no significant differences between those who responded to the survey and those who did not, nor between those who asserted the null and those who did not. Clinicians were represented in all major categories in about the same proportion.

Of the nearly half who did not choose to suggest incurable disorders, there were many calm but forceful lectures on the philosophy and logic of science: "You cannot demonstrate that a disease is incurable: only that it is curable," and "I don't like the term incurable; it implies an absolute," and "None (are incurable), ultimately, by definition." Some expressed feeling: "I feel no human illness is potentially incurable" (leaving nonhumans in limbo). Others modestly stressed their information limits: "To my knowledge no human illness is incurable" (again, ignoring nonhuman animals). Many requested a definition of terms: "Without a definition of incurable, I cannot judge any human illness as such" (still no concern for animals). There were the cautious optimists: "In the *long run,* nothing is incurable"; those who relied on faith: "I am unwilling to believe that any illness is incurable"; the inspirational: "Were we, as a nation, to dedicate ourselves to commitment to medical research we should ultimately find cures, I believe, for all that plagues mankind. . . ."

In contrast, one of the most pessimistic providers of incurable disorders asserted that "*Every* disease is incurable to at least a certain unlucky few . . .," a sentiment similar in effect to the Buffalonian's credo: 'No good deed goes unpunished.'

In sum, the first survey, to the extent the respondents were representative, suggested that about half of American psychologists probably assert the null hypothesis of incurable disorders. Only one in five of the disorders so asserted are commonly designated mental disorders.

A second survey was immediately launched to poll physicians of every major speciality including psychiatry.[1] Again, using the relevant national associations' biographical directories 271 Distinguished Scientist Survey forms were sent out to randomly selected applicants (100 of whom were psychiatrists). About a third (88) of the 271 responded. Of the respondents, 75 (85%) asserted incurable disorders. Again, about a fifth of the supposedly incurable complaints were mental disorders. When it came to asserting incurables, the 32 responding psychiatrists were not much different from the 51 psychologists in either choices of content labels or in the proportion of mental disorders found hopeless. The non-psychiatric physicians listed significantly ($p < .05$) more organic incurables than psychiatrists or psychologists, usually in their own area of specialization. The psychiatrists as a group were more defeatist than the psychologists ($p < .05$) and less defeatist than the other physicians ($p < .05$): 24 (75%) chose to assert incurable problems. Physicians, not counting psychiatrists, named incurable disorders: 51 of the 56 respondents (91%). (All comparisons were by chi square.)

Physicians' responses, including psychiatrists, generally followed psychologists' responses in content, if not proportion, although more self-authored books were plugged and substance addictions were added to the list of incurables. Some began positively but shifted gears midway: "I know of no illness that is 100% incurable—by the above I mean that is always incurable—I am excluding the following...." Another could not hold himself to ·only three incurables, adding "and many, many others—particularly...." Some responses sparkled: "No disease is incurable for, given the time, the potential for cure is there, be it physical, emotional or philosophical illness. Anyway, the word cure stems from 'to take care of,' Latin-curare, and so amelioration is as good as cure any day." One respondent took two full handwritten pages to tell me that I was wasting his time.

In sum, the second survey (to the extent the respondents were representative) suggested that, compared to psychologists, an even larger majority of psychiatrists and other medical specialists are willing to assert the null of incurable disorders, often in their own area of expertise. The best-guess estimate of the prevalence of *non*-defeatist practitioners is: one of every two psychologists, one of every four psychiatrists, and one of every ten non-psychiatric medical specialists. Every disorder named as incurable by any respondent has had successful intervention approaches promoted in contemporary publication.

Cross-validation surveys, using the same format and population of practitioners, were done in 1973 (Campbell[2]) and again in 1974 (Burley-Allen[3]) with essentially the same results. Similar unpublished studies have been done most recently in California and Colorado over the last few years by some of my students as class exercises with, again, similar results in local context.

Null Assertions: Contemporary Case Histories

Awareness of probabilities based on systematic observations in controlled studies in the core of the scientific method, a method that helps keep us from being misguided optimists or iatrogenic pessimists. The issue is what is probable, not what is possible.

Yet, in 1973, Abraham B. Bergman asserted that theories can only be critically tested by the opinions of one's "scientific peers." With this as his decision-making base, he pronounced the "sudden infant death syndrome" (crib deaths) "neither predictable nor preventable" in a national news magazine read by millions. Dr. Bergman was President of the National Foundation for Sudden Infant Death, Inc., in New York (cf. *Newsweek* 82 (September 3, 1973): 12).

Dr. Lauretta Bender, author of the *Bender Motor-Gestalt Test,* Chief Psychiatrist at New York's Bellevue for many years, an outspoken advocate of ECT for children, asserts that "Schizophrenia may be treated but not cured" (Bender 1971). She reported that a study following her own patients over the years found none of them to have been helped in a lasting way. Such overgeneralization matches the biostatistician who, after a summer night in a cabin filled with *No Pest* strips, declared the mosquito an endangered species.

The probability of change and growth is always present.

Mortality and Aging

Doubling your life span is not impossible, but without basic changes in the lifestyle of most of us it is highly improbable. However, death probabilities have too often been taken as fixed in past experience and overgeneralized from limited environments.

A distinguished Stanford microbiologist, Leonard Hayflick, discovered that human embryo cells in a test tube subdivide 50 times (+ 10) and no more. Older tissues have fewer divisions. In much published work over the last decade he concluded that a biological clock must determine the speed of subdivision and thereby aging (Hayflick 1965, 1970, 1974a, 1974b). Hayflick's research was seized upon by professional defeatists as clear evidence that the maximum human life span, reflected in the limit of 50 cell divisions was immutable, indicative of built-in limits, perhaps God-given, and will never be transcended. Those arguing this way were to some extent successful in arranging funding priorities in age research such that the extension of longevity was unlikely to be financed. Then, as is typical of the history of science, the clear limit we cannot exceed was exceeded. First, Macieria Coelho (1966) and Cristofalo (1974) reported hydrocortisone (5 mg/ml culture medium) extended the number of cell doublings by 30 to 50%. Next, Packer and Smith (1974) of Berkeley more than doubled the number of cell divisions by adding an antioxidant, Vitamin E, to the culture. Even at the 97th doubling 95% of the cells were still viable (able to synthesize DNA); Vitamin E had also protected these cells against stress induced by visible light or high oxygen tension. Now: the Hayflick studies in being promoted (via cell division frequency) as an index of human longevity were now prefatory work to an illustration that, if the analog holds, longevity can be doubled by proper dosage of hydrocortisone or vitamin E. (Obviously, this would have to be very carefully tested first on live humans in addition to tissue in test tubes.) Perhaps to declare a limit to progress is to be a catalyst for exceeding that limit.

For more than a decade now, we have had a practical method for testing the individual rate of human aging (Morgan 1968a, 1969a, 1969c, 1970, 1972, 1977a, 1977b, 1977c, 1981a, 1981b; Morgan & Fevens 1972; Morgan & Wilson 1983). With this and related procedures, the specific impact of various stresses, nutrients, therapies, and other interventions on human individuals can be evaluated (Morgan & Wilson 1983). Such information leads to greater life extension: clearly age can no longer be exclusively treated as an independent variable.

Child Development Norms

Sadly, the assertion of the status quo has had its place in the history of American psychology not too long ago and the remnants still retard our understanding of behavior. Often psychologists trained in child development prior to 1950 were taught that the infant's cortex was "non-functional" and would remain that way for two years independent of the environment. Much environmental retardation was supported by this, a self-fulfilling prophecy of sorts (I once had the delightful experience of bringing my one-year-old to class to argue the point with such a 'non-functional' psychologist). How did this destructive interpretation evolve? Decades ago, careful behavioral studies were made of small groups of American children. The average behavior observed at each age observed was tabulated as normal or "norms" for American children. Not much attention was given to how representative these children were of all American children since it was assumed all children of the same species were much alike. Further, the norms were seen as platonic biological guidelines describing what a child *can* do at a given age. Variance measures were not reported. Cultural and home environment influences were considered ineffective in changing these biologically based competencies of infants. Today, of course, we realize that these norms are *primarily* a reflection of culture and environment, expressed with genetic and other individual differences of structure much broader than anticipated. And, they reflected poorly on both home and culture. This holds true today as well. Let us briefly examine a few valuable child-normed tests in current use: the Bayley Scales of Infant Development (Bayley 1969), the Vineland Social Maturity Scale (Doll 1965), and the Pre-school Attainment Record (Doll 1966). Some uninformed testers still interpret the norms of these tests as biologically based behavioral limits rather than ability samples of fairly small groups of children at each age observed and thereby more context-specific than species-specific. Bayley based her test on 83 to 94 children per month evaluated (1,262 total) while Doll based his on 20 per age evaluated (620 total). Since both were carefully done, these tests may be of good use to *estimate* what is normal for many children in our culture but not what is normal for children of *every* culture nor what is *impossible* for children of any culture. It turns out that using their data, the normative expectation in our culture is that a typical child:

> Must be two years to: hop on one foot, dry own hands.
> Must be three years to: wash hands unaided, throw objects, know own sex, tell own name.
> Must be four years to: wash face unassisted, dress self except tying, count to four and catch.
> Must be five years to: blow nose, copy triangle, know own age, name colors.
> Must be six years to: use table knife for spreading, bathe self assisted, color drawings, go to bed unassisted.
> Must be seven years to: ride play vehicles.
> Must be eight years to: bathe self unaided, use table knife to cut.
> Must be 14.95 years to: communicate by letter.

An adaptation of the Denver Developmental Screening Test was condensed and presented to the public in the American Medical Association's well distributed monthly magazine (*Today's Health*) in late 1972. Parents were told not to expect their children to vocalize for two months, say three words for twenty-one months, kick a ball or scribble until two years, jump in place until three years, hop two or more times until five years.

Those of you who have traveled foreign lands the likes of Mexico or Hong Kong and there were beguiled by three-year-old flower salesgirls *know* that human children can learn to blow their own noses before five, catch a ball before four, know their own sex and name and hop twice before three! In Bali, children of three may be accomplished musicians of a year to two's experience. No: what we have here are the sad norms of children whose development is on the average far less than what it could easily be. Perhaps our self-fulfilling fantasies of helpless infancy have held our children back. But the relative cultural disadvantage illustrated above is not the issue here. What is [the issue] is that the role of assessment is to clearly describe a present state and *not* an invariant unchangeable characteristic, to chart progress and not limit according to preconceived "reality." Of course, all the above is from the bias of a psychologist. High school students have been known to be volleyed back and forth like ping pong balls between school psychologists pushing them to grow satisfying career fantasies and school guidance counselors pushing them to shrink their fantasies to fit careers realistic to their limitations. One can earn a living in our day and age either helping people transcend their limits or accepting their realities.

Cortical Decay

Another example of the frustration of the search for immutable realities can be found in research on the aging of the brain: A basic limitation to the credibility of the cell division studies as an analog of aging is the fact that some cells do not reproduce even once in our life span. Among the most crucial of these are the neurons, building blocks of our brain and the entire nervous system. Most introductory physiology and psychology texts will report that brain weight decreases with age, past middle age, and this reflects progressive loss of nerve cells. The nerve cells, not being able to reproduce, are not replaced. Biostatisticians calculate weight loss curves and then conclude that, if the rate of loss remains constant, there would be little brain left to see long-lived adults through a second century (although cell loss would not be enough to create serious damage in our present life-span). This, then, again seems to create a limit on how long we can expect to extend life. A cortical ceiling on the length of intelligent life has in this way been integrated into the gerontology text. But, let's look closer. Assuming it were so, we would still have the potential for developing ways for neurons to reproduce. Another approach would be to find methods for reducing the constant rate of decay; this constancy being the substance of the dismal predictions for great longevity. We're already aware of ways to *speed up* this decay: drugs, alcohol, radiation, stress, etc. And now, another logical possibility: if the preceding negative events, so common in our culture, can promote decay of neurons *perhaps this common rate of decay so reliably observed is the result of our noxious environment and not a biologically ubiquitous necessity.* Once again it may be that observations correctly describing a group have been misunderstood as defining its limitations. If so, a removal of noxious environmental stimuli would extend the cell life, a logical possibility. Science fiction? The data suggest it is not. Let us look at the basis for the claim of reduced brain weight with aging: autopsies on deceased humans. While they do demonstrate, in our culture, that brain weight has decreased, they cannot indicate what was the rate of decay or when it occurred or even why. Only in the last few years, via careful animal and human studies, have we learned that in fact the greatest amount of brain cell death occurs from birth to maturity (Brody 1970) and not during adult life! This might be due to a greater vulnerability of youth to the accelerators of cultural decay. This early decay could be masked by the ongoing growth processes of childhood. What of the lesser decay that *does* take place in adult life? Buetow (1971) demonstrated that animals in properly protected environments show very little decay as adults. We can now conclude that the decay rate *can* be slowed by changes in the environment, that children are the *most* vulnerable to neuron deaths, and that we therefore must begin any serious longevity program designed to include a functional brain by special interventions from infancy on.

A more recent study (Carlen et al. 1978) demonstrated reversible cerebral atrophy in eight chronic alcoholics who maintained abstinence. Respect for good data and a philosophical bias for change over limitation has taken us to a very different conclusion than that promoted by past textbooks. We have seen a cherished biological "reality" revised: progressive cortical decay can be slowed and possibly halted; decreasing brain weight may not be a hallmark of adult aging; aging is not immune to conquest.

Research and Practice in Human Genetics

A famous cataloguer of aging research was quoted recently as guaranteeing that our present maximum life span will not be doubled or tripled by any scientific breakthrough. His rationale is that such an increase would violate the genetic code that determines our life-span. This is a common way of looking at aging and reflects, philosophically, a steady state view of genetics: we will die when 'our number' is up and there is little we can do about it but go out with dignity. Not only is this defeatist philosophy but it is poor genetics as well.

Dr. Lissy Jarvik, one of the most important living pioneers of the study of genetics and aging, has this to say: "It is a common fallacy to assume that because a condition is genetically determined, it is unalterable, immutable, and incurable. Nothing could be farther from the truth. Actually, if we can demonstrate the hereditary transmission of a condition, a search for its biological correlates is bound to be eventually successful. Once a cause has been determined it *can* be altered. Indeed the area of mental deficiency provides the example par excellence of how knowledge of genetic factors has enabled us to interfere and to prevent intellectual deficits in individuals genetically predisposed toward them. . . . Phenylketonuria, a form of mental deficiency based on the inherited inability to metabolize the amino acid phenylalanine, can now be prevented in most cases by judicious dietary management from earliest infancy" (Jarvik 1975, 581). She added: "The attitude of hopelessness, when it comes to aging, is not only unwarranted but has probably been the greatest impediment to progress in the field. It has resulted in restricted financing of research, in a lack of interest on the part of the young—except for those in our few gerontology centers—and in an attitude of self-deprecation on the part of the aged themselves" (Jarvik 1975, 582).

Bernard Strehler, another age geneticist of stature, has promoted research in a variety of ways to increase maximum species-specific life span (the conventional wisdom was usually that only average life span could be increased with the maximum life span, the longest a member of the species has lived, as an absolute limit). Among these promising interventions are genetic selection, chemically suppressed deterioration rate, environmental manipulations, and the reactivation of controller genes affecting the cell production needed for continuing existence: "Because the nature of these controller substances may be more simple than was previously supposed and might well be inserted into cells in a very precise manner, the chance for a chemical modification of the maximum life span is probably closer to realization than most persons anticipate" (Strehler 1971, 48).

Strehler too decried in 1971 the starvation diet of funds the government offered biological gerontology. In fact, subsequent genetics research in areas other than aging moved so quickly and effectively that enough fear was generated to impose an eighteen-month embargo on such research, an unprecedented step in the history of American science. Concern that change is not possible has increasingly been replaced by concern that it is, and in what direction such change will take us.

The fields of aging and of assessment, part of all scientific inquiry, therefore continue to employ some who devote their professional life to setting limits to progress and others who devote their professional life to exceeding these limits. Perhaps the negative catalyst is useful, but it is more difficult to row the boat when someone drops anchor.

Senility

Harvard psychologist Robert White authored what for many years was the definitive college text on mental disorders: *The Abnormal Personality*. In the 1956 edition (and all subsequent editions) he asserted: "It is obvious that not much can be done for senile patients except to make them comfortable, keep them in physical health, provide occupations that are within their powers, and protect them from necessary difficulties." Kolb, in his equally prestigious *Modern Clinical Psychiatry* (8th edition, 1973) tells us "the prognosis of advanced senile dementia is manifestly hopeless." Five years earlier, Muller and Ciompi wrote in their landmark text *Senile Dementia:* "Whereas organic dementias were formerly thought to be irreversible and incurable states of decay, their prognosis has changed with the progress of new therapeutic means" (Muller & Ciompi 1968). Also years earlier, group psychotherapy focusing on the present and the future (strategies for coping with the threat of personal death) proved effective with many senile psychotics (Morgan 1965, 1967a). Woodruff's work (1975) with applied biofeedback suggests another promising new approach. Of course, we still have substantial time gaps between the published literature and the established text or practice. The consequences of such a gap are too often the tragic waste and warehousing of senior citizens in custodial geriatric programs not truly designed to return their clients to independent satisfying lives.

Variable Intelligence

Along with aging and senility, the surveys never failed to include at least one practitioner or scientist who believed mental retardation was incurable.

In 1971, the city and county of San Francisco's Department of Public Health distributed a weekly bulletin to the public on mental retardation which asserted: "Unlike mental disorders, mental retardation is an inevitable lifelong condition. Therefore, adjustment and acceptance rather than a return to normal functioning is the goal..." (Curry 1971). Was taxpayers' money being paid only to adjust people to their disorders rather than curing them? Actually, some of the psychologists working in the county system had some extremely effective programs going in which their clients did indeed reach normal functioning. Ultimately, the Department of Public Health retracted their statement of hopelessness. Unfortunately, many, if not most, structured public programs for mental retardation still set their goals only for clients' tranquility and behavioral adjustment while the very same disorder is often under successful attack only a county or a state away.

In Prince Edward County, Virginia, the schools were closed for four years and three thousand children felt the impact: the average intelligence of children in the county fell into the retarded range, as much as a mean drop of thirty IQ points from pre-closing levels (Green, Hoffman, Morse, Hayes & Morgan, 1964). We learned, dramatically, how much a child's expressed intelligence depends on the school (Green, Hoffman, Morse & Morgan 1965; Green, Hoffman & Morgan 1967; Green & Morgan 1969). A conservative estimate made from nearly all quarters of the field is that at least four of every five diagnosed cases of retardation are non-organic, that is, something went wrong in the child's environment. For more than a decade now, the literature has been overflowing with exciting new special or compensatory education approaches to successful intervention with all children, including the retarded or disadvantaged (Pines 1966; Morgan 1969b; Morgan & Toy 1970). Even more encouraging are the many viable prenatal and birthing interventions, nutritional to psychological, often classified as "wholistic health care" (Morgan 1977b).

Again, as long as the public is led to believe that progress is impossible, it becomes more difficult to bring the newest progress to them.

New Directions

There are many important new approaches to doing what our surveys told us so many distinguished scientists felt was impossible to do. One might point to the rapidly accelerating number of applications of clinical biofeedback, particularly with children (Toomim & Toomim 1973). The guided imagery used to combat cancer (Halsell 1976; Simonton, Simonton & Creighton 1978) would be another example of an apparently promising assault, psychological in nature, on the most commonly asserted "incurable" human ailment. There are now conditioning techniques to make such imagery externally accessible to ordinary people (Morgan & Bakan 1965); there are hypnosis techniques by such leaders as David Cheek and Leonard Elkind for assault on problems of aging, birthing, bleeding and, more positively, for the enhancement of the mental abilities of all of us (Morgan 1981a, 1981b, 1983).

Those who hold the purse strings for research and treatment as well as those who contribute to them must not continue to be overwhelmed by the iatrogenic impact of prestigious defeatism. Equally important, the training programs of future scientists or clinicians should not be led by those whose professional reputations rest on emphatic assertions of defeatist limits.

In 1953, Scott and Marston published a classic early study most relevant to the iatrogenic psychology of practitioners' defeatism. Fighting mice who suffered rigged defeats in their early adulthood developed nonadaptive behaviors, no longer responded to fight training, and persisted in their retreat from other mice even after a two-month rest. Subsequent studies with a wide variety of species, including ours, have demonstrated success to be increasingly less likely after rigged defeats in early childhood or even adulthood. The superior symbolic capacity human speech provides our own species, allows us to suffer defeat experienced, or even anticipated, by others.

Unless we are to experience the fate of Scott's mice, we must discontinue providing cultural credibility to those who would program us for the self-fulfilling prophecy of failure.

FOOTNOTES

[1] R. F. Morgan. Distinguished Scientist Survey I. Unpublished survey, California School of Professional Psychology, San Francisco, 1972.

[2] K. Campbell. Distinguished Scientist Survey II. Unpublished survey, San Francisco State University, 1973.

[3] M. Burley-Allen. Distinguished Scientist Survey III. Unpublished survey, San Francisco State University, 1974.

BIBLIOGRAPHY

American Psychiatric Association. *Diagnostic and statistical manual of mental disorders (DSM-II)*. Washington, D.C.: Mental Hospitals Service, 1968.

Bayley, N. *Manual for the Bayley Scales of Infant Development.* New York: Psychological Corp., 1969.

Bender, L. Alpha and omega of childhood schizophrenia. *Journal of Autism and Childhood* 1 (1971):115-118.

Bergman, A. B. Crib death. *Newsweek* 82 (September 3, 1973):12.

Brody, H. Structural changes in the aging nervous system. *Interdisciplinary Topics in Gerontology* 7 (1970):9-21.

Buetow, D. E. Cellular content and cellular proliferation in the tissues and organs of the aging mammal. In *Cellular and molecular renewal in the mammalian body,* edited by I. L. Cameron and J. D. Thrasher, 86-106. New York: Academic Press, 1971.

Carlen, P., G. Wortzman, R. Holgate, D. Wilkinson and J. Rankin. Reversible cerebral atrophy in recently abstinent chronic alcholics measured by computed tomography scans. *Science* 200 (1978): 1076-1078.

Cristofalo, V. Aging. In *Concepts of development,* edited by J. Lash and J. R. Whittaker, 429-447. Stamford, Conn.: Sinauer Assn., 1974.

Curry, F. J. Mental retardation program. *Weekly Bulletin, City and County of San Francisco, Department of Public Health* (December 27, 1971):1.

Deemer, W. L. The power of the t-test and the estimation of required sample size. *Journal of Educational Psychology* 38 (1947):329-342.

Denver Development Screening Test (adaptation). *Today's Health* 50 (September 1972):35.

Doll, E. A. *Vineland Social Maturity Scale.* Circle Pines, Minn.: American Guidance Service, 1965.

——. *Preschool Attainment Record.* Circle Pines, Minn.: American Guidance Service, 1966.

Fisher, R. A. *The design of experiments.* 4th ed. London: Oliver and Boyd, 1947.

Green, R. L., L. J. Hoffman and R. F. Morgan. The effects of deprivation on intelligence, achievement and cognitive growth: a review. *Journal of Negro Education* 36 (1967):5-14.

Green, R. L., L. J. Hoffman, R. J. Morse, M. Hayes and R. F. Morgan. *The educational status of children in a district without public schools.* Washington, D.C.: United States Office of Education, 1964. (Cooperative Research Project 2321 Report.)

Green, R. L., L. J. Hoffman, R. J. Morse and R. F. Morgan. *The educational status of children during the first school year following four years of little or no schooling.* Washington, D.C.: United States Office of Education, 1965. (Cooperative Research Project 2498 Report.)

Green, R. L. and R. F. Morgan. The effects of resumed schooling on the measured intelligence of Prince Edward County's black children. *Journal of Negro Education* 38 (1969):147-155.

Halsell, G. Mind over cancer. *Prevention* 28 (January 1976):118-127.

Hayflick, L. The limited in vitro lifetime of human diploid cell strains. *Experimental Cell Research* 37 (1965):614-636.

——. Aging under glass. *Experimental Gerontology* 5 (1970):291-303.

——. The longevity of cultured human cells. *Journal of the American Geriatrics Society* 22 (1974a):1-12.

——. The strategy of senescence. *The Gerontologist* 14 (1974b):37-45.

Jarvik, L. Thoughts on the psychobiology of aging. *American Psychologist* 30 (1975):576-583.

Kolb, L. C. *Modern clinical psychiatry.* 8th ed. Philadelphia: Saunders, 1973.

Macieria-Coelho, A. Action of cortisone on human fibroblasts *in vitro. Experientia,* 22 (1966):390-393.

Morgan, R. F. Note on the psychopathology of senility: senescent defense against the threat of death. *Psychological Reports* 16 (1965):305-306.

——. Memory and the senile psychoses: a follow-up note. *Psychological Reports* 20 (1967a):733-734.

——. Relationship of ethnic background, religion, diagnosis, memory and other variables to presence of shock "therapy" history for a sample of hospitalized mental patients: preliminary investigation of the lasting effect of shock treatment on behavior. *InterAmerican Journal of Psychology* 1 (1967b): 251-261.

———. The Adult Growth Examination: preliminary comparisons of physical aging in adults by sex and race. *Perceptual and Motor Skills* 27 (1968a):595-599.

———. The need for greater use of efficiency percentages to supplement reports of statistical significance. *Perceptual and Motor Skills* 27 (1968b):338.

———. Are you older than you think? *Science Digest* 66 (August 1969a): 20-21.

———. Compensatory education and educational growth. In *Racial crisis in American education,* edited by R. L. Green, 186-219. Chicago: Follett, 1969b.

———. How old are you? *London Sunday Times* 39 (October 19, 1969c).

———. Techniques for assessing differential aging. *The Canadian Magazine* (February 28, 1970):2-4.

———. The Adult Growth Examination: validation, analysis and cross-cultural utility of a compact brief test of individual aging. *InterAmerican Journal of Psychology* 6 (1972): 245-254.

———. Revising DSM-II by adding iatrogenic disorders and recognizing celibacy as a sexual deviation. *Journal of Irreproducible Results* 21 (1975):31.

———. The Adult Growth Examination: a follow-up note on comparisons between rapidly aging adults and slowly aging adults as defined by body age. *InterAmerican Journal of Psychology* 11 (1977a):10-13.

———. *Conquest of aging: modern measurement and intervention.* 2nd ed. Pueblo, Colo.: Applied Gerontology Communications, 1977b.

———. An introduction to applied gerontology. *Long Term Care and*

Health Services Administration Quarterly 1 (1977c):168-178.

———. *Measurement of Human Aging in Applied Gerontology.* Dubuque, Iowa: Kendall/Hunt, 1981a.

———. *Interventions in Applied Gerontology.* Dubuque, Iowa: Kendall/Hunt, 1981b.

Morgan, R. F. and P. Bakan. Sensory deprivation hallucinations and other sleep behavior as a function of position, method of report and anxiety. *Perceptual and Motor Skills* 20 (1965):19-25.

Morgan, R. F. and S. K. Fevens. Reliability of the Adult Growth Examination: a standardized test of individual aging. *Perceptual and Motor Skills* 34 (1972):415-419.

Morgan, R. F. and T. B. Toy. Learning by teaching: a student-to-student compensatory tutoring program and the Educational Cooperative. *Psychological Record* 20 (1970): 159-169.

Morgan, R. F. and J. Wilson. *Growing Younger.* New York: Stein & Day, 1983.

Muller, C. and L. Ciompi. *Senile dementia.* Bern, Switzerland: Huber, 1968.

Packer, L. and J. Smith. Extension of the life span of cultured normal human diploid cells by vitamin E. *Proceedings of the National Academy of Sciences, USA* 71 (1974): 4763-4767.

Pines, M. *Revolution in learning: the years from birth to six.* New York: Harper & Row, 1966.

Scott, J. P. and M. V. Marston. Nonadaptive behavior resulting from a series of defeats in fighting mice. *Journal of Abnormal and Social Psychology* 48 (1953):417-428.

Simonton, C., S. Simonton and J. Creighton. *Getting well again.* Los Angeles: J. P. Tarcher, 1978.

Strehler, B. L. Genetic and cellular aspects of life span prediction. In *Prediction of life span,* edited by E. Palmore and F. Jeffers, 33-49. Lexington, Mass.: Heath, 1971.

Toomim, M. K. and H. Toomim. Bio-feedback—fact and fantasy: does it hold implication for gifted education? *Gifted Child Quarterly* 17 (1973):48-55.

Woodruff, D. S. Relationships between EEG alpha frequency, reaction time and age: a biofeedback study. *Psychophysiology* 12 (1975):673-681.

PART TWO

CONCEPTUAL AND SCIENTIFIC CONTEXT

ROBERT E. ALEXANDER

2

The Velikovsky Affair: Case History of Iatrogenic Behavior in Physical Science

Bob Alexander has been able to blend rigorous logic with a scholar's open mind and candor without losing any humanistic drive or personal warmth. If we can approach iatrogenics with his Velikovsky example fresh in our minds, we may just learn something new; if not, no matter how lofty the goal, the effort will stagnate, conforming only to those ideas that have come before. Beware of Occam's razor: neither the simplest explanation nor the one fitting all presently accepted theory must turn out to be correct. **R.F.M.**

The Earth almost died in 1450 B.C. A near collision occurred with the newly born planet, Venus, and the results were catastrophic: tidal waves, earthquakes, meteorite showers noted by the Bible in Egypt and Palestine, and other disasters in places as divergent as China and Mexico.

In 1950, a Russian-born psychiatrist, Immanuel Velikovsky, documented historical and physical evidence for these events. His book, *Worlds In Collision* (Velikovsky 1950), was an immediate best seller. However, Velikovsky incurred such wrath from the scientific "establishment" that his publishers were blackmailed into dropping the book.

Why was there such a violent reaction by scientists? In spite of earlier twentieth century revolutions, many scientists were still committed to the ideas of Newton and Darwin. These theories had provided a stable view of celestial mechanics and terrestrial life, and this stability was threatened by Velikovsky's new view of things.

"This book is a heresy if Newton and Darwin are sacrosanct," Velikovsky admitted. However, he expected that science was open to question—a vital, changing body of ideas rather than static dogma. In this, he was wrong. His treatment as a scientific heretic will be discussed after a survey of his views.

The Venus Affair

Evidence of Catastrophes Due to Venus
Beginning with reports of catastrophes in the Old Testament and other ancient writings, Velikovsky shook the consensus of archeology and an-

cient history with a revised chronology for the cultures of the Middle East (Velikovsky 1952).

Velikovsky theorized that, after erupting from Jupiter, the comet that became Venus moved in front of the Earth's orbital path in 1450 B.C. For days, this conflict of forces wreaked havoc on the Earth, havoc which appears in biblical records of the Exodus.

Entering the tail of the comet, the Earth was first pelted with red dust which poisoned all surface water, giving it the appearance of blood. A shower of hot meteorites and blazing petroleum followed. During the intense darkness that descended, the only light came from massive lightning between the two bodies. Velikovsky also said there was a radical change in the direction of the Earth's rotation, causing earthquakes and tidal waves (the parting of the Red Sea), and moving people to terror by the sight of the sun rising in the West.

Velikovsky's research turned up surprising confirmation of several biblical events. He said that, during a fifty-year interval when the disturbances caused by Venus subsided, those who had survived were supplied a honey-like substance (mana) that condensed like frost. Following this, Venus made another close pass, causing earthquakes which were probably the historical basis for the destruction of the walls of Jericho, and slowing the Earth's rotation for a few hours (making the sun appear to stand still) during Joshua's battle at Beth-horon.

For the next 600 years, the Earth was peaceful enough for new calendars to be made. Instead of a 360-day year made up of ten 36-day months, there were now found to be twelve 30-day months in the same length year. Venus, however, did not remain idle. By 776 B.C., after being disturbed by Venus, Mars began the first of four menacing passes at the Earth in the next ninety-one years. Mars in smaller than either the Earth or Venus, so the upheavals were less colossal.

The Axis of the Earth was tilted ten degrees and reversed by the same amount on the next pass. On the final pass about 687 B.C., Mars established itself as the "God of War" by destroying 185,000 soldiers in Sennacherib's army in one day with an enormous electrical discharge.

There was also a shorter lunar month (29.5 days) which no longer coincides with the calendar month. The heavens have remained stable with a longer year (365.25 days).

World in Collision was based on evidence largely from ancient cultural remains such as paintings, astronomical charts, calendars and scriptures from Palestine, Egypt, Mexico, India and China. Five years later, Velikovsky repeated his theories in *Earth In Upheaval* (Velikovsky 1955). This time he used fossils, glacial remains and earth formations to prove his case.

The evidence from the last twenty years of space probes to Venus, Mars, Jupiter and the Moon is more in line with Velikovsky's predictions than with traditional scientific expectations. Quite a surprise for many people.

Scientists in the "establishment" had predicted that Venus would be about the same temperature as Earth; Velikovsky had stated that it would be extremely hot, since it would not have had time to cool down from its recent life as a blazing comet. Venus probes have indicated temperatures of over 500 degrees Celsius.

Velikovsky also expected magnetic irregularities which were then found in moon rocks. National Aeronautics and Space Administration (NASA) scientists were surprised. They did not mark rock samples for orientation on the moon until later flights, although Velikovsky had publically pointed out the importance of such data on the eve of the first Apollo flight (Pensée 1976, 253).

The Scientific Implications of the Venus Affair
The scientific theories of Velikovsky have far-reaching implications. They have the potential to completely change our understanding of how the world developed. Geological changes, like the ice ages, may have happened in a few days rather than inch by inch over millions of years. How else, Velikovsky asks, can we account for instantly frozen mammoths found with tropical vegetation in their stomachs?

In celestial mechanics, the view of the solar system as a series of billiard balls governed only by Newtonian gravity may no longer be sufficient. Instead, he suggests that electrical charge differences between planetary-size bodies also affect their motion.

In addition, Velikovsky's ideas account for some of the puzzles in ancient records. In spite of the fact that Venus is highly visible in our heavens as Morning and Evening star, many ancient observers never refer to seeing it. Nevertheless, they knew the precise orbits for Mars and tiny Mercury.

Later records refer to Venus as being so bright that it outshines the Moon and rivals the Sun in brilliance. Such records (found as far apart as in India and Mexico) now suggest that our predecessors were accurate observers of the sky, rather than superstitious primitives.

The Velikovsky Affair

Not all new theories proposed by those technically outside the scientific profession can be accepted or even tested; time is short and resources are scarce. But science cannot afford to reject new ideas merely because they appear to contradict what is "known." There are no guarantees in science or anywhere else.

Scientific Suppression by Blackmail and Ridicule
Since Velikovsky declared he was taking issue with some of the fundamental views of Newton and Darwin, a number of influential scientists decided he must be mistaken. Their action resulted in an attempted suppression of Velikovsky's works.

Instead of acting in the role of objective observers by suspending judgment until crucial tests were made, high ranking scientists organized a campaign to boycott Velikovsky's publisher. Within two months of publication, Macmillan fired a senior editor for accepting *Worlds In Collision* and the rights were sold to Doubleday, a trade book publisher, relatively immune to a boycott from academics.

After this, Velikovsky continued to publish and the scientific journals criticized his theories without giving him the opportunity to respond in print. By 1963, *The American Behavioral Scientist* magazine devoted a whole issue to the controversy, eventually published as *The Velikovsky Affair* (deGrazia, Juergens, Stecchini 1966).

In spite of the attempted suppression of his work, Velikovsky did not fade away. Space probes were now bringing back evidence that his predictions (e.g., those concerning Venus), were mostly true.

As mentioned earlier, the extreme high temperatures on Venus has been forecast by Velikovsky in 1950: by late 1962, Mariner II had documented a surface temperature of 500 degrees Celsius on the surface of the planet.

For ten years after his first publication, Velikovsky faced derision for "creating" electromagnetic forces in space whenever his theory needed them (Gardiner 1957). Then, the Van Allen belts were discovered, and Pioneer V conclusively showed that space is literally full of magnetic fields and electric currents, instead of being empty as Newtonians thought.

A tiny handful of scholars and scientists encouraged Velikovsky. They included Einstein (a collaborator with him on a scholarly project in Berlin in the 1920s), who was open-minded enough to read and comment on his writings. Einstein was so impressed with the confirmation of Velikovsky's prediction of radio noise from Jupiter that he suggested some further tests of the theory. With the loss of such prestigious support when Einstein died in 1955, the tests were never carried out.

By 1972, the journal *Pensée* was devoted entirely to the elaboration and criticism of Velikovsky's views later published as *Velikovsky Reconsidered* (*Pensée* 1976). International conferences on the controversial scientist were held at Lethbridge, Alberta, and Hamilton, Ontario, culminating at the 1974 annual meeting of the American Association for the Advancement of Science in San Francisco.

This forum could have been a belated but serious look at some of Velikovsky's claims in the light of puzzling data from space. Instead, it became a media event, dominated by personal conflict. Carl Sagan was the main spokesman for traditional views. Once more Velikovsky became the subject of ridicule. Seventy-eight-years-old, with flowing white hair, he looked the part of an eccentric, and his theories were dismissed as the products of a religious mania.

Unfortunately, only one side of this session was published as *Scientists Confront Velikovsky* (Goldsmith 1977). Partly to counteract its negative impression, *The Age of Velikovsky* (Ransom 1976) was written as an introduction to the ideas and the controversy. Therein, Ransom reveals the unethical tricks, distortion and sloppiness of Velikovsky's opponents.

Iatrogenic Behavior Under the Banner of Truth and Objectivity

The behavior of highly reputable scientists at San Francisco, indeed the whole scenario, is one of the most fascinating and troubling episodes in the twentieth century. It is fascinating because, in the words of one critic, "Velikovsky's ideas would be of the utmost importance if they were correct: well-established concepts in a host of disciplines would then fall like leaves in the wind" (Goldsmith 1979, 21). The matter is also troubling: the opposition to Velikovsky's new ideas destroys our traditional belief in the scientist as dispassionate observer.

Bruno's burning at the stake and Galileo's forced recantation were caused by a fanatical response to religious dogma apparently under attack. But modern science is supposed to be composed of testable and revisable theories, not dogma. If its beliefs come under attack, they must be defended by reasonable criticism, not by suppression.

Of course, in dealing with "pure" science, we are also dealing with human scientists. As individuals, they have a vested interest in status and ego protection. Their work can never be a completely altruistic search for truth. Like endeavors in education, health and government, the point of science often gets obscured and subverted by personal concerns and by internal professional or institutional pressures.

Velikovsky's treatment at the hands of the scientific community reveals a problem: we view the specialist with a kind of awe and he is likely in return to view the layman's ideas with contempt. Velikovsky was not formally trained as an evolutionary biologist, an astronomer, nor even an ancient scholar, so the experts regarded him (and rightly so) as an amateur. This assumption (wrongly) caused the offhanded rejection of his ideas.

The famous Italian mathematician, Bruno de Finetti, offers another reason. "Velikovsky ... challenged the right of their [the scientists'] fossilized brains to rest in peace," he said. Such disrespect for the layman, he thought, might transform the great clan of scientists "into a sort of despotic and irresponsible Mafia" (deGrazia, Juergens, Stecchini 1966, 133).

This unsavory page in the history of science is not primarily iatrogenic in the sense of "error-producing"; the large issues have not been conclusively settled as truth or error, although some of the smaller ones have been. Both opposing theories are global, problematic and unfinished, so overall judgments about error are premature and issue-begging.

"The cure is worse than the disease," however, does apply when we take it to mean "suppressing the 'heresy' is worse than letting it be discussed and perhaps believed." It hindered potential improvements in the received theories of Newton and Darwin where Velikovsky revealed new difficulties. Left alone, even widespread belief in the Venus affair would have had little practical impact on everyday affairs other than perhaps a small loss of face for scientists who were thought to be wrong. As it was, the scientific community lost a great deal of respect for its unethical behavior, even if the traditional theories turn out to be completely vindicated.

The best view of scientific suppression is that it is *likely* to be "error-producing," that is, iatrogenic in the sense of "bias-producing." By definition, unbiased methods of inquiry are less likely to result in error and biased methods are less likely to result in truth, though both sometimes have unlikely results. Much of contemporary philosophy of science is a debate of iatrogenics in this sense (Feyerabend 1978; Kuhn 1970; Magee 1973; Popper 1959, 1968, 1972).

If a little knowledge is a bad thing, it is no worse than a lot of knowledge. The crucial factor is not what you know, but how well you can sift through what yourself or others claim to know. The existence of "experts," since they often disagree among themselves, means our ordinary decisions are harder, not easier to make.

Whether one is assessing Velikovsky's view of Earth's history, the recommendation of a professional helper or the advice of a friend, the only reasonable approach is a fair and open mind—one that acknowledges the likelihood of iatrogenic tendencies in all human judgments.

BIBLIOGRAPHY

deGrazia, A., R. E. Juergens and L. C. Stecchini, eds. *The Velikovsky Affair: Scientism vs. Science.* New Hyde Park, N.Y.: University Books, 1966.

Editors of *Pensée, Velikovsky Reconsidered.* New York: Doubleday, 1976.

Feyerabend, P. *Against Method: Outline of an Anarchistic Theory of Knowledge.* London: Verso, 1978.

Gardiner, M. *Fads and Fallacies in the Name of Science.* New York: Dover, 1957.

Goldsmith, D., ed. *Scientists Confront Velikovsky.* Ithaca, N.Y.: Cornell University Press, 1977.

Kuhn, T. S. *Structure of Scientific Revolutions.* Chicago: University of Chicago Press, 1970.

Magee, B. *Karl Popper.* New York: Viking Press, 1973.

Popper, K. *The Logic of Scientific Discovery.* New York: Basic Books, 1959.

———. *Conjectures and Refutations: The Growth of Scientific Knowledge.* New York: Harper & Row, 1968.

———. *Objective Knowledge: An Evolutionary Approach.* Oxford: Oxford University Press, 1972.

Ransom, C. J. *Age of Velikovsky.* New York: Dell, 1976.

Velikovsky, I. *Worlds In Collision.* New York: Doubleday, 1950.

———. *Ages in Chaos.* New York: Doubleday, 1952.

———. *Earth In Upheaval.* New York: Doubleday, 1955.

DAVID H. FREY

3

Level of Care, Therapy Mode and Iatrogenesis in Mental Health

David Frey is in the first rank of epidemiologists: those hunters of causes in a professional milieu sceptical of determinism in any field setting. I met Frey some years ago when I hired him to teach statistics to graduate students. Few courses offer greater challenge to dedicated teachers: Frey's colleagues had been known to try hypnosis on their students to breach the fear of applied mathematics. He prevailed and succeeded with more individualized care, attention, rigor, patience and clarity than I've ever experienced. This is also the manner in which Frey tackles etiology in his chosen area of work today, also with much success. Share then, a model from his perspective . . . **R.F.M.**

An iatrogenic disorder originally was an abnormal mental or physical condition induced in a patient by a physician or surgeon. The concept combines two Greek root words: *iatros* or physician and *genman* to produce. In modern times, iatrogenesis also implies that the physician could have avoided the negative/traumatic effect if proper and judicious care was applied. Historically, even from the times of Hippocrates and Galen, iatrogenic inducing behaviors on the physician's part violate a basic medical ethic: "It's better to do nothing than to make things worse." From early on, all experienced and wise physicians knew that each treatment could be used for both benefit and harm. To some degree, each potion is a poison and each surgical procedure is a wound.

In short, therapeutic procedures can be seen as intrusions. Therapeutic methods are to be respected and applied judiciously, with a light hand. The application of each treatment revolves around two principles. The first asks that we respect the potency of our therapeutic techniques. The second demands respect for the client's right to refuse treatment and to bear his/her own consequence.

One can quickly imagine how these principles evolved given the sorts of treatments available in more primitive times, e.g., the Middle Ages. Treatments such as bleeding and volatile purgatives often bordered on being lethal. It seems apparent that some treatments were not only unable to arrest the disease's progress but were often more dangerous than the disease itself. Home remedies and good nursing care often seemed more effective and certainly less dangerous than the prescribed treatments.

Thus, the wise physician ultimately learned to bide his time, let nature take its course and intervene in a gentle, light-handed manner. This position didn't necessarily reduce the prevalence of illness, but, at least, it didn't produce iatrogenesis.

Much of this traditional wisdom changed in modern times with technological medicine, improved pharmacology, modern hospitals, advanced surgical techniques and effective pain killers. These advances, bolstered by an uncritical faith in science and reinforced by some impressive cures, caused the physician to become more bold. The boldness necessitated increased reliance on doctors' remedies and often was accompanied by disdain for the older, more restrained model. This older model demanded a degree of humbleness in the face of powerful illnesses and rather puny treatments.

Some of the boldness is caught up with our interest and extension of the scientific or mechanistic metaphor for organizing natural data (Pepper 1942). While many of the outcomes from this line of inquiry are truly heroic, the organizing world view in mechanism, by definition, discounts alternative forms of proof and other forms of data. Thus, we are left with a conceptual scheme that only accounts for certain parts of the human condition. Purists (often calling themselves "medical scientists") argue strongly for tighter boundaries around the mechanistic metaphor and its succeeding principles while others (in all forms of which the holistic school is now most popular) want a medicine that is more organic and contectual (Pepper 1942).

Thus far, the distinction between physical treatment and mental health care has not been highlighted. Certainly, one cannot deny that each has a separate and long history of its own. The point is that mental health personnel have looked to physical medicine for models of treatment. One often sees an uncritical acceptance of the power of a given technique too often accompanied by a naive awareness of side effects (Frey and Heslet 1975). Certainly some stable marriages have been sacrificed to misguided notions of self-fulfillment or openness. Similarly, some people may have wasted precious hours and money in insight-based psychotherapy when their malady was environmentally induced and no amount of insight could alter the toxic situation. Therapists who seek unabashed self-actualization or probe the depths of the unconscious are not alone in their blame. Behavioral treatment and community mental health are also not immune to the invariant effect of unwanted and harmful side effects. In fact, the selection of therapy or combination of therapies is bought at a price. One constantly needs to arrive at a treatment cost that balances as much therapeutic benefit against lesser amounts of negative side costs. Wise counselors or therapists know how to make these therapeutic deals best. They are expert in charting the tricky course between treatment and side effects.

Before continuing these arguments, the development of an aside to enrich the point will be given. There is no intent here to deny or take the edge off beneficial modern advances. The arguments given are not designed to negate the purposeful and slow advance of significant research data and clinical wisdom that separates our interventions from those of primitive peoples or superstitious quackery. We know more than we used to and that is to our, and our clients' advantage. Moreover, there seems little advantage in holding an anti-technology philosophy that shrinks from anything drawing on the mechanistic model or advanced medical science. Such a sophomoric position forces one to return to folk medicine or overly simplistic concepts of holistic health.

In counseling and psychotherapy, the rejection of modern advances often leads to thinking of intervention in simple terms—two caring persons existentially encounter each other purely and simply. Such a stance undercuts the need for technical skill, knowledge, wisdom and experience. Given the typical presenting problem today, positive regard and active listening are rarely enough (Warnath 1981).

There is, however, a reasonable middle course between unabashed technocracy and medical wishful thinking. A fine line exists between a simplistic and sometimes romanticized view of treatment and the seemingly scientific and critical position. The former skeptically rejects empirical evidence by fiat while the latter accepts an over-parsimonious view of the human condition by imposing mechanistic frameworks over complex contextual human phenomena. Both miss the target. Perhaps, one hits the mark best by returning to common sense, by integrating in creative ways the information generated by each case and then developing treatment plans that are in concert with the facts and values present in each situation (Pepper 1942).

The Etiology of Iatrogenesis

Any intervention has positive and negative effects. Each intervention system, drawing on its philosophy, values and technology, brings with its application an *apriori* predisposition to error in certain ways. For example, those who choose a romanticized and naive humanistic psychology often err in undertreating severe cases. Deep and chronic psychopathology demands more than a warm, supportive therapist with an active ear. Similarly, the technocrat too often overtreats because inherent in his/her therapeutic system is the tendency to add more and more services (i.e., if one session a week is not working then two are needed; if one unit of the drug is not achieving the goal, then let's try two or three units).

When left to its processes, each intervention system will maximize its potential to make iatrogenic errors. Something is needed to counter the automatic pull to keep doing more of the same in a more deliberate and powerful way. One factor that is effective in countering this inertia is knowledge of disease and the particular socio-cultural forces that interact with a particular disease in a particular location, at a particular time, for a particular person. Thus, one must draw on both the natural history of the disease and its shape and form in a given context (McDermott 1977, 146).

For clarity, the etiology of iatrogenesis may be roughly divided into two forms: maladies coming from undertreatment and neglect, and maladies coming from overtreatment. Of the two forms, we most often hear about the first. Both the popular and professional press often cite cases of populations that are underserved for various reasons (i.e., the aged in inner cities, the infants of racial minorities in American urban centers, the rural poor, and so on). These situations make, from time to time, strong news stories, especially when an investigative reporter links poor care with political negligence or fraud. Without lessening the terrible impact of epidemic level of disease and undertreated populations, the focus here will be on the second iatrogenic error, overtreating. Primarily, this focus was chosen because we hear less about it and others have written about undertreatment at length. By centering on the issue of overtreatment, one cannot argue that undertreatment is less damaging to public health or that its epidemiology may even be more serious if we could eventually calculate mortality and morbidity rates across iatrogenic types. The point is rather to highlight certain factors in overtreatment. It is easier to argue against neglect and/or indifference than to argue against overcommitment, extensive care, intense application of treatment and the search for more powerful remedies. Thus, there may be an error in discussing overtreatment at the expense of an appreciation for undertreatment, but it is an error made in an attempt to set the balance.

Figure 1 graphically describes how iatrogenesis of the first and second type interact with treatment. In each instance, it is possible to commit error not only in the amount of treatment given but also in the kind or type of treatment. Thus, we see an interaction of level of treatment with properness of treatment. One could undertreat with both proper and improper methods and overtreat with proper and improper interventions. A mental health example will clarify the model. Consider the case of a middle-aged male going through a racalibration of life goals, including a career or life-style change. The man is typically caught between mounting

Figure 1: Level of Care, Proper Therapy and Iatrogenesis

	Undertreatment	Overtreatment
Type A: proper therapy	Cell A: correct therapy given *below* level of effectiveness for that therapy	Cell B: correct therapy given *beyond* level of effectiveness for that therapy
Type B: improper therapy	Cell C: incorrect therapy given *below* acceptable standards for that therapy	Cell D: incorrect therapy given *beyond* acceptable standards for that therapy

anxiety about possible changes and fear stemming from lack of knowledge about the environment. Without going into all of the case details here, let's assume that an active career-counseling program modeled on a brief-therapy philosophy is the proper therapy. Given these brief data, then Cell A could describe a situation in which career counseling was given in a totally rational way and the client's values, feelings and fears about the emerging change are undercut. Likewise, Cell B could describe a career-counseling program that continually added exercises, psychological tests and therapy sessions to such a degree that the client never was able to make the transfer from counseling to trial exploration in the real world. In short, the proper therapy was given in too full a measure. Cell C might describe a situation in which the therapist moved the client into long-term, psychodynamic-based therapy and administered the intervention poorly. Not only is the client getting "improper" care, but he is also the benefactor of poor interpretations, therapeutically dangerous countertransferences and so on. The final cell, Cell D, might model the improper psychoanalytic counseling administered in such a way that the treatment overwhelmed the condition. In this case, the client may have been asked to see the therapist three or four times a week over a long period of time. In like fashion, other hypothetical cases could be applied to the model, showing the four types of iatrogenic error described here.

The Natural History of Disease

In the course of a particular treatment, the various iatrogenic errors modeled in Figure 1 interact with the nature of the disease. Although the use of the term *disease* moves the meaning of the client's malady too far toward the infectious and physical illness side of things, the term will be retained for no other reason than its universal usage. In addition, other terms such as *presenting concern* or *mental problems* lack the definitional compactness of the word disease.

The natural history of a disease is the progress the disease takes without treatment (McDermott 1977; Morris 1975). The idea focuses on the natural pattern of the disease process as it functions in the client's system. In a sense, the natural history of a disease is like the native anthropological behaviors of primitive peoples when uninterpreted by modern times or the intrusions of the field worker doing ethnography. The natural history of a disease answers the question: Given the complaints, the symptoms and the context how might this client progress if we did nothing? In some cases, the lack of intervention could be life threatening. However, in no cases can the judgment to intervene or not intervene be made properly if one has little knowledge of the conditions of the natural history, including epidemiologic rates. Knowledge of the natural history of a disease necessarily increases the therapist's ability to make more reliable prognostic statements and to more effectively plan interventions. One then, of course, may minimize the chances of making iatrogenic errors.

The natural history of the disease forms a "window" through which we view treatment and can better avoid over or undertreatment or the selection of an improper therapy (Vaillant and Milofsky 1980). In an everyday sense, we are all familiar with these concepts. The common cold tends to go away in a week or ten days with or without treatment (unless there are complicating factors). An explosive friend with a hystrionic personality style may verbally abuse us one day only to forget his/her rage a day or two later. In such a case, an intense rational intervention during the outburst may do little more than prolong the episode. A depressed colleague may bottom out only to find his/her mood elevated with or without love or support. At best, a basic knowledge of these factors helps in dealing with the cold, the interaction with explosive persons and helping a depressed friend.

Some examples are now at hand to show that by using the natural history of disease "window" or frame of reference one can better avoid making iatrogenic errors. During Victorian times, the shock of syphilis was only exceeded by hearing that one had inoperable cancer. Syphilis meant that one's marriage was over, the brain and spinal cord would be destroyed, one would be blind, the heart would be damaged and all of one's children would be infected too. Patients believed this and so did physicians. Some liberal physicians thought early treatment could prevent a few of these terrible consequences, but both the doctor and patient knew it was really hopeless.

However, Gjestland (1955) in Norway followed a large population of untreated syphilis cases and found that the chances of development of a truly serious late form of the disease were about fifteen in one hundred. This meant two things: although penicillin might prove relatively ineffective in preventing late forms of the disease (which from other evidence is almost certainly not the case), eighty-five of one hundred patients with untreated syphilis would go through life virtually unscathed; and the unlucky fifteen would really be no worse off than their contemporaries who suffered a heart attack or stroke in late middle age. Thus, from the Victorian period until Gjestland's research, thousands of people had to live with a devastating fear of disease (an iatrogenic effect) that was mostly a paper tiger.

Gjestland's research data on the natural history of syphilis mandated changes in treatment. First, it became possible for the physician to calm the fears of patients, knowing that penicillin works in most cases and that the disease doesn't follow its worst form in all cases. Second, data were generated across time that allowed the physician to locate key intervention points that maximize positive effects. As a result, fear and hand wringing may now be replaced by both effective treatment and lessened iatrogenic effects.

Another example of the use of natural history of a disease in lessening iatrogenic effects may be seen in Billings' (1974) research of 620 suicidal individuals. For a minimum of twenty-four months, these 620 suicidal individuals were followed in order to determine suicide/nonsuicide after an initial hospitalization for depression, suicidal thoughts or a suicide attempt. Subjects in the study were allowed to follow the regular assignment procedures for various treatment modalities: individual psychotherapy, day treatment centers, inpatient treatment, no treatment at all and an experimental suicide treatment group. After making a statistical adjustment to standardize rates for the various modes, the data supported two conclusions. First, treatment in general was more effective in preventing death than no treatment at all. Second, even though, on the average, treatment was better than no treatment there was a vast range of effects within treatment modes. For example, the suicide rate for day treatment was 13.4 percent (the most ineffective treatment) and the rate for a group therapy program especially designed for suicidal clients was 1.0 percent. *The death rate for no treatment at all was 10.4 percent.* In short, given the natural history of suicide about one in ten high risk suicidal patients committed suicide. Some treatments, especially day treatment, appeared to have an iatrogenic effect. On the other hand, a therapy program specially designed to meet the needs of depressed/suicidal clients significantly reduced mortality (Frey, Motto & Ritholz 1981).

Given the above examples, the point seems to be that there is a therapeutic advantage in knowing the history of a disease if one is to plan non-iatrogenic treatment programs. Gjestland's work with syphilis could certainly lessen patient anxiety and Billings' research tells us that certain therapies are more effective than others in treating suicide and, in some cases, no treatment at all may be more effective than certain treatments for some clients. However, tailoring the treatment to the specific needs of the client appeared to have real benefits in the case of suicide rates. Frey, Motto and Ritholz (1981) based much of their treatment on certain key factors in suicidal processes (i.e., isolation, helplessness, hopelessness, repressed rage, poor social skills, maladaptive work habits, etc.). It seems then that by attempting to have the treatment processes positively interact with the various stages of suicidal/depressive reactions the clients seemed to benefit by the treatment.

These are but two examples of how treatment and the natural history of a disease interact. The therapeutic advantage is in knowing the disease process well enough so that one's interventions are optimally matched to client's needs. Clearly, this is not an easy task. This sort of balance is never truly achieved, but perhaps in the pursuit of this balance one is more likely to maximize benefit and lessen iatrogenic effects of the type that overtreats.

In summary, the conceptual model that is being built here presents us with sets of questions that help in effective treatment planning. The first set of questions rest in the natural history of the phenomena. These questions arise from our expertise about the condition itself unfiltered by a particular circumstance. Secondly, we must ask questions about type of treatment or mode of therapy. These questions center on maximizing the interactive benefit between therapies and the natural history of the disease. Finally, we must consider the level of care, avoiding both under and overtreatment. Iatrogenesis is minimized when one understands the disease process, selects proper treatments and arrives at a proper level of intervention. The linchpin in the system is the natural history of the disease, the antecedent probabilities of the process in the population (Meehl and Rosen 1955).

Factors Influencing Overtreatment

Certainly, there are a host of social, political, cultural and economic factors that reinforce the posture to overtreat. Only a few of these factors will be highlighted here. Moreover, attention will focus on iatrogenic effects in mental health rather than to carefully cite reasons for its causes.

Economic Advantage

There are definite financial benefits to overtreatment. This is obvious. Clients who remain in treatment for long periods of time become an economic constant in the therapist's economic resources. Fewer referrals are needed. Less initial costs (e.g., intake sessions and diagnostic procedures are incurred). Less client turnover relieves the therapist of professional marketing activities that often have low economic return per unit of time expended. Similarly, agencies, schools and community health services can show greater utilization rates from long-term users, and this is often a key factor in arguing for a larger budget.

Not only are economic advantages associated with direct one to one or small group services, but auxiliary services (e.g., physical therapy, pharmacy services, pastoral services, etc.) also reap the benefit of more long-term patients in the system. Thus, the decision to terminate often entails more than just patient interest. Too often, termination mandates economic considerations about the loss of client resources. In areas where the patient to therapist ratio is quite low (e.g., communities with large universities or medical training centers) the economic pull to overtreat can be considerably strong.

Reliance on Technical Means

As Illich (1973) pointed out, tools have a mandate, a power of their own. This mandate takes its form in drawing the physician or therapist to use, play with, practise on and implement the technology. It is as if the tool looks for application. A new expensive machine is rarely left unused, for to do so would not only "waste" capital but also interrupt the magnetic attraction between man and his technology. Thus, psychologists use up their test protocols, surgeons their operating rooms and pharmacists their drugs.

We are drawn to the latest technology and may tend to overevaluate the positive effects it can have in treatment. More and more technology demands more and more service and more and more time. Ironically, the technology that we hoped might reduce human effort and speed up efficiency can do just the reverse. More elaborate technical processes can complicate diagnosis without adding to reliable taxonomic classification and can render interventions less parsimonious and to the point. Too often technology paves the way to overtreatment.

Unrealistic Concepts of Pain and Suffering
Pain is truly a four-letter word. We don't like it. We don't expect to have it, and we don't want to know it exists. Modern life is supposed to be pain free. Thus, when we suffer the normal and rather predictable pains of psychological development, we too often conceptualize these painful but normal periods as extraordinary and thus needing treatment. We too often want the therapist to make "it go away."

As most of us realize when we think about it for a while, the expectation of a painless life is unrealistic. Pain and suffering are endemic to the human condition. In fact, as the existentialists tell us, a well-lived life will have pain—the pain of living in the world—the pain of feeling and experiencing our environment where death, illness and disappointment are not uncommon.

Clearly, it is not the point here to relish or accept painful circumstances. Rather the idea is to show that the reasonably healthy individual knows of the possibilities of pain in one's life and hopes to cope with these possibilities when they arise and as best as he/she can. Such persons don't expect a painless life. They want a full life within which they can handle the stresses and strains as well as can be expected. Sometimes, they may need professional help in handling these difficulties.

However, when one's pains become totally unnatural, then the tendency to ask for relief may be extended. For many, this could mean constant therapeutic support. They could choose to be in counseling or psychotherapy a lifetime, constantly wanting to live a painless existence. Since the goal is unattainable for mortal humans, the result may then be overtreatment.

The Medicalization of Society
There are many reasons why medicine, in all its forms, plays an increasingly important role in our lives. The pursuit of a painless existence is one of these. We spend more of our natural resources on health than we have in the past. Therapists and physicians are often key personalities on television talk shows. Hospitals are our birthplaces and deathbeds (Knowles 1977; Illich 1973).

Institutions are expected to take care of our needs. We have transferred a great deal of power to the institutions of society and thus, rather than attempt to cure ourselves, we hope that the institutions will do it for us. Treatment then becomes standardized, too often overly technical and overextended. Services delivered become prepackaged and not rooted in the context of each person's life. The scene is set for iatrogenic effects.

Disregard for the Idea of Therapeutic Range
A therapeutic range for any intervention defines the range from lower-bound limit (the point when the treatment has its initial positive effect

and below which there is no therapeutic effect) to upper-bound limit (the point when the treatment loses its therapeutic effect, typically having toxic effects). The model tells us that any intervention can be underadministered and overadministered. When we disregard this principle, we can easily move into iatrogenesis. In terms of overtreatment, we may begin to think that more and more of a good, effective treatment is therapeutically useful. In this way, we may forget to monitor for toxic effects, failing to note that point when we move from benefit to potential harm.

Conclusion

An attempt has been made here to express the interaction between three concepts: iatrogenic effect in mental health, causes for iatrogenesis and the natural history of disease. The purpose of drawing these interactions is to highlight the diagnostic and treatment dynamics that influence both the level and kind of treatment given, especially as these dynamics negatively support iatrogenic effects. Special attention was given to overtreatment.

My intent was not to make radical changes in therapeutic practice but rather to raise level of awareness. If a limited number of readers can now look at their attitudes and expectations of disease in a new light, then their awareness has been raised. If a few therapists begin to question their automatic assumptions about treatment independent of the natural history of the disease, then there is also heightened awareness.

BIBLIOGRAPHY

Billings, J. The efficacy of group treatment for depressed and suicidal individuals in comparison with other treatment settings as regards the prevention of suicide. Ph.D. dissertation, California School of Professional Psychology, 1974.

Frey, D. and F. Heslet. *Existential Theory for Counselors.* Boston: Houghton Mifflin Co., 1975.

Frey, D., J. Motto and M. Ritholz. Group therapy for persons at risk for suicide: An evaluation using the internal design. *Psycholotherapy: Research, Theory and Practice.* In press.

Gjestland, T. The Oslo study of untreated syphilis: An epidemiologic investigation of the natural course of the syphilistic infection based on a restudy of the Boeck-Bruns-gaard material. *Acta Dermatology and Venereology* 35 (1955).

Illich, I. *Medical Nemesis.* London: Bantam Books, 1976.

——. *Tools for Conviruality.* New York: Harper and Row, 1973.

Knowles, J. *Doing Better and Feeling Worse: Health in the United States.* New York: W. W. Norton & Co., 1977.

McDermott, W. Evaluating the physician and his technology. In *Doing Better and Feeling Worse: Health in the United States,* edited by J. Knowles, 135-158. New York: W. W. Norton & Co., 1977.

Meehl, P. and A. Rosen. Antecedent probability and the efficiency of psychometric signs, patterns, or cutting scores. *Psychological Bulletin* (1955).

Morris, J. *Uses of Epidemiology.* London: Churchill Livingstone, 1975.

Pepper, S. *World Hypotheses.* Berkeley: University of California Press, 1942.

Vaillant, G. and M. Milofsky. Natural history of male psychological health: IX. Empirical evidence for Erikson's model of the life cycle. *American Journal of Psychiatry.* (November 1980) 1348-1359.

Warnath, C. The relationship in counseling: Some potential contradictions with service realities. Unpublished paper, Oregon State University, Corvallis, Oregon, 1981.

PETER R. BREGGIN

4

Iatrogenic Helplessness in Authoritarian Psychiatry

Dr. Peter Breggin is a leading expert on some of the more iatrogenic treatments still in vogue (see his chapter 21 on shock treatment). He is also one of the prime movers of blending a scientist's data with an activist's techniques for change. Dr. Martin Luther King Jr. and others foresaw decades back that good intentions were never enough: a movement without a systematic search for truth would ultimately defeat itself by its own fresh dogma. Having identified some change that is clearly justified by data, one is left with generating the means to create that change. This chapter develops the process theory behind the professional behavior maintaining the iatrogenic content Breggin relentlessly opposes. **R.F.M.**

Fear and helplessness are the twin problems of mankind. Fear underlies most of the painful emotions we commonly experience (e.g., guilt, shame and anxiety). Helplessness is the most debilitating response to this fear (Breggin 1980a).

Because human beings suffer from fear, and because they so often become helpless in the face of this fear, authority thrives in human life. Reliance upon authority is the individual's attempt to deal with feelings of fear and helplessness (Breggin 1980a).

In psychiatry, authority has often been promoted as *the* answer to the helplessness and fear which typically dominate psychiatric patients, as well as the rest of mankind. Indeed, the entire structure of psychiatry seems built upon the maintenance of authority over the patient.

To the extent that psychiatry promotes its own authority, it also promotes helplessness and fear. Authority, by its very nature, encourages fear and helplessness upon the part of the individual over whom it is exercised. Authority, and psychiatric authority in particular, can be said to cause *iatrogenic fear and helplessness*. The sources of the fear and helplessness are always there within the individual—within every living individual. We all find much to be afraid of within life, and much to be afraid of about death. We often struggle with a sense of helplessness which urges us to seek out the answers in one kind of authority or another, rather than within our own autonomous ability to reason and to make decisions. But nearly all forms of psychiatry prey upon this helplessness and fear, in order to gain further authoritarian control over the patient.

Fear

Fear is so much a part of human life that an analysis of fear is tanta-mount to an examination of life itself. All I can attempt here is to outline some of the major sources of fear and their relationship to guilt, shame and anxiety.

From a very early age, a child experiences fear. Probably it begins with pain—the pain of hunger, of indigestion, of uncomfortable positions, loud noises, and sometimes, of physical punishment. Very quickly fear also begins to generate in the child's relationships to others; the young infant will become "cranky" or uneasy when the parent is out of sorts or upset. Over the first few years of life, the child learns about abandonment, loss and disappointment of all kinds. The fear of death itself sets in early, certainly within the first few years. By the time the child is two or three years old, he/she can easily become dominated by fears which may explode in sheer terror at being left alone, or being punished, or being unloved or being threatened by imagined monsters.

Soon the parents or other authorities, including older siblings, become closely tied to *the production of fear* and *the protection from fear.* The authorities produce fear by inflicting pain upon the child, and by punish-ing in various other ways. They also inflict pain in unavoidable ways: by not always meeting the child's needs, and by leaving the child when it does not want to be left. But while the authorities, from the child's viewpoint, seem to cause much of its pain, they are also the child's sole source of protection from pain. The child becomes dependent upon the very people it fears. This ambivalent relationship becomes the prototype for later relationships with authorities, who will be seen as fearsome and yet needed.

Helplessness

Helplessness is the most debilitating response to fear (Breggin 1980a). In helplessness, the child, or grown individual, gives up or foresakes the concept that he/she cannot do anything about the fearful circumstance. Helpless according to the American Heritage Dictionary (1969) means:

1. unable to manage by oneself; defenseless; dependent.
2. lacking power or strength; impotent; ineffectual.
3. without help.
4. unable to be remedied.

In this typical definition, two aspects of helplessness are mixed, the subjective experience and the objective reality. From an objective view-point, there are times when we are more or less helpless. I cannot avoid eventual death. I probably cannot escape paying my taxes. The influence I can exert upon my wife, children or friends is limited. Whether this article is read and appreciated is somewhat out of my hands. These are objective limits.

But there is a more subjective aspect to helplessness, and this subjective helplessness disposes the individual to submit to authority. Subjective helplessness is a form of "giving up," a surrender of one's abilities and autonomy. In particular, it is a surrender of the ability that I call self-determination (Breggin 1980a). Self-determination is the capacity of the individual under any and all circumstances to "keep his head" or to maintain rationality. This rationality can then be used to exert whatever influence is possible over the inner world of subjective thoughts and feelings, and the outer world of events. The individual may be limited severely in his capacity to effect events: he may be locked in prison or suffering from a debilitating disease. Indeed, in so many ways, all of us are locked in various prisons, from our bodies to our nations, and all of us have a debilitating disease, the aging process. But if we remain self-determining, rather than helpless, we can rely upon ourselves to make the most of whatever situation in which we find ourselves. Above all else, we can attempt to control our personal, subjective responses to these situations. Helplessness, from the viewpoint of the psychology of self-determination, is an inner, subjective state, characterized by the giving up of self-control and self-direction. It can vary from slight feelings of "I can't do anything" to overwhelming panic and catatonia. Helplessness is one response to fear. Self-determination is the other.

Real or objective helplessness in regard to external events in the world is the obvious situation of the infant at birth. Subjective helplessness develops over the years. Certainly by the age of one or two, children can be observed to develop subjective helplessness. A child, for example, when stymied by a puzzle may become frustrated and upset, and refuse to try any further. The child may throw a temper tantrum over the failure, becoming wholly subjectively helpless.

Subjective helplessness often develops in the child as a response to authorities. Mom wants the child to get dressed by himself, but the child just cannot seem to get his arms and legs co-ordinated properly. It is a case of studied, chosen helplessness. Later this obviously volitional helplessness can become so embedded in the child's consciousness that the child is unaware that he/she once chose helplessness as a means of evading the commands of the parents. This is a typical example of what I mean in the *Psychology of Freedom* when I speak of how children choose their life styles of helplessness. They eventually forget that choices were made. Adult maturity requires undoing these original choices and deciding, instead, to become self-determining.

Guilt, Shame and Anxiety

Fear is the root emotion behind all the other negative emotions in life, such as guilt, shame and anxiety. Typically the process involves what I call self-oppression (1980a). The child is afraid of the authority, and cannot bear to have a confrontation with it. It is too dangerous to meet Mom or Dad head on in a fight or disagreement. So the child, instead of being afraid of the parent, and consequently angry at the parent, instead turns on itself and helplessly identifies itself as the cause of the problem.

The parent or other authority encourages this process. Thus, guilt is a form of turning anger on oneself in an effort to avoid confrontation with the authorities. Guilt becomes a form of helplessness in the face of fear, a subjective sense that one is "bad" and, therefore, cannot take any effective actions to remedy the situation.

Shame and anxiety are similar expressions of self-oppression in the face of a fearful confrontation. Shame says "I am worthless, meaningless or inconsequential and hence, I am helpless." Anxiety says, "I do not know what is going on, and hence, I am helpless." Either way, helplessness continues to dominate.

Ultimately, most forms of self-oppression, and hence, most forms of guilt, shame and anxiety can be understood as subjugation to authority. The individual who is not submissive to authority (either external authority or internalized authority) is a self-determining, rational being who can make independent choices.

Life Styles of Failure

In *The Psychology of Freedom,* I describe the origins of the various life-styles of failure. Here I can only summarize them briefly. *Paranoia* is a helpless response to fear in which the individual blames others or outside forces for his failure to remain self-determining. It does not matter if the outside force is real. Perhaps we *are* influenced by radio waves from outer space. Perhaps the Martians have landed. Certainly, real life threats can be included in the paranoid person's viewpoint. What matters is the *helpless* attitude.

Depression is still another form of helplessness in which the individual blames himself/herself, rather than others or outside forces. The depressed person feels or expresses self-hate, and says, in effect, "I am bad. I am no good." As in paranoia, the issue is not the truth or falsehood of the moral observation, but the helplessness with which it is felt and uttered. In depression, the self-blame is used as one more *excuse* for remaining helpless: "I am bad, therefore, I cannot do anything about the things in life that I fear."

In *anxiety,* unlike depression and paranoia, the individual blames no one and nothing. In effect, the individual becomes confused, stupid or unknowing rather than face his/her fears. This life style, like the others, can usually be traced back many years as a consistent method of dealing with the world.

Individuals frequently vacillate between depression, anxiety and paranoia. The common thread is the *helplessness.* When the individual decides no longer to be helpless, but rather to be self-determining, and in particular, to use reason in the service of dealing with the various fears in life, the individual begins to leave behind the life styles of depression, paranoia and anxiety, and the various associated emotions of guilt, shame and anxiety.

Schizophrenia, which Szasz (1976) has aptly called "the sacred symbol of psychiatry," is nothing more than an expression of total helplessness, including helplessness in the control of one's own mind. The person who develops "loosening of associations" or "delusions" has become totally irresponsible, or totally helpless, in regard to control over the inner world (Breggin 1980a). Such a person feels at the mercy of his own thoughts, rather than in charge of his own thoughts. For the person who is bordering on "going crazy," these concepts can be immensely helpful. The individual can grasp responsibility for self-determination of his/her own mind.

Self-determination

In *The Psychology of Freedom* I develop the concept of self-determination as based upon the twin principles of personal sovereignty and personal freedom. *Personal sovereignty* designates the right and the capacity to be in charge of one's own internal, subjective world. It reflects the individual as an agent who can make moral and ethical decisions. Personal sovereignty has no known limits. Individuals are forever developing new thoughts and concepts, and making new decisions. Sometimes these experiences remain wholly private; at other times, they are communicated and become real to others as well.

Personal freedom designates the right and the capacity of the individual to implement his/her thoughts, feelings and decisions in the world. All philosophies advocate certain limits on personal freedom, especially a limit on infringing upon the liberties of others. "Thou shall not kill" is a paradigm of the moral limit on personal freedom. Personal freedom is also limited by objective reality. We all live in bodies, and that places grave limits on us.

The psychology of self-determination, based upon the libertarian principles of voluntary association, states that the individual can and should strive for ever-increasing degrees of personal sovereignty and personal freedom. The sole injunction is against the use of force (except in self-defense) (Breggin 1980a).

Types of Authority

The opposite of self-determination is other-determination, or subjugation to authority. Authority can take many forms (Breggin 1980a). The only benign form of authority from my viewpoint is the authority of expertise. In this context, it really should not be called authority. An individual may rationally decide that another person offers great expertise or sound advice. The individual, in this process, does not give up authority or dominion over himself. He retains the right to judge the value or reliability of the informant or guide with whom he is dealing. He is not forced or emotionally compelled to conform to the wishes of this individual. In contrast, most forms of authority are oppressive, and they encourage self-oppression. They encourage the individual, by emotional pressure or by force, to accept the control of the authority.

Moral authorities are those which rely mostly upon emotional pressure. They encourage guilt, shame and anxiety in the individual, rather than rational decision-making. They emphasize faith rather than rational judgment. Nearly all religions are based on moral authority. The individual must sacrifice an element of self-determination, or rational decision-making, in order to "believe in" such an authority.

Political authorities are ones which enforce their position through a combination of emotional pressure and physical force. The state is the ultimate political authority. It fosters moral authority in the form of patriotism, but it *forces* itself upon the individual whether or not this emotional pursuasion succeeds. Everywhere in the world individuals are born into nations and, in most cases, they have little opportunity to leave their countries. Based on the fear and helplessness first developed in childhood, these individuals go from believing in the authority of their parents to believing in the authority of the state. Along the way, public education, backed by parents and state alike, reinforces the transition from obedience to parents to obedience to state.

Religion, of course, plays a key role in the development of authority over the individual. In some nations, the power of religion is largely moral; it is maintained through emotional control. In other nations, religion is directly tied to state authority. In communist states, the dogma of communism (religious authority) is inextricable from state authority. Throughout the world, the vast majority of individuals out of fear and helplessness live their lives under the shadow of various authorities, including parents, priests and politicians.

Psychiatry and Authority

Psychiatry possesses both moral and political authority. In the Western world, and increasingly throughout the entire world, psychiatry as a moral authority has to a great extent replaced religion as the institution which enforces standards of ethical conduct for its citizens (Szasz 1965, 1974, 1976; Breggin 1974, 1975, 1980a). Under the old religious order, the question might be asked "Is homosexuality wrong?" Under the new psychiatric order, it is asked "Is homosexuality sick?" The language has changed somewhat, but the issue is the same—a positive or negative value judgment on conduct. In the Soviet Union, where official policy has set itself against religious authority, psychiatry has become the ultimate church-state combination. Deviation from state authority is called "mental illness," and deviants are "treated" in psychiatric prisons (Fireside 1979; Breggin 1981a).

Everywhere throughout the Western world, psychiatry is a formidable political authority. That is, psychiatry is maintained and backed by state authority. The most obvious political authority of psychiatry is the power of certification and commitment. Through certification, a physician, typically a psychiatrist, can determine that any particular citizen should lose his freedom, his civil rights and be forcibly admitted to a mental hospital. The grounds for this vary from place to place, and include "mental illness," "need for treatment" and "dangerousness to self and others." It makes little difference. Fundamentally we are dealing with the power of one person, in the role of psychiatrist, to determine that another person no longer has the ordinary rights of citizenship because of his state of mind or non-criminal conduct that is considered "wrong" or "harmful."

In most places throughout the world, psychiatry has many more connections to the state than certification and civil commitment. In the United States, psychiatrists play various roles in the legal system. As an expert witness, the psychiatrist may be called upon in court to testify whether or not the individual was "sane" (the actual wording varies from state to state) during the commission of a crime. In effect, he is being asked to make a moral judgment upon the reprehensibility of the crime. He may be called upon to decide if the individual is fit to stand trial in the first place, and after conviction, he may be called upon to render an opinion that will influence the sentencing and disposition of the prisoner. When the parole period is reached, he may be called to render still another decision on the individual's fitness for parole.

Psychiatry is also tied into the state through various funding procedures. In the United States, psychiatry is supported by a variety of grants and legislative programs. More indirectly, psychiatry is supported and controlled through government policies concerning medical schools and medical licensure.

Jonas Robitscher, in *The Powers of Psychiatry* (1980), catalogues and questions many varieties of psychiatric authority. Among the more interesting is the moral-political role played by psychiatrists who wrote letters calling for the deferment of draftees on the grounds that they were "mentally ill." We might also note the adversary role played by the federally-employed psychiatrists who had the final say on whether or not the young men were indeed morally fit to serve in the army.

Psychiatric Authority and the Enforcement of "Craziness"

Authority lives upon fear and helplessness, and therefore, upon the various life styles of helplessness (paranoia, depression and anxiety) and the various emotions of helplessness (guilt, shame and anxiety). In the extreme, it is easy to see how a dictator bent upon whipping up a patriotic fervor in his subjects can play upon any one of these life styles and their associated emotions. The more helpless his subjects feel, the more likely they will respond to his authority. Psychiatry is no different from any other authority in this regard. Ultimately, most forms of psychiatry cannot "succeed" according to a value system based upon self-determination because they undermine self-determination. Thus psychiatry tends to produce *good patients* rather than *free and independent individuals*. Psychiatry has developed the art of *iatrogenic helplessness*.

The methods by which psychiatry enforces its own authority, and correspondingly, the helplessness of its patients, are legion. Nearly all the officially supported and sanctioned methods of psychiatry tend to be authoritarian. The aspects of psychiatry which I am now analyzing in this regard are obviously overlapping.

Civil commitment and certification—Every psychiatrist has the power to initiate and sometimes to carry out the process of depriving a citizen of his civil rights, placing him in confinement in a mental institution. The justification, it might be argued, is that the individuals in question are helpless and need someone to take over their lives for them. Indeed, most people who are committed are being subjectively helpless, or they would not fall into the psychiatric trap. But by declaring the individual helpless, and then treating him as if he is helpless, *psychiatry actually reinforces the individual's sense or conviction of helplessness.* Thus psychiatry reinforces the patient's problem and takes advantage of it, so that the patient who feels subjectively helpless is actually rendered still more helpless from an objective viewpoint. He is incarcerated, and worse, his mind will be blunted and disrupted by various physical "therapies." This is why psychiatric commitment and psychiatric treatment in general do so little good for anyone (except the psychiatrists); these processes prey upon the very helplessness that is already plaguing and even destroying the individual.

Like the child who both fears and needs the authorities around him, the mental patient comes to fear and to need the authorities around him. He needs their good will and approval if he is ever to get free of them. The child, at least, can look forward to emancipation as a routine matter of growing older. The patient remains a child at the discretion of the committing psychiatrists.

Diagnosis and the disease model (Szasz 1974)—This plays a crucial role in enforcing the psychiatrist's authority and the patient's helplessness. Psychiatric diagnosis reinforces the worst elements of paranoia, depression and anxiety as expressed by the patient himself/herself. The depressed person believes "I am bad, and therefore unable to do anything about my life." The diagnosing psychiatrist says, "No, you are not morally bad, you are biochemically bad. You have a disease. It is called manic-depressive disorder (or whatever). *You* are helpless in the face of it, but *we* have these treatments..." The patient, by conceiving of himself as morally bad, was at least on the right track. He knew, perhaps, that morality and ethics and ultimately choice might be involved in some way. The diagnosing psychiatrist removes the issue one step further away from human decision-making, and declares the problem utterly out of the hands of the patient.

The paranoid person says "I am being controlled by forces outside myself." The diagnosing psychiatrist says, "These forces are the environment, heredity or your hormones." Whatever the particular bias of the psychiatrist, the basic message is the same "Yes, you are helplessly at the mercy of forces beyond your control." Once this helplessness is confirmed, the psychiatrist can move in with his treatment.

The anxious person says, "I don't know what is happening to me." The diagnosing psychiatrist says, "We don't know the cause of your illness, but we have empirical treatments."

Every psychiatric diagnosis carries within it the same kernel of helplessness expressed by the life styles of paranoia, depression and anxiety. It does not matter a great deal whether the ideology involved is Freudian (your unconscious controls you), behavioristic (environmental cues, in combination with heredity, control you) or biological (your aberrant neurotransmitters control you). In each case, the psychiatrist's authority goes up and the patient's authority over himself goes down. It is no wonder that "eclecticism" is so rampant nowadays; it is all cut from the same cloth of authority.

The mental hospital system—This is the epitome of an institution created to induce helplessness. The history of the state mental hospital system (Breggin 1964, 1971a, b; 1974, 1979) is the history of seizing relatively helpless individuals in order to render them still more helpless, and hence, docile within custodial institutions. Private psychiatric hospitals follow the same model. In none, is the autonomy or independence of the patient fostered. In all, being "improved" and "ready for discharge" means conforming to the authority of the institution. This authority aims at maintaining a helpless, child-like state in the individual.

Psychotherapy—With individuals, and sometimes with couples or groups, psychotherapy probably has the greatest potential to serve the individual as a self-determining being (Breggin 1980a; Szasz 1965). But as Szasz has thoroughly documented in *The Myth of Psychotherapy* (1978) and as I described in "Psychotherapy as Applied Ethics," (1971b) most psychotherapies, including classical psychoanalysis, reinforce the ethic of heteronomy, or submission to others. The very concept of "psychotherapy," drawn from medicine, smacks of authority. In *The Ethics of Psychoanalysis* (1965), Szasz describes a contractual approach to therapy which mitigates much of the authoritarianism inherent in the situation. In *Psychology of Freedom* (1980a), I systematically develop a psychology of self-determination based upon free will and personal freedom. Undoubtedly many individual psychotherapists in private practice treat many or most of their patients in an autonomous fashion. They do this on the basis of their own personal values. Almost anything they read and almost everything they have experienced in their psychiatric training will run counter to their more libertarian, autonomous practices.

Psychiatric technology—As a tool of oppression and control psychiatric technology has already received an enormous amount of my attention. My efforts were at first focused upon the paradign of destructive therapies, psychosurgery (Breggin 1980b, 1981c), then upon electroshock (1979, 1981b) and finally upon psychiatric drugs (1982). I developed the brain-disabling hypothesis which states that all the major psychiatric technologies *disable the normal brain* rendering the individual *more helpless,* and hence, easier to manage or to ignore. Each of the major psychiatric treatments—psychosurgery, electroshock, the major tranquilizers and lithium were originally developed in order to subdue and control unruly, difficult patients in the state mental hospital system (Breggin 1979, 1974, 1975, 1981a). Eventually each was rationalized as a "treatment" for "diseases," and their use spread from the state mental hospitals to private hospitals, clinics and private practices.

The brain disability (and associated mental dysfunction) produced by the major psychiatric treatments is an iatrogenic illness. The illness is what the psychiatrist calls the "improvement."

The brain-disabling effects of psychosurgery are perhaps the most easy to understand. By producing lesions in the frontal lobes or the limbic system, the surgery reduces the higher capacities of the individual, rendering him less autonomous, and hence, less troublesome to others and possibly to himself. The therapeutic or clinical effect is only indirectly related to the loss of abstract reasoning, creativity, emotional sensitivity and other mental functions. It is most directly related to the inability to generate independent (and hence, inconvenient) choices and actions. Kalinowsky and others (Breggin 1979, 1982) have referred to the "emotional indifference" as the key to this treatment; but the emotional indifference is what makes the patient more managable, less "symptomatic" and less troublesome to others. While this blunting usually results in varying degrees of apathy, it may also result in euphoria. If depressed patients become euphoric, they will be considered "improved" when actually suffering from an iatrogenic disease.

Electroshock is also relatively easy to understand in terms of the brain disabling hypothesis (Breggin 1979). All patients on electroshock become, to one degree or another, victims of an acute organic brain syndrome, which includes global disruption of all mental functions, including abstract reasoning, memory, judgment and emotional stability. The patient may become either apathetic or euphoric, but will no longer seem depressed. Depression, like all the life styles of self-oppression, requires a relatively well functioning brain. As the acute organic brain syndrome clears, the patient may be left with permanent mental disabilities (Breggin 1979). To the extent that it completely clears, the patient is likely to lapse back into depression, now complicated by his/her traumatic experiences at the hands of the psychiatrist.

My latest investigations of brain-disabling therapy, *Chemical Lobotomy* (1982), focus upon the effects of the major tranquilizers, antidepressants and lithium. All produce severe brain dysfunction, and should be considered neurotoxins. Instead of specifically ameliorating biochemical effects, they produce global brain dysfunction.

The antidepressants produce an acute brain syndrome (or toxic delirium), in many ways similar to electroshock, in a large proportion of patients, without producing as much strait-jacketing or apathy as the major tranquilizers. Hence, their apparent efficacy in retarded depressions.

The major tranquilizers (neuroleptics or antipsychotics) are especially effective in suppressing overactive, rebellious or difficult patients. The generalized neurotoxicity produces a pacifying or subduing effect on all individuals (and animals). The major tranquilizers share this effect with lithium and the antidepressants. But the specific dopamine disruption in the limbic system produces a virtual chemical lobotomy unique to these drugs. In addition, the various neurologic disorders can aid in controlling the patient by means of the chemical strait jacket. Unhappily, these drugs, in addition to producing tardive dyskinesia in many if not most patients, also produce other associated defects in the higher centers of the brain, resulting at times in irreversible lobotomy, irreversible psychoses and dementia (Breggin 1981-2). The widespread use of the major tranquilizers is reaping a grim harvest of millions of brain-damaged individuals, many with severe, irreversible disorders of higher brain function.

Iatrogenic Denial

In order to designate an important effect of the major psychiatric technologies, I coined the term *iatrogenic denial*[1] (Breggin 1981c). Iatrogenic denial involves the infliction of brain damage and dysfunction upon the patient to encourage the patient in the process of denying the existence of both his personal problems and the iatrogenic brain damage.

Throughout history, medicine in general, as well as a multitude of quackeries, has relied upon the placebo effect and suggestion to achieve various effects in the patient. The authority of the physician or quack usually plays a key role in the process. Only in psychiatry, however, is the suggestion, "You are better now." reinforced by damaging the patient's brain and hence, his judgment, encouraging him to lapse into apathetic submission or an unrealistic high.

Denial and confabulation can be found in almost any brain damaged individual; the difference in iatrogenic denial is the purposeful infliction of the damage in order to encourage these primitive defense mechanisms and to enforce the authority of the physician (Breggin 1979; 1980b, 1980c).

The brain-disabled patient, above all else, is a fit subject for control by an authority. In the typical mental hospital today, where 90 percent or more of the patients are intoxicated with one or another brain-disabling agent, the authority of the physician and the institution are assured by the helpless state of the patient. The patient who enters into the psychiatric system because he subjectively *feels helpless* is rendered *objectively helpless* by mind-disabling treatments and by involuntary treatment and incarceration.

Conclusion

Life, for every individual, is fraught with fear. Too often the individual responds to these fears with an attitude of helplessness, rather than an attitude of self-determination. Once the route of helplessness has been taken, the individual tends to rely upon authority for guidance and for protection from the fears.

Psychiatric patients invariably suffer from an excess of helplessness in the face of their fears. They are primed to respond to authority. Psychiatry, instead of reversing this process, encourages the patient to spiral downward deeper into helplessness, and hence, more complete reliance upon the authority of the psychiatrist. Frequently, the psychiatrist will damage the brain of the patient with the major tranquilizers, antidepressants, lithium, electroshock or psychosurgery rendering the patient still more helpless and still more subject to the authority of the psychiatrist. Thus, the psychiatric treatment induces iatrogenic denial and iatrogenic helplessness in which the helpless patient submits to the psychiatrist without facing his own personal subjective helplessness or the objective helplessness induced by psychiatric treatment.

Involuntary treatment, diagnosis and the disease model, the mental hospital system, most psychotherapies and the various treatment technologies, such as electroshock and the major tranquilizers, encourage helplessness and submission to the authority of the psychiatrist.

There are alternative approaches which foster the individual's self-determination. Szasz (1965) and I (1971b, 1980a) have promoted the ethic of autonomy as a more rational principle upon which to develop re-educational approaches to individuals suffering from personal helplessness.

In *The Psychology of Freedom* (1980a) I have developed a systematic psychology of self-determination based upon the individual's right and capacity to be his/her own authority in life. In this approach, personal or subjective helplessness in the face of fear is recognized as the fundamental cause of most human problems. Even the most debilitating "psychiatric syndromes," such as depression, paranoia and recurrent anxiety, can be understood as particular styles of ethical failure. Instead of reinforcing helplessness and submission to authority, the psychology of self-determination presents principles through which individuals can take rational control of their own lives.

FOOTNOTE

[1] Iatrogenic denial is one aspect of iatrogenic helplessness. I have elaborated upon the latter term for the first time in this chapter.

BIBLIOGRAPHY

Breggin, P. R. Coercion of voluntary patients in an open hospital. *Arch Gen Psychiatry* 10 (1964):173-181.

——. *The Crazy from the Sane*. New York: Lyle Stuart, 1971a.

——. Psychotherapy as applied ethics. *Psychiatry* 34 (1971b):49-75.

——. Therapy as applied utopian politics. *Mental Health Soc* 1 (1974): 129-146.

——. Psychiatry and psychotherapy as political processes. *Am J Psychiatry* 29 (1975):369-382.

——. *Electroshock: Its Brain-Disabling Effects*. New York: Springer, 1979.

——. *The Psychology of Freedom: Liberty and Love as a Way of Life*. Buffalo, N.Y.: Prometheus Books, 1980a.

——. Brain-disabling therapies. In *The*

Psychosurgery Debate, edited by C. Valenstein. San Francisco: W. H. Freeman, 1980b.

——. Libertarian psychiatry. *Psychiatric Quarterly* (Spring 1981a).

——. Electroshock as brain-disabling therapy. In *Controversies in Psychiatry,* edited by M. Dongier. New York: Harper and Row, 1981b.

——. Psychosurgery as brain-disabling therapy. In *Controversies in Psychiatry,* edited by M. Dongier. New York: Harper and Row, 1981c.

——. *Chemical Lobotomy: The Brain-Disabling Effects of Psychiatric Drugs.* New York: Springer, 1982.

Fireside, H. *Soviet Psychoprisons.* New York: Norton, 1979.

Robitscher, J. *The Powers of Psychiatry.* New York: Houghton Mifflin, 1980.

Szasz, T. S. *The Ethics of Psychoanalysis.* New York: Basic Books, 1965.

——. *The Myth of Mental Illness,* rev. ed. New York: Harper and Row, 1974.

——. *Schizophrenia: The Sacred Symbol of Psychiatry.* New York: Basic Books, 1976.

——. *The Myth of Psychotherapy.* Garden City, N.Y.: Anchor Press, 1978.

W. FRANK EPLING AND J. B. WOODWARD

5

How to be a Successful Psychotherapist No Matter What the Effect on Behavior: The Corn Soup Principle

Dr. Thomas Nelson, Professor and Chairman, of the psychology department at the University of Alberta in Edmonton, strongly recommended we take a close look at the Corn Soup Principle proposed by two of his clinical colleagues, Epling and Woodward. This notorious principle, unfortunately too frequent in actual practice, follows. Their irony underlines the need for measureable/accountable objectives for the variety of meaningful and honest feedback purposes that keeping realistic track of successes and failures could serve. How often we have heard eminent therapists answer the question: "How do you know your work is successful?" with: "My patients don't come back" or "My patients send me Christmas cards." **R.F.M.**

Summary—An accidental discovery in the Union Hospital Cafeteria, Yorkton, Saskatchewan, led to the formulation of non-therapeutic intervention. This paper describes how therapy may be successful for the therapist, independent of changes in the client.

Like many of the great scientific advances of the twentieth century, this paper brings together the vast clinical experience of two psychologists and a serendipitous happening that occurred one day in the hospital cafeteria. While enjoying the scrumptuous cuisine, which is the standard fare of most hospital cafeterias, the senior author noted that his corn soup was bereft of corn, and contained only a yellow tasteless fluid. The importance of this observation was immediately seized upon by the junior author. After an intense discussion, the philosophical implications became apparent. "Ah," you might ask, "but what does corn soup have to do with psychotherapy?" On the following few pages we shall strike to the heart of the matter and reveal the kernels of wisdom implicit in this observation.

It is no easy task to engage in therapy that reliably leaves the client unchanged, and at the same time maintain professional standards. However, if dietitians can make corn soup that does not contain corn, surely

From *Behav. Res. & Therapy* 14 (1976):482-484. Reprinted with permission of Pergamon Press.

psychotherapists can design psychotherapies that contain no therapy. It is important in designing these therapies that one have a thorough understanding of the utility of therapy for the therapist. First, and probably most essential, the therapist must continue to be paid, regularly and lavishly. Second, the therapist must win and hold the esteem of his colleagues. This means that therapy must be designed so that no criticism is possible. Finally, clients must be happy with the therapeutic process, even though there is no change in their behaviour. The outstanding non-therapist will continue the therapeutic process as long as the client is alive. We are, of course, indebted to the highly complex psychodynamic schools of thought, which have laid squarely in the tradition of non-therapy. Other scholars, amongst them R. G. Jensen (1974), have identified some of the crucial features of the "Corn Soup Principle"; to illustrate, Jensen has stated

> another fundamental approach to a successful failure requires that the conceptualization and goals of the program be kept relatively obscure. If the treatment principles and goals become too concrete, there is some likelihood that an astute observer (e.g., a parent or trainee involved in the program) might ask impertinent questions such as, "Why are you doing that?" and expect a concrete answer. Failure becomes more difficult once treatment principles and techniques are open to public scrutiny. One means of maintaining a certain level of confusion is to make decisions on these matters, but insure that the decisions are not made known until the program is well under way.

Selection of Clients

Clients must be selected very carefully. The ideal client is one who seems to be reasonably happy, and is not sure why he or she has come to see a therapist. There are many such clients available, but in case of difficulty in obtaining them, it is the therapist's responsibility to let it be known that everyone has their "hang-ups" and that all of us may strive to become more "fully actualized." The unhappy client should be avoided since they have a tendency to complain about the length and outcome of therapy, and are more prone to end the therapeutic relationship. Clients with concrete problems (e.g., marriage failing, cannot hold a job) should also be avoided. There is a great danger that these people will recognize that therapy has not changed their behaviour. In addition, this type of client may complain to other professionals and thereby reduce the esteem of the successful non-therapist. Two additional qualifications of the ideal client are as follows: Clients should be young adults and they should be gullible. A handy guide for identifying gullible clients comes from *Theories of Personality* (Hall and Lindzey 1968), "a gullible person, for example, is one who is fixated on the oral incorparative level of personality; he will swallow almost anything he is told. Biting or oral aggression may be displaced in the form of sarcasm and argumentativeness." Good therapeutic practice requires a lifetime's dedication on the part of the client (some therapists have been known to give free dance lessons). Additionally, the therapist is typically older than his clients, and for this reason, at retirement the successful therapist will be able to sell his practice (this, of course, includes clients) and will thereby increase his retirement fund.

The Corn Soup Principle in Action or How to Conduct Therapy

It is essential that on the first meeting the therapist says only those things that the client wants to hear. The client should also be assured that he has made a positive step forward by entering the therapeutic relationship. It is additionally helpful to hint that had the client not come to you, something disastrous may have happened. These steps should be taken so that the therapist may be assured that the client will return for the next therapeutic session.

The therapist should strive to keep interaction at this level for a considerable amount of time (the length of time depends upon the brilliance of the therapist). The road to no behaviour change is strewn with many pitfalls that the unwary therapist can fall into. First it is important that the therapist strenuously resist setting any goals for therapy. It is to be remembered that many therapists have stated, "It is the process of therapy, and not the outcome, that is important." It should be noted here that if goals are set for therapy, only one of two things can happen. Either the client achieves the goal and therefore terminates therapy, or the client does not achieve the goal and is dissatisfied with the therapeutic relationship. In either case, this represents failure on the part of the client to live up to his responsibilities to the therapist.

Under no circumstances should the therapist observe behaviour or record observations. Some of the more outstanding therapists in the field do not even keep a record of the date, and it is well known that one quite successful therapist could not remember his name, much less those of the clients. Accurate data keeping has led to many case terminations. For those of you who work in public institutions that require accurate record keeping, we suggest forging them, or at best, do them all at the end of the month. As an alternative to behavioural observations and subsequent data keeping, the therapist should focus his attention on the clients earliest childhood experience, in an attempt to unravel the psychosexual history. It is of particular importance that toilet training of the client be unravelled. This developmental stage has only recently been re-evaluated and its importance underscored. For example, J. W. Hamilton (1974) has demonstrated a connection between psychosexual development and some automobile accidents. In concluding his article, Hamilton says, "The rear end collision can be seen as an attempt to master the fear of anal rape by the father via identification with the aggressor in the striking of another car from behind." This, by the way, is an excellent example of the sort of meaningless remark that the non-therapist should rehearse. There are, of course, many other useful phrases that the therapist can call upon. These phrases should be inserted in the therapeutic communication, in so much as possible, in a random manner. For example, Jung (1938) has said, "a complex may behave like an autonomous personality, which has a mental life and a motor of its own." Other illustrative examples from the authors are as follows: "Um hum, it probably has to do with the way you have grown." "It seems to me that you have made some steps forward," and "Get in touch with your feelings." Feelings have that nebulous quality that non-therapeutic therapy demands. They cannot be adequately described or properly identified, hence years of innocuous dialogue may be obtained by concentrating on these "facets of personality."

In order to avoid an analysis of the client's current behaviour in relation to its environment, the therapist should under no circumstances see the client anywhere but in his office, between the hours of 10:00 a.m. and 3:00 p.m. This serves to make the environment as artificial as possible and therefore reduce the frequency of deviant behaviour (this reduction in frequency occurs only in the office). In this regard, the office environment itself should be made as unusual as possible. Once this is done, the therapist may utilize learning theory principles while, at the same time, remaining assured that the newly conditioned behaviour will not generalize to the natural environment. It is helpful in the design of these office environments that one consult Hollywood movies made in the period 1927-1935.

Miscellaneous, sometimes extraneous, points that the successful non-therapist must be cognizant of

Confusion—"There is no such thing as truth or reality for a living human being, except as he participates in it, he is conscious of it, has some relationship to it," (May 1960). This clearly states the ideal client-therapist relationship. It is apparent that the client can only understand reality as he participates in it with the therapist. In as much as this is true for the client, it is true for everyone. *No one can understand reality or participate in it without the help of the non-therapist.* As long as the non-therapist keeps the therapeutic relationship obscure, the ideal of a lifetime of therapy is laid upon a firm foundation. Buytendijk (1960) elaborates by stating, "the phenomenological approach to feelings and emotions starts from the undeniable fact that consciousness is always a being conscious of something else and that we are conscious of our existing, that means our being physically subjugated to a given situation." Quite obviously, Buytendijk is here referring to the therapist. These clearly defined considerations must be uppermost in the therapist's mind at all times.

Testing—Psychological testing is one of the most powerful tools available to the non-therapist. A vast array of clinical instruments are readily available. There are only two justifiable uses of psychological tests. The first is that the therapist may sound very learned when conversing with other professionals, as for example, when the therapist says, "the high elevation of scale 6 to scale 8 in the 8-6 profile type is consistent with the uniform diagnosis of the sample as paranoid schizophrenics (Gelberstadt and Duker 1965). The second major reason is so that clients may be assigned a psychiatric diagnosis. This allows quick and efficient description of clients to other professionals. For example, "My 303.2 is getting in touch with his feelings." This is also useful when one is designing a filing system or when clients are to be shuffled from one ward to another, thereby being dealt with. One of the outstanding advantages of personality testing is that classification has little or nothing to do with therapy and typically assumes that the problem lies "deep within the client." Since testing has little to do with treatment, the therapist may satisfy himself with a testing session that looks good on the records and does not require a change in therapeutic direction. Finally, it must be pointed out that this can be an additional source of income that must not be sneered at.

Interpretations or more confusion—Again and again, the successful non-therapist is called upon to make interpretations in the course of therapy. As a guide to interpretations, we suggest the following, "again, generally speaking, interpretations should be offered only if and when all data pertinent to the issue under interpretive investigation appear to be covered by the interpretation and if the psychiatrist feels reasonably certain that the interpretation he has in mind is one which he considers correct and valid among several other possibilities." (Fromm-Reichmann 1950). Interpretations serve two useful purposes: first of all, they are fun for the therapist: second, an astute non-therapist can keep the client (and sometimes colleagues) completely confused.

Confrontation—Never confront the client, as this can serve no useful purpose for the therapist. The only exception is when the client becomes aggressive and the therapist must confront in order to reduce the aggression (Carkhuff and Berenson 1967). If clients become too aggressive, they may (1) terminate therapy or (2) make the therapeutic session unpleasant for the therapist. It is therefore essential that the therapist be as impassive, placid and non-directive as possible.

Summary

It is important that therapists do not observe or record behaviour, rather talk about feelings and early history. Do not set goals, rather set hazy objectives that neither client nor therapist fully understand. Keep the therapeutic relationship and environment as artificial as possible. Several tactics are available; confusing the client and psychological tests are excellent examples. Offering interpretations of verbal behaviour in obscure language is another excellent practice. Finally, it is suggested that clients should not be confronted with misbehaviour of any sort, as this serves, at best, to make therapy unpleasant for the therapist.

We realize that numbers of therapists function quite well without the insight of "the Corn Soup Principle." However, it is only by clearly stating basic principles of action that progress may be made.

REFERENCES

Buytendijk, F. J. J. 1950. The phenomenological approach to the problem of feelings and emotions. In *Feelings and Emotions,* edited by M. L. Reymwert, 127-141. New York: McGraw-Hill.

Carkhuff, R. R. and B. G. Berenson. 1967. *Beyond Counseling and Therapy.* New York: Holt, Rinehart and Winston.

Fromm-Reichmann, Frieda. 1950. *Principles of Intensive Psychotherapy.* Chicago: The University of Chicago Press.

Gilberstadt, H. and Jan Duker. 1965. *A Handbook for Clinical and Actuarial MMPI Interpretation.* Philadelphia: W. B. Saunders.

Hall, C. S. and G. Lindzey. 1968. *Theories of Personality.* New York: John Wiley.

Hamilton, J. W. 1967. The rear end collision—a specific form of acting out. *J. Hillside Hosp.* 16:3-4, 187-204.

Jensen, R. G. 1974. How to be a failure as a psychologist in programs for retarded children. *Mental Retardation* 12:10-11.

Jung, C. G. 1938. *Psychology and Religion.* New Haven: Yale University Press.

May, R. 1960. Existential psychology. In *Existential Psychology,* edited by R. May, 16-35. New York: Random House.

MICHAEL K. MILLER

6

Health Systems vs. Sickness Systems: Implications for the Physical Well-being of Americans

While at Cornell, sociologist Miller exploded a media bombshell under the sober manpower deliberations occurring across the continent. In the *Journal of Health & Social Behavior* (1978) and *Rural Sociology* (1980), he demonstrated that increasing hospital facilities and trained physicians in a community may *increase* rather than *decrease* mortality. Based on twenty years of data from 145 counties, Miller argued persuasively that increasing the numbers of community health nurses (with their emphasis on preventive work like nutrition and health education) and the availability of prepaid health maintenance organizations (where unnecessary surgery would work against the profit motive) would be more to the real advantage of medical consumers. His attention, data based, to the serious and widespread iatrogenic disasters within our present system and the profit incentive for medical overintervention as a remediable structural deficiency of the service delivery system was a landmark example in the constructive application of data to create pressure to combat iatrogenesis. **R.F.M.**

Abstract—The medical care system in the United States is a societal subsystem with a mandate to preserve, repair and enhance the health status of Americans. It is assumed, however, that the existing system is structured in such a way that it operates only on the negative dimension of health. The structure of the existing sickness system is elaborated and its impact on mortality is evaluated relative to community structure. The results indicate that the stratification system among communities is far more important in explaining differential mortality than is the medical care system. Further, while some elements of the medical care system demonstrate positive impacts on health (i.e., registered nurses), other elements (concentration of surgeons and utilization) appear to contribute materially to iatrogenic disease. It is concluded that if improved health is the goal, priorities should be shifted from a sickness care to a health care system. This latter system would focus on the behavioral (life style) and environmental (to include social inequalities) determinates of health. Improved public well-being should be realized by the focus on positive and primary preventative health.

The paper is a revision of the keynote address to the Oregon Nursing Convention, Portland, Oregon, April 9-11, 1980. Reprinted with permission of the Director of the Arkansas Agricultural Experiment Station which supported the research.

Introduction

From the turn of the century, the physical health status of Americans has improved dramatically. In 1900 the infant mortality rate in the United States approached 162 infant deaths per 1000 live births (Kotelchuck 1976). By 1940 the rate had declined to 47.0 and in the twelve months ending with July 1979, 1000 live births were accompanied by approximately 13.3 infant deaths (Monthly Vital Statistics Report 1979). Other indicators have shown equally impressive declines. Maternal mortality rates have declined from approximately 730 to less than twelve. Death rates for tuberculosis have dropped from 194 in 1900 to virtually nothing in 1980. Americans are also living longer than ever before. In the early 1900s Americans could expect to live only forty-seven years. Today, the average life expectancy is 72.8 years, with females outliving males by 7.6 years.[1] Thus, even though deaths from such things as malignant neoplasms have shown a steady increase over the last century, most indicators point to an improved physical health status for Americans.

Accompanying this dramatic improvement in population health status has been an ever expanding, evermore costly and complex medical care system. In 1950 the health care enterprise cost $12 billion and accounted for roughly 4.6 percent of the gross national product (GNP). Fueled by costs that are rising faster than those in any other sector of the economy (with the current exception of energy),[2] the health care industry had ballooned to $160.6 billion in 1977 (8.6 percent of the GNP) and established itself as the third largest industry in the nation behind agriculture and construction (Culliton 1978; Walsh 1978). Current projections put the 1980 price tag for medical care at almost 10 percent of the GNP (approximately $900 for every man, woman and child) (Warner 1979).

The growth of the American health empire has flourished for a number of reasons. Professional autonomy, a capitalist, political philosophy and historical precedent all serve as partial explanations (Duval 1977; Knowles 1977; Rogers 1977; Wildavsky 1977). Probably the most important reason for the expansion, however, has been the public's estimate of the role medicine played in the historical improvement of health, and the further estimate of the role it plays in the contemporary production and will play in the future production of health (McKeown 1976; Rogers 1977; Thomas 1977).

The American people want to live as long as possible and to live well (Duval 1977). The common assumption is that the accomplishment of that end requires the application of "more and more complex" medical knowledge and technology, whatever the price. But, as a number of recent authors (Carlson 1975; Illich 1976; McKeown 1976; Miller and Stokes 1978; Mendelsohn 1979) and not so recent (Dubos 1960; Cochrane 1972) have pointed out, the assumption may be largely unjustified. The impact that medical care has actually had or is having on health is, by and large, assumed but unsubstantiated. Indeed, using historical data from England and Wales, McKeown (1976) demonstrates most convincingly that the bulk of mortality decline was due to the reduction of deaths from infectious diseases.[3] Further, the primary influences that led to the reduction, both from infectious and noninfectious causes, were nutritional, environmental (particularly improvement in water and food sources), behavioral (reduced natality), and intrinsic resistance resulting from interaction of organism and host. In most instances mortality rates were declining long before effective immunization or treatment procedures became available, and the subsequent rates of decline were virtually unchanged (McKeown 1976; Knowles 1977). In short, medical intervention via vaccination had little or no impact on the historical decline in mortality.

What about the more recent situation? Vaccination did produce some additional decline in the rates of smallpox in the nineteenth century.[4] In this century vaccines contribute to declines in diptheria, poliomyelitis, tuberculosis and measles. Still, over the past one hundred years, vaccinations probably accounted for less than 10 percent of the overall reduction in mortality (McKeown 1976). The contribution made by the introduction of medical and surgical therapy, particularly antibiotics and tumor excision, is even smaller (Knowles 1977).[5]

The aforementioned data provides some evidence that the formal medical care system did contribute (albeit very minimally) to historical mortality reduction. Some recent literature suggests that, under certain circumstances, the existing system can even further reduce mortality and morbidity rates in the United States (Minnesota Systems Research 1972[6]; DHEW 1972; Gordis 1973; Kessner 1973; Radtke 1974; Lipscomb 1978). Others are less convinced by the available evidence and suggest that the contribution of the medical care system to health status has been significantly overstated and potentially misinterpreted. The result of the misinterpretation has been a severe misuse of resources and a distortion of the role of medicine (Kisch 1974; Carlson 1975; Illich 1976; McKeown 1976; Callahan 1977; Knowles 1977; Wildavsky 1977; Miller and Stokes 1978; Mendelsohn 1979). The remainder of this paper is an empirical examination of the relative impact of the medical care system on the physical health status of the population of the United States.

Theoretical Operation of the Medical Care System: A Macro Sickness Model

The previous section suggested the existence of a deeply held belief about the functioning of the American health care system. The assumption can be succinctly explicated as one which puts virtually unquestioning faith in the investigation and treatment of diseases by formally trained medical personnel (particularly physicians and to a somewhat lesser degree, nurses and physician assistants) (Callahan 1977). Malady intervention is deemed critical, not only as a restorative strategy for the acutely ill, but also as the solution to long-term health prospects (Thomas 1977).

It is this presumption about the efficacy of medicine to produce and restore health (a presumption made by both the profession of medicine and the general public) that serves to justify the massive investment in medical care (Bennett 1977) and to provide a theoretical underpinning for the continuation of a functional sickness care system.[7]

Recent literature (Field 1973; Levy 1977; Miller and Stokes 1978) has defined the macro health care system as a societal mechanism, however ineffective, that has been mandated to preserve, repair or enhance the capacity of social actors whose role performance is imperiled by ill health or premature death. As such, the system would include the aggregate of resources (to include manpower in designated roles) that society actually imparts to the health concern. While such a definition is conceptually appealing, operationally the elements of the existing system are considerably more restricted. The existing system is not a comprehensive integrated system with health as the target. More realistically, it is a rather loosely assembled class of medically related elements with malady and mortality as the focus. Our investment in "health" is based on the assumption that, as a collectivity, we are ill and need to be made healthy and that medical intervention is the way to accomplish that health (McKeown 1976). But, if collective good health is the goal, there is a paradox in the way the medical care system is structured. The most characteristic function of the elements of the system lies in the diagnosis and treatment of disease in the individual patient (Black 1968; Reiser 1977). Hence, the great majority of medical manpower will never be concerned with *positive health, preventative health* or *community health*. The focus on individual acute curative medicine leads away from a consideration of the environmental and behavioral etiology of disease. But, in post-industrial American society, such "public health" considerations are potentially the most realistic path to decreased mortality and improved positive health.

Even though the medical care system is not comprehensively integrated with positive health as the focus, it is nonetheless possible to specify a general structure for the more restricted sickness system. The minimum commitments that society makes to the medical care subsystem can be organized into four major categories: knowledge, manpower, physical facilities and economic resources. Embodied in the knowledge commitment are such things as basic biomedical research and training of manpower to fill specialized roles within the system. The manpower commitment includes all personnel directly involved in the sickness concern (e.g. nurses, x-ray technicians and, of course, physicians). The physical facility component embraces all objects which are primarily instrumental in fostering fulfillment of the roles filled by the existing manpower. Central among these facilities are hospitals, clinics and sundry forms of technical equipment.

The economic resource component is, of necessity, rather ubiquitous and plays a central role in all of the three aforementioned commitment areas. In addition, it includes more direct elements such as per capita expenditures for health and actual medical care payments.

Organized in this manner, the medical care system can be formally conceptualized as an input-outcome system. The four components, knowledge, manpower, facilities and economic resources, constitute the inputs to the system and population health status is the outcome.

For subsequent analytic purposes, it is useful to differentiate between internal and external components of the system. The output of the internal components remain within the system but eventually have an influence on the services provided by the system (Field 1973). Conversely, the output of the external components go directly from the system to the existing maladies of society. For example, the specialized training of manpower indirectly contributes to the treatment of the disease. The actual application of that training is provided through existing manpower activities and available techniques. The major modalities employed by the external components of the system are: diagnosis, treatment and rehabilitation.[8]

The sickness system is a differentiated subsystem of society. As such, it is neither unconstrained nor self-supporting, but rather operates in a given structural or community context with a target population of defined scope. Hence, the structure of the community constrains the operation of the system and thus influences what impact the system can theoretically have on the physical well-being of the population (Rushing 1971). Different settings demonstrate widely varying abilities to furnish the needed supports for the system to function optimally. At the same time, the very structure that constrains the operation of the system also demonstrates a direct impact on the health status of the target population.

The nature of the impact is perhaps best summarized by the phrase "cumulative advantage" or "cumulative disadvantage." Community characteristics are interdependent and mutually reinforcing. Those with strong economies attract more and more professional industries. In turn, well-educated people with relatively high socio-economic status are attracted because of lucrative opportunities for employment. To accommodate the clientele, high quality services are developed and supported. The inevitable outcome of the process is a stratification system *among* communities that parallels the system of inequalities at the individual level (Blau 1977; Miller and Stokes 1978). Hence, theoretically, the health status of a given population will be a function of both the general structure of the community and the specific medical care system operating within the constraining structure. Diagramatically, the system is depicted in figure 1 (*see* page 64). The intent of the current analysis is to assess the relative importance of community structure and the medical care system on differential mortality rates in the 3079 counties of the continental United States.

The Concept of Community Malady

To make the task manageable, the focus of this paper is on physical health status to the exclusion of the mental and/or social dimension of the health triangle. However, as Goldsmith (1973) has pointed out, there are certain types of data that are more widely accepted as policy relevant by health planners and legislators than others: infant mortality rates, rates of preventable deaths, mortality rates by major causes and health facilities data. And, as pointed out previously, this type of focus is consistent with

Figure 1: Theoretical Structure of the Medical Care System

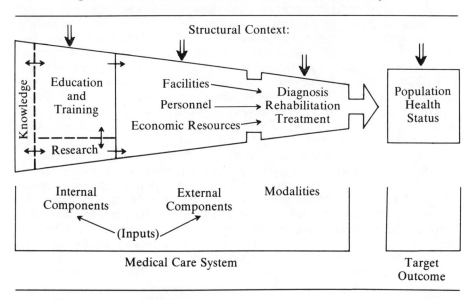

Where ⟹ is interpreted as influences

the focus of the existing malady system. Accordingly, two separate measures of mortality are employed to evaluate collective physical well-being:[9]

1) Infant mortality rates, and
2) Age-sex standardized death rates for all causes.[10]

Although there is not complete consensus, infant mortality is considered by many to be the single most sensitive index of "the level of health existing in an area" (Anderson 1973). Further, to the extent that the etiology of the life-threatening maladies are postnatal and somewhat tractable, the medical care system is, theoretically, capable of exerting some positive impact. This is true for many nongenetic causes of death and thus an appropriately adjusted death rate (all causes) can legitimately serve as an overall measure of physical health status for a population. Employing this rationale, it is possible to operationally define community health (or malady) in a straightforward relative framework. Any one community can be judged to have a higher health status than any other community when the mortality rate in one is smaller than the rate in the other.

Consistent with this theoretical framework, data also were collected on medical care resources, utilization and structural characteristics of the population for every county in the continental United States. Indicators of germane structural characteristics of the population include: percent non-white population, median school years completed for all persons 25 years and older, percent of the labor force classified as white collar, median family income, percent of homes with no plumbing and percent urban population. All indicators were selected as structural properties that differentiate among communities. Most importantly, when considered in combination, the indicators allow for examining the existence of hierarchic differentiation (Rushing 1975). Communities that are relatively advantaged in terms of the structural mix (i.e., those with cumulative advantage) will, theoretically, have lower mortality rates than those lower in the hierarchy.

A total of eight indicators was used to measure medical care resources for the age-sex adjusted mortality model. Manpower resources were indexed by: medical specialists per 1000 population, surgical specialists per 1000 population, general physicians per 1000 population, registered nurses per 1000 population and licensed practical nurses per 1000 population. Physical facilities were measured by: number of hospital beds per 1000 population, presence or absence of at least one hospital in the county and presence of two or more hospitals in the county. Finally, items selected to represent utilization of existing resources include: inpatient days per 1000 population, and outpatient visits per 1000 population.

The model for infant mortality employs basically the same indicators of population structure, but adds one indicator of poverty: average number of Aid to Families With Dependent Children (AFDC) recipients per 1000 population. In addition, the medical care system is now more complex. The indicators of manpower are unchanged, but several additional indicators of physical resources pertaining directly to infant mortality have been included: presence or absence of a hospital with a neonatal intensive care unit, presence or absence of a hospital with a premature nursery, presence of two or more hospitals with premature nurseries, presence or absence of a pediatric program in the county and presence or absence of an obstetrical/gynecologic (OB/GYN) program in the county. Finally, because of known variation in mortality and resource distribution, an explicit control for region of the country was included in both models.

The Relative Determinants of Mortality: Medical Care vs. Community Structure

The fundamental intent of the current research is to examine empirically whether or not mortality is influenced by the existing medical care system, as well as by the structural characteristics of the population. By examining the information in the first column of table 1, it is apparent that, as specified, the model explains only 38 percent of the variation in age-sex adjusted death rates and less than 18 percent of the variation in infant mortality. This finding alone indicates that much more work needs to be done before a full understanding of the determinants of mortality can be achieved. However, the information in the four remaining columns of table 1 lend some insight into the relative explanatory power of the medical care system and the general structural makeup of the population.

Contrary to the opinion of some authors, the medical care system does have a net impact on mortality. The magnitude of the impact is not, however, large either absolutely or relative to that of the community structure. In absolute terms, the medical care system accounted for only 4.02 percent of the variation in age-sex standardized death rates and still less (1.4 percent) of the variation in infant mortality. As relative percentages, those figures represent 10.5 percent and 7.8 percent of the total variance expained by the standardized mortality model and infant mortality model respectively.

Table 1: Variance in Mortality

Percentage of variance explained by:				
(1) **Medical care system and population structure**	**(2)** **Structure**	**(3)** **Medical care system**	**(4)** **System with structure controlled**	**(5)** **Ratio col. 4 to col. 1**
Age-Sex Adjusted Death Rates				
38.00	35.40	5.06	4.02	.105
Infant Mortality				
17.85	16.68	4.88	1.40	.078

Although the data in table 1 provide some information concerning a general explanation for mortality differentials, it is instructive to examine the nature of the effects for individual indicators. For example, what is the impact of having one more doctor, one more nurse or one thousand dollars more income? The partial regression analysis presented in tables 2 and 3 provide the relevant data. By comparing the magnitude and the signs of the beta coefficients it is possible to determine the nature of the impact as well as the relative importance of the indicators in explaining mortality. Because the explanatory variables exhibit diverse impacts on age-sex standardized death rates and infant mortality rates, the results of the analysis will be presented separately.

The Age-Sex Standardized Mortality Model

By examining the beta coefficients in the second column of table 2, several general observations can be made. First, it is apparent that the stratification system among communities is important in explaining differential mortality rates. After controlling out the impact of the medical care system and region of the country, those communities that have higher average income ($-.07$), higher educational levels ($-.05$) and a relatively small nonwhite population (.40) have lower levels of mortality. It is instructive to note that although the percentage of the labor force engaged in white collar occupations and the percent of homes with no plumbing are relatively important explanatory variables in the bivariate situation (column 4 of table 2), their impacts are virtually eliminated when other variables in the model are controlled. Further, the degree of urbanization tends to be unimportant in both the controlled and the uncontrolled situation. Finally, although all of the community structural variables in the model are not large enough to be statistically significant predictors of differential mortality, the nature of their impact (i.e., + or −), is consist-

Table 2: Regressions of Age-Sex Standardized Death Rate on Structural Characteristics and Medical System Resources

	b	β	Probability of β	r
Manpower				
Medical Specialities/1000	−152.285	−0.154	<0.001	−.062
RN/1000 1972	−8.631	−0.126	<0.001	−.133
Surgical Specialities/1000	121.764	0.162	<0.001	−.007
Physicians/1000 1969	−4.428	−0.023	0.374	−.066
LPN/1000 1967	2.845	0.023	0.168	−.003
Facilities				
Hospital Bed/1000 1970	3.512	0.100	0.009	−.016
One Hospital 1970	−0.416	−0.002	0.938	.035
Two + Hospitals 1970	−5.463	−0.023	0.403	−.057
Utilization				
Inpatient Days/1000 1970	0.005	0.035	0.362	.013
Outpatient Visit/1000 1970	0.005	0.043	0.009	.063
Structural Characteristics				
Percent Nonwhite 1970	3.024	0.401	< 0.001	.502
Percent Urban 1970	0.045	0.011	0.643	−.066
Percent White Collar 1970	−0.110	−0.008	0.745	−.152
Median Education 1970	−4.650	−0.056	0.079	−.317
Percent Homes No Plumbing	0.399	0.041	0.237	.394
Median Family Income 1970	−0.005	−0.077	0.006	−.225
Region				
Eastsouthcentral	−59.072	−0.166	< 0.001	.189
Mid-Atlantic	7.547	0.014	0.575	.039
Mountain	−51.379	−0.128	< 0.001	−.034
Eastnorthcentral	−34.127	−0.103	0.006	−.011
Pacific	−71.170	−0.126	< 0.001	−.082
South Atlantic	−46.002	−0.153	< 0.001	.308
Westnorthcentral	−113.600	−0.396	< 0.001	−.311
Westsouthcentral	−122.569	−0.383	< 0.001	−.095

Constant = 1075.30
R^2 = .380

When employing dummy variables in a multiple regression equation, the form is $y = a + b_1 d_1 + b_2 d_2 + b_3 x_1 + \ldots b_i x_i$. a = the mean ($\bar{x}$) of the excluded category, adjusted for all other variables in the equation. The slope coefficients on the remaining dummies are interpretable as differences from that adjusted intercept. In the current analysis, region of country is handled as a nine category dummy variable with Northeast being employed as the excluded category.

ent with theoretical expectation. Cumulative advantage/disadvantage does appear to operate in contemporary American society. The same phenomena appear to operate for the regional variation as well. As evidenced by the regional coefficients, communities that are located in the Northeast (the excluded category for the present analysis) and the mid-Atlantic region (b = 7.5) have the highest overall death rates. Conversely, communities that are located in the westnorthcentral (b = −113.6) or the westsouthcentral (b = −122.5) part of the country have lower overall mortality rates than any other geographic location.

Although the aforementioned regional and socio-economic variations are important, the most striking piece of information relative to the extant stratification system in this country is the fact that the percentage of nonwhite residents in a community is the single most important predictor of increased death rates. This is true even after all other socio-economic, regional and medical care factors have been statistically controlled. In short, macro inequalities in mortality still have a significant racial component in the latter part of the twentieth century.

Turn to an examination of the nature of the impact of the medical care system. Consistent with the macro system model developed earlier, the three categories (manpower, physical facilities and utilization) all contain variables that are statistically significant predictors of differential mortality. Specifically, communities that have relatively high concentrations of medical specialists (6 = −.15) and registered nurses (6 = −.12) tend to have lower death rates. Conversely, as hospital beds increase (.09), as utilization rates increase (.04) and as surgical specialists become more concentrated (.16), the mortality rates in communities also increase. In fact, except for the percent nonwhite in the population the concentration of surgeons is the single most powerful negative predictor of mortality differentials among communities. Conversely, the concentration of registered nurses and medical specialists are the two most powerful positive explanatory variables in the model. Hence, the data demonstrate that 50 percent of the elements of the medical care system have no statistically significant impact on mortality, and those variables that do demonstrate significant impacts do not affect mortality in the theoretically expected fashion in all instances. A discussion of these findings and the implications is included in the final section of the paper.

The Infant Mortality Model

If attention is turned to table 3, it become apparent that the medical care system operates quite differently for the more narrowly defined problem of infant mortality. The nature of the difference is simple. The existance and concentration of medical manpower, programs and facilities have no impact on infant mortality rates. The only statistically significant coefficients are for utilization (hospital admissions .10 and inpatient days .10). And, even though the increased utilization demonstrates a constant nega-

Table 3: Regression of Infant Mortality on Structural Characteristics and Medical System Resources

	b	β	Probability of β	r
Manpower				
Physicians/1000 1975-1976	−0.186	−0.022	0.570	−.083
Medical Specialities/1000 1970	0.029	0.001	0.990	−.086
Surgical Specialities/1000 1970	−3.463	−0.079	0.058	−.090
RN/1000 1972	0.062	0.015	0.680	−.150
LPN/1000 1974	0.038	0.008	0.725	.051
Facilities				
One Hospital 1976	−0.050	−0.004	0.930	.054
Two + Hospitals 1976	−0.031	−0.002	0.963	−.063
Hospital Bed/1000 1975-1976	−0.203	−0.079	0.129	.003
One + Hospital Neonatal Intensive Care 1976	−0.493	−0.024	0.370	−.055
One Hosp., Premature Nursery 1976	0.123	0.008	0.714	−.013
Two + Hosp., Premature Nursery 1976	0.409	0.021	0.481	−.047
One + Pediatric Program 1971-1972	−0.874	−0.028	0.401	−.038
One + OBGYN Program 1971-1972	0.437	0.016	0.641	−.039
Utilization				
Hospital Adm./1000 1975-1976	0.008	0.105	0.020	.034
Inpatient Days/1000 1975-1976	0.001	0.105	0.018	.019
Outpatient Visits/1000 1975-1976	<0.001	0.001	0.965	.001
Structural Characteristics				
Per Capita Income 1974	<0.001	0.013	0.762	−.274
AFDC Recip./1000 1975-1976	0.013	0.065	0.022	.257
Percent White Collar 1970	−0.078	−0.102	0.006	−.179
Median Education 1970	0.137	0.027	0.566	−.273
Median Family Income 1970	>−0.001	−0.071	0.154	−.284
Percent Nonwhite 1970	0.100	0.239	0.001	.365
Percent Urban 1970	0.025	0.101	0.003	−.073
Percent Homes No Plumbing	0.035	0.061	0.241	.306
Region				
Eastsouthcentral	2.155	0.107	0.039	.136
Mid-Atlantic	1.561	0.053	0.110	−.064
Mountain	2.750	0.105	0.006	−.019
Pacific	1.935	0.063	0.060	−.061
South Atlantic	1.794	0.108	0.075	.130
Westnorthcentral	0.456	0.024	0.637	−.125
Westsouthcentral	2.359	0.127	0.027	.095
Eastnorthcentral	0.966	0.049	0.294	−.123

Constant = 13.47
R^2 = .178

tive impact on infant mortality, the magnitude of the coefficients are sufficiently small to conclude that the relationship is tenuous.[11]

By examining the coefficients for the structural characteristics, it is again apparent that the macro stratification system is operating to produce cumulative advantage/disadvantage among communities. However, a different (i.e., different from the age-sex standardized death model) set of variables are important in explaining differential infant mortality. In this case, communities that have lower concentrations of AFDC recipients (.06), higher percentage of the labor force in white collar occupations (−.10), a smaller percentage of the population living in urban areas (.10) and a relatively low percentage of nonwhite population (.24) have lower infant mortality rates. As with the earlier model, the percent of nonwhite population is the single most powerful negative contributor to increased infant mortality rates in a community.

Although there is some net regional variation in infant mortality rates, it is not as pronounced as for the standardized mortality model. An examination of the regression coefficients suggests that there are only two broad regional differences. The Northeast (the excluded category in the regression analysis), eastnorthcentral, westnorthcentral and the mid-Atlantic regions tend to cluster as areas with relatively low infant mortality rates. Relative to those regions the eastsouthcentral, Mountain, Pacific, South Atlantic, and westsouthcentral areas have, ceterus parabus, relatively high rates of infant mortality.

Summary

One of the major underlying justifications for spending billions of dollars on the medical care system in the United States has been the assumed validity of what Wildavsky (1977) has termed the "Great Equation, to-wit: Medical Care Equals Health." Given this equality, it is presumed by many that the real problem with the American medical care system, and thus, by definition, with American health status, is basic insufficiency (Thomas 1977). There are not enough doctors, there are not enough nurses, there are not enough medical schools and there are not enough hospitals. Clearly then, if there was only enough money to expand manpower and resources, the medical care system could function to enhance good health in the population.

The evidence does not support such a contention. As McKeown (1976), Duval (1977), Wildavsky (1977) and a number of other authors have suggested, most of what the medical care system does, or is capable of doing, is irrelevant to collective good health. The evidence presented in this study suggests that the system is also impotent in the more narrowly defined charge of curtailing preventable death or prolonging lives. Access, equal or not, is not equivalent to health. Indeed, the marginal value of putting one thousand or several billion additional dollars into the existing medical care system to equalize access will be very close to zero in terms of preventing death, let alone improving the collective health status of Americans. This is not to say that the medical care system, its practitioners and its technology does not help in individual instances. Bones do get mended, ruptured appendices do get removed and innoculations do get administered. But, at the level of the societal collectivity, the effectiveness pales. Even so, there are elements of the system that are beneficial at the macro community level. The concentration of registered nurses tends to

be associated with lower community mortality rates. One possible explanation for this relationship has recently been proposed (Miller and Stokes 1978). Although nurses do engage in some therapeutic activity, that would not appear to be their primary function. Hence, to the extent that nurses avoid highly risky undertakings, the potential of medical misadventure is limited. But this would only explain the existence of no relationship between community mortality rates and nurse concentration. To explain the presence of the positive impact requires further examination of the nursing role. As Miller and Stokes (1978) and Kane and Kane (1978) point out, the traditions of nursing not only deemphasize diagnosis and therapy, but are inextricably tied into the nurturing requirements of long-term care. Further, in many instances, the nursing role tends to emphasize health promotion (or at least sickness prevention) via health education efforts (Anderson 1973).[12] If this interpretation of the findings is correct, it would imply the need to examine closely the impact on health of changing the function role of nurse practitioners. At the very least, it would suggest the need to maintain many of the supportive, health promoting activities of traditional nurses.

While it is possible to provide tentative explanations for the relationship between nurses and mortality, plausible explanations for the relationship between medical specialists and mortality are less evident. Again, a partial explanation may be found in the roles performed by the various specialists. To the extent that specialists deal with well-defined maladies, and to the extent that minimally risky curative technology is available and employed to treat such maladies it is reasonable to expect the system functions as expected (i.e., it reduces death or prolongs life). This logic would, however, lead to the necessity of examining individual specialty fields to determine which are providing maximum benefit. For example, which specialities employ (on the average) less risky, more beneficial technologies?

It is a simple fact that no diagnostic or therapeutic procedure is free from potentially harmful effects.[13] This is true even if the procedure is administered appropriately by a highly competent person. Surgical procedures (as a group) are probably among those with the highest attached risk. Hence, the more surgical procedures that are used, the higher the probability of some iatrogenic disease resulting. This situation is aggravated in the United States by several different factors: the quantity of surgery in a population is positively associated with the concentration of surgeons and the concentrations of surgeons continues to rise, and the fee-for-service payment system in the United States gives the surgeon incentive to perform more and more complex (i.e., high cost) surgery (House of Representatives Committee on Interstate and Foreign Commerce 1976; Kristein et al 1977). Consistent with these system structures is the fact that the concentration of surgeons and the rate of elective surgery in the United States are among the highest in the world (i.e., we have twice as many surgeons and twice the rate of surgery per capita as has England). Even more disconcerting is the fact that within the United States the rates of surgical admission and general hospital use is approximately twice as high for fee-for-service populations as for those under prepaid group plans (Social Security Administration 1975). The situation is further exacerbated by the health insurance payment guidelines (i.e., they pay for in-hospital care of a curative nature). Given these system realities, it is entirely consistent, even highly predictable, that as the concentration of surgeons increase in a population so do the general mortality rates. It is an inescapable conclusion that although some people may be helped by the system, some may also be harmed. Clearly, a cost accounting is appropriate in such instances.

If the goal is actually improved health and if, for whatever reason, the existing medical care system does not address many of the factors that ultimately have an impact on health, there appears to be a great deal of rethinking and reallocation of funds that is necessary.

The data presented in the current study is conclusive in identifying race as a major contributing factor to differential mortality in the United States. However, race is not tractable from a policy perspective. This would suggest the need to identify and examine those things that are associated with the racial factor but are more amenable to public policy solution. In this context, it is increasingly evident that many health problems in the United States have their genesis in social class difference generally, and associated personal behavior patterns. Hence, in some communities, those relatively low socio-economic status (SES) communities, the major maladies result from environmental conditions and behavioral patterns (e.g., sewage disposal, water supplies and food supplies, hygiene and reproductive practices) that are not conducive to good health. At the other extreme are the relatively affluent communities that have equally deleterious, but very different, environmental conditions and collective behavior patterns. Over-consumption of alcohol, fatty foods and tobacco, combined with a sedentary, generally stressful life style are clearly not health producing.

The conclusion is inescapable. There are priority changes that must be made if an improvement in the health status of Americans is to be realized. One general priority shift is from a sickness care to a health care system. There are a number of alterations that loom large as needed first steps. First, it is essential that it become common, but more importantly, *accepted* knowledge by the consuming public, the policy makers and the profession of medicine that health cannot be purchased. Life style, social inequality and environmental conditions are the prime determinants of health, or its antithesis, death. A system of acute, curative, "compliant-responsive" hospital-based medicine—a sickness system—is not a viable contender for improving the plight of the population. Second, it will be necessary to invest significant resources, part of which may indeed be gerimandered from the current medical care system, into the health education of Americans.[14] It is a sad fact that of the billions of dollars spent annually on health, only ½ of 1 percent is spent on health education (Knowles 1977). This becomes particularly disheartening when it is realized that significant strides in improved health status could very probably be realized by convincing the public to observe simple and prudent behavioral guidelines relating to exercise, diet, rest and personal habits. Three meals each day at regular times, moderate exercise, adequate sleep, maintenance of a reasonable weight, no smoking and alcohol only in moderation (if at all) can do more for health, and at far less expense, than all the efforts of the medical care system combined.

In addition to the aforementioned, it will be necessary for the commitment to environmental health research and primary preventative "medicine" to be substantially increased. What kind of logic encourages attempted medical cure of cancer when existing knowledge indicates that the vast majority of human neoplasms (80% to 90%) have their genesis in environmental factors such as the food we eat, the water we drink, the air we breathe, self-indulgent habits (we spend $30 billion plus for cigarettes and alcohol) and even the occupations we choose (or are forced into)? Obviously, there is a misalignment between cause and concern, both on the part of the medical establishment and the public. If a workable (i.e., one that improves health), health system is to be developed, it will require a rational setting of priorities and a much different distribution of scarce resources.

Finally, there is a constantly expanding literature, including the current study, that demonstrates the lack of impact as well as the probable existence of iatrogenic disease. Hence, what is needed is more fundamental than a shift in resources among existing services. What is needed is a complete, thoughtful reappraisal of the entire structure of the medical care system. That will probably be a long time coming. In the interim, control of the quality of care (to include effectiveness, efficiency and standards) should be the central focus of efforts to improve health via the existing medical care system. Such efforts may not have a great deal of positive impact directly on health, but they would force some systematic cost benefit analysis of the present medical care system and its operation. This would potentially lead to structural modifications that would ultimately serve to shift the focus from sickness to positive and primary preventative health. Subsequently, progress toward improved public health would hopefully be realized.

FOOTNOTES

[1] It should be pointed out that the improvements in life expectancy reflect, by and large, improved survival rates for infants and the very young. Additionally, most of the change in expectation of life occurred pre-1950.

[2] Past Secretary Califano indicated that from 1975 to 1977, costs for medical service rose at a rate of 9.5 percent—one and one-half times the overall rate for all consumer prices. Hospital costs (a major contributor to escalating costs, accounting for 40 percent of the health care bill) have been increasing at an average annual rate of 17.3 percent (Culliton 1978).

[3] McKeown also notes that infanticide and starvation may have contributed substantially to the overall reduction, but that an assessment of the actual impact is virtually impossible.

[4] Knowles (1977) points out that by 1968 the costs of vaccination for smallpox in the U.S. outweighed the benefits. In that year, the vaccine resulted in over 8000 complications, 152 of which were major, including nine deaths (one per million vaccinations). All of this happened twenty years after the last reported case of the disease (i.e., 1949).

[5] Kisch (1974) notes in this regard that the death rate from complications of medical procedures more than doubled in the period 1950-1970.

[6] It is significant to note that the positive impacts reported in these studies resulted from preventative and primary care programs, including nutrition programs designed to serve high-risk populations (i.e., poor largely nonwhite ghetto areas of large cities).

[7] It is necessary to point out that health status (or sickness status) has a reality both for the individual and for the community (i.e., entire populations). It follows that the societal subsystem that purportedly provides for health needs theoretically operates at both levels (Levy 1977). The focal point of this paper is macro. Specifically, the intent is to examine the population's state of health and empirically assess the assumed existence of an organic link between the health "state" and the medical care subsystem.

[8] Field (1973) enumerated six major activities: diagnosis, treatment, rehabilitation, custody, prevention and health education. It is the contention of this paper, as well as several other authors (Black 1968; Knowles 1977; Reiser 1977), that at least the last two, prevention and health education, are not fully integrated modalities of the existing sickness system.

[9] The literature that grapples with the conceptualization and measurement of health status is massive and growing rapidly. (See the ongoing Health, Education and Welfare publication, *Clearinghouse on Health Indexes.*) While there are some exciting new developments in the area, many require the use of data that are very expensive and, by and large, unavailable for use in macro modelling efforts. Further, given the focus of the existing medical care system, the most valid assessment of its impact may indeed be on how well it explains differential mortality as opposed to some more complex measure of positive health.

Additionally, as McKeown (1976) points out, declines in mortality have been accompanied by rather large declines in morbidity. Hence, it is unlikely that the utilization of mortality rate to gauge the health status of a population will be very misleading. The reader should consult Sanders (1964) for an opposing view.

[10] Since the two primary determinants of differential mortality are age and sex, the measure employed in present research adjusts for both. Race is also an important determinant, but racial composition is explicitly included in the analysis.

[11] A comparison of the signs of the coefficients for the two models (tables 2 and 3) implies that the nature of the impact exerted by the medical care system varies substantially. However, given the extremely small and statistically insignificant coefficients in table 3, it is debatable whether it is appropriate to discuss the nature of the relationships for the infant mortality model. The only legitimate conclusion would seem to be one of no impact.

[12] To the extent that the long-term health promotion activities actually reflect the nursing role, it would partially explain why there is a

stronger impact on age-sex adjusted death rates than on infant mortality.

[13] Noteworthy is the observation that the death rate from accidents representing complications of medical procedures has more than doubled in the past twenty years.

[14] It is instructive to note that although the data employed in this study are aggregate county data, essentially the same conclusions were reached by Linda Bilheimer (1980) using micro data for the State of Arkansas.

REFERENCES

Anderson, J. G. 1973. Causal models and social indicators: Toward the development of social system models. *American Sociological Review* 38 (June):285-301.

Bennett, Ivan L. Jr., M.D. 1977. Technology as a shaping force. In *Doing Better and Feeling Worse: Health in the United States,* edited by John H. Knowles, M.D., 125-134. New York: W. W. Norton & Co.

Bilheimer, Linda. 1980. *Health Care in Arkansas: Paying too Much for the Wrong Thing.* Little Rock, Arkansas: Winthrop Rockefeller Foundation.

Black, D. A. K. 1968. *The Logic of Medicine.* Edinburgh and London: Oliver and Boyd.

Blau, Peter M. 1977. *Inequality and Heterogeneity: A Primitive Theory of Social Structure.* New York: The Free Press, Macmillan Publishing Co., Inc.

Callahan, Daniel. 1977. Health and society: Some ethical imperatives. In *Doing Better and Feeling Worse: Health in the United States,* edited by John H. Knowles, M.D., 23-34. New York: W. W. Norton & Co.

Carlson, Rick J. 1975. *The End of Medicine.* New York: John Wiley and Sons.

Cochrane, A. L. 1972. *Effectiveness and Efficiency: Random Reflections on Health Service.* London: Nuffield Provincial Hospitals Trust.

Culliton, Barbara J. 1978. Health care economics: The high cost of getting well. In *Health Care: Regulation, Economics, Ethics, Practice,* edited by Philip H. Abelson, 41-43. Washington, D.C.: American Association for the Advancement of Science.

Department of Health, Education and Welfare. 1972. *Infant mortality rates, socioeconomic factors.* Publication No. 72-1045.

Dubos, Rene. 1960. *The Mirage of Health.* London: George Allen and Unwin Ltd.

Duval, Merlin K. 1977. On the science and technology of medicine. In *Doing Better and Feeling Worse: Health in the United States,* edited by John H. Knowles, M.D., 185-192. New York: W. W. Norton & Co.

Field, Mark G. 1973. The concept of the 'health system' at the macrosociological level. *Social Science and Medicine* 7 (October):763-785.

Galbraith, John Kenneth. 1969. *The Affluent Society,* 2nd ed. rev. Boston: Houghton Mifflin Co.

Gaus, C., B. Cooper and C. Hirschman. 1975. *Contrasts in HMO and Fee for Service Performance.* Washington, D.C.: Office of Research and Statistics, Social Security Administration.

Goldsmith, Seth B. 1973. A re-evaluation of health status indicators. *Health Services Reports* 88 (December):937-941.

Gordis, Leon. 1973. Effectiveness of

comprehensive care programs in preventing rheumatic fever. *New England Journal of Medicine* 289 (August):331-335.

House of Representatives Committee on Interstate and Foreign Commerce. 1976. Cost and Quality of Health Care: Unnecessary Surgery. (Report by a subcommittee) Washington, D.C.: Government Printing Office.

Illich, Ivan. 1976. *Medical Nemesis.* London: Calder and Boyars.

Kane, Roger L. and Rosalie A. Kane. 1978. Care of the aged: Old problems in need of new solutions. In *Health Care Regulation, Economics, Ethics, Practice,* edited by Philip H. Abelson, 55-60. Washington, D.C.: American Association for the Advancement of Science.

Kessner, David M. 1973. *Infant Death: An Analysis of Maternal Risk and Health Care.* Washington, D.C.: Institute of Medicine, National Academy of Sciences.

Kisch, Arnold L. 1974. The health care system and health: Some thoughts on a famous misalliance. *Inquiry* 11 (December):269-275.

Knowles, John H., M.D. 1977. The responsibility of the individual. In *Doing Better and Feeling Worse: Health in the United States,* edited by John H. Knowles, M.D., 57-80. New York: W. W. Norton & Co.

Kotelchuck, David, ed. 1976. *Prognosis Negative: Crisis in the Health Care System.* A Policy Advisory Center Book. New York: Random House.

Kristein, Marvin M., Charles B. Arnold and Ernst L. Wynder. 1977. Health economics and preventive care. In *Health Care Regulation, Economics, Ethics, Practice,* edited by Philip H. Abelson, 55-60. Washington, D.C.: American Association for the Advancement of Science.

Levy, Emile. 1977. The search for health indicators. *International Social Science Journal* 29 (No. 3):433-463.

Lipscomb, Joseph. 1978. Health status and health programs. *Health Services Research* 13 (Spring):71-77.

McKeown, Thomas. 1976. *The Role of Medicine: Dream, Mirage, or Nemesis?* London: Nuffield Provincial Hospitals Trust.

Mendelsohn, Robert S. 1979. *Confessions of a Medical Heretic.* Chicago: Contemporary Books, Inc.

Miller, Michael K. and C. Shannon Stokes. 1978. Health status, health resources, and consolidated structural parameters: implications for public health care policy. *Journal of Health and Social Behavior* 19 (September):263-279.

Minnesota Systems Research. 1972. Children and Youth Projects Report, Series 18 and 20. Minneapolis-St. Paul: Minnesota Systems Research.

Radtke, Hans D. 1974. Benefits and costs of a physician to a community. *American Journal of Agricultural Economics* 56 (August):586-593.

Reiser, Stanley Joel, M.D. 1977. Therapeutic choice and moral doubt in a technological age. In *Doing Better and Feeling Worse: Health in the United States,* edited by John H. Knowles, M.D., 47-56. New York: W. W. Norton & Co.

Rogers, David E., M.D. 1977. The challenge of primary care. In *Doing Better and Feeling Worse: Health in the United States,* edited by John H. Knowles, M.D., 81-104. New York: W. W. Norton & Co.

Rushing, William A. 1971. Public policy, community constraints, and the distribution of medical resources. *Social Problems* 19 (Summer):21-36.

——. 1975. *Community, Physicians, and Inequality.* Lexington, Kentucky: Lexington Books.

Sanders, Barkeus. 1964. Measuring community health levels. *American*

Journal of Public Health and the Nation's Health 54 (July):1063-1070.

Thomas, Lewis. 1977. On the science and technology of medicine. In *Doing Better and Feeling Worse: Health in the United States,* edited by John H. Knowles, M.D., 35-46. New York: W. W. Norton & Co.

U.S. Dept. of Commerce, Bureau of the Census. 1971. Statistical Abstract of the United States 1971. Washington, D.C.: U.S. Dept. of Commerce, Bureau of the Census.

Walsh, John. 1978. Federal health spending passes the $50 billion mark. In *Health Care: Regulation,* *Economics, Ethics, Practice,* edited by Philip H. Abelson, 44-48. Washington, D.C.: American Association for the Advancement of Science.

Warner, Kenneth E. 1979. The economic implications of preventive health care. *Social Science and Medicine* 13C (December):227-237.

Wildavsky, Aaron. 1977. Doing better and feeling worse: the political pathology of health policy. In *Doing Better and Feeling Worse: Health in the United States,* edited by John H. Knowles, M.D., 105-124. New York: W. W. Norton & Co.

JEFFREY A. BUCK AND MARK S. KAMLET

7

Approaches to Cost-Benefit and Decision Analysis of Iatrogenic Effects of Psychotherapy

Clinical psychologist Jeffrey Buck is a fellow in the Program in Public Policy and Applied Social Science Research at Carnegie-Mellon University where mental health policy analysis and mental health economics form the center for his research. Buck, in turn, collaborated with Dr. Mark Kamlet, assistant professor of economics and public policy, at Carnegie-Mellon's School of Urban and Public Affairs. Kamlet has done much work in the areas of decision theory, organization theory and budgetary processes. The impact on national health policy (and survival) from prevailing economic forces is immense. An intelligent policy, building on the information and cautions exemplified by Miller and other authors herein, is long overdue. Buck and Kamlet make an important statement and proposal along these lines.   **R.F.M.**

Introduction

The scientific investigation of psychotherapy has focused on developing and understanding treatments and their outcomes. The orientation of economics and policy analysis has rarely entered into this research. This situation is changing as the tools of policy analysis become capable of being applied in a wider range of contexts and as mental health professionals are increasingly challenged to demonstrate not only the efficacy of their techniques, but their worth as well. This paper considers some aspects of the application of cost-benefit analysis (CBA), cost-effectiveness analysis (CEA), and decision analysis (DA) to the evaluation of psychotherapy. In particular, attention is directed to possible iatrogenic effects of psychotherapy and how such effects can be incorporated into CBA, CEA and DA.[1] Additionally, this focus suggests that the perspectives of policy analysis may help refine what is meant by an iatrogenic effect.

At the outset it should be stressed that quantitative tools of policy analysis such as CBA, CEA and DA are not meant to replace scientific research in psychotherapy. Quite to the contrary, such tools complement

The authors gratefully acknowledge the encouragement and critical comments of Dr. Charles Kiesler in the preparation of this paper.

the scientific understanding of treatments and their effects. They are concerned with the implications of the given state of scientific understanding for mental health program design, treatment practice and government funding in the area of mental health services. Even within this domain of use, techniques of policy analysis are not meant to determine the "right" answers to questions in complicated policy areas. They simply provide one source of information to be used in making policy decisions.

Despite these limits, techniques of policy analysis can be of great importance and use. They allow the application of explicit standards for evaluating the relative importance of treatment effects, and the difficult but necessary tradeoffs between associated resources and the alternative uses to which they can be put. These standards are not absolute. Nevertheless, in reaching decisions about where to allocate funds or what types of treatment programs to sponsor, some standards, regardless of their source, must be applied. Techniques of policy analysis simply make such standards explicit and insure some consistency in their application.

In the area of mental health services, analytic techniques such as DA, CBA and CEA can be applied in a variety of contexts. They might be used by an individual mental health professional to select the proper mode of treatment, by a private clinic to design a particular mix of services or by a government agency to determine which treatment facilities to sponsor or the level of support for such facilities. In each case, the objectives to be accomplished and the available alternative actions to accomplish these objectives may differ dramatically, but the analytic techniques used are quite similar. This paper will focus primarily, but not exclusively, on how a government agency might employ such techniques.

With this brief statement of the purposes and limitations of the tools of policy analysis in mind, the following discussion begins by briefly reviewing the debate over the issue of negative effects of psychotherapy. The limits of this debate for the development of mental health policy are outlined, and the rationale for the use of techniques of policy analysis is presented. The use of CBA, CEA and DA is then described in greater detail, particularly as they apply to the evaluation of psychotherapy. Finally, the interpretation of iatrogenic effects in a policy context is considered.

Evidence Concerning Iatrogenic Effects

Bergin and his colleagues have probably been the most vocal in their contention that deterioration can occur in psychotherapy (e.g., Lambert, Bergin & Collins 1977; Bergin & Lambert 1978). In their efforts to establish the existence of this phenomenon, they have cited numerous studies in which a proportion of subjects deteriorated in the course of treatment. Critics of this approach have charged that the demonstration of deterioration within a treatment group is insufficient to establish the existence of iatrogenic effects. Rather, changes as a result of treatment must be compared with a relevant control group before any conclusions can be drawn as to their cause. The simplest of such comparisons is between the means of the two groups. Using this criterion, support for at least the occasional occurrence of negative effects is provided by the meta-analysis of 475 psychotherapy outcome studies by Smith, Glass & Miller (1980). This analysis equated different results through the calculation of an effect size (the difference in the means of the treated and control groups divided by the standard deviation of the control group) for each outcome measure. Using this criterion, 9 percent of the effect-size measures produced were negative, indicating a net deterioration for the treated group. Nevertheless the authors conclude that this small percentage does not generally support the existence of negative effects, although it does suggest their occurrence under certain atypical conditions.

Many researchers, however, contend that the use of the mean deterioration criterion is insufficient to cover many conceivable manifestations of negative effects. Specific individuals within a treatment group may fare worse than if they were not treated, even if there is a positive mean effect for the treatment as compared to a control group. Along these lines, Lambert et al. (1977) suggest that a definition of deterioration should "include not only worsening symptoms but also lack of significant improvement when it is expected and even the acceleration of ongoing deterioration."

Two possible indexes of deterioration involving the comparison of treatment and control groups that can partially account for these concerns are differences in the variance between pre- and post-test or between treatment and control groups on post-test. The most obvious example of negative effects using these criteria would be a situation where a majority of cases have improved but a minority have deteriorated relative to controls, resulting in greater variance for the treatment group. (Increased variance of treatment groups relative to controls is a frequent finding in experimental psychology.) Lambert et al. (1977) correctly point out that both increased and decreased variance may be associated with negative effects, implying the need to have knowledge of the range and means of outcomes to adequately evaluate this criterion.

Using both the mean and variance criteria, Mays and Franks (1980) reviewed the literature supporting the existence of negative effects cited by Bergin and his colleagues. They concluded that the evidence did not support the conclusion of a causal relationship between psychotherapy and deterioration. Strupp et al. (1977), although finding the data suggestive, identified only one study demonstrating negative effects as meeting their criteria of sound methodology. After examining the variances of treatment groups in their meta-analysis, Smith et al. (1980) found little support for the existence of negative effects.

In response to these criticisms Bergin (1980) defended his contention of the existence of negative effects by stating that studies investigating hypothesized causes of deterioration cannot be done for ethical reasons and that evidence for negative effects must rely on natural experiments for the provision of the data that is available. He contends that much of the evidence he cited is as sound as the rest of the outcome literature and that given the drawbacks mentioned, several studies were exceptional in the strength of their support.

Thus, the major disagreements among researchers studying iatrogenic effects have centered around the criteria used to link deterioration to treatment and, to a lesser extent, the degree to which studies indicating deterioration meet such criteria. Despite these disagreements, there nevertheless seems to be agreement on several points. First, a survey of experts in the field of psychotherapy indicates that nearly all believe that iatrogenic effects can occur, although opinions differ on how such effects should be defined (Strupp, Hadley and Gomes-Schwartz 1977). Second, some individuals deteriorate during the course of treatment, although the cause of such deterioration is not agreed upon. Research to determine such causes poses both ethical and methodological dilemmas. Third, regardless of the effect on specific individuals, when compared to a relevant control group, the mean effect of psychotherapy is usually positive and beneficial.

In sum, while the possibility of iatrogenic effects of psychotherapy is agreed upon, its presence has not been established to the satisfaction of all of those concerned with this area. The continued attention to iatrogenic effects, though, reflects a legitimate concern about the implications of such effects for the understanding and practice of psychotherapy. The identification of negative effects and their causes is a prerequisite for reforming practices or factors which contribute to their existence.

Policy-Related Considerations

The process of understanding treatments and their effects is an important one for the advancement of service technology. However, for several reasons this process and its associated knowledge base are often limited in their usefulness for policy-related decisions. The chief reason for this limitation is that policymakers must take into account factors not typically considered by scientifically-oriented researchers, and treat them from a different perspective.

For instance, from a policy perspective, research that focuses solely on the cause and extent of iatrogenic effects is somewhat misguided. Iatrogenic effects are only a subset of the range of possible outcomes associated with psychotherapy. The entire range of outcomes, the values placed on each outcome and side-effect, and the probability that each outcome level will result, all must be taken into account in determining the desirability of a treatment. Similarly, while determinations of causality are important for understanding and reforming therapeutic practice, policymakers must be concerned with the range of outcomes associated with different treatments regardless of their source.

Even given information concerning the range, probability and values of treatment outcomes, decisionmakers are still faced with choices among different courses of action. Ceasing treatment altogether is only one possible response to the demonstration of negative effects. The choice of this

alternative, or any of a number of others, depends not only upon knowledge concerning the factors outlined above, but also upon considerations of variables such as alternate uses of resources and costs associated with service provision.

To say that these concerns should be taken into consideration in service design does not imply they are never done so. Rather, such factors often are implicit in many decisions concerning treatment. Yet, a high potential exists for biases to enter into such decisions, even if quite unintentional, when such factors are only accounted for implicitly. This is particularly true when there is substantial uncertainty about key variables (Tversky and Kahneman 1974, 1981). These biases may lead individuals to over or underestimate the value or likelihood of an outcome despite information to the contrary. This form of distortion can clearly occur in judgments concerning the application of a treatment which has a certain probability of helping, harming or leaving unaffected a particular individual or group of individuals.

The Case for Formal Analysis

In situations where significant iatrogenic effects may result from the application of a treatment, a formal analysis will allow for the systematic treatment of information concerning outcomes, values and uncertainty in a way which minimizes the bias inherent in individual decision making. In doing so, it also has the potential to incorporate the range of perspectives of different parties concerned with the area, and to insure that all relevant factors enter the decision. In this way points of concern and disagreement can be isolated for further treatment or discussion rather than obscured under a general debate over the "worthwhileness" of a particular procedure. Similarly, the opinions of experts can be incorporated in the absence of consensus concerning the effects of particular treatments.

Additional motivation to perform such analyses is increasingly coming from government concerned about costs associated with government sponsored or supported health and mental health programs. With respect to the latter, the United States Congress has expressed concerns over the "safety and efficacy" of psychotherapy and prompted the Office of Technology Assessment to investigate the current state of cost-effectiveness investigations of psychotherapy (OTA 1980b). Although the application of formal policy analysis to this area is in its infancy, continuing government concern about costs and program alternatives in the health and mental health areas is likely to lead to an increased emphasis on such analyses of this kind in the future.

Determining Costs and Benefits of Psychotherapy

The best known methods of analysis for determining the desirability or worth of a public undertaking are cost-effectiveness analysis (CEA) and cost-benefit analysis (CBA). Related, but somewhat more general, is the framework of decision analysis (DA). All of these techniques of analysis begin by explicitly considering the alternative actions that might be taken and the effects of each action. Here, the actions might be the type and extent of psychotherapy provided to particular types of patients. Listing alternative actions is "the most creative part of the decision process." (Howard 1975:359.) Listing the effects of each action is often the most difficult part of the analysis, although certainly one of the most valuable.

What are the effects of psychotherapy? Our list is possibly incomplete but is illustrative of the different types of effects that must be considered. These effects are those that might be associated with the treatment of a mild neurotic living in a family setting. To begin with, there are psychic effects for the individual involved. Collectively these effects constitute personal well-being. There are many components of this sense of well-being including, for example, the degree of anxiety, self-esteem and somatic complaints. Job performance, employability and absenteeism are also often affected by psychotherapy, with many of the resulting benefits accruing to the individual involved. On the other hand, there are costs born by the individual such as travel expenses, time, monetary payment for therapy time and possible stigma associated with treatment.

There are also significant *externalities* in psychotherapy: costs and benefits borne by those other than the individual being treated. There is evidence, for instance, that psychotherapy reduces the load on the medical system (Jones & Vischi 1979). Cummings and VandenBos (1981) indicate that a substantial amount of regular physician time is spent dealing with psychological problems. To the extent these clients receive psychotherapy instead, these physician resources are freed. There is also evidence that reductions in the demand for medical services as a result of psychotherapy extend years beyond the period of treatment. In such cases, benefits are generated that extend beyond those experienced by the individual being treated. Externalities may also include some of the job performance effects of psychotherapy that are borne by society as well as the individual in the form of welfare and unemployment payments. Finally, there are psychological externalities experienced by those in contact with the patient at home, at work, and on the street.

Having derived a list of the types of benefits and costs for a given psychotherapy for a given population of individuals with a certain disorder, we can imagine a vector listing of these benefits and costs at time t,

$$V_t = (B_{1,t} \ldots, B_{N,t}, \qquad C_{1,t} \ldots, C_{M,t}).$$

Each $B_{i,t}$ or $C_{i,t}$ represents a type of cost or benefit associated with psychotherapy such as those listed above. For example, $B_{1,t}$ may be the change in absenteeism on the job during time period t (say the next three months) as a result of psychotherapy. $C_{1,t}$ may be the out of pocket costs to the individuals treated for the therapy during this time period. In decision theory terminology, each type of cost or benefit (each dimension of the vector) is referred to as an *attribute*.

CBA supposes that each attribute can be converted into a comparable

monetary level reflecting social cost. This involves three major contentions. The first is that for each point in time each benefit and cost level
can be translated into an independent monetary equivalent. The second is
that one can account for the time factor in the analysis by calculating the
present value of each cost and benefit stream using a social discount rate.
That is, there is some discount factor r such that a benefit of X dollars in
year t – 1 is equal to a benefit of $X/(1-r)$ in year t.[2] The use of such a rate
is simply a way of incorporating the idea that a present effect is valued
differently from a future one. The last contention is that the resulting
expected net social value is a normatively compelling criterion to assess
efficacy; that is, that the cost-benefit criterion is valuable information for
setting policy.

These contentions imply that alternate actions can be ranked in terms
of their desirability based on their net present value (NPV) where,

$$
NPV = \sum_{i=1}^{N} \left(\int_{t=0}^{\infty} f_i(B_{i,t}) e^{-rt} dt \right) - \sum_{i=1}^{M} \left(\int_{t=0}^{\infty} g_i(C_{i,t}) e^{-rt} dt \right)
$$

In this formula, r is the social discount rate and f_i and g_i convert the
measures of benefits and costs into their monetary social benefit or cost
equivalent. The summation signs reflect the assumption that each attribute can be treated independently and in a simple additive fashion. The
integrals and e^{-rt} terms indicate that one can discount in the traditional
manner. If the benefits remain constant over time, $B_{i,t}$ could be replaced
by B_i, although this appears unlikely to be justified empirically. As Smith
et al. (1980) conclude after extensive review and analysis of the literature,
"the benefits of psychotherapy are not permanent, but then little is." How
does one determine the social costs or benefits of the various outcomes
that result from a given action or program? In the context of the NPV
formula, this is the same as asking how one determines the f_i and g_i
functions. Cost-benefit analysis assumes that the appropriate measure of a
benefit is the amount someone is willing to pay for the it (or willing to
pay to avoid a negative benefit). The appropriate measure for the cost of
resources used in a project (labor, capital, etc.) is the value of those
resources in their next-best alternate use. This notion of cost is called
"opportunity cost." Sometimes deriving values for willingness-to-pay and
opportunity costs are relatively straight-forward. For instance the appropriate measure of the opportunity cost of the staff involved in a given
undertaking may be their market wage. Frequently however, deriving
willingness-to-pay and opportunity cost is very difficult. Assessing the
value of health benefits—mental and physical—is always particularly troublesome and much of the work over the last twenty years in cost-benefit
analysis has been concerned with this issue of measurement.

The framework of cost-benefit analysis can be applied not only to
questions such as the type and extent of psychotherapy to be provided to
a particular group but more generally to issues such as the proper level of

government support or intervention for a given mental health program. It is here that externalities play a critical role. Private benefits and costs that accrue solely to the individuals involved may be best evaluated by individuals themselves in a private market context. Welfare economics, from which cost-benefit analysis emerges, is devoted in large part to specifying when the private market will adequately take account of the benefits and costs of programs and activities. One instance where the private market will not function in this respect is when there are significant externalities. Since this situation is common in the mental health area, the policy analyst is likely to be most interested in the external public effects of psychotherapy. This highlights the fact that from a policy perspective research may be better devoted to assessing the external effects of psychotherapy rather than focusing upon changes in personal well-being.

Other cases in which the private market will fail to adequately capture the costs and benefits of a given service occur when those experiencing the service either do not have sufficient information as to the effects of such services or are not capable of evaluating the relevant information, and when services are provided in markets that are not competitive. These are conditions which are particularly relevant for the provision of mental health services. Accordingly, cost-benefit analysis and welfare economics can be of particular value in addressing the question of governmental versus private market provision of mental health services.

Problems with Cost-Benefit Analysis

It would take us too far afield to offer a detailed critique of CBA. Many of the possible problems are common to a wide range of public programs (Haveman and Margolis 1977; Mishan 1976). Some of them, however, may be particularly prevalent in assessing psychotherapy. For instance, CBA only focuses on the sum of benefits of a given program or treatment and the sum of the costs, not the distribution of these benefits and costs across different individuals. That is, it does not account for the effect of programs on the distribution of income or general welfare. The criterion employed to determine if a given enterprise is worthwhile is simply whether the total benefits accruing to all individuals exceed total costs. It is reasoned that if this is the case, there can always be some transfer of wealth among the individuals involved such that all are made better off than they were previously. As such, the project or enterprise being examined is justified on economic efficiency grounds. Since this theoretical transfer scheme need not actually occur, there may be substantial impacts on the distribution of income.

Distributional considerations are particularly important in assessing many mental health policy issues. For instance, as McGuire (1981) notes, " ... coverage for one branch of medicine, private psychiatry, has basically been excluded from [national health insurance] bills, partly on distributional grounds." On the other hand, Weisbrod and Schlesinger (1979) point out that many programs in the health area often have goals that include a bias toward low income populations in the distribution of resources. Regardless of the direction of the distributional effects, the suggestion in both cases is that the distributional impacts of a program should be weighed alongside cost-benefit gains in determining its overall desirability.

Another problem in applying CBA is that many of the benefits in mental health are private intangibles. That is, while they accrue to the individuals treated, benefits such as increased self-esteem or decreased anxiety are not commodities that are traded or have a market price reflecting their value. At the very least, this makes the task of assigning value to them much more challenging. Moreover, the additive form of the basic cost-benefit equation may not always be valid. For example, the value of a given increase in self-esteem for an individual may not be independent of the level (or change in the level) of anxiety experienced. In this case one cannot derive monetary equivalents for particular benefits and costs without considerings the levels of the other benefits and costs.

This does not mean that one should not try to make value judgments that allow trade-offs among benefits and between benefits and costs, only that it may be methodologically and empirically difficult. Initially it may seem callous to compare costs, often measured directly in monetary units, and benefits concerning health and welfare. Nevertheless, trade-offs among costs and benefits are inherently made in allocating resources for any health or mental health program. CBA makes such trade-offs explicit, so that they can be applied consistently and debated on their own merit. Certainly no moral or ethical equivalent is being made between dollars and lives, for instance. What is sought is that limited resources be applied so that the maximum level of the benefits, even if they are intangible, be achieved.

Tangible benefits and costs may be as difficult to evaluate as intangible ones. Resources consumed, such as psychiatrists' time, are sometimes provided in markets that are not competitive. Also, there may be imperfect information available to potential consumers of psychotherapy in terms of efficacy, total costs and nature of experience. Special divergences may exist between privately borne costs and true opportunity costs due to the distortions introduced by third party payments. Finally, the "rationality" and "consumer sovereignty" assumptions underlying the microeconomic welfare implications of competitive markets, assumptions which posit each individual being able to realistically assess his or her condition and choose the appropriate treatment, may be unrealistic for some of the clients involved in psychotherapy. In all of these cases, market prices may not equal social opportunity cost and social value. Such prices must be "corrected" in the presence of these conditions if they are to serve the purposes of CBA.

A final critique of cost-benefit analysis as applied to mental health issues is the large amount of uncertainty about the effects of any given treatment on a given individual or population. The effect of psychotherapy on a given individual may not be known with certainty, since one cannot be sure what would have happened to the individual in the absence of psychotherapy. Moreover, the state of scientific knowledge is very often such that one cannot gauge precisely the full range of treatment effects for particular populations. A serious potential danger occurs when, in the extreme case, a cost or benefit is ignored because of uncertainty as to its likely level. In such instances, systematic bias can enter into the analysis. In order to take account of costs and benefits for which there is substantial uncertainty, their levels must be constructed partly from the subjective estimates of experts, practitioners or policyanalysts in addition to available outcome measures. This process may be very difficult. For example, stress may be measured by physiological measures and self-esteem by personality inventories or therapist ratings. These outcomes are clearly related to such attributes as psychic well-being and job perform-ance, but in ways currently understood only partially at best.

Possible Solutions

The use of cost-effectiveness analysis is a means of avoiding some of the difficulties associated with intangible benefits. CEA can be used to evalu-ate alternative actions which have the same set of benefits. When benefits are the same for two alternative activities, analysis can be directed to the cost side of a program, with the desired activity simply being the one with the lowest costs. As an example, Smith et al. (1980) suggest that the mode of psychotherapy seems to make little difference in the benefits provided across a wide range of outcome measures. If so, CEA would argue that the cheapest mode should be chosen.

The advantage of CEA is that one does not have to come up with value trade-offs between costs and benefits. Its corresponding limitation is that it can only be applied to activities generating the same set of benefits. Even in this case it can only identify which activity among several with identical benefits should be selected, not whether a project should be undertaken at all.

Decision analysis and multiattribute utility theory (MAUT) are addi-tional methods of dealing with some of the problems inherent in CBA. Decision analysis allows one to take into account all the issues in which a given decisionmaker or policyanalyst is interested. In particular, it allows a policyanalyst to account for equity and distributional effects of a pro-gram, as well as the efficiency implications as revealed through CBA. Decision analysis does not indicate how to take equity considerations into account; but if a policyanalyst views such effects as important, it allows him or her to deal with them however he or she sees fit, and to do so in a consistent manner, allowing trade-offs between efficiency and equity objectives in the analysis. As an example of how this might be accom-plished, Keeney (cited in Watson 1980), in a study of river control policy, included as explicit and different attributes the consequences to four different categories of users. Rather than simply being added together, these attribute values were combined in a nonlinear, nonadditive func-tional form reflecting the relative importance of costs and benefits to different constituencies.

In cost-benefit analysis, uncertainty is usually accounted for through sensitivity analysis, using various values of the uncertain variables and determining if conclusions are sensitive to the changes. Decision analysis though, allows one to deal more systematically with uncertainty than CBA. It does this in two ways. First, the framework of DA recognizes that much of the objective data that might be desired in applying CBA is lacking, while at the same time experts are not totally ignorant about likely levels of benefits and costs. Such experts have subjective beliefs about the likelihood of given outcomes of a given action (a treatment, program, government activity, etc.). These beliefs are often valid and valuable assessments incorporating past experience and available evidence. DA, particularly MAUT, also recognizes that there may be disagreements across individuals concerning value trade-offs (between equity and efficiency objectives, for instance). DA has developed a variety of formal and methodologically rigorous elicitation techniques by which to determine a set of subjective beliefs and values from a policymaker, expert or practitioner.

The second advantage of DA over CBA in handling uncertainty is that it adopts a Bayesian statistical decision theory perspective and evaluates the various alternatives on the basis of these beliefs and values using subjective expected utility theory. This theory is one of the central developments and accomplishments of decision analysis and microeconomics in general in the post World War II period. It provides a rigorous base for the normative (i.e., prescriptive) evaluation of alternative actions in the presence of uncertainty. This evaluation is derived from an individual's beliefs, value trade-offs and risk preferences. It does not say what these beliefs, value trade-offs and risk preferences should be, but it insures that they are dealt with consistently and that their impact on the analysis is made explicit. For important decisions and policies in which there is substantial uncertainty about key benefits and/or costs, DA provides a much more satisfying method of evaluation than CBA.

Finally, DA is more suited than CBA to determining the proper course of actions for multistage decision problems. While some tpyes of decisions —such as the proper level of federal or state support for certain prespecified mental health services—are basically one-stage decisions, other types of mental health policy issues involve a sequence of potential actions. For instance, the issue for a given treatment is usually not simply to treat or not to treat, but, once treatment has begun, when to cease treatment, when to shift to an alternative treatment if the initial treatment does not seem to be effective, etc. Decision analysis, through use of "decision trees," is oriented toward determining the proper course of action at each choice stage, taking into consideration all the relevant information for each choice situation as it arises. CBA is oriented more towards once-and-for-all selections of one of a set of prespecified alternative actions.

Interpreting Iatrogenic Effects in a Policy Context

The discussion of cost-benefit and decision analysis techniques has illustrated the kinds of variables that must be considered in the evaluation of treatment from a policy perspective. As this discussion suggests, the relevant concerns for analyzing iatrogenic effects for policy purposes can be different than those relevant for purely scientific investigation. From a policy orientation, perhaps the most important of these differences is that the analysis of iatrogenic effects has little meaning independent of an assessment of the entire range of treatment outcomes. Even in the extreme case in which the only options are to continue or cease treatment (as opposed to options to modify or shift treatments), the entire range of possible effects, their respective probabilities, and their relative values must be accounted for in determining the proper action. Similarly, in the presence of multiple output effects, even a mean negative effect for one output is not a sufficient argument to discontinue treatment if other output effects are positive. One must consider how the various output effects trade-off against one another in the overall determination of efficacy.

The policy perspective also suggests that the disagreement among researchers concerning the definition of iatrogenic effects of psychotherapy is basically semantic. What is important is not how iatrogenic effects are defined, but how negative effects, however classified, affect the overall assessment of psychotherapy. The absence of any kind of negative effect does not guarantee that a particular treatment is worthwhile, since the costs associated with treatment may outweigh any benefits. Nor does the presence of negative effects mean that the treatment should be discontinued, even if the individuals who are likely to experience these negative effects cannot be determined beforehand.

The alternative definitions of iatrogenic effects found in the literature focus on different aspects of outcomes—changes in the mean or variance of a treatment group as compared to a control group vs. changes to specific individuals, for example. Insisting that iatrogenic effects be tied to changes in specific individuals seems the least useful from a policy perspective if such individuals cannot be identified prior to treatment. However, because information concerning the direction and degree of changes in the population as a whole is very necessary in policy evaluation, investigation of iatrogenic effects through the evaluation of the means, ranges and variances of experimental groups do represent important information.

Finally, in determining the efficacy of a given treatment, the way in which the different levels of outcome effects translate into social benefits is of great importance. For example, consider some measure of the outcome of a particular psychotherapy for a particular type of client with a particular type of disorder. Assume, as will often be the case, that this measure (e.g., a physiological index of stress) is not identical with the measure of benefit with which one is ultimately concerned (e.g., a sense of psychic well-being). In this case, through a calibration scale, one must translate the outcome measure into the type of benefit measure that will prove useful in analyzing the efficacy of a given treatment.

Of special import for evaluating iatrogenic effects is the fact that this calibration need not be linear. For instance, an improvement of 20 percent in an outcome measure may not lead to twice the level of benefits as an improvement of 10 percent. If these kinds of nonlinearities are present, then possible deterioration in psychotherapy may have a greater or lesser impact on the analysis of its efficacy than would be indicated by simply the proportion of its occurrence. In this situation, knowledge of only differences in means is not very useful. For instance, psychotherapy that has the effect of improving everybody experiencing it by a certain, fixed positive amount would clearly be viewed as representing a positive benefit. If instead half the clients improve by a certain amount, a, while the other half's condition deteriorated by an amount β, then the mean improvement is greater than zero if $a > \beta$. Yet, even in this instance, the second situation may not represent a positive benefit if the weight attached to a benefit of a is much less than the weight attached to a deterioration of degree β. This kind of concern is particularly important in situations where a net positive effect is accompanied by a greater variance compared to a control group.

Implications

A recent Office of Technology Assessment review (1980a) of the use of CBA/CEA techniques in evaluating medical technology concluded that such techniques should not be used exclusively to make decisions concerning medical treatments or procedures. Nevertheless, it did conclude that these techniques have great potential to inform such decisions by making explicit the array of costs and benefits associated with particular techniques. The previous description of decision analysis has illustrated how uncertainty and subjective beliefs and values may be incorporated rigorously into such an evaluation. Decision analysis is also particularly useful for multistage decision and policy problems. These techniques hold the promise of allowing better definition and examination of the full range of outcomes associated with psychotherapy, and a better understanding of its worth as a result.

A policy-oriented approach to evaluating psychotherapy has particular implications for the focus of research and the interpretation of outcomes in this area. For instance, research on the effects of psychotherapy that concentrates on various components of the client's well-being may be less valuable for policy purposes than research devoted to external effects such as the client's future health care needs, job performance or demands on the welfare system. These external effects are central for justifying government support of mental health service provision while, for some forms of mental health treatment, private benefits and costs may be adequately captured in a private market context. These external effects are not well measured at present, while their exclusion from analysis clearly makes psychotherapy less efficacious than may actually be the case.

Another implication of the policy perspective for scientific research is that when the only available options are to treat or not to treat a certain population, knowledge of the cause of particular outcomes is less important than knowledge of the variety and direction of such outcomes. The distinction between "spontaneous" deterioration and that caused by treatment becomes irrelevant within such a context. Similarly, psychotherapy outcome measures are often derived from a particular therapeutic orientation or related to an individual's presenting complaint. Although helpful in understanding the therapeutic process, such measures are less useful in other contexts. Specifically, a measure may be sensitive to change, but that which changes may not be valued highly. Another measure may be more important because changes in it are highly valued. The difference between measures of self-esteem and job absenteeism is one such example. It may be difficult for scientifically-oriented researchers to accept this concept. However, outcomes on measures such as job absenteeism are particularly salient for legislators who are reluctant to fund programs or treatments which can only demonstrate that they make people "feel better." Research concerning the effects of psychotherapy on medical utilization represents a step in this direction.

A policy orientation suggests that knowledge is also needed about the ways in which the various parties participating in the policymaking process value particular outcomes for particular populations. The history and pattern of government appropriations in mental health already imply that improvement in certain diagnostic groups and degrees of disability are valued more highly than others. Attempts to formally elicit such values offer the potential of better informing policy-related research and decision-making.

It has already been noted that it is possible for psychotherapy to be beneficial but "worthless." However, it is also possible that psychotherapy is worth more than the current outcome literature suggests. The potential for these types of findings suggests how policy-oriented research may expand the current debate over the possible negative effects and general efficacy of psychotherapy. In the absence of such research, policy decisions affecting the utilization of psychotherapy will continue to be made subjectively in the relative absence of data concerning the full range of relevant effects. Those who believe that psychotherapy "works" are often disappointed with the results of such decisions. Efforts to better identify the costs and benefits of psychotherapy and to objectively incorporate such information into decisions concerning its use, holds the opportunity both for improving the understanding of psychotherapy's effects, and to make such understanding relevant to the policy process.

FOOTNOTES

[1] In the following discussion the terms iatrogenic and negative effects will be used interchangeably.

[2] If there is a social discount rate of r, a benefit of \$X in t years has a present value of Xe^{-rt} when there is continuous compounding. A time stream of benefits, X(t), thus has a present value of $X(t)e^{-rt}dt$.

BIBLIOGRAPHY

Bergin, A. E. Negative effects revisited: A reply. *Professional Psychology* 11 (1980):93-100.

Bergin, A. E. and M. J. Lambert. The evaluation of therapeutic outcomes. In *Handbook of psychotherapy and behavior change: An empirical analysis.* 2d ed., edited by S. L. Garfield and A. E. Bergen. New York: John Wiley & Sons, 1978.

Cummings, N. A. and G. R. Vanden-Bos. The twenty year Kaiser–Permanent experience with psychotherapy and medical utilization: Implications for national health insurance. *Health Policy Quarterly: Evaluation and Utilization* 1 (1981):159-175.

Edwards, W. How to use multiattribute utility theory for social decision analysis. *IEEE Transactions on Systems, Man and Cybernetics* SMC-7 (1977):326-339.

Fischer, G. W. Willingness to pay for probabilistic improvement in functional health status: A psychological perspective. In *Health: What is it worth? Measures of health benefits,* edited by S. J. Mushkin and D. W. Dunlop. New York: Pergamon Press, 1980.

Haveman, R. H. and J. Margolis. eds. *Public Expenditure and Policy Analysis.* Chicago: Rand-McNally, 1977.

Howard, R. A. Social decision analysis. *Proceedings of the IEEE* 63 (1975):359-371.

Jones, K. R. and T. R. Vischi. Impact of alcohol, drug abuse and mental health treatment on medical care utilization: A review of the research literature. *Medical Care* 17 (1979):1-82. (Supplement).

Lambert, M. J., A. E. Bergin and J. L. Collins. Therapist-induced deterioration in psychotherapy. In *The therapist's contributions to effective treatment: An empirical assessment,* edited by A. S. Gurman and A. M.

Razin. New York: Pergamon Press, 1977.

Mays, D. T. and C. M. Franks. Getting worse: Psychotherapy or no treatment—the jury should still be out. *Professional Psychology* 11 (1980): 78-92.

McGuire, T. G. National health insurance for private psychiatric care: a study in distribution of income. *Public Finance Quarterly* 9 (1981):183-196.

Mishan, E. J. *Cost-Benefit Analysis.* New York: Praeger Publishers, 1976.

Office of Technology Assessment, U.S. Congress. *The implications of cost-effectiveness analysis of medical tehnology* (GPO stock No. 052-003-00765-7). Washington, D.C.: U.S. Government Printing Office, 1980a.

Office of Technology Assessment, U.S. Congress. *The implications of cost-effectiveness analysis of medical technology. Background paper #3: The efficacy and cost effectiveness of psychotherapy* (GPO stock No. 052-003-00783-5). Washington, D.C.: U.S. Government Printing Office, 1980b.

Smith, M. L., G. V. Glass and T. I. Miller. *The Benefits of Psychotherapy.* Baltimore: Johns Hopkins University Press, 1980.

Strupp, H. H., S. W. Hadley and B. Gomes-Schwartz. *Psychotherapy for better or worse: The problem of negative effects.* New York: Jason Aronson, Inc., 1977.

Tversky, A. and D. Kahneman. Judgement under uncertainty: Heuristics and biases. *Science* 185 (1974): 1124-1131.

——. The framing of decisions and the psychology of choice. *Science* 211 (1981):453-461.

Watson, S. R. Decision analysis as a replacement for cost/benefit analysis. Unpublished manuscript, 1979.

Weisbrod, B. A. and M. Schlesinger. Benefit-cost analysis in the mental health area: Issues and directions for research. In *Economics and Mental Health*, edited by T. G. McGuire and B. A. Weisbrod. DHHS Pub. No. (ADM) 81-1114, Washington, D.C.: U.S. Government Printing Office, 1981.

THOMAS S. SZASZ

8

A Right to Treatment or a Right to Treat?

Dr. Thomas Szasz has long been the acclaimed leader of the movement for psychiatry to clean its own house. His challenge to the medical model as traditionally practiced, conceptually and ethically, is well known and relentless. If one were to name the top few key thinkers and shapers of the resistance to iatrogenesis, Szasz would never be left out. From the time of his classic book *Myth of Mental Illness* (1961), he has maintained perhaps the strongest opposition of any to the clinical status quo. After reading the frame of reference article for this handbook, Dr. Szasz requested he be represented by chapter 8 from his book *Psychiatric Slavery* (1977). **R.F.M.**

I

The subject of the mental patient's so-called right to treatment has received much attention in recent years. It is impossible to assign an exact date to the origin of this idea, as the notion is clearly coeval with the practice of mad-doctoring. Ever since the seventeenth century, when psychiatry in its modern sense began, madness was conceived of as some sort of malady, and the madman was viewed as someone who does not know his own best interests. It was an integral part of this image that the madman ought to be cared for by others. Although this care consisted of brutal confinement, this seemingly altruistic idea became increasingly attractive to its purveyors and to the public. From the start, then, the madman's right to care was, in fact, the mad-doctor's right to confine him; and now the plea for the mental patient's right to treatment is, in effect, a plea for the psychiatrist's right to treat him.

Although it is difficult to discuss the right to treatment without considering what constitutes treatment and what the disease is for which it is supposed to be a remedy, I shall resist the temptation to take up this subject here. Suffice it to say that a great deal of so-called psychiatric treatment has as its aim a change in the patient's beliefs and behavior. Regardless of their particular psychiatric persuasion, most psychiatrists— and most non-psychiatrists—agree with this view. If such change of belief occurs voluntarily—with the subject's consent and, indeed, with his active cooperation—then it presents no special moral, legal, or constitutional issue. This sort of personality change falls readily into the general category of learning. However, what if such change in belief is imposed on a person against his will? It then presents a very obvious moral, legal, and constitutional problem.[1] If coerced personality change affects religious belief or conduct, then it clearly conflicts with the First Amendment guarantee of freedom of religion. How, then, should coerced psychiatric personality change be viewed?

I do not see how it is possible to deny that coerced psychiatric personality change—even (or especially) if it entails "helping" a person to give up his "psychotic delusions"—closely resembles coerced religious conversion. If so, it is obvious not only that there can be no such thing as a "right" to involuntary psychiatric treatment, such as Bazelon, Birnbaum, Ennis, and others are advocating, but that such an involuntary intervention is itself a clear constitutional "wrong." The Supreme Court actually gave a ringing affirmation of this view in a suit concerning whether the state can require Jehovah's Witnesses to salute the flag. The court reasoned that such a salute "require(s) the affirmation of a belief and an attitude of mind" which it is constitutionally impermissible to create by coercion. In phrases that I submit are applicable equally to coerced psychiatric treatment, the court declared that,

> (I)f there is any fixed star in our constitutional constellation, it is that no official, high or petty, can prescribe what shall be orthodox in politics, nationalism, religion, or other matters of opinion, or force citizens to confess by word or action their faith therein. If there are any circumstances which permit an exception, they do not now occur to us.

As befits an *inimicus curiae,* I would like to remind the justices of the Supreme Court of what evidently never occurred to them: namely, that they have always made an exception to this rule in the case of psychiatry. In fact, what never even occurred to the justices is that involuntary psychiatric treatment constitutes an instance of "forcing citizens to confess by word or act their faith" in a social reality interpreted by institutional psychiatry. Therein, precisely, lies the tragedy of psychiatric slavery.

II

Although the idea of depriving persons of liberty on the grounds of insanity is not of American origin, it fell on fertile soil in the United States. We are thus confronted with an astonishing, seemingly paradoxical, spectacle: Namely, that although American political reformers have done more to enlarge and secure individual liberty than has any such group anywhere in the world, American psychiatric reformers have done more to constrict and endanger it than has any such group anywhere in the world. From Benjamin Rush and Isaac Ray, through Dorothea Dix and the crooks of the "cult of curability," to Alexander, Menninger, Bazelon, and the other terrorists of the Therapeutic State—American psychiatric reform has been characterized by an implacable hostility to individual dignity, liberty, and responsibility, and by a corresponding zeal to replace personal self-control with the controls of pseudo-medical despots. A few citations from the writings of some psychiatric "greats" will illustrate how well they loved, not liberty, but psychiatry.

In 1783 Benjamin Rush, the undisputed father of American psychiatry, whose portrait adorns the official seal of the American Psychiatric Association, wrote to a friend: "Mankind considered as creatures made for immortality are worthy of all our cares. Let us view them as patients in a hospital. The more they resist our efforts, the more they have need of our services."

Rush's life and writings reveal him to be a zealous therapeutic inquisitor who would have made many a theological inquisitor seem tame by comparison. He declared his own son insane and locked him up in his own hospital, where the son languished, except for one brief "remission," for twenty-seven years. On January 2, 1811 Rush wrote to Jefferson: "He [John] is now in a cell in the Pennsylvania Hospital, where there is too much reason to believe he will end his days."

As for Rush's criteria for commitment, he articulated them in his classical *Medical Inquiries and Observations upon the Diseases of the Mind,* hailed by psychiatrists as the first American textbook of psychiatry, as follows:

> Miss H. L.... was confined in our hospital in the year 1800. For several weeks she [displayed] every mark of a sound mind, except one. She hated her father. On a certain day, she acknowledged, with pleasure, a return of her filial attachment and affection for him; soon after she was discharged cured.

The next "giant" in American psychiatry, Isaac Ray, offered this opinion in 1838 about the constitutional limits that ought to be placed on the deprivation of personal freedom under psychiatric auspices:

> When the restoration of the patient is the object sought for, as it always is or should be, in recent cases, no unnecessary restrictions should be imposed on this measure. The simple fact of the recency of the case should be sufficient, when properly attested, to warrant his seclusion, if it be deemed necessary for his care.

These phrases recur with remarkably little change throughout the rest of psychiatric history and are advanced today as if they constituted a novel and revolutionary scientific program. At the core of Ray's recommendation for involuntary mental hospitalization lay a clear reordering of moral and political priorities—the promise of mental restoration in the asylum displacing the problems of personal liberty in society. As classic liberals and modern libertarians want a minimum of "unnecessary restrictions" on individual freedom, so institutional psychiatrists and psychiatrically enlightened jurists want a minimum of such restrictions on therapeutic coercions.

In 1929 Franz Alexander actually committed this horror to paper:

> The neurotic criminal obviously has a limited sense of responsibility. Primarily he is a sick person.... If he is curable, he should be incarcerated for the duration of psychiatric treatment so long as he still represents a menace to society. If he is incurable, he belongs in a hospital for incurables for life.

For three decades following the publication of the foregoing sentences, Alexander was one of the most respected and influential psychiatrists and psychoanalysts in the United States.

Karl Menninger, himself one of Alexander's students—who went on to become the acknowledged dean of American psychiatry in the 1950s and 1960s—has continued to spread the gospel of social security through institutional psychiatry. Menninger is an enthusiastic advocate of preventive psychiatric detention. He advocates replacing penal sanctions with psychiatric sanctions—claiming even that although punishment is a crime, crime is a disease:

> Eliminating one offender who happens to get caught *weakens* public scrutiny by creating a false sense of diminished danger through a definite remedial measure. Actually, it does not remedy anything, and it bypasses completely the real and unsolved problem of *how to identify, detect, and detain potentially dangerous citizens* (emphasis in the original).

Karl Menninger, president of the American Psychiatric Association, uncompromising advocate of psychiatric coercion, and the proprietor-leader of a famous private insane asylum named after his family, has occupied and continues to occupy a prominent position in the American Civil Liberties Union.

III

David Bazelon is one of the most prominent advocates of psychiatric coercion concealed as care and cure. He has succeeded in deforming liberty by ostensibly reforming criminology and psychiatry—an enterprise whose worth he has gravely misjudged, partly by thinking that it is good when it is evil, and partly by believing that it rests on new discoveries when in fact it rests on old deceptions.[2] Thus in 1960 Bazelon offered this plea for psychiatric-legal reform:

> When the sentence has been served, the warden of the penitentiary signs a certificate to that effect, and the prisoner rejoins society—even though it may be obvious that the punishment has worked no cure.... On the other hand, the inmate of a mental hospital is released only when certified by the staff as cured, or at least not dangerous to himself or others.... Is it not evident that treatment rather than punitive incarceration offers society better protection?

O'Connor and Gumanis acted on just these principles in treating Donaldson, and many of Bazelon's fellow jurists reared up in righteous indignation against them.

By 1967 Judge Bazelon had managed to get rid of personal choice and will altogether. In this process he also disposed of the individual, as we know this concept and use this term when we speak of individual freedom and responsibility:

> Scientists now generally agree [and Bazelon is obviously agreeing with them] that human behavior is caused rather than willed. . . . What is usually required of the [psychiatric] expert is a statement in simple terms of why the accused acted as he did—the psychodynamics of his behavior. . . . Where it occurs, under the Durham rule [handed down by Bazelon], the accused may be seen as a sick person and confined to a hospital for treatment, not to prison for punishment.

Here it is in its naked horror: one of the most widely known and respected American judges advocating that persons accused of offenses be deprived of their constitutional right to trial by defining them as mad and locking them up in the madhouse. Indeed, as a judge, Bazelon has not only advocated this course of action but has also practiced it. It is not surprising that he is a much-decorated hero in the struggle for psychiatric justice, having received both a Certificate of Commendation and the Isaac Ray Award from the American Psychiatric Association. In 1970 Bazelon served as the President of the American Orthopsychiatric Association, one of the constituent bodies of the Mental Health Law Project—the "psychiatric liberties" group that shepherded the *Donaldson* case through the courts. In 1967 Bazelon was a leading member of an official United States Mission on Mental Health to Russia. In the Soviet Union, Bazelon saw nothing of the much-heralded Communist abuse of psychiatry but saw much to admire and praise. The following passage from his report on that trip conveys both his judgment of Soviet psychiatry and his position on involuntary mental hospitalization:

> [I]nstitutionalization is a significant part of the Russian approach. Even if a patient opposes hospital commitment, it is deemed voluntary if it is sought by the patient's family, his trade union, business organization, or polyclinic doctor. The Russian attitude seems to be that under these circumstances the patient himself would want hospitalization if he could make rational decisions. As a result, only three or four percent of all commitments are termed involuntary. I must hasten to add that many of our own psychiatrists share the same underlying attitude. . . . They justify this on the ground that they are acting for the patient's benefit. . . . And, of course, these psychiatrists may be right. Perhaps people who need treatment should be involuntarily hospitalized for their own benefit, even if they are not dangerous. But clearly this is a decision which must be made by society as a whole—not by the psychiatric profession alone or by individual psychiatrists.

Nothing could show more clearly how devout a believer Bazelon is in mental illness and the psychiatric cures for it. He accepts as a given, as something too obvious to challenge, that every civilized society must have involuntary mental hospitalization. Indeed it is so important that just as war must not be left to the generals alone, so commitment must not be left to the psychiatrist alone: The decision must be made by society as a whole.

assumption is psychiatric illness

To be sure, Bazelon's views on psychiatric incarceration are not original: They are simply the faithful reflections, undistorted by doubt, of the prevailing psychiatric imbecility in the mirror of judicial inhumanity. To illustrate the extent to which psychiatric incarceration forms the backbone of official psychiatry, I want to cite a typical passage from *Noyes' Modern Clinical Psychiatry* (Seventh Edition), whose author, Lawrence C. Kolb, was for many years professor of psychiatry at Columbia University and is now the Commissioner of Mental Hygiene in New York State. In a chapter on "Personality Disorders," under the section "Sexual Deviation," Kolb offers these revealing remarks:

> If the offender has not been guilty of violence, it is usually desirable that he be confined in a hospital atmosphere. . . . Through therapy and subsequent parole, some such offenders, if their desire for improvement is strong, may be enabled to channel their impulses into constructive activities.

Exactly what sort of non-violent sex criminals is Kolb referring to here? In the three pages immediately preceding the passage quoted, he presents the pathology and treatment of the following sexual deviations: homosexuality, pedophilia, fetishism, transvestism, and exhibitionism. It is the non-violent practitioners of any or all of these perversions, then, that Kolb believes are best treated by coerced psychiatry and parole. His opinion, as befits so sage an expert, is of course not his alone. In support of it, he cites the recommendations of the most liberal and enlightened division of all the branches of the psychiatric establishment, a clique that has aptly called itself the Group for the Advancement of Psychiatry (GAP). Here is what Kolb cites from a 1949 GAP pamphlet, *Psychiatrically Deviated Sex Offenders:* "If the offender is curable he can be eventually released to society; if not, he should never be released. . . . The Committee is unreserved in its opinion that the committed sex offender should be actively treated in a non-penal institution."

If this sounds like Franz Alexander's classic totalitarian line about neurotic criminals, it is because the members of GAP who wrote it probably derived their ideas from Alexander. It is important to note that the GAP is unreserved in its endorsement of coerced psychiatric treatment; that Kolb is unreserved in his endorsement of this position; and that Kolb's book is the most authoritative and widely used text in American medical schools and psychiatric residency programs. Such, then, is the "official" American psychiatric position on psychiatric justice and psychiatric slavery.

IV

At the present time the chief interpreter of and spokesman for the official American psychiatric position on matters concerning law and psychiatry is Alan Stone, Professor of Law and Psychiatry at Harvard University, and the chairman of the American Psychiatric Association's Commission on Judicial Action. When Christianity was an established faith in the West, leading theologians distinguished themselves by writing Christian apologetics. Today, when psychiatry is an established faith, leading psychiatrists distinguish themselves by writing psychiatric apologetics.

After the Supreme Court handed down its ruling on the *Donaldson* case, Stone wrote a review of the history and present status of the concept of the right to treatment, unequivocally supporting it. Why does he like it? Because it supports the medical legitimacy of psychiatry, is a useful vehicle for seeking more public funding for psychiatry, and offers a justification for urging the liquidation of the private practice of medicine and its replacement by national health insurance.

Stone cogently observes that in the history of the early right-to-treatment cases, "not one of them arose in the context of the more numerous and familiar cases of civil commitment of the mentally ill. All of the cases involved men who, although diverted from the prison system into hospitals, had been originally charged with crimes."

From this Stone infers that because they were charged with crimes, all these men "had extensive access to legal counsel"; which, in turn, "is illustrative of the lawyer's contention that without the right to counsel all other rights are bootless."

I submit a different inference, namely that these cases illustrate the propensity in forensic psychiatry to remedy one injustice by adding another one to it. The problem in these cases lay not in the lack of treatment but in the diversion from the criminal process. If lawyers, psychiatrists, and civil libertarians had insisted that persons charged with crimes ought to be tried, sentenced if guilty, and discharged by the courts if innocent, the very problem of people languishing in mental hospitals as quasi-criminals would never have arisen.

When these problems did arise, they inexorably brought with them their own solution: the newly discovered constitutional right to treatment. Thus, according to Stone, in the celebrated case of *Rouse* v. *Cameron,* "Judge Bazelon found the right to treatment in his interpretation of the statute of the District of Columbia, [and] indicated there might be a constitutional right as well; he alluded to the question of cruel and unusual punishment and of due process and equal protection of the laws."

Judge Bazelon did not, however, allude to the possibility that diversion from the criminal to the psychiatric route of social control was itself unconstitutional! In other words, he preferred to fashion a *new* constitutional right for these persons incarcerated in insane asylums rather than to find the established constitutional right to trial applicable to their cases.

I want to recall at this point the Fifth Circuit's decision in *Donaldson,* as it was premised on the concept of the right to treatment; and to note some of the problems, so far not considered, which such a quasi-medical approach to involuntary mental patients raises. The central claim that *Donaldson* placed before the Court of Appeals—and which that court upheld, but the Supreme Court rejected—was that "Where nondangerous patient is involuntarily committed under civil commitment procedures to state mental hospital, only constitutionally permissible purpose of confinement is to provide treatment and patient has due process right to such treatment as will help him to be cured or to improve his mental condition."

This claim is a tissue of nonsense, and a dense one at that. I say this because it seeks to justify depriving an innocent person of liberty on the grounds that he is mentally ill and will receive treatment for it, a reasoning that implies—as essentially unchallengeable—that the subject has, in fact, an illness; that it is treatable; that the treatment will be forthcoming; and that it will be effective. Actually, each of these premises may be false. The "patient" may not have an illness at all, for example, because "mental illness" is not an illness; or he may not have the illness imputed to him, although such an illness exists, because he was falsely diagnosed; or, once confined, he may not be treated; or the treatment may be ineffective or even harmful.

What procedural protection is there, in a ruling such as was advanced in behalf of Donaldson, to protect healthy persons against false diagnoses of illness? Doctors are fallible human beings. Mistaken diagnoses are an ever-present medical possibility. Who shall bear the risk of such error in cases where the very act of making a diagnosis is imposed involuntarily on the so-called patient?

The risks of diagnosing and treating disease are generally well appreciated. They are borne by patients, or would-be patients, in the hope that future medical benefits will accrue to them. Where such hope is absent— for example, in the fatally ill person—permission for further diagnostic explorations is often withheld, and wisely so. Once the diagnostic intervention is wrenched out of its traditional voluntary context, the very word "diagnosis" loses its meaning. For if the consequence of a positive finding of mental illness is psychiatric confinement, and if such confinement is undesired, the persons subjected to diagnostic studies of mental illness would inevitably regard the intervention not as diagnosis but as self-incrimination. If a person accused of a crime for which the penalty is only a fine has, nevertheless, a right against self-incrimination, how could that right be denied a person accused of a mental illness for which the treatment is incarceration? If, however, the right against self-incrimination is extended from the penal context to the psychiatric, then in all cases of involuntary psychiatric interventions, there will be a fresh conflict between two constitutional rights—the right against self-incrimination and the right to treatment. Which of these rights ought then to prevail? The right-to-treatment advocates stubbornly evade such questions. Instead, they extoll the obvious nobility of their cause, as does Stone when he writes:

> The constitutional right to treatment has now become an accepted part of our legal order, but it lacks the imprimatur of the Supreme Court. . . . The Supreme Court actually dealt with the [*Donaldson*] case in a manner that leaves all the important right to treatment questions unanswered.

Thus, neither the fact that *Donaldson* left all the important right to treatment questions unanswered, nor Chief Justice Burger's opposition to the concept of the right to treatment dampens Stone's enthusiasm for the idea. "There is," he remarks approvingly, "already an avalanche of decisions [affirming a right to treatment] in every area of noncriminal confinement." The practical implications of the doctrine, as Stone sees them, are painfully familiar—that is, a demand and a justification for more tax monies for institutional psychiatry:

> In the end the real solution to the problems addressed by the right to treatment cannot come from complicated judicial discourse about civil rights and civil liberties. It must come in the form of a system of national health insurance that includes adequate mental health coverage for inpatient as well as outpatient treatment and for chronic as well as acute mental illness. To some, this will seem unrealistic or too expensive or too much like socialized medicine. But is there a humane alternative that psychiatrists can endorse?

Yes. Leaving people alone. Offering them help but eschewing coercion.

V

It seems fitting to conclude this critique of the concept of the right to treatment with a careful consideration of the views of Morton Birnbaum, the man often said to be the proud father of this anencephalic monster.[3] Birnbaum began his campaign for the right to treatment in 1960, from an observation that is both valid and important—namely, that people in public mental hospitals generally do not receive what one ordinarily would regard as medical treatment. There are at least two immediate and obvious conclusions that might be drawn from this observation. One is that such hospitals are medical institutions in name only. The other is that they are *bona fide* medical institutions in which more medical treatment ought to be dispensed. I drew, and continue to draw, the first conclusion. Birnbaum drew, and continues to draw, the second.

In 1960 in an article in the *American Bar Association Journal* Birnbaum advocated "the recognition and enforcement of the legal right of a mentally ill inmate of a public mental institution to adequate medical treatment of his mental illness."

In 1963 in *Law, Liberty, and Psychiatry* I rejected this proposal because, "it supported the myth that mental illness is a medical problem that can be solved by medical means." Furthermore, I view the care provided by compulsory mental treatment as potentially much more harmful than the metaphorical disease it is supposed to cure.

Despite the millions of words that have since been said and written for and against the right to treatment, the argument has advanced very little. I continue to insist that, because it is an evil like slavery, involuntary psychiatry should be abolished. Birnbaum continues to insist that, because it is a good like curing the disease of an unconscious patient, the involuntary treatment of the involuntary mental patient should be a right guaranteed and enforced by the courts.

As fresh evidence that mental illness is unlike bodily illness keeps cropping up, Birnbaum and I continue to interpret it in diametrically opposite ways. Obsessed with the idea of the right to treatment, Birnbaum declares—as if saying it made it so—that "Medicaid and Medicare statutes are in reality federal right-to-treatment statutes." In fact, Medicaid and Medicare are methods of third-party payment for various medical interventions many of which may not be therapeutic, such as diagnostic procedures or hospitalization of the dying patient. But never mind; to Birnbaum everything that doctors do is treatment.

Having offered his personal definition of Medicare and Medicaid, Birnbaum indignantly declares: "I was quite surprised that in 1965 the initial Medicaid legislation . . . totally excluded only one group among the nation's poor and infirm: state mental hospital patients under 65." That is a fact. Again, the question is: What shall we make of it? What Birnbaum makes of it is that "This is simply another example of how a sanist Congress elected by a sanist society handles this most complex problem in planning to deliver adequate health care to our nation." What I make of it is that this is another example supporting the view that the status of state mental hospital inmates is more like that of children than of adult medical patients. Since such state mental hospital patients are, ostensibly, already cared for by the state, as *parens patriae,* Congress has concluded that there is no need for additional support for them.

Birnbaum, however, is incensed at this exclusion, perhaps the more so because he keeps telling himself it is all due to what he labels "sanism": "As I believe that the decision was incorrect and was sanist, I am now [1974] considering further petitioning of Congress to end this exclusion, filing a formal complaint with the United Nations Human Rights Council concerning Congressional sanism." This threat is at once ridiculous and repellent. Birnbaum actually proposes to denounce his own country, still the freest in the world, to that bastion of super-morality, the United Nations! Are the Russians and their allies, who after all are quite influential in the U.N., not also "sanist"? Are they so nice to mental patients? Birnbaum's belief that the U.N. is more compassionate or moral than the U.S. Congress is, I submit, deeply revealing of his fundamental hostility to traditional American values of individual freedom and dignity.

On September 25, 1975 *The New York Times* reported on a new case filed by Birnbaum that seems to support the worst charges of psychiatric totalitarianism that could be brought against him. According to this story, Birnbaum has filed suit against federal and New York State officials in a case designated as *Woe* v. *Weinberger* (Woe being the pseudonym of the patient and Weinberger being Caspar Weinberger, the former Secretary of Health, Education, and Welfare), contending that the plaintiff had been committed against his will to the Brooklyn State Hospital where he is receiving care that costs $25 a day. "Dr. Birnbaum argues that the court that committed Mr. Woe could have sent him to the psychiatric ward of Downstate Medical Center across the street, where psychiatric care costs $250 a day . . . But because Downstate . . . will not accept involuntary patients, Mr. Woe went to the state hospital."

Birnbaum's posture is naively self-incriminating. A self-declared champion of the rights of the mentally ill, he is here championing the rights of involuntarily hospitalized mental patients to affirm their identities through their illnesses, and by means of a kind of psychiatric affirmative action program, their right to demand the most expensive treatment available for their diseases.

VI

Urging a right to treatment for involuntarily hospitalized mental patients commits one, linguistically and logically, to accept, first, that there is such a thing as mental illness; second, that persons afflicted with such an illness may be legitimately incarcerated in mental hospitals; and third, that such involuntary patients can be effectively treated by means of psychiatric treatments. Each of these propositions is highly questionable, to say the least. I articulate them here to re-emphasize that Birnbaum embraces all of them with the greatest enthusiasm. Significantly, Birnbaum's suit is based on the claim that his client was harmed not *by being committed* to the Brooklyn State Hospital, but *by not being committed* to the Downstate Medical Center!

The Downstate Medical Center is the name of the medical school and affiliated hospitals of the State University of New York in Brooklyn. Because of its university affiliation, this hospital is a prestigious institution. The fact that such an institution refuses to accept involuntary mental patients—a practice unheard of a few decades ago—betokens a changing view of commitment among some leading psychiatrists. If one wanted to be optimistic, one might even speculate that today's refusal by some university and private hospitals to admit involuntary mental patients may be a harbinger of tomorrow's general rejection of this practice. Whether such a change is in the air or not, Birnbaum comes down squarely for the preservation, and indeed extension, of the practice of involuntary mental hospitalization.

Birnbaum charges that his client, Mr. Woe, requires involuntary confinement in a mental hospital; and he charges, further, that he should rightly be confined at the Downstate Medical Center. The real object of Birnbaum's argument can therefore be one thing and one thing only: a demand for state intervention to correct such psychiatric discrimination by ordering the Downstate Medical Center (and similar institutions) to admit involuntary mental patients.

This proposition is exquisitely ironic. In all my years in psychiatry, I have never heard even the most ardent institutional psychiatrist complain about hospitals that refuse to admit involuntary patients. Now, Birnbaum, stalwart defender of the mental patient, complains about precisely this breach in the psychiatric front. His demand, in *Woe* v. *Weinberger,* is:

> That a declaratory judgment be entered that the involuntarily civilly committed must constitutionally be integrated with the voluntarily hospitalized in the separate, unequal, and superior general hospital psychiatric facilities where they can receive the adequate and active care they need, and which is constitutionally required.

In short, Birnbaum now demands, first, that the courts compel mental hospitals—both public and private—to admit involuntary mental patients; second, that voluntary and involuntary mental patients be compulsorily integrated; and third, by implication, that psychiatrists practicing in mental hospitals (and perhaps even those not so practicing) be compelled to accept involuntary subjects as their patients. These fresh demands in the name of the right to treatment are, indeed, the inexorable consequences of the paternalistic-psychiatric imagery inherent in this doctrine. That they are advanced just at this moment in the history of the struggle between the psychiatric totalitarians and the psychiatric libertarians is of the greatest symbolic significance.

Like many people, Birnbaum believes that some people are so seriously mentally ill that they must be confined in mental hospitals against their will. This belief, as I suggested, is like the belief that some people are so subhuman or childlike that they must be enslaved. The ideology behind slavery requires that, ideally, all blacks be slaves and that all whites who can afford it be slave owners. If some blacks are free and survive in freedom, the ideology is threatened. And if some whites reject slave holding, the ideology is threatened even more. All this was clear enough during the days of Negro slavery in America. Hence, for example, the fugitive slave laws.

To uphold the dignity of the glorious institution of psychiatric slavery, Birnbaum is now suing the United States government, claiming that his client was deprived of his constitutional rights because some psychiatrists refused to accept him as a committed patient. The logic behind this is sound: If every psychiatrist treated involuntary mental patients, whether voluntarily or under state compulsion, then the hands of all psychiatrists would be equally bloody. It would be less likely that any would then object to the practice. At present a few psychiatrists reject psychiatric slavery as immoral, refuse to participate in the psychiatric slave trade, and either try to help psychiatric slaves escape to freedom, or, if the slaves prefer a secure bondage to an uncertain liberty, leave them alone. These psychiatric abolitionists represent an intolerable threat, at once practical and symbolic, to the psychiatric slave holders. Birnbaum endeavors to rid psychiatry of this threat: His aim is not to liberate the involuntary mental patient but to enslave the voluntary psychiatric patient (by compulsorily integrating him with the involuntary mental patient) and the free-market psychiatrist as well (by compulsorily transforming him into a court-dominated slave-master of his psychiatric slave-patient).

All this is in the best tradition of paternalistic social reformers who cannot tolerate human differences, which they first call inequalities, then inequities, and finally deprivations of constitutional rights. The upshot is that if they cannot raise the black man to the level of the white, or the poor to that of the rich, or the sick to that of the healthy, they can at least reduce the latter to where, in each case, he is indistinguishable from the former. So it is now with the differences between the sane and the insane. Mental health reformers like Birnbaum and the MHLP are not satisfied with setting the insane free by abolishing psychiatric slavery. Why not? Because it would leave many mentally ill individuals palpably still less well off than some other persons not so categorized. What these therapeutic totalitarians want is not freedom but equality. This is why what they advocate is not the abolition of psychiatric coercion but the abolition of the psychiatric inequities between the sane and the insane and between various classes of the insane. By claiming that we ought to protect involuntarily committed mental patients from "deprivations of their constitutional rights to treatment," they are leading us further down the road toward the Therapeutic State.

FOOTNOTES

[1] More than a half-century ago, Karl Jaspers, the great German psychiatrist-turned-philosopher, emphasized that the concept of treatment is not applicable to so-called psychotics:

Rationale treatment is not really an attainable goal as regards the large majority of mental patients in the strict sense ... Admission to hospital often takes place against the will of the patient and therefore the psychiatrist finds himself in a different relation to his patient than other doctors. He tries to make this difference as negligible as possible by deliberately emphasizing his purely medical approach to the patient, but the latter in many cases is quite convinced that he is well and resists these medical efforts.

Nevertheless, contemporary psychiatrists and jurists prattle not merely about the treatment of just such individuals but also about their right to it.

[2] In *Make Mad the Guilty*, Richard Arens documented how, in his quest for psychiatric salvation, Judge David Bazelon's judicial decisions have sacrificed both common sense and civil liberties.

[3] In view of the historical record of psychiatry, current claims for a right to treatment for the institutionalized mentally ill, especially as advanced by Bazelon and Birnbaum and their followers are simply absurd and obscene. These psychiatric reformers write and talk as if their proposal for a right to treatment were a new scientific and humanitarian idea. Actually, more than one hundred years ago, the National Association of Madhouse Keepers agitated for what were, in effect, right-to-treatment laws. In 1868, in a unanimous resolution, the members of the Association of Medical Superintendents of American Institutions for the Insane, declared that "believing that certain relations of the insane should be regulated by statutory enactments calculated to secure their rights ... [we] recommend that the following legal provisions be adopted by every state whose existing laws do not, already, satisfactorily provide for these great ends."

BIBLIOGRAPHY

The Age of Madness: A History of Involuntary Mental Hospitalization Presented in Selected Texts, edited by T. S. Szasz. Garden City, N.Y.: Doubleday Anchor, 1973.

Alexander, F. and H. Staub. *The Criminal, the Judge and the Public: A Psychological Analysis* [1929]. Rev. ed. Glencoe, Ill.: The Free Press, 1956.

Arens, R. *Make Mad the Guilty: The Insanity Defense in the District of Columbia.* Springfield, Ill.: Charles C. Thomas, 1969.

Bazelon, D. The law and the mentally ill. *American Journal of Psychiatry* 125 (November 1968):667.

———. Justice stumbles over science. *Trans-action* 4 (July-August 1967): 13.

———. The awesome decision. *The Saturday Evening Post* (January 23, 1960):33, 56.

Binger, C. *Revolutionary Doctor: Benjamin Rush, 1746-1813.* New York: Norton, 1966.

Birnbaum, M. The right to treatment: Some comments on its development. In *Medical, Moral and Legal Issues in Mental Health Care,* edited by F. J. Ayd, 128. Baltimore: Williams & Wilkins, 1974.

———. The right to treatment. *American Bar Association Journal* 46 (May 1960):499.

Contemporary Literature. Report of the proceedings of the Association of Medical Superintendents of American Institutions for the Insane, at their twenty-second annual meeting, Boston, Mass., June 2-5, 1868 in *The Quarterly Journal of Psychological Medicine and Jurisprudence* 2, edited by W. A. Hammond, 495. New York: D. Appleton and Company, 1869.

Donaldson v. *O'Connor* 493 F. 2d 507 (5th cir. 1974):508.

Herndon, A. New right-to-treatment suit filed in New York. *Psychiatric News* 10, no. 1 (November 5, 1975):27.

Hunter, R. and I. MacAlpine. *Three Hundred Years of Psychiatry, 1535-1860.* London: Oxford University Press, 1963.

Jaspers, K. *General Psychopathology* [1923], trans. by J. Hoenig and M. W. Hamilton, 839-840. Chicago: University of Chicago Press, 1963.

Kolb, L. C. *Noyes Modern Clinical Psychiatry.* 7th ed. Philadelphia: Saunders, 1968.

Menninger, K. *The Crime of Punishment.* New York: Knopf, 1968.

Ray, I. *A Treatise on the Medical Jurisprudence of Insanity* [1838]. Cambridge, Mass.: Harvard University Press, 1962.

Rensberger, B. New suit presses "right to treatment" for mentally ill. *The New York Times* (September 25, 1975):26.

Rush, B. Letter to Granville Sharp, November 28, 1783. *Journal of American Studies* 1 (April 1, 1967):20.

———. *Medical Inquiries and Observations Upon the Diseases of the Mind* [1812]. New York: Hafner, 1962.

Skultans, V. *Madness and Morals: Ideas of Insanity in the Nineteenth Century.* London: Routledge, 1975.

Stone, A. A. Overview: The right to treatment—Comments on the law and its impact. *American Journal of Psychiatry* 132 (November 1975):1125-1134.

Szasz, T. S. *The Manufacture of Madness: A Comparative Study of the Inquisition and the Mental Health Movement.* New York: Harper and Row, 1970.

———. The right to health. *Georgetown Law Journal* 57 (March 1969):734-751.

———. *The Ethics of Psychoanalysis: The Theory and Method of Autonomous Psychotherapy.* New York: Basic Books, 1965.

———. *Psychiatric Justice.* New York: Macmillan, 1965.

———. *Law, Liberty and Psychiatry: An Inquiry into the Social Uses of Mental Health Practices.* New York: Macmillan, 1963.

West Virginia Board of Education v. *Barnette* 319, U.S. 624 (1943):633, 642.

STUART W. TWEMLOW AND GLEN O. GABBARD

9

Iatrogenic Disease or Folie à Deux?

While Tom Szasz retains pre-eminence as the articulate philosopher/scholar of what may be characterized as an existential resistance to iatrogenic practice, it must be recognized that there are other points of view. Our "Corn Soup" contributors certainly fit within a behavioral world view, while still retaining key criticisms cutting across all views. The psychoanalytic movement is also still alive, well and capable of making conceptual points on iatrogenics from within contemporary practice models. Two psychiatrists affiliated with the Menninger Foundation have taken our well-founded and justifiable reluctance to "blame the victim" and asked us to take a second look. Their contribution gives us yet another point of view on the wide spectrum of conceptual framework for those challenging iatrogenesis. Gabbard is a much awarded, honored and published practitioner whose background includes the theatre arts; Twemlow has spearheaded some of the most intriguing research into human potentials and transpersonal psychology I've yet encountered. Both have interrupted their role on the cutting edge of discovery long enough to share some cautionary thoughts on iatrogenic practice. **R.F.M.**

The term *iatrogenic behavior* may, in fact, be a misnomer. Implicit in the etymological origins of the word *iatrogenic* is the notion that the physician actively induces an untoward effect in his patient, who passively experiences the assault. Twentieth century psychiatry has taught us that what is passively experienced may, in reality, be actively perpetrated in the unconscious. The victim, in other words, may be a collaborator in his own victimization. In this chapter we will try and summarize evidence for the view that so-called iatrogenic disease is often an unconscious collusion between doctor and patient resulting in a matrix of miscommunications in which the smoothness of the transaction between the two is disrupted, resulting in damage to the patient and often also to the doctor. Iatrogenic horror stories occur daily and are sufficiently publicized. We will focus on the much more subtle results of this folie à deux. It may well be that much of iatrogenic disease might not exist if expectations between doctor and patient were clear; that is, strengths and limitations of the doctor and strengths and limitations of the patient were clear to each person and what each expects of the other was equally clear. The pernicious effects of

---

A shorter paper on this theme has subsequently been published by the authors in *American Family Physician* 24, no. 31:129-134.

such distorted communication seem to us to result from the fact that they are unconscious and thus, not subject to the scrutiny of logic and reason.

One of the first recorded traditional medical treatments involved an *iatrogenic* case (Schipkowensky 1977). Hippocrates illustrated a very familiar theme in one of his treatments in which he listened to the patient and attempted to sort out miscommunications resulting from previous treatment. There was much competition in ancient times between medical schools, particularly those of Cnidus and Kos. At that time, Perdiccas II, King of Massadonia (433-413 B.C.), was losing weight and energy. He was under the treatment of Euryphon, head of the Cnidus School. Euryphon tried many procedures (sweets, sour honey, milk, buttermilk) in vain, while all the time complaining, "There are young men who are trying to revolutionize time honored medical practice by referring to their allegedly new discoveries." In spite of the failure of his treatment, he claimed that his remedies might have been successful had they been used on a Greek but had proved nonbeneficial to a Barbarian, thus blaming the patient.

Young Hippocrates first discontinued all drug medication and ointments. He had long talks with the patient, and helped him understand his dreams. He found that Perdiccas was facing a very perplexing problem from which he was unable to extricate himself. Interestingly enough, this problem concerned conflicting feelings between respect for his late father and love for Phila, his former playmate who later became his father's favorite. Hippocrates helped Perdiccas decide in favor of Phila with complete recovery in mind and body. However, such an account fails to highlight the role of the patient in the situation. The patient, in many of the numerous writings on doctor-patient relationships, is often depicted as a helpless victim. Since we know that the vast majority of physicians are quite well-trained, fairly humble, hard-working conscientious people, who are neither psychotic sadists nor cold and calculating psychopaths interested in filling their own money bins, then we have a difficult problem to solve in explaining *iatrogenic* disease.

Models of Illness

Man's basis for action in health and disease is a composite of many things, but one crucial variable is the way he *sees* or perceives the situation of disease and all the social ramifications that accompany it. Man is in constant interaction with his environment. From the multiple stimuli that impinge on him, he must select those to which he will attend and must interpret them in some meaningful way as the basis for his subsequent behavior. To put it another way, an individual brings a complex of assumptions or psychological sets to each situation that confronts him. For example, if one is sitting on an airplane next to a man wearing a clerical collar, one will *see* a lot more than the collar alone. Communication with him may lead one to avoid profanity and perhaps to take care in the choice of certain topics of conversation. A patient in a doctor's office is supposed to feel free to discuss his problems with complete openness and without censorship so that the best objective judgment of them can be made and the best treatment prescribed. However, the matrix of expectations (i.e., the psychological set of doctor and patient), vastly influenced the nature of the transaction. The subtlety of these transactions, both verbal and nonverbal, are well summarized by Blum (1972).

As Balint (1961) points out, to understand people professionally requires two types of understanding: *intellectual,* where emotions should be kept at a low level, and *emotional,* where the understanding lies further from the field of the exact sciences and is thus much more complicated. Medicine has been called the art of making a judgment on the basis of insufficient evidence. Emotional understanding presupposes a keen appreciation of what emotions under observation mean to the observed and the observer in a context of imprecise language. The basis for more accurate emotional understanding is through identification and empathy. This depends on a desire and willingness by the doctor to understand the patient. He may even, for a brief few moments, feel as if he were that person and may make a conscious effort to try and see the world as the patient sees it. Thus, he must also be secure enough and aware enough of himself, his own roles, his likes, dislikes and problems so that he can separate those from those of his patients. Although such self-awareness is fundamental in all forms of psychiatric treatment, it is not so explicitly necessary in the day-to-day nonpsychiatric office practice.

Michael and Enid Balint's group from the Tavistock Clinic in London performed an invaluable service by an in-depth, long-term study of the way in which general practitioners and their patients interact, resulting in a number of publications on the doctor-patient relationship and the various ways in which the patients present their difficulties (Balint 1961, 1964). Among the numerous findings, we wish to highlight certain difficulties or impediments to the doctor's understanding of the patient. Balint calls these "apostolic functions" (1957). Balint says: "It was almost as if every doctor had revealed knowledge of what was right and what was wrong for patients to expect and to endure, and further, as if he had a sacred duty to convert to his faith all the ignorant and unbelieving among his patients. An especially important aspect of the apostolic function is the doctors urge to prove to the patient, to the whole world, and above all, to himself that he is good, kind, knowledgeable and helpful."

These "apostolic functions," implicit and usually unconscious, in the doctor-patient relationship have multiple determinants. In a number of books that we have reviewed on the doctor-patient relationship, it is uncommon to find references to the impact of the *models of illness* on the doctor and on the patient. Since we believe that these rarely explicit models are important contributors to the unconscious collusion which often results in iatrogenic disease, we will now proceed to a discussion of these illness models.

In conventional medicine the major responsibility is given to, and accepted by, the physician (i.e., the physician is *doing* something for or to the patient who *takes* what is done to or for him). Sometimes this is called the *medical* model. In its counterpart, the *psychological* model, there is a practical open contract between patient and physician where it is made explicit that the final responsibility for health lies with the patient and with his own essential efforts. In this latter model, the physician is willing to become involved, but only as a facilitator and catalyst for these efforts. Apparently iatrogenic disease may result from an inappropriate application of the medical model, where the passive subordinate role of the patient results in confused expectations, followed by anger when these magical needs are not adequately met. This phenomenon may perhaps provide a partial explanation for the burgeoning number of malpractice suits in the United States.

In some of the writings on the medical and psychological model (Gill 1977), other terms are being proposed for these models primarily because of the often unwitting and naive confusion with the disciplines involved. In these two models, the doctor's position is sharply different. However compassionately employed, in the medical model the doctor does not see, at least theoretically, the patient's comfort as of primary importance. The doctor applies certain findings from natural science to the patient's body and the patient's comfort is seen primarily in terms of his capacity to adhere to a treatment program. Examples are obvious from surgical and medical sciences, but they also exist in many branches of medicine where the interventions are primarily psychological. For example, one way of looking at the placebo effect is to see it as a situation in which the patient feels he is *passively* experiencing relief from his doctor (medical model) when in reality, he is *actively* perpetrating it himself unconsciously (psychological model). The placebo is administered to the patient by his doctor, but the palliative action is brought about by the patient's own unconscious process which influences physiological responses.

In the psychological model the doctor recognizes that he is inevitably involved as a participant in a dyadic interaction. Such a model is much more obvious in certain forms of psychotherapy, for example, the client-centered psychotherapy of Carl Rogers, but is also most important in the day-to-day nonpsychiatric office practice. Thus, it would seem incorrect to assume that the psychological model is relevant only to psychological therapies, a fact now becoming more widely recognized by the development of "holistic medicine" in the United States (Twemlow & Chamberlin 1980). A practitioner who wishes to operate across a broad spectrum of disorders, for example, a family practitioner, has to have the flexibility to shift from one model to another. Put in another way, the practitioner must be flexible in the degree of *activity* and *passivity* of his involvement with the patient. Undue activity of the physician results in the oversimplified paradigm in which illness is an invading enemy which victimizes the patient, and which the doctor assaults all the skill and technology at his command. The danger of being seduced into undue activity is most common when the patient is seriously ill. Intensive care units foster helplessness and dependency because, as is often the case, time is running out. Even in such situations, activity of the patient can be encouraged with great benefit to avoid iatrogenic failures. Norman Cousins (1976, 1979) describes in his own serious attack of ankylosing spondylitis how a combination of heavy doses of vitamin C and periodic laughter, induced by Candid Camera movies, helped him to control his illness, which had been unresponsive to traditional interventions. Cousins highlights the great importance of his highly sensitive physician friend, who was able to take control when Cousins was failing and instill trust and hope (the active mode), and when Cousins felt more in control, took a much more passive and compliant approach. He respected, for example, his patient's wishes to experiment with unusually heavy doses of intravenous vitamin C and to discharge himself from the hospital to a hotel to engage in his own healing efforts (passive mode). Cousins describes his physician: "He encouraged me to believe I was a respected partner with him in the total undertaking. He fully engaged my subjective energies."

A good example of the unintended iatrogenic effects of *undue activity* is the sensitization of the patient to observing himself too closely for symptoms. Widespread efforts to acquaint patients with early signs of diseases such as carcinoma of the lung, tuberculosis, etc., have resulted in what Blum (1960), in the five-year Stanford study of the doctor-patient relationship called *sensitization*. He feels that people develop a justifiable fear of return of their pathological condition. The state of alarm is created by over-activity of the physician in warning the patient. In a highly judgmental phrase Blum says, "the physician has 'infected' the patient with that anxiety." Since that early study, these facts have become fairly widely recognized in intensive cardiac care units where the demoralizing and frightening effect of flashing lights and buzzing warnings have, as Cousins suggests, probably been involved in the precipitation of cardiac arrests.

Undue passivity on the part of the *doctor* can be equally pernicious and iatrogenic. We have described elsewhere (Bowen & Twemlow 1977) a case of a remarkable recovery from serious depressive symptoms and peptic ulceration in a thirty-year-old sailor, who was treated by psychotherapy and tranquilizers for what later turned out to be a rare form of chronic polymyositis. The patient's personality interfered with communication with numerous doctors, who adopted a wait-and-see attitude. Strikingly, the final diagnosis of a serious organic illness was made by a psychiatrist. The passive, *not doing* mode seems more appropriate to psychotherapy. However, most physicians recognize that we know less about the human mind than any other part of the human organism as a whole, and thus would be more cautious in intervening in conditions that seem primarily *mental*. The true art of the doctor-patient relationship involves also the appreciation of the pernicious and infantilizing effects of too much activity, causing the patient to adopt a regressed, dependent position.

It would seem to us to require a rather extraordinary agility to move between the active and passive modes, and although experience teaches much, it is possible to assist the lessons of experience by a closer look at three basic patterns of collusion between doctor and patient. Each is avoidable if consciously appreciated by the doctor and by the patient early in the process. This early detection might well lead to an avoidance of so-called iatrogenic illness.

Three Basic Patterns

To recapitulate some of our points so far, we have noted that *psychological set* influences the way in which two people communicate, based on certain selective inferences and assumptions each makes about how the other will respond. To an extent this type of thinking is automatic. The individual is not consciously aware of going through this process of sorting and categorizing before he responds. Obviously, it is important to sort the barrage of incoming stimuli since it is not possible to respond to all of the various stimuli to which we are exposed every minute of the day. This sorting and categorizing enables us to respond, to select the most important stimuli, and thus to make an effective and efficient action rather than the confused sorts of responses that are known to occur in people who have serious problems in filtering sensory stimuli. However, the mode of operations of these filtering mechanisms is influenced by a vast collection of unconscious beliefs, distortions and expectations, which have been built up over a lifetime of experience. In our initial example, to sit by a man wearing a clerical collar on an airplane may lead to a socially appropriate, consciously experienced control of the use of profanity. But there the similarity between individuals' responses to our cleric will stop. A spectrum of such responses may vary from one of extreme anger, in those with strongly negative religious opinions, to a form of passive obsequiousness in others, who have had childhood experiences of awe and dependency in relation to religious figures. It is this latter group of unconscious responses which we now wish to address.

Transference and Countertransference

Transference and countertransference are concepts derived from psychoanalytic theory and practice, and refer to unconscious tendencies of both doctor and patient to project on to each other certain attitudes and feelings derived from early experiences with family figures. The irrational element in the response is that it is inappropriate to the present object and to the present situation. *Transference,* simply defined, is the unreal attributes which the patient believes he sees or feels to be present in the doctor. The phenomenon of transference is ubiquitous. One authority on communication points out the process of transference is one of the basic elements in communication and in relationships (Meerloo 1958). Transference is believed, therefore, to operate behind every conversation and in every human contact.

Today the concept of transference has been extended to include not only projected unconscious percepts which give the irrational element to the patient's response but also reaction to traits in the physician's personality, realistically perceived by the patient. Similarly, *countertransference* refers to the irrational responses which the patient's personality evokes in the doctor. Some more broadly define it to include all of the doctor's feelings and reactions directed towards his patient and towards his work with that patient. For example, countertransference reactions are involved in likes and dislikes for particular types of patients (e.g., "I just cannot treat fat women!"). Besides the individual idiosyncratic response of the doctor to his patient determined by his own early experiences, the role of the doctor in somatic medicine has a built-in kind of transference. The doctor expects to be able to manipulate the individual without resistance. He is in control of the situation. Later, after his practice on cadavers at medical school, if this pattern of activity persists in an exaggerated way, he may tend to overlook the fact that the individual is a live human being. Any form of specialization has a built-in form of countertransference which may result in scotomata on the part of the doctor for the personhood of the patient. Thus, the patient often feels infantilized and depersonified and may react by regression or undue passivity and compliance (e.g., the patient does not ask why procedures are performed, what the expectations are, what the pitfalls are and what the possible benefits are).

Problems that are referred to as iatrogenic may actually result from *transference-countertransference* paradigms which develop at an unconscious level between doctor and patient, and therefore fit better into a coequal collusion model than into a persecutor-victim model. It is obviously not possible to cover here all the various idiosyncratic transferences and countertransferences in the individual doctor-patient dyad. Each patient has his own preferences: older gray-haired doctors; young, enthusiastic, energetic doctors; male doctors; female doctors; and so on. There are, however, some useful points that can be made with regard to transference and countertransference to the role of doctor (expert) and to the role of patient (non-expert).

Although the role of doctor has many deeply buried historical social attributes, three concepts resulting from transference-countertransference paradigms can be delineated. These are *generalization, oversimplification* and *stereotypy* (Blum 1972). A gray-haired and distinguished doctor may invoke the feeling of being in the presence of a competent father, and thus induce a sense of confidence and hope, often without any other real grounds for such an opinion. This transfer of response from an original stimulus to a subsequent one having similar components is called generalization. Although it has constructive aspects in that it enables the establishment of a trusting relationship rather quickly, it also beclouds and distorts perception, leading to irrational attitudes.

When an individual response to one outstanding impression discounts other cues, the response is said to be oversimplified, for example, the tendency of doctors to refer to patients by categories. Medicine has an inherent propensity to oversimplification by its use of diagnostic labels. Such labels were derived scientifically to improve and to make for more efficient and effective communication between physicians, but they can be used in an irrational and degrading way (e.g., "Mrs. B. is just a hypochondriac."). *Stereotypy* is a term frequently employed to point up the limiting effects of oversimplification upon the process of judgment. Often such stereotypes are transmitted to the individual during childhood through attitudes expressed by parents and other adults. The stereotype is born largely through suggestion, with the uncritical acceptance of another individual's judgment. The tendency to stereotype people has obvious serious consequences for the doctor-patient relationship.

Using the concept of the transference-countertransference paradigm and all of the implications of that for the effective treatment of illness, we can now proceed to examine three basic patterns which are common in doctor-patient relationships and which serve as underpinnings of iatrogenic disease:[1]

The needy child—omnipotent parent posture—The neediness of a patient is rather obvious and not to be regarded as necessarily a negative concept. Doctors exist to fulfill the needs of patients. The point here is to note the *unconscious* and thus irrational aspects, where the doctor treats the patient as if he is a needy child when he is not, in fact, a needy child, and where the patient treats the doctor as an omnipotent parental figure, when the doctor clearly does not possess these properties. A visit to the doctor has the reasonable expectation that needs will be met. It would all be very well if it could be kept on such a reasonable and logical level. Our observation from our combined experiences in psychoanalytic practice, general psychiatry, surgery and general practice, including obstetrics, is that it does not remain at the rational level, especially in seriously disturbed patients. The dependency on the doctor/leader is for nourishment, material and spiritual, and protection. Bion's work with groups points out that highly sophisticated people make these sorts of assumptions, and there is clearly no relationship between level of education or social status and the capacity to get enmeshed in this transference-countertransference paradigm. What is destructive is that the patient denies his own responsibility for his problems and his treatment, and the doctor denies the limitations of his own ability, both emotional and intellectual. This process of idealization of the doctor is said by some workers to cover deepseated fears of abandonment, and fears that the doctor will be sucked dry by the patient's neediness. Idealization in this way can be defensive and destructive by virtue of its oversimplification and stereotyping.

An implication of this distortion is that the patient acts as if he must be passive (i.e., totally compliant), that he must accept whatever the doctor's whims are without question. It is very easy then for the doctor to be seduced into the omnipotent and highly stereotyped response to the patient. A not uncommon example of a rather subtle iatrogenic situation is the following: A forty-eight-year-old housewife had headaches, vomiting and gait ataxia developing progressively over a three-month period. She had seen her family doctor three times with the concern that "something is seriously wrong." Each time her family doctor reassured her, without taking the time for a detailed neurological examination, that it was just "nerves." The patient accepted his word each time, thinking that "he was the doctor" and knew what he was doing. She later said that if he had told her to lie down in the middle of the street, she would have done so. Finally, she verbalized her worst fears and told him she thought she had a brain tumor. In his most fatherly tone of voice, the doctor replied: "No, my dear, you do not have a brain tumor." Two months later a cerebellar astrocytoma was removed from her posterior fossa at a university medical center.

The Pollyanna posture—An observation of this paradigm in action can be seen every day in a busy hospital ward. The patient acts as a naive empty-headed optimist, whose optimism has a hypomanic quality to it. The doctor colludes with this optimism with back slapping, insincere joking and with remarks which are thought to be supportive, for example, "You're looking well today, Mrs. X," when she looks terrible, or, "How are you feeling? You're looking fine." The patient, in the naive and regressed position, believes that love and hope will prevail, denies hopelessness and loneliness and excuses the rushed doctor for having done his best. "I will not trouble the busy man with my complaint," he says to himself. Any patient who comes to an office takes time off work, expends a considerable amount of money, waits several hours, only to come into a consulting room with minimal symptoms, saying that he is "feeling fine," is a candidate for such a collusion. Psychologically, this is a form of pairing, in which the doctor and patient unite together with the same general goal, to deny the underlying anxiety and the potential for destructiveness to operate in the dyad. A doctor's office that is "too happy" may be encouraging such collusion. An unusual quality of such a relationship is its unrealistic hope. For the feelings of hope to be sustained, it is essential that the cure should be *unborn,* that is, it is a person or idea, not present, that will save the situation from feelings of hatred, destructiveness, and despair. But obviously, in order to do this, this messianic hope must never be fulfilled. Only by remaining a potential does it persist. Hope is, of course, a highly positive aspect of any treatment process; however, we are describing a magical hope, which does not allow for the acknowledgement of shortcomings in the physician or his methods, and which ultimately may lead to bitter resentment and disillusionment. Moreover, it may lead to the covering up of symptoms or complaints that need to be investigated.

The persecutor-victim posture—This paradigm is present in the most dramatic examples of iatrogenic disease, but is probably much less common than the other two. By now, the unconscious collusions have resulted in many unproductive attempts at treatment. The relationship, especially to onlookers such as family and friends, has assumed an unreal and pathological quality. The patient may see the doctor as a persecutor, while at the same time he is able to consciously acknowledge the fact that for other people, the doctor is a very good doctor. He may see no apparent contradiction. Statements of such patients are often quite extreme. The doctor acts as a persecutor. He gets irrationally angry with the patient, accuses the patient of noncompliance, does not monitor his treatment efforts carefully and, as in the case of Hippocrates treatment, begins to get almost as irrational as Euryphon. The doctor often is aware of the impending disastrous quality of this paradigm, becomes fearful that colleagues will follow up his mistakes and omnipotently states that such a patient is not treatable by anybody. In fact, valid orders may not be followed, with devastating consequences. For example, a middle-aged lady with carcinoma of the breast, felt she was treated rudely by a physician who "demanded," according to her, bone scans. She refused because she felt that he was not courteous toward her and because he poked her rudely during his examination. She, in fact, did not receive adequate follow-up treatment, was discharged from the hospital and later readmitted with extensive metastatic deposits which might have been controlled with appropriate treatment. She blamed the doctor, failing to see her role in the *victimization*.

Conclusion

A lesson may be learned from the more primitive systems of medicine, in which partly because of relatively ineffective technology, and partly because of social expectations, the main cure was felt to come from the patient himself. The Shaman doctor activated or catalyzed the healing process. The responsibility was always with the patient, and failure of the cure was rarely ascribed to failure of Shamanistic rituals. There may be many cultural-anthropological explanations for this phenomenon, including the fact that gods or spirits may not be expected to have faults. Scientific medicine with highly sophisticated technology is seen to encourage the three basic patterns described, which on a day-to-day basis result in so-called iatrogenic disease, often of a not particularly dramatic quality. Clearly, certain diseases, for example, drug-induced agranulocytosis, have little patient collusion involved. However, it is our opinion, that when doctors treat patients not merely to protect themselves from malpractice suits, but with the holistic view that patients are *collaborators* in cooperative attempts to overcome disease, then there will be much less iatrogenic disease, and certainly far fewer malpractice suits. Probably all physicians have made errors of judgment which have had devastating effects on the patients. In our experience, and each of us have had such disasters, a frank discussion with adequate attention to our defects and mistakes has resulted in an amicable outcome, with an increased understanding from both patient and doctor.

These models of relationship may in fact apply to many situations where expert advice is sought, but the doctor-patient relationship is of course a more dramatic example because of the potentially more devastating effects of miscommunication, than might, for example, occur when one calls an electrician to repair an electrical fault in one's house. Since the power of the word has been universally acknowledged, we suggest that it may be more accurate to replace the word *iatrogenic* with an equally ugly, but perhaps more accurate and descriptive term, *syndyadogenic*, literally, a disease caused by two people working together.

FOOTNOTE

[1] The concepts of Wilfred Bion (i.e., his basic group assumptions: dependency, pairing and fight-flight) have been the source of ideas for these three paradigms. Bion derived his ideas from the observations of small group process and to our knowledge has not applied the concepts to dyads. (Bion, W. R. *Experiences in Groups.* New York: Basic Books, 1959.)

BIBLIOGRAPHY

Balint, M. *The Doctor, His Patient and the Illness.* 2d ed. London: Pitman Co., 1964.

Balint, M. and E. Balint, *Psychotherapeutic Techniques in Medicine.* London: Tavistock Publication, J. B. Lippincott Co., 1961.

Bion, W. R. *Experiences in Groups.* New York: Basic Books, 1959.

Blum, L. H. *Reading Between the Lines.* New York: International Universities Press, 1972.

Blum, R. H. *The Management of the Doctor-Patient Relationship.* New York: McGraw-Hill Co., 1960.

Bowen, W. T., S. W. Twemlow and I. Lewis. Alcoholics: the double carousel phenomenon. *Social Casework* 58, no. 1 (1977):41-43.

Cousins, N. Anatomy of an Illness (as perceived by the patient). *New England Journal of Medicine* 295, no. 26 (1976):1458-1463.

——. *Anatomy of an Illness as Perceived by the Patient—Reflections on Healing and Regeneration.* New York: W. W. Norton Co., 1979.

Gill, M. M. The two models of the Mental Health Disciplines. *Bulletin of the Menninger Clinic* 41 (1977):79-84.

Meerloo, J. A. M. *Conversation and Communication.* New York: International Universities Press, 1958.

Schipkowensky, M. *Psychotherapy Versus Iatrogeny.* Detroit: Wayne State University Press, 1977.

Twemlow, S. W. and C. R. Chamberlin. Holistic Medicine: Rethinking attitudes to health care. *Journal Kansas Medical Society* (November 1980).

The authors would like to thank Ms. Alice Brand, Chief Librarian, Menninger Foundation, for help with reference materials.

JUANNE N. CLARKE

10

The Iatrogenic Consequences of the Physician as Moral Entrepreneur

Dr. Clarke is a sociology professor at Wilfrid Laurier University and leader of the ad hoc gerontology group there. As a sociologist, she has traced the moral decision-making inherent in the medical model of practice and, using contemporary data from Canada and the United States, argues for more sensitivity to the need for social change in addressing many of our most powerful disease-producers. Through her own strong principles, ability and charismatic style, Professor Clarke herself presents a living antidote to iatrogenesis. **R.F.M.**

Introduction

A purpose of this paper is to explore the iatrogenesis which may result from the fact that the physician acts as a moral entrepreneur in normal work as a doctor. This involves an explanation of the ways in which the moral character of the work of the doctor, along with evidence as to the growth of the power of the physician can be seen as having deleterious consequences for the health of the population. The first section is the argument that a medical diagnosis is also a moral diagnosis. The second part is the discussion of the implications of this in a society in which the physician has an increasing amount of influence and power. It suggests that depoliticization of deviant behavior through the application of the label of illness serves to maintain ill health in our society.

The Social Construction of Medicine

It is generally believed that the job of the doctor is to identify physical anomalies, to apply scientific principles to their explanation and to prescribe a treatment on the basis of these principles. As part of this, a lay person is seen simply to observe clear symptoms of illness, and then to go to the doctor to have the illness cured. Research in the sociology of medicine suggests, however, that the processes through which the patient comes to recognize symptoms and seek treatment and the doctor subsequently comes to treat these symptoms actually result from the solutions to a number of social dilemmas.

The patient's recognition of self-illness seems to be related to ethnicity, sex, social class, religion, age, family status and degree of community involvement, degree of im pairment in work and in social functioning, cost of medical services and distance from medical services (Mechanic 1978). And the diagnosis of the medical practitioner seems to depend on the sex, social class, area of speciality and religion of the practitioner and, reflexively, on the ethnicity, social class, sex, type of illness, age, social functioning and religion of the patient, among other things (Mechanic 1978). It appears as if the model of a straightforward scientific diagnosis of illness with a group of clearly ill lay people is not a wholly accurate representation of the system involved in the recognition and treatment of illness. Health and illness are social constructs. They are not simply the result of physiological processes.

Medical, As Moral, Diagnosis:
The Physician As Moral Entrepreneur

One of the most direct links between medical and moral considerations in medical decision-making comes from the work of Talcott Parsons (1951:428-447) through Eliot Freidson (1970:205-277). In his seminal discussion of the sick role, Parsons argued that medicine has the power to legitimize, or construct, illness provided that the *patient* plays the sick role in the normative way. To be exempted from social responsibilities due to illness and from responsibility for the condition, the patient is expected to want to get well, to seek technically competent help and to co-operate with the helper in getting well. Legitimation is a moral process, as are the behavioral constraints and expectations associated with the legitimation. The sick role, in the Parsonian sense, is the social role enacted by people who believe that they are ill.

Freidson's argument elaborates upon Parsons' work. He suggests that because medicine is the authority on what illness is, it *creates illness* as a social role. And, because illness is generally assumed to be unwanted and people are expected to desire good health—"to want to get normal"—is a type of deviance from the norms defining *normal* health.

> Human, and therefore social, evaluation of what is normal, proper or desirable, is as inherent in the notion of illness as it is in notions of morality. Quite unlike neutral scientific concepts like that of "virus" or "molecule," then, the concept of illness is inherently evaluational. Medicine is a moral enterprise like law and religion, seeking to uncover and control things that it considers undesirable. (Freidson, 1970:208)

Illness is a form of legitimated deviance. The physician, as the labeller of illness, can be thought of as a moral entrepreneur. Calling behavior illness rather than sin is a moral act. The consequence, for instance, of labelling alcoholism an illness rather than a moral weakness has resulted in the minimization of punishment and the avoidance of moral condemnation. The alcoholic person is treated with sympathy rather than with opprobrium. This is an ethical decision, and an instance of what Zola calls medicalization (1972).

The definition of illness is only one instance of the moralizing of the physician. Decisions, other than diagnoses, which must be made in the work of the doctor may also be seen as moral decisions. Tuckett enumerated a number of typical medical conflicts (1976:192-200). In each case a decision would be formed by the religious and moral values of the decision-maker. Physicians are faced with numerous moral conflicts in their practices which they must resolve on their own. Sometimes the care of one patient necessitates the neglect of another patient or group or class of potential patients. Dialysis with one patient faced with severe renal failure means that the expensive technology that this treatment requires is available to one but not another. The present needs of an individual patient may be incompatible with the future needs. News of a terminal illness may cause immediate despair which may later be turned to acceptance. At times the hopes of family members may contravene the hopes of a patient. An elderly person may want to remain in his own home while his family desire his incarceration in a nursing home. Serving one patient may conflict with service to the state or other formal organization. An individual may want exemption from military duty, for instance, while the military desires personnel. These are a few of the specific concerns enumerated by Tuckett.

Uncertainty is a fundamental aspect of diagnosis, prognosis and treatment. While the lay person expects the physician's work to be straightforward, the physician is constantly in a position of having to make judgments in situations lacking in clarity (Burkett and Knaft 1974:82). When faced with ambiguous situations, the medical practitioner generally tends toward active intervention (Parsons 1951:466-469; Freidson 1970:244-277; Scheff 1963:97-107).

Scheff has called this tendency to act in a situation of uncertainty the *medical decision rule*. Medical decision-making in Scheff's model is not unlike statistical and legal decision-making. Statisticians have developed techniques which are designed to protect an interpreter of data against the possibility of rejecting the correct finding or of failing to reject the incorrect finding on the bases of errors due to sampling fluctuations. One rejects or fails to reject the *null* hypothesis (i.e., the hypothesis of no illness). If one rejects the null hypothesis, the level of statistical significance tells you the probability of a type I error. In a type I error there is no illness but illness is diagnosed. A type II error occurs when the null hypothesis is not rejected, but is false. In a type II error, there is undiagnosed illness. This error is usually considered to be the more reprehensible. A physician who fails to diagnose or treat a patient who is ill and who suffers later from the effects of the unnoticed disease may be sued for malpractice, may have his license revoked and may be the subject of the moral condemnation of colleagues. Consequently, the decision rule used by doctors probably is "if in doubt, call it illness" (Scheff 1963:105-127). On the other hand, the treatment of a person who is not ill may have deleterious physical consequences. Hospitalization, drug use and X-rays are among the medical treatments that are known to have negative effects (Illich 1976).

Several studies which document this decision rule have been done. In a now classic study, Bakwin (1945) has reported on physicians who judged the advisability of tonsillectomies for 1000 school children. Of these, 611 were judged to need, and subsequently had, their tonsils removed. Those remaining were examined by another physician, and an additional 174 were selected for tonsillectomies. Finally, 205 children remained. They were examined by another physician and still another 99 were judged to require a tonsillectomy.

In another common treatment, antibacterial drug prescription, a similar tendency toward action in the face of uncertainty is evident. Most sore throats are not sore because of an infection due to strep bacteria (the treatment of which requires antibiotics). Yet the administration of anti-biotics, which at times are known to have negative side-effects, does not always depend on proof of the existence of strep bacteria. Meyers has shown that the tendency to prescribe prophylactic antibacterial drugs is, in part, a function of the particular hospital milieu in which the doctor works. Thus, in some hospitals the policy is to use prophylactic drugs in all cases; in other cases the policy is to use these drugs hardly at all (Meyers 1961). Meyers investigated the use of antibacterials in twenty-four community hospitals, and found that their use, after hernia surgery, varied from 9.2 percent to 100 percent. While the administration of these drugs should technically vary with the actual physical conditions of the patients, Meyers noted that they were in fact used 38.2 percent of the time in simple hernias but not used in 47.8 percent of all complicated hernias where the risk of infection is greater. The issue here is not simply one of failing to prescribe a drug according to the technical requirements of a physiological situation. It is more complex than that because the side-effects of antibacterials can be destructive.

In the field of roentgenology, studies of diagnostic error are apparently more highly developed than in other areas of medicine. Garland (1959) reports that in 14 867 X-rays for tuberculosis, there were 1216 positive readings which turned out to be clinically negative, and twenty-four nega-tive readings which turned out to be positive. Thus, the likelihood of diagnosing tuberculosis when it doesn't exist is greater than the reverse. There are few examples of such error because the evaluation of the validity and reliability of diagnosis is not a well-developed field. Never-theless, Scheff's contention that physicians tend toward active intervention is repeatedly demonstrated in these examples.

Clifton Meador (1970) has explored this tendency and has suggested some of the social sources of medical diagnoses. One is that there is no category of illness called nondisease. Because the physician's job is to diagnose illness, not health, the designation of diagnostic categories, and the language of diagnosis are biased. They omit a very important addi-tional set of categories. These are those which indicate the absence of a suspected disease. Somewhat whimsically, Meador suggests that there is some prevalence of nontuberculosis, nonbrain tumor, noninfluenza, and so on.

Mildred Blaxter (1978) has commented on the categorization of illness. She notes that the most generally accepted and complete list of medical categories of diagnoses, the International Statistical Classification of Diseases, Injuries and Causes of Death (ICD) includes a great number of different models of diseases. Some classes of disease are virtually assertions about the cause (e.g., cut on finger); others are simply descriptions of visually obvious or verbally presented symptoms (e.g., high blood pressure). Some are classified by site (e.g., diseases of the stomach); some are categories of symptoms (e.g., headache); others are the names of syndromes which include the nature, symptoms, cause and prognosis (e.g., Tay-Sachs disease). This list of categorizations could be extended. But the point is that disease diagnosis is not a straightforward and unequivocal procedure. Diseases vary fundamentally in their certainty, ranging from the best defined (e.g., major anatomical defects caused by trauma), to the least, with unknown etiology and variable description. Given variability in the meaning and labelling of disease, it is not surprising that the process of diagnosis is sometimes considered to be an art rather than a science.

This general tendency toward *medicalization* or active intervention depends on the categories of illness available, the social situation in which the diagnosis occurs, and on characteristics of the patient. Sudnow (1967), in a study of hospital emergency rooms, has shown that the age, the social background and the perceived moral character of patients affect the amount of effort that is made to attempt revival of the patient when *clinical* death signs are detected. Just as one case example, consider the following statement.

> Generally speaking, the older the patient, the more likely is his *tentative* death taken to constitute *pronounceable* death. Before a twenty-year-old in the emergency room with a presumption of death attached in the form of the ambulance driver's assessment will be pronounced dead by a physician, very long listening to his heartbeat will occur, occasionally efforts at stimulation will be made, oxygen administered and often times stimulative medication given. Less time will elapse between the initial detection of an inaudible heartbeat and a nonpalpitating pulse and the pronouncement of death in the person who is forty years old, and still less if he is seventy . . . (Sudnow 1967:103).

In the *Sanctity of Social Life* (1974), Crane provides additional evidence that physicians respond to social variables in treating the chronically and terminally ill. In making a prognosis, they consider the extent to which patients are capable of interacting with others. Thus, the treatable patient is one who is most capable of interacting with others. The social status or prestige of the patient, is also an important consideration. Crane notes considerable differences among physicians of varying specialties in terms of the types of decisions made with regard to treatability. The social status of the affiliated hospital in which the medical practitioner works apparently affects his judgement in predictable ways. For instance, physicians in more prestigious institutions tend toward active intervention when compared with those in less prestigious ones.

To recapitulate: A central aspect of the work of a physician is the diagnosis of illness. Such diagnosis involves social, moral and physical considerations. It does not refer to an objectively defined physiological occurrence that is independent of cultural meanings. Various physical states do exist. Whether they are called health or illness does not depend directly on the physical states but, rather, on the evaluation of the states by those who label them. Health and illness, grace and sin are integrally tied to one another.

Iatrogenic Consequences

The integral linkage of health and illness to morality is a universal phenomena (Dreitzel 1971; Freidson 1975; Mechanic 1977). As Dreitzel argues, religion, medicine and morality are frequently found together in the behavioral art or event, and *folk medicine* becomes *social medicine* to an extent not found in industrial societies (1971:1). It becomes a problem, however, in a complex industrialized society such as ours is in which the medical and the religious institutions are said to be separate. The official perspective is that doctors deal with physiologically evident illness while the clergy and the courts deal with moral concerns. The realms are believed to be distinct. Moreover the doctor is accorded a good deal more power, prestige and influence in our society than the clergy (Clarke 1979). This power is granted because of the view that the doctor is universalistic, collectivity-oriented, specific and altruistic (see Parsons 1951) in his work. In fact, however, as we have demonstrated, the doctor provides moral judgments and this occurs in ever-widening spheres of life (Clarke 1979; Illich 1974; Zola 1972; Conrad 1975).

Physicians tend to act in the face of uncertainty, to diagnose disease, not nondisease and to consider social characteristics of patients in their diagnostications and treatments. In a variety of ways the job of the doctor is to *label* or *create an illness* definition in the individual who attends the doctor.

The paradox inherent in this is that doctors concentrate their diagnoses, prognoses and treatment on individual patients. But in doing so, they are given power as the legitimate experts regarding both health and illness. But the real factors in the major causes of death and morbidity are neither relevant to an individualized, *physically* oriented training and expertise of the doctor nor amenable to treatment by the doctor. Let us take a brief look at the chief causes of death in our society today.

The overall mortality rate for Canadian men and women has decreased significantly from 1940 to 1971. The average life expectancy in that thirty-year period of time has increased from 63.0 years to 69.4 years for males and from 66.3 years to 76.5 years for females (Lalonde 1974:19). The major cause of the increase is the large drop in infant mortality from 61 deaths for 1000 births in 1941 to 17.5 deaths for 1000 births in 1971.

Once a Canadian male has lived beyond childhood, however, there has been very little improvement in the subsequent life expectancy (Lalonde 1974:19). Thus while a twenty-year-old male would have lived to be 69.6 years in 1941, in 1971 he will live to be 71.8. The improvement in life expectancy of adult females has been greater. While in 1941 the average life expectancy at twenty was 71.8 years, in 1971 the average life expectancy is 78.2 (Lalonde 1974:19). Furthermore, if we examine the current causes of death that are indicated in the following two tables (Lalonde 1947:20, 22), we note the prevalence of death resulting from environmental factors.

Table 1: Years of Life Lost, Canada, 1971

Major Cause of Death	Years of Life Lost (age 1-70)	
	Male	Female
Motor vehicle accidents	154,000	59,000
Ischaemic heart disease	157,000	36,000
All other accidents	136,000	43,000
Respiratory disease and lung cancer	90,000	50,000
Suicide	51,000	18,000
	588,000	206,000

From these tables we see that more years, for both males and females, are lost through accidents (motor and other) than from any other cause of death. Accidents are not preventable through the skills of the individual clinical practitioner, nor are they generally biologically or physiologically instigated. It has been estimated that deaths from automobile accidents could be reduced 50 percent if everyone wore seat belts and if the laws regarding drinking and driving were more strictly enforced. It is not, therefore, medicine that we must turn to in order to minimize this aspect of our mortality rate but it is rather our life styles and the relationships between human beings and the environment. Coronary disease is the single largest cause of death for those over forty. It is found to be largely resultant from the following factors: genetic inheritance, the relative absence of estrogen in men, smoking, obesity, high fat diets, high serum cholesterol, lack of exercise and stress (Lalonde 1974:13).

Table 2: Major Causes of Death, Canada, 1971

Major Causes of Death	No. of Deaths	Percentage of all Deaths	Predominant Ages
Ischaemic heart disease	48,975	31.1%	40 and over
Cerebrovascular disease	16,067	10.2%	65 and over
Respiratory diseases and lung cancer	15,677	10.0%	Under 1 year and 55 and over
Motor vehicle and all other accidents	12,031	7.6%	All ages
Cancer of the gastrointestinal tract	7,947	5.1%	50 and over
Cancer of the breast, uterus and ovary	4,816	3.1%	40 and over
Diseases specific to the newborn	3,299	2.1%	Under 1 week
Suicide	2,559	1.6%	15 to 65
Congenital anomalies	1,967	1.3%	Under 1 year
TOTAL	113,338	72.1%	
ALL DEATHS	157,272	100.0%	

Clearly the treatment for many of these causes of morbidity and mortality is neither individual clinical treatment nor medical technology per se. It is rather large scale changes in life style and in public health and education. Smoking is known to be important in the genesis of respiratory diseases and lung cancer. Alcohol addiction is said to be associated with one quarter of the admissions to psychiatric hospitals. While a good deal of illness is defined as mental illness and a good deal of somatic illness is said to have psychological causes, expenditures on this aspect of health are generally greatly neglected. Moreover, the suggested typical medical treatments for these socially *caused* deaths have not been particularly noteworthy. Thus the treatment of cardiovascular disease has been elaborated in complex and expensive intensive care cardiac units. In the United States 3000 units were completed by 1971 and these units were using ten percent of all trained nurses. This sounds like a wise financial investment given the destructive effects of cardiovascular disease, but unfortunately this major investment has yielded very little in the way of returns. The only randomized controlled study comparing hospital and home treatment failed to show any benefit of note accruing to treatment in the hospital cardiac care unit (Illich 1976:106).

Conclusion

In this paper, it has been argued that doctors act as moral entrepreneurs in that they actively seek to define illness and act to ameliorate it once it is discovered. This has inherently iatrogenic side effects since the major causes of illness and death are environmental, occupational and life style. Only widespread social change can diminish the disease-generating aspects of these institutions. Doctors, who are our *health experts* largely ignore these both in their medical education and in everyday medical work. In this way, the medical practice is *iatrogenic.*

BIBLIOGRAPHY

Bakwin, H. Pseudodoxia Pediatrica. *New England Journal of Medicine* 232 (1945):691-697.

Blaxter, Mildred. Diagnosis as Category and Process: The Case of Alcoholism. *Social Science and Medicine* 12 (1978):9-17.

Burkett, Gary and Kathleen Knaft. Judgement and Decision-Making in a Medical Specialty. *Sociology of Work and Occupations* (1974):82-109.

Clarke, J. N. Medicalization in the Past Century in the Province of Ontario: The Physician as Moral Entrepreneur. Ph.D. dissertation, University of Waterloo, Waterloo, Ontario, 1979.

Conrad, Peter. The discovery of hyperkinesis: notes on the medicalization of deviant behavior. *Social Problems* 23 (Oct. 1975):12-21.

Crane, Diana. *The Sanctity of Social Life: Physicians' Treatment of Critically Ill Patients.* New York: Russell Sage Foundation, 1975.

Dreitzel, Hans Peter, ed. *The Social Organization of Health: Recent Soci-*

ology No. 3. New York: The MacMillan Company, 1971.

Freidson, E. *The Profession of Medicine: A Study of the Sociology of Applied Knowledge.* New York: Dodd Mead Publishing Co., 1970.

Garland, L. H. Studies of the Accuracy of Diagnostic Procedures. *American Journal of Roentgeneology* 82 (1959):25-38.

Illich, Ivan. *Medical Nemesis.* New York: Panther Books, 1976.

Lalonde, Marc. *A New Perspective on the Health of Canadians: A Working Document.* Ottawa: Information Canada, 1974.

Meador, C. K. The Art and Science of Non-Disease. *New England Journal of Medicine* (1965):272-292.

Mechanic, David. *Medical Sociology: A Comprehensive Text.* New York: The Free Press, 1978.

Meyers, R. S. Quality of Patient Care: Measurable or Immeasurable. *Journal of Medical Education* 36 (1961):776-784.

Parsons, Talcott. *The Social System.* Glencoe, Ill.: Free Press, 1951.

Scheff, Thomas J. Decision Rules, Types of Error, and Their Consequences in Medical Diagnosis. *Behavioral Science* 8, no. 2 (1963):97-107.

Sudnow, D. *Passing On: The Social Organization of Dying.* New York: Prentice Hall, 1967.

Tuckett, David, ed. *An Introduction to Medical Society.* London: Tavistock Publications, 1976.

Zola, I. K. Medicine as an Institution of Social Control. *Sociological Review* 20 (1972):487-504.

RICHARD V. MASON

11

Self-Defeating Qualities of Professionalism

Richard Mason is angry. He is affronted as a person and appalled as a sociologist. While holding out hope for humanistic and nonexploitive professional practice, his model of the bureaucracies within which we function suggests a powerful iatrogenic influence therein to overcome. Dr. Mason presents his conceptual model with candor and passion, demanding a fresh examination of the social forces inhibiting creativity and critically aware clients from our services. In his continuing consultation and education roles in Canada and the United States, Mason has done much to encourage the resurgence of principle, candor and confrontation in the social and professional sciences: this in a world where the Emperor has no clothes, but the populace keep buying his wardrobe. Some critics feel Mason overstates or exaggerates the destructiveness of our bureaucratic systems. Mason, I would guess, hopes they are right.   **R.F.M.**

Abstract—Individuals who work in the helping professions must defend and justify their professional image in an increasingly competitive job market. Members of the helping professions, like all other professionals, defend their professional status in two general modes or images: by manipulating their clients critical awareness and self respect or by striving to inform and sustain critically aware clients who will—we hope—respect and defend (pay for) our work. In actual fact, most professions, and particularly the helping professions, don't operate as *pure types* of either image mode but adapt some combination of both in response to changes in client or general social attitudes.

Either professional image imposes significant limits in our individual or collective ability to learn from, work with or teach about clients or our actual on-going social process. Type 1 (manipulative) professionalism is built on the systematic confoundment and brutalization of critical human ability. In this mode, helping professionals deny or ignore much of their personal interactive experience to gain the label of manipulative standardized professionalism and, by their denial, destroy the very insight and critical learning they must have to understand themselves, their clients or the actual challenges of our on-going social process. This is the iatrogenic, self-defeating double bind of manipulative professionalism that can selectively and systematically destroy both our personal and professional ability to actualize the human service potential of the helping professions.

To understand or critically survive the actual pressing demands of our on-going society, members of the helping professions periodically must critically reconsider the ramifications of their professional image and assess the implications, both personal and collective, of defending that image.

To understand the self-defeating qualities of professionalism in the helping professions, we must critically examine what people who work in those roles actually experience. This critical examination seldom appears in the formal literature because it requires the recognition of rather ugly, embarrassing aspects of our actual work-a-day life. Many of the formal values and ideals of our profession appear informally in our work-a-day experience as petty, self-serving rationales; formal ideals of the profession are too often the cover agenda for the actual purpose of avoiding criticism of our service or ability. In hostile defense, we turn to ridicule and character assault to avoid persons who present critical challenges to our work or profession. Using ideals of scientific or professional excellence (*high standards*) as a justifying rationale, we exact informal sanctions to suppress the critical person while avoiding any formal recognition of their legitimate concern. This is the self-serving mode of professionalism examined in this essay. To sustain or actualize the human service potential of the helping professions, and, in that process, to critically assess our own changing options, we must periodically re-examine the formal and informal aspects of our actual work and life space (Myrdal 1944).

Formally, any person who is employed as a helping professional has survived through some level of a competitive certification process and must continue, as a truly life-long process, to react to the shifting values that structure both the formal and informal values of those programs (Bucher & Strauss 1961; Berger & Luckman 1967).

> Although, in general, the larger universities are still the freest of places in which to work, the trends which limit the independence of the scholar are not absent there. (Given the social pacification service of many helping professions, hard times mean more client dilemmas and increased stress on "professional quality"—**RVM.**) The professor, after all, is legally an employee, subject to all that this fact involves. Institutional factors naturally select men for these universities and influence how, when and upon what they will work and write (and teach). Yet the deepest problem of freedom for teachers is not the occasional ousting of a professor, but a vague general fear—sometimes politely known as "discretion," "good taste" or "balanced judgment." It is a fear which leads to self-intimidation and finally becomes so habitual that the scholar is unaware of it. The real restraints are not so much external prohibitions as control of the insurgent by the agreements of academic gentlemen (Mills 1959:296-297).

As teaching professionals, when academics achieve institutional and professional status, they reasonably assume that their fears via *good taste* must be imposed on the raw rabble of students or junior colleagues to maintain the quality of their professions. This presents, over time, the paradoxical situation where many of the senior members of an academic community are not the critical, innovative persons the formal rationale would suggest but rather ego involved and hyperanxious: at once ultra-timid of peer disapproval and ultra-ruthless toward more vulnerable students, staff and junior faculty (to prove their professional rigor and scientific excellence). The institution adaptability and need to please superiors insures that most academic or professional organizations are staffed by persons who still need to be directed by more powerful, prestigious persons. For critical persons to survive in this selective process they must have some formal or informal support group to keep or sustain their critical awareness and endure the resultant pain and frustration of constant harassment by fearful, manipulative critics. The literature, with my research, consulting and personal experience, indicate that no isolated critical person can survive the sanctions of manipulative harassment because assessment of one's academic or professional service and related occupational survival requires an ethical stance from others who value that work. When manipulative sanctions or fear of them prompts withdrawal of that colleague support, there are no options allowed to the person thus isolated.

In a similar sense, people who are certified and paid as helping professionals are members of an institutional interest group that claims, as a result of their training, a unique, special ability to understand problems and provide help or resources to other people—clients—so their problems can be constructively resolved. It is formally claimed and asserted, that in this process, clients, as well as society in general, are provided with valuable services and resources that are beneficial to all. People recruited to the helping professions are often initially attracted and later sustained by this humane, social service potential claimed as the special mission of their profession.

To develop any critical insight or valid information about the actual occurrence of professionalism and iatrogenic behavior, it is absolutely essential to call this political process of power accumulation to public account. This is exactly the accounting so strenuously avoided by successful, powerful professions. To even outline this paradox, much less understand or resolve it, we must examine the larger social context of professionalism. To understand how members or clients of the helping professions relate to each other, we must account for the legitimation process that sustains the stratification of the larger social context:

> In any given political order, we may expect to find both *conscience* and *coercion*, and it is the element of conscience, of voluntary obedience, that engages our attention, even though we keep in mind the fact that regardless of the type and extent of conscience, all states practice coercion.
>
> An adequate understanding of power relations thus involves a knowledge of the grounds on which a power holder claims obedience, and the terms in which the obedient feels an obligation to obey. The problem of the grounds of obedience is not a supra-historical question; we are concerned rather with reconstructing those central ideas which in given institutional structures in fact operate as grounds for obedience. Often such ideas are directly stated and theoretically elaborated; often they are merely implied, left inarticulate and taken for granted. But, in either case, different reasons for obedience prevail in different political institutions.
>
> *Power* is simply the probability that men will act as another man wishes.

This action may rest upon fear, rational calculation of advantage, lack of energy to do otherwise, loyal devotion, indifference or a dozen other individual motives. *Authority,* or legitimated power, involves voluntary obedience based on some idea which the obedient holds of the powerful or of his position. "The strongest," wrote Rousseau, "is never strong enough to be always master, unless he transforms his strength into right, and obedience into duty."

Most political analysts have thus come to distinguish between those acts of power which, for various reasons, are considered to be *legitimate,* and those which are not. We speak of *naked power* as, for instance, during warfare, after which the successful tries to gain *authority* over the defeated; and we speak of *authority* in cases of legitimate acts of power, and thus, of *public authorities,* or *ecclesiastic* or *court authority* and so on. In order to become *duly authorized,* power needs to clothe itself with attributes of *justice, mortality, religion* and other cultural values which define acceptable *ends* as well as the *responsibilities* of those who wield power. Since power is seen as a means, men ask: "Whose power and for what ends?" And most supreme power holders seek to give some sort of answer, to clothe their power in terms of other ends than power for power's sake (Gerth & Mills 1951:194-195).

While this is the formal, legitimating claim of helping professions, what people actually experience in the informal work-a-day role is significantly different.

What actually occurs is an ongoing ingroup vs. outgroup exchange of sanctions that has been reasonably termed the *department feud* (Bensman 1967). Bensman describes two sources for department feuds that my own research and experience confirm: disagreements about academic schools of thought (and related *high quality* professional work) and the necessity of appearing to be busy (therefore, productive; therefore, worth one's salary and status). The *appearance* of being busy and productive is the most important because it tends to subsume the first sooner and because it is directly involved with the peer evaluation (and related sanctions) of one's professional contribution and, ultimately, of one's job security or tenure. Feuds typify much of our actual, informal professional or academic experience:

> These feuds become the major basis for the way of life of significant numbers of the academic community. (But *especially* of those individuals who assume personal responsibility for enforcing sanctions to insure professional quality-RVM.) ... For the work ethics the significance of the feud is that it allows suspension of all ethical norms during its course. Or rather, ethics (professionalism-RVM.) becomes an instrument in the feud. One can practise any morally leprous act as long as the response to the act does not endanger one's own tenure. At the same time, one uses *ethics* as a rallying cry, to indicate the unethical behavior of one's enemies as they reciprocate. ... Aside from the use of ethics as a device in organizational feuding, the feud overrules all other ethical considerations. As a result, there are no forms of ethical leprosy that are beneath the participants of a feud (Bensman 1967:141-142).

As noted before, this has been and will continue to be a major selective limit on critical research or teaching as an effort to sustain or actualize the humanistic potential of the helping professions.

Why Teachers Burn Out

A relatively new occupational affliction is taking hold in America. It is spreading through the ranks of those from whom our young take tutelage. It is known as *teacher burnout*. Among its symptoms are a sense of discouragement, plummeting morale and an emptying of dedication and desire among teachers, chiefly in the public schools.

Many men and women who went into teaching to help shape and stretch young minds are becoming fed up. They are getting out. Dispirited and disillusioned, they are quitting the classroom in unparalleled numbers, by all the indications tracked by *The Trend Report* which monitors societal trends at the grassroots as a division of the research firm of Yankelovich, Skelly and White, Inc.

Burnout is also manifested by the growing numbers of teachers who stay home, notably on Mondays and Fridays, with nonexistent illnesses. In many areas, the rate of absenteeism among teachers is twice that in private industry.

A number of social and economic factors, intertwined, are turning teachers into some "of the most vocally unhappy workers in the nation," in the view of *The Trend Report*.

A loss of public faith in the schools is rife. People don't feel they're doing a good job. In their frustration with the educational system, taxpayers are venting their ire at teachers, who in turn resent being made the scapegoats for what's wrong with the schools. Public animus toward the pedagogy is stoked by the growing militancy of some in the profession. Last fall, for example, strikes closed schools in more than a dozen states.

Amid rampaging inflation, taxpayers are taking a harder line toward educational expenditures. Bond issues and tax levies are being voted down. Declining enrollments are leading to tighter budgets. Less money is available for teachers' salary increases.

Time was when teaching was stable work, offering job security virtually invulnerable to economic hard times. No longer. As a result of slumping enrollments, layoffs of teachers are commonplace. Some 3000 were let go in California alone last year.

With the breakdown of discipline among students, there's more violence than ever in the schools. Fear stalks the classrooms and corridors. Drugs and booze are finding their way even into the elementary grades. Students beat up teachers, assault them sexually, steal from them. In some cities, teaching has become a raw physical struggle for survival.

Teachers complain that they're burdened by more and more administrative chores and that the mounting pile of paperwork cuts into the time they can spend on academic duties. The rising incidence of burned-out teachers who are retiring early, and quitting outright, raises questions about the caliber of their replacements. In educational circles, there's deep concern about the future of what used to be one of the most honored professions. Business is worried, too, that the best and brightest young prospects will go into other careers. That would leave second-raters to teach America's young. It's a chilling thought (*Harpers* July 1980:7).

As a resource area for the evasion of client or social accountability, the academic community offers a uniquely adaptive setting where *objective, scientific scholars* define the accomplishments and professional qualities of people actually working in the helping professions. As both an initial certification source and as a life-long authority, academic professionals must first resolve their own formal/informal values in order to then serve their proclaimed role of *experts*. Academic professionals experience significantly more conflicting expectations and stress than people in other occupations:

> In practically no other occupational area are participants willing to stoop so low. Thus, all the ethical norms we have described become fictitious in the feud ... In no other institution is there as much cruelty and barbarism openly practised as among ethically superior academic men ... This situation is not at all rare. In fact, I have observed some form of it in every school I have been able to observe in any depth. Thus, the contradiction between ethical ideals or ideology and practice in the university is greater than in most institutions. But it is more than this contradiction that highlights the level of practice. The actual level of ethical practice is probably lower than in any other professional organization in America (Bensman 1967:142-143).

There really isn't anything new in this information; we experience variations of it every day and trade accounts of the more destructive events during the informal bar lounge conversations at our learned professional conferences. What would be new and critically productive would be the acknowledgement and discussion of these feuds as part of the formal agenda. But that critical, formal acknowledgement would seriously compromise the power of informal sanctions used by the vested interest groups that actually manipulate professional certification programs. Sanford (1971) calls this shadow agenda the *conspiracy of silence* where members of a professional group never openly acknowledge the conflict between formal and informal norms. As a result, most teaching professionals live in a social climate of *vague, general fear* (Mills 1963) and even the most prestigious research professor is aware and apprehensive of his/her survival should the informal norms be used against them.

Far from a part-time influence, this informal, shadow world or agenda is actually the dominant influence for self-defeating professionalism. It also enforces the conflicting expectations, sanctions and resulting stress that selectively brutalizes persons who remain sensitive to the humanistic potential of their profession. For any initial insight into this self-defeating process, it is important to recognize the actual ingroup vs. outgroup dynamics of professionalization. Members of the helping professions, like all other professionals, defend and sustain their professional status by adapting or using two general but contrasting modes of images. A professional group can defend their status by manipulating their client's critical awareness and self respect as competent persons or by striving to inform and sustain critically aware clients who will—it is hoped—respect, defend, and support (pay for) the profession's work.

Whether within the professions or in interaction between professions and clients, or the larger society, most professions—particularly the helping professions—don't actually operate as pure types of either image mode but adapt some combination of both in response to members' identity needs as related to changes in client or general social response. If the dominant informal norm of the professional ingroup is a naive desire to be *pure* scientists, they will tolerate very little concern for client abuse from social agencies. They will be, in all probability, very hostile to any critical review or teaching about the relation of their profession to social stratification or other, more powerful, vested interest groups (Ph.D., consulting, personal experience).

This has generated a very destructive paradox for graduate student recruits or junior faculty colleagues who wish to join the profession for its human service potential. As noted earlier, people are often attracted to the helping professions by the social service ability formally claimed by the profession or any group offering certification-graduate programs for the profession. Informally, many new people find they are ridiculed, harassed and, should they refuse to conform, systematically flunked out or ostracized from *their* profession because they try to actualize the human service potential of the profession. In many informal, subtle ways, people established in a professional group inform (more by action or inaction than by direct communication) what they will accept as the proper attitude for reasonable concerns of *competent* aspiring professionals. Because of this subtle, nameless norm enforcement—the vague, general fear (Mills 1963) enforced through a *conspiracy of silence* (Sanford 1971)—many professional certification programs continue to operate on the self-defeating, absolutely ruthless level of systematic brutalization where no ethical hypocrisy is beneath the participants in the department or professional feud.

Either professional mode imposes significant limits on how we perceive, approach or will expect to learn from clients. Manipulative professionalism is built on the systematic brutalization of critical human ability because the self-serving rationales used to defend the profession must distort and evade the actual relationships or human dilemmas of our changing society. In this mode, helping professionals are expected to deny or ignore their personal interactive experience or insight of the client's world to sustain and gain credibility from manipulative professionalism. By that denial and need to sustain an abstracted professionalism, helping professionals destroy the very insight and critical learning they must have to understand the motive needs of themselves or their clients.

Critical professional modes significantly reduce the sense of isolation between professional and client and the client's frustration, pain and hostility in dealing with paradoxical social dilemmas becomes real for the professional. The source of accomplishment or professional success involves recognition and respect from clients as well as from one's professional colleagues. In certain situations, the critical professional may actually accept criticism from manipulative groups as a personal and professional complement and vice versa: "Given what *those* characters are about, their refusal to give any credit to my work is the most reassuring compliment I've had in a long time" (Ph.D. interview). Perhaps such contentions could be productive if both groups are allowed basic survival resources but the goal is to move to one or the other form of *high quality professionalism* and tolerance is a rather rare professional quality, especially within departments.

In fairness, when one is not being destroyed by such a feud, it becomes obvious that the enforcing members are really not able or competent to provide any ethical protection or strength to others without incurring the wrath of norm enforcement themselves. As a result, professional status seldom provides critical independence but, quite the reverse, an increased level of personal pain should the senior person fall into disfavor. Competent reasonably self-secure people would not condone nor perpetuate the vicious destructive feuds that actually structure so much of the professions; helping, or others. My research and work by others (Bensman 1967; Berth & Mills 1951; Sanford 1971; Berger & Luckman 1967); and those who have studied the dynamics of professionalization process indicates that it is often the most ruthless, ethically unprincipled member of a profession that feels complimented and the terms of their personal self-respect confirmed by the destructive process of professional feuds.

This process where the most destructive individuals claim and use conflicting sanctions of professionalism is the iatrogenic, self-defeating, double bind of manipulative professionalism. Individuals, whether as new members/students or as certified participants, to the extent that they try to actualize the human service potential of their profession, will experience significant sanctions from the powerful interest groups and individuals of their profession. Because this process of systematic brutalization occurs as such a subtle complex of sanctions enforced within an informal, shadow world—a world at almost total odds with the professed, formal norms of the profession—critically motivated persons, as they strive to achieve professional resources, may also serve as effective agents—possibly the most effective agents—in confounding the actual delivery of helping professions.

In very rough outline, I have attempted to describe how bureaucratics can operate in concert with other bureaucratic interest groups to push at every level of our personal and collective experience a pseudo-reality, a warped, dehumanized perspective about the facts or potential of our human existence.

Granting that, how do we minimize the destructive aspects of our professional experience? Ironically, even when we glimpse the futility of bureaucratic *progress* or *security,* our consciousness, our critical human capacity has been so crippled by bureaucratic concepts that we can often not feel any trust or hope in our personal or collective ability *to act,* to move toward our own reality. We may have been so thoroughly programed to feel and trust only absolute, competitively standardized, lifeless *facts* and rewards that we experience the feeling of our actual potential life process only as emotional pain and frustration.

Certainly there are no simple universal solutions to such pervasive complex problems but understanding how bureaucratic education first structured our perception and now continues to frustrate and limit our critical consciousness suggests ways we can grow around and past its effects. To survive or endure as humane people we must remember that we are dealing with and against a constant, life-long social process that has massive influence. No one is ever outside of or beyond the bureaucratic definition of their existence.

Any critical consciousness we develop requires the *time* and *effort* for repeatedly pushing the crippling concepts of professional bureaucracies *back* into focus. And that constant process of refocusing requires us to re-experience frustration, disappointment and pain. It is the avoidance of this frustration and pain that often—over an extended period of time and interaction—literally wears down our critical human consciousness, our capacity to feel or be alive either to our own or other people's human potential.

But consider that as long as you still feel pain and frustration you are still alive to the intense joy and excitement of human interaction and learning. You/I/we can still experience and learn from nonexploitative existence, we can experience the sensation of being in need or of being a friend to someone or ones who need, and by our collective experience, learn and grow beyond the competitive, exploitative, dead, standardized, pseudo *security* of the bureaucracy.

When we experience that pain and frustration and *act* to modify it for ourselves and others, we move toward the humanistic, nonexploitative aspects of our private and collective experience, we are in the process of living and learning from our lives instead of being driven by our bureaucratic existence, we are in the process of living the answer, of being the answer to bureaucratic education.

Perhaps the only way to avoid the service of manipulative professionalism as one tried to actualize critical, human service potentials is to constantly include both contrasting realms within one's analysis, teaching and personal self-concept. Both as individual persons and as members of the helping professions, we continue to evolve in reaction to our experiences of larger social relationships. As long as we can still perceive both modes of our professions and, perhaps most important, feel the resultant joy of critical service or frustration/pain of manipulative professionalism, the human service potential of the helping professions endures.

BIBLIOGRAPHY

Bensman, Joseph. *Dollars and Sense.* New York: Macmillan, 1967.

Berger, Peter L. and Thomas Luckman. *The Social Construction of Reality.* Garden City, N.Y.: Doubleday, 1967.

Bucher, Rue and Anselm Strauss. Professions in Process. *American Journal of Sociology* (January 1961):325-334.

Freire, Paulo. *Pedagogy of the Oppressed.* Trans. Myra Bergaman Ramos. New York: Seabury Press, 1970.

Gerth, Hans and C. Wright Mills.

Character and Social Structure. New York: Harcourt, Brace & World, 1951.

Gonick, Cy. *Inflation and Wage Controls.* Winnipeg: Canadian Dimension, 1976.

Humanistic Survival as an Environmental Issue: A Critical Perspective. *Left Review.* Kent, Ohio: Kent State University, Spring, 1978.

Martell, George. *The Politics of the Canadian Public School.* Toronto: James Lorimer, 1974.

Mason, Richard V. The Critical Potential of Knowledge: Environmental Studies and the Matrix of Power. Ph.D. dissertation, OISE, University of Toronto, 1978.

Mills, C. Wright. *The Sociological Imagination,* New York: Oxford University Press, 1959.

——. *The Social Role of the Intellectual.* New York: Oxford University Press, 1959.

Myrdal, Gunner et al. *An American Dilemma.* New York: McGraw Hill, 1944.

Power, Politics and People: The Collected Essays of C. Wright Mills. Edited and introduction by Irving Louis Horowitz. New York: Oxford University Press, 1963.

Sanford, Nevitt. Academic Culture and the Teacher's Development. *Soundings* LIV, no. 4 (Winter 1971):357-371.

Straus, Robert. Departments and Disciplines: Status and Change. *Science* (November 30, 1973):895-898.

Trow, Martin. The American Academic Department as a Context for Learning. *Studies in Higher Education,* 1, no. 1 (1976):11-22.

ROBERT ROSENTHAL AND LENORE JACOBSON

12

Teachers' Expectancies: Determinants of Pupils' I.Q. Gains

What evidence do we have for the kind of bureaucratic iatrogenesis Mason warned of? Using the school system again as focus, we move to an earlier level of training.

Some years ago, one of my graduate students did a project on Grade 2 art instruction in Nova Scotia as practised in several different ability groupings. The I.Q.-based groups were named the *Eagles,* the *Dogs* and the *Turtles;* their respective I.Q.'s might be guessed. During their class, the art teacher gave the Eagles a wide variety of art supplies to choose from and requested they do a winter scene. She then consulted with each individual as requested during the drawing: the ultimate art reflected this creative atmosphere. During their class, the art teacher instructed the Dogs to copy a snowman she drew for them on the board. Each had a piece of black paper and white chalk. She guided each in terms of making an accurate copy. The Turtles were given the same assignment but were ignored and did whatever they wished. Their drawings were mostly chalk scribbles. The teacher felt she was being an effective teacher by "fitting the instruction to the abilities of the class." She did not realize her important socializing role in determining those very abilities. The Eagles were to become (and were children of) the owners of factories or the leaders and professionals of the community. The Dogs were, of course, those who would become (and were children of) the workers in those factories. The Turtles were to become the misfits and clients of the community's various institutions. Eagles were trained in thinking for themselves; Dogs in following directions exactly or conformity; and Turtles in failure. We recall that the basis for forming the Eagles/Dogs/Turtles in the first place was tested I.Q. Such a mistake does not take into account the many possibilities of error in the instrument nor the demonstration by Dr. Robert Green and colleagues[1] (based on testing thousands of Virginia children displaced from school for four years) that I.Q. is profoundly affected by schooling.

Robert Rosenthal, Harvard University social psychologist, has been identified more with the theory of experimenter bias and self-fulfilling prophecy than any other social scientist. One can see his theory in action throughout our daily life. Lenore Jacobson teamed up with Professor Rosenthal in a classic study demonstrating such iatrogenesis in the classroom. Although the bias in this handbook is for new material and a statement on the state of the art, I think the following study (much since replicated and debated) is even today a crucial paper to present and to understand. **R.F.M.**

Reprinted with permission from *Psychological Reports* 19 (1966):115-118.

Summary—Within each of eighteen classrooms, an average of 20 percent of the children were reported to classroom teachers as showing unusual potential for intellectual gains. Eight months later these *unusual* children (who had actually been selected at random) showed significantly greater gains in I.Q. than did the remaining children in the control group. These effects of their teachers' expectancies operated primarily among the younger children.

Experiments have shown that in behavioral research employing human or animal Ss, E's expectancy can be a significant determinant of S's response (Rosenthal 1964). In studies employing animals, for example, Es led to believe that their rat Ss had been bred for superior learning ability obtained performance superior to that obtained by Es led to believe their rats had been bred for inferior learning ability (Rosenthal & Fode 1963; Rosenthal & Lawson 1964). The present study was designed to extend the generality of this finding from Es to teachers and from animal Ss to school children.

Flanagan (1960) has developed a nonverbal intelligence test (*Tests of General Ability* or TOGA) which is not explicitly dependent on such school-learned skills as reading, writing and arithmetic. The test is composed of two types of items, *verbal* and *reasoning*. The *verbal* items measure the child's level of information, vocabulary and concepts. The *reasoning* items measure the child's concept formation ability by employing abstract line drawings. Flanagan's purpose in developing the TOGA was "to provide a relatively fair measure of intelligence for all individuals, even those who have had atypical opportunities to learn."

Flanagan's test was administered to all children in an elementary school, disguised as a test designed to predict academic "*blooming*" or intellectual gain. Within each of the six grades in the school were three classrooms, one each of children performing at above average, average and below average levels of scholastic achievement. In each of the eighteen classes an average of 20 percent of the children were assigned to the experimental condition. The names of these children were given to each teacher who was told that their scores on the "test for intellectual blooming" indicated that they would show unusual intellectual gains during the academic year. Actually, the children had been assigned to the experimental condition by means of a table of random numbers. The experimental treatment for these children, then, consisted of nothing more than being identified to their teachers as children who would show unusual intellectual gains.

Eight months after the experimental conditions were instituted all children were retested with the same I.Q. test and a change score was computed for each child. Table 1 shows the mean gain in I.Q. points among experimental and control Ss in each of the six grades.[2] For the school as a whole those children from whom the teachers had been led to expect greater intellectual gain showed a significantly greater gain in I.Q. score than did the control children ($p = .02$, one-tail). Inspection of Table 1 shows that the effects of teachers' expectancies were not uniform across the six grade levels. The lower the grade level, the greater was the effect (rho $= -.94$, $p = .02$, two-tail). It was in the first and second grades that the effects were most dramatic. The largest gain among the three first grade classrooms occurred for experimental Ss who gained 24.8 I.Q. points *in excess* of the gain (−16.2) shown by the controls. The largest gain among the three second grade classrooms was obtained by experimental Ss who gained 18.2 I.Q. points in excess of the gain (−4.3) shown by the controls.

Table 1: Mean Gains in I.Q.

Grade	Controls		Experimentals		Diff.	t	p†
	M	σ	**M**	σ			
1	12.0	16.6	27.4	12.5	15.4	2.97	.002
2	7.0	10.0	16.5	18.6	9.5	2.28	.02
3	5.0	11.9	5.0	9.3	0.0		
4	2.2	13.4	5.6	11.0	3.4		
5	17.5	13.1	17.4	17.8	−0.1		
6	10.7	10.0	10.0	6.5	−0.7		
Weighted M	8.4*	13.5	12.2**	15.0	3.8	2.15	.02

* Mean number of children per grade = 42.5
** Mean number of children per grade = 10.8
† one-tailed

An additionally useful way of showing the effects of teachers' expectancies on their pupils' gains in I.Q. is to show the percentage of experimental and control Ss achieving various magnitudes of gains. Table 2 shows such percentages for the first and second grades only. Half again as many experimental as control Ss gained at least 10 I.Q. points; more than twice as many gained at least 20 I.Q. points; and more than four times as many gained at least 30 points.

An important question was whether the gains of the experimental Ss were made at the expense of the control Ss. Tables 1 and 2 show that control Ss made substantial gains in I.Q. though they were smaller than the gains made by experimental Ss. Better evidence for the proposition that gains by experimental Ss were not made at the expense of control Ss comes from the positive correlation between gains made by experimental and control Ss. Over the seventeen classrooms in which the comparison was possible, those in which experimental Ss made greater gains tended also to be the ones where control Ss made greater gains (rho = .57, p = .02, two-tail).

Table 2: Percentages of Experimental and Control Ss

I.Q. Gain	Control Ss*	Experimental Ss**	x^2	p†
10 points	49	79	4.75	.02
20 points	19	47	5.59	.01
30 points	5	21	3.47	.04

* Total number of children = 95
** Total number of children = 19
† one-tailed

Retesting of the children's I.Q. had been done in classroom groups by the children's own teacher.[3] The question arose, therefore, whether the greater gain in I.Q. of the experimental children might have been due to the teacher's differential behavior toward them during the retesting. To help answer this question, three of the classes were retested by a school administrator not attached to the particular school. She did not know which children were in the experimental condition. Results based on her retesting of the children were not significantly different from the results based on the children's own teachers' retesting. In fact, there was a tendency for the results of her retesting to yield even larger effects of teachers' expectancies. It appears unlikely, then, that the greater I.Q. gains made by children from whom greater gains were expected could be attributed to the effect of the behavior of the teacher while she served as an examiner.

There are a number of possible explanations of the finding that teachers' expectancy effects operated primarily at the lower grade levels, including: (a) Younger children have less well-established reputations so that the creation of expectations about their performance would be more credible. (b) Younger children may be more susceptible to the unintended social influence exerted by the expectation of their teacher. (c) Younger children may be more recent arrivals in the schools' neighborhood and may differ from the older children in characteristics other than age. (d) Teachers of lower grades may differ from teachers of higher grades on a variety of dimensions which are correlated with the effectiveness of the unintentional communication of expectancies.

The most important question which remains is that which asks how a teacher's expectation becomes translated into behavior in such a way as to elicit the expected pupil behavior. Prior research on the unintentional communication of expectancies in experimentally more carefully controlled interactions suggests that this question will not be easily answered (Rosenthal, in press).

But, regardless of the mechanism involved, there are important substantive and methodological implications of these findings which will be discussed in detail elsewhere. For now, one example, in question form, will do: How much of the improvement in intellectual performance attributed to the contemporary educational programs is due to the content and methods of the programs and how much is due to the favorable expectancies of the teachers and administrators involved? Experimental designs to answer such questions are available (Rosenthal, in press) and in view of the psychological, social and economic importance of these programs the use of such designs seems strongly indicated.

FOOTNOTES

[1] Green, R. L. and R. F. Morgan. The effects of resumed schooling on the measured intelligence of Prince Edward County's black children. *Journal of Negro Education* 38 (1969):147-155.

Green, R. L., L. J. Hoffman and R. F. Morgan. The effects of deprivation on intelligence, achievement and cognitive growth: a review. *Journal of Negro Education* 36 (1967):5-14.

Morgan, R. F. Compensatory education and educational growth in *Racial Crisis in American Educa-*

tion, edited by R. L. Green, 186-219. Chicago: Follett, 1969.

[2] There were no differences in the effects of teachers' expectancies as a function of Ss' initial level of educational achievement: therefore, the three classrooms at each grade level were combined for table 1. In one of the three classrooms at the fifth grade level, a portion of the I.Q. test was inadvertently not re-administered so that the data of table 1 are based on seventeen instead of eighteen classrooms.

[3] Scoring of the tests was done by the investigators, not by the teachers.

BIBLIOGRAPHY

Flanagan, J. C. *Tests of general ability: technical report.* Chicago, Ill.: Science Research Associates, 1960.

Rosenthal, R. The effect of the experimenter on the results of psychological research. In *Progress in experimental personality research.* Vol. I, edited by B. A. Maher, 79-114. New York: Academic Press, 1964.

——— . *Experimenter effects in behavioral research.* New York: Appleton-Century-Crofts, in press.

Rosenthal, R. and K. L. Fode. The effect of experimenter bias on the performance of the albino rat. *Behavioral Science* 8 (1963):183-189.

Rosenthal, R. and R. Lawson. A longitudinal study of the effects of experimenter bias on the operant learning of laboratory rats. *Journal of Psychiatric Research* 2 (1964): 61-72.

ROBERT F. MORGAN

13

Methodology Footnotes: Efficiency Percentages and Gender Genetics

To complete this section on conceptual and scientific context, two short articles are herein reprinted. Both deal with critical reading of studies upon which personal, community or social decisions can be based. Being aware of multiple causality and individual differences, how efficient are our statistical findings in genuinely and helpfully describing groups? And, if misinterpretation of scientific studies has at times been iatrogenic, how iatrogenic indeed has been our stereotyping of the female and male genders? The second article was meant to be a satire and yet (with modern genetic research) it could now be done in part. How quickly reality actualizes fantasy; how often a joke at the expense of others (in this case, those overstating genetic or gender impact on human behavior) can become an unfunny joke on us all. Decades later, the stereotypes remain; some even more iatrogenic than ever. **R.F.M.**

Need for Greater Use of Efficiency Percentages to Supplement Reports of Statistical Significance[1]

When something is more true of one group than another, it is not enough to report this something as statistically significant. We need to know what percentage of all groups the finding holds true for. Too often abstracts and popular understanding lack this safeguard.

Stereotypes are often based on such error. A minority attribute can be accepted as typical of the entire group if its incidence, albeit low, is significantly more common than other groups show. If white males show a statistically significant increment of 4% more impotence than Negro males, we have unearthed an interesting variable. Yet, if more than 90% of both race groups are sexually potent, it would be misleading to characterize Negro males as sexually more vigorous than whites. The average man in either group fails to possess the variable examined.

Validity testing of psychological measures, frequently skipped entirely, needs to include efficiency percentages, predictive validity, more often than presently used. If for example a social scientist aided gun licensing

Reprinted with permission from *Perceptual and Motor Skills* 27 (1968):338. © Southern Universities Press 1968.

organizations by contributing our present understanding of violence in the form of a psychological screening test, we would be concerned with the efficiency of preventing both Types I and II errors. We would probably need more than 90% efficiency in separating potential gun murderers from peaceful sportsmen before public officials could accept such a test.

This author's only personal brush with 100% efficiency[2] recently occurred when, of 46 college students, 22 reported being punished in grade school days by being forced to write "I will never again . . ." in multiples of 100. Every one of the 22 having this early experience presently suffered serious difficulty in getting himself to sit down and write letters or class assignments; none of the rest of the class reported this problem. While this was not a controlled study and may not be representative of the general population, I was nevertheless more impressed by the fact that all the students exposed to the treatment showed the same effect than by any chi square significance I might have demonstrated.

The Definitive Method for Assessing the Genetic Basis for Behavioral Differences Between the Sexes[1]

In recent decades, psychological research has unearthed overwhelming empirical support for the power of environmental and psychogenic variables to over-ride the influence of genetic and developmental variables on human behavior. Because of this, the present author has followed the general drift to psychological research exclusively of environmental and psychogenic factors. To counteract this, a vigorous attempt will be made in this note to refocus attention on genetic relevance by innovating methodology designed to isolate innate behavioral differences due solely to membership in either the male or female sex.

Sex is one variable so ubiquitously assessed in psychological research, as a matter of rote, that we know very little about it. For every pro study there is a con, for every thesis there are tables of sex differences among *Ss*. For example, even though every 'rat' psychologist knows that male rats are less excitable than females, the proof of this has always been confounded by the incontrovertible fact that both male and female rats are the 50-50 genetic products of a male and a female, just as are humans. Reflecting this, both male and female hormones, in varying proportions, are found in each rat and man, regardless of sex. Further, the majority of rats and men are raised in the presence of adults of both sexes. However, definitive research can get around all this.

The first step is to isolate totally laboratory rats by sex. Twelve male couples are housed in individual cages in one room; 12 female couples are housed in individual cages in a second room. Next, we apply the most familiar method for assessing genetic effects on behavior (Ratner & Denny, 1964). Using a selective breeding procedure for at least 10 genera-

Reprinted with permission from *Perceptual and Motor Skills* 27 (1968):90. © Southern Universities Press 1968.

tions, males are mated to males and females are mated to females. Just as Tryon (1940) used this procedure to produce "intelligent" strains of rats, so do we intend to produce "all male" and "all female" strains of rats as grist for serious behavioral assessment.

At present, sexually isolated, single-sex couples have been observed to be cooperative, even friendly, but the first litter is slow in coming.

FOOTNOTES

[1] *Editors' comment*—Fascinated by the experiment reported here, we repeated it on a small sample of 19. Ten reported the experience described by the author. Accepting his conclusions regarding that group, we concentrated on the remaining nine. Three reported punishment by paddling and today not only had difficulties sitting down and writing letters and assignments but reported difficulties sitting down and doing anything. Three reported dusting erasers after school as punishment. They were all found to be seated farthest from the blackboard. Three reported never to have been punished. All three refused to cooperate with *E*. Indeed, one reported *E* to the Dean for invasion of privacy. (WBW)

[2] This does not include a method, discovered several years ago by the author, to motivate ants with 100% efficiency to learn a one alley runway. The ant was put at the extreme end of the runway and its half of the apparatus was immediately submerged under water. All those proceeding to subsequent trials demonstrated learning (Morgan 1981).

BIBLIOGRAPHY

Morgan, R. F. Learning in the submerged FORMICA RUFA. *Psychological Reports* 49 (1981):63-69.

Ratner, S. C. and R. Denny. *Comparative psychology.* Homewood, Ill.: Dorsey, 1964.

Tryon, R. C. Genetic differences in maze-learning ability in rats. *Yearb. Nat. Soc. Stud. Educ.* 39 (1940):111-119.

PART THREE

TREATMENT CONTEXT: CASE HISTORIES

CARL R. ROGERS

14

The Case of Mr. Bebb: Analysis of a Failure Case

Simply stated, Carl Rogers is one of the century's central personality theorists and the still evolving leader of the most widely practised counseling approaches. His humanistic persona has led to the addition of "Rogerian" as a label synonymous with empathic insightful person-centered partnership in the resolution of human problems. In a strictly Rogerian style, Dr. Rogers responded to the initial invitation to join in this handbook by agreeing that our effort was a good one, yet choosing a contribution to illustrate that even those with the best of intentions can be iatrogenic, an iatrogenesis of omission rather than commission: the search for errors to correct must always, candidly and continuously, begin with ourselves. To quote Dr. Rogers: "This case is typical of my experience; while we were not of much help to the young man, neither did we harm him. There is a definite difference between failure to help and really hurting the individual, a difference of which I am sure you are aware." **R.F.M.**

I: Introduction

The purpose of this chapter is to present a body of research and clinical data bearing on an individual who must, by several criteria, be regarded as a "failure" in psychotherapy. There are a number of reasons for regarding this as worth-while. Very few unsuccessful cases have been presented, and the portrayal of such a case is thus a step in the consideration of the whole range of therapeutic effort. Further, the fact that a wealth of objective information is available on this client makes the value of the presentation greater to the profession. Finally, there is the long-standing and distressing fact that, though each therapeutic orientation has fairly clear-cut hypotheses to explain those instances in which constructive change occurs, the hypotheses offered to explain failures are vague, confusing, and often contradictory. We stand in need of more significant hypotheses to account for lack of change, and it is hoped that analysis of such a case may provide some leads for better hypotheses.

Reprinted with permission from *Psychotherapy and Personality Change*, edited by Carl R. Rogers and Rosalind F. Dymond. Chicago: University of Chicago Press, 1954.

II: The Client and His Therapist

The Gathering of Data from the Client

"Mr. Bebb," as we shall call this client, was a young man of foreign birth, a student, who came to the Counseling Center at the suggestion of a friend. He agreed to participate in the research, with the understanding that his therapy would in no direct way be influenced by the research. In terms of our experimental design he was assigned to the own-control group and was immediately given the battery of tests utilized in the first block (Block I) of our research: the Thematic Apperception Test (TAT); a set of one hundred Q-sort cards with self-referent items which he sorted to portray himself, the self he would like to be, and the ordinary person; the Willoughby Emotional-Maturity Scale (E-M Scale); and the Self-Other Attitude Scale (S-O Scale). He was then asked to wait for sixty days before the first appointment with his therapist. At the end of the sixty-day period all the tests were repeated before his first interview, giving a control period of sixty days without therapy. The first through seventh interviews were held in the next thirty-one days, all interviews being recorded. At the conclusion of the seventh interview he was requested by the psychometrist to again carry out the threefold Q-sort. At this time the counselor also sorted the Q-cards as he thought the client would sort them. There were two more interviews in the next twelve days, and he then concluded therapy after the ninth interview, therapy having extended over a six-week period. After he had concluded therapy, the whole battery of tests was repeated. After a follow-up period of six months the battery of tests was readministered, and he was interviewed by both the psychometrist and the therapist in regard to his experience during and since therapy. This concludes the contacts through which the objective data were collected.

Each of the instruments used was selected to test one or more specific hypothesis concerning the process or the outcome of therapy. The hypotheses for each portion of the study will be stated in the appropriate section in which the data are given (Secs. IV through IX of this chapter).

The Client as Seen by the Therapist

The therapist supplied the following qualitative description of Mr. Bebb very shortly after the conclusion of therapy.

> When I first saw Mr. Bebb, he seemed to me to be an extremely shy, deferential, rigid, frightened person. He was concerned about himself because of physical symptoms (heart palpitations) which he had been told by a physician were psychological in origin. These seemed to be part of a general anxiety.
>
> In his interviews he revealed himself as having extremely high expectations for himself. In comparison with these standards, he thought of himself as completely worthless. He tentatively revealed some auditory hallucinations, which he never thoroughly explored. He felt that he must have guidance in his thinking and that he could not possibly make any choices on his own initiative. He wanted very much to have some external and objective decision as to his normality.

His progress in therapy was evident but centered around a very limited issue. As he discussed the necessity of being guided by external standards, he explored the different answers he might receive and recognized that some of these answers he would accept and others he would reject. Evidently the impact of these discoveries struck him between interviews, and he came in, in the ninth interview, with a decidedly changed view. He had concluded that he *was* capable of making evaluations himself and that he could accept himself as having this capacity. With this interview, he concluded therapy.

The therapeutic process was clear cut in that he achieved the courage to place the locus of evaluation within himself. It was also clear however that he was a long way from having achieved integration. I cannot predict whether therapeutic change will continue beyond the end of the interviews. If not, he will at some point need further help, because he did not fully admit all significant experiences to awareness. I regard the case as successful in a limited way.

The Relationship

Because of the probable importance of the relationship to the process of therapy, the counselor was asked to give his impression of the relationship between himself and Mr. Bebb. These are his comments.

Mr. Bebb was such a frightened and self-depreciating person that a real relationship was very difficult to establish. I felt warmly toward him, partly I am sure, because he was so obviously in need of help. It seemed to me that he was never able to accept my feeling for him, because he could not believe it.

In the relationship he frequently wanted and asked for guidance and for answers. I did not feel in any sense pushed by these requests, because the desperate need for inner assurance showed through these so clearly. I usually handled such requests by trying to understand the feeling behind them. When he wanted very much to have an objective evaluation of his normality, I dealt with this in somewhat the following fashion: "It seems to you that, if I would tell you that in my judgment you are normal, this would settle the issue for you, and that, on the other hand, if I said you were definitely abnormal, then you could accept that and be guided by it." This helped him to explore his own feelings much further and to discover resources of self-confidence of which he had been unaware.

His confidence in himself took a sharp upward turn which was fairly dramatic. I was surprised to have him conclude his interviews at this point, however, and thought it likely that he would return. In our parting I expressed my sincere attitude of willingness to see him again if at any point, then or later, he felt a need of further help. To date he has not returned.

Counselor Ratings

The ratings of the case, made by the therapist at the conclusion of the interviews, give in summary form his judgments of the somewhat contradictory elements in the situation. The judgment was made that therapy for this client had been largely an intellectual-cognitive process and only to a small degree an emotional-experiential one. It was felt that Mr. Bebb had made very little use of the relationship itself for therapy. As for over-all ratings regarding outcome, it was judged that at the beginning of therapy the client was near the extreme of highly defensive psychological organization and that in therapy he made only slight progress toward real integration. (On the "degree of personal integration" he was rated on the nine-point scale as being at 2 at the beginning of therapy and at 4 at its conclusion.) As to his life-adjustment, it was felt that this was poor and that little progress had been made. (Rating of 3 at beginning, 4 at conclusion.) As to "outcome of therapy," the counselor first gave him a rating of 5 but then changed it to 6 on the nine-point scale, feeling that the therapeutic process had been clear cut and positive, even though the gains were relatively small.

III: The Dynamics of the Therapeutic Interviews

Undoubtedly the reader will wish to form his own clinical judgment as to the basis of the failure of personality or behavior change to occur in this case. For this reason, numerous and somewhat lengthy excerpts have been taken from the nine interviews, and they are presented in this section. Since it was obviously impossible to present the whole case, selections had to be made. The effort was made to include all the segments which appeared to have the most meaning to the client, those excerpts which seemed to have any bearing on the therapeutic process, and those portions where questions might be raised as to the adequacy of the therapist's handling. It is believed that this basis of selection has provided, in a relatively small number of pages, an accurate picture of the client, the process, and the relationship. The material will be presented with a minimum of interpretation to facilitate the forming of independent judgments.[1]

In presenting the material, it may be helpful to state that the client's voice was very low and hesitant and that sometimes it would trail off into such self-directed mumblings that it was inaudible to the therapist. The client was quite inarticulate, and speech was slow, with many pauses. This seemed to be a matter of temperament rather than a matter of speaking in other than his childhood tongue.

First interview—In the first moments of the first interview Mr. Bebb states his problem as he sees it.

> **C.:**[2] I just...had a general feeling of being depressed..... And, well, it's the way it...it...manifested itself that sort of...worried me..... The way I became aware of it was more or less in the physical manifestations, I mean, palpitations of the heart..... and, I seen the doctor over at the hospital, and, well, he tried to say that...it's a functional disease...some sort of a psychiatric...that's what's wrong.

He tells how he saw a psychiatrist for two interviews and was told that his difficulty was an Oedipus complex and that he should think about it and come back in three months. He has tried to think about it but to no avail.

> **C.:** (Pause.) I mean, I've been thinking about this stuff, but...I've tried to get at it and really...I mean seek it out, seek out the problem and...try to

recognize it. But... I mean, all I'm confronted with, ever, I think, it just the effects... The cause is completely... unidentified, completely concealed. And ... it's just like... diving, I mean, with a hood over your head or something. You don't know just where to look for it.

T.: M-hm. You tried very hard to look within yourself...

C.: Yeah. M-hm.

T.: ... and see what the cause could be but it's just... the causes just remain completely unknown to you, and you're scrabbling around in the dark. (Pause.)

C.: And the... I mean, the physical effects are still there and... that gives me reason to believe that whatever is the catalyzer, initiator of the whole thing, is still there.

He tells something of his childhood and talks of his feelings both of inferiority and of superiority.

C.: People generally thought I was... a kind of idler or idle person..... and ... had no ambition or no backbone. And... also in the school I went... which was... well, it's sort of an orphanage and sort of an... institution... which I was put into after my father and my mother was divorced. And there the... well, the kids always made fun of me because I was sort of dull, inactive... in their activities, and... which I'm quite sure gave me a sort of inferiority complex..... Then I have the opposite feeling, namely that..... I'm really much better than some people..... Sometimes, I mean, I just feel depressed, morbid, and I just feel that I'm no good; and other times I feel... very elated. That is I... I... just feel that... well, practically ready to take on anybody because I feel that, sometimes, I'm so much better than they are. But there's never really any... any... golden medium.

Second interview—In the second interview he compares this country and his own and his feelings about going back. In this segment he also presents again the two views of himself.

C.: I'm actually... sometimes I'm fearful of the fact of... going back and... well, then, I think, I believe I've changed a great deal since... since I lived in my own country, you see. My... people in my country, they know me..... Mean, I have this notion of feeling compelled to do something which is really good and worth while before I can go back..... And I still feel that there's a certain amount of prejudice involved in... people I know in my country... in respect to my individuality, my personality, which... is not the case here because... I don't, well, I don't know what you would call it, maybe a bad impression, but... well, I guess you could say that. I don't think that that has been the case over here. And (pause) it's (pause) mean, my (pause) well, my achievements... regardless of how small they may be, have been... been greater in this country than they have in my own. And... but the people in my country don't... don't seem to be aware of it, perhaps because of... I told you when I went to this orphanage when I was... ten till I was fifteen, well, they considered me sort of dull. But I don't know... I mean, somehow the—I mean a great many times I knew that... for instance in studying, I mean, I was among the lowest in the class and... but still 'way in myself I felt..... that I knew more, I mean about the courses that we focused on, our studies, than, the... persons who were considered to be the best in the class. I just felt that I... I wasn't recognized. I don't know why that is. Seems I was, well, rather sort of emotional because sometimes, somehow I mean, I'd just start crying. I don't know, that . . . meant nothing and . . . so I mean they'd make fun of it, I mean, the kids . . .

T.: So that one of the reasons why you feel quite sure that you couldn't really be accepted back there unless you do something quite important and quite significant over here is that . . . there is quite a discrepancy between the way you felt inside yourself where you felt even in those younger days that you *did* know something, you really knew more than some of the others and so on; but because of your feelings and emotions, somehow that didn't get expressed, and so others had a poor opinion of you. Is that something like it?

C.: Yeah. It's also this . . . well, now, when I look upon those years, I also thought that I sort of . . . withdrew myself, and probably it easily could have been . . . probably justified, and . . . considered sort of dull or . . . inactive . . .

He is annoyed that he cannot believe in himself, and two statements from the remainder of the interview will indicate his attitudes on this point.

C.: Now I'm working on a novel in my own language, and I just thought maybe if I could finish that and have it published in my country that maybe . . . Somehow I just get, I mean get sort of angry with myself because I feel that I have to do something before I dare show up, mean I just get angry with myself because I don't have, seem to have, enough faith in my, in own capabilities.

T.: (*Later, responding to a statement client has just made.*) You want so much to prove to them, "I am worth while; I am somebody."

C.: Yeah. But of course I mean, it would also prove to myself something.

T.: Feel it isn't only to them that you have to prove this; it's to yourself too.

C.: Yeah. But, sorta feel, I mean, I'm more convinced essentially . . . than . . . I feel they are. (Long pause: 2 minutes.)

Third interview—The third interview was spent mostly in expressing his comparative attitudes about this country and his home country. Much of the material was not very deeply related to himself. At one point he expresses his need of belonging.

C.: Well, I mean, somehow . . . I still feel a need of belonging by common . . . consent . . . I mean, to (pause) living or (pause) more or less be part of some (pause) collective mentality which is in . . . is in concord with one's own, I mean, my own . . . way of looking at things.

T.: You want to be identified with some group or with its way of living and its culture. With a group that sees life somewhat in the same terms that you do. Is that . . . ?

C.: M-hm. (Pause.)

Fourth interview—The fourth interview is very full of quotable material, as he plunges more and more deeply into his own attitudes. First is his desire to be told and then his fear about his sanity.

C.: (Long pause.) (*Sighs.*) I feel like (*deep sigh*) I wish you could tell me what you wanted me to say. And I don't know . . . talk about something (pause).

T.: You mean you'd be quite willing to talk about something if I would indicate what . . . what it might be useful or helpful to talk about, hm?

C.: Yeah. (Long pause.) I don't know why, I mean (*sighs*) always seem to . . . want to have . . . I mean, be told things like . . .

T.: M-hm. (Pause.) As though there's a certain amount of ... *satisfaction* in being ... guided, is that ... ?

C.: Well not (pause), not necessarily being guided, but (pause) just (pause) at least just have suggestions ... be given suggestions ... having suggestions made about ... things which ... I'm not sure about. Like about myself somehow. And (Pause.)

T.: That is, in areas where you're not *sure*, like about yourself (pause) you prefer it if somebody *else* gives you a lead a little bit ... or makes a little suggestion.

C.: Yeah. (Pause.) Sometimes I just feel that (pause) I'm not ... fully sane and I just ... want somebody to have some sort of ... test made, you know, or just be ... I mean, I want somebody to ascertain whether it's true or not. I mean I just sort of (pause) feel in doubt, or dubious. And ... I mean I can't ... ascertain that for myself because I don't feel, I mean I don't feel I have capacity for—either the capacity or the competence for it in that sense. (*Sigh of relief.*)

T.: M-hm. When you ... when you wonder if you really are normal or if you're abnormal, or insane, then it seems as though—if someone who was more competent than *you* would test you, would judge you ... and say, either "Yes, you are," or "No, you aren't" ... that ... there would be something about this that you'd like ... very much.

C.: Yeah. M-hm. That's it. (Pause.) There occurs ... (*clears throat violently*) within myself I find, I mean, such ... a sort of ... dichotomy between ... well, not ... maybe it's two selves or ... maybe there's just ... two halves of the one ... I mean, it's just two extremes, and (*sighs*) sometimes I just feel the one is normal, and the other one is abnormal, by others' preconceived standards, judgments. And ... then ... I just wanta ... *know* whether it would (pause).

T.: Is this it, that when you feel such a deep *discrepancy* within your*self* ... as you say, maybe between two selves (pause), and then it's ... well, I'm not quite sure there. Then it seems to you as though perhaps one self is abnormal and the other one ... is *not* ...

C.: Is not, yeah. This ... is the way it seems to me, but then ... I mean in cases like that I'd just like to have some competent person, I mean, who knows about it ... tell me just ... which is which and ... then I feel that maybe I could look at it differently rather than ... being aware of the ... of the ... symptoms or whatever it is ... Not know ... just ... how they are to be interpreted or ... what they mean.

In discussing this, he tells of trends in himself toward turning within and turing out.

C.: (Long pause.) And then sometimes I (pause), I don't know if this makes sense, but ... sometimes I just feel that ... I want to exist, so to speak, completely ... within myself, I mean, within ... without any ... normal social intercourse, and then ... but when I feel like that I (*sighs*), I sort of feel sorry for myself. And then I become sorta depressed. And then (*sighs*) at other times I feel that I don't want to exist within myself at all because it ... brings sort of agony or torment or sort of mental ... hardships. And then I just want to ... indulge in complete ... normal ... social ... relationships, and I don't want at all to exist within myself, but (*sighs*), well, then I become ... then I feel it's that somewhat ... mean I feel that's good. And then I become ... rather elated. And I (*sighs*), I feel that ... I've taken the right course ... but I mean I don't know ... again I mean, there's nothing, there's nothing in between. (*Sighs.*)

T.: Sort of swings back and forth, but there are the two ... two pulls, as I get it. That sometimes you feel pulled in the direction of just living completely within yourself and never mind relationships with anyone else; only then you ... feel dissatisfied and depressed somewhat by that feeling. Then again the pull is in the other direction, to ... live in your relationships with others; and that feels very good, but it ... doesn't necessarily last that way. Is that what ...?

His desire for social relationships makes him realize his need for affection, and this in turn makes him angry.

C.: But then when I ... when I get this feeling that ... I need affection, then ... I become angry ... at myself because I ... or become angry at other people because they ... bring about my realization that I do need it ...
T.: M-hm. You feel ... angry at others because they kind of awaken in you that ... that sense of *need* for affection, and then you feel angry at yourself because ... why are you so weak or something as to ... need any affection from others? Is that something like it?
C.: Yeah. M-hm. (Long pause.)

Later in the interview his desire for outside evaluation is explored much more deeply, and he comes to realize the positive opinion he has of himself.

C.: I feel that (pause) if you, if you should tell me something now ... something which you ... thought would-would sum me up ... I mean, sum my personality up pretty well and pretty accurately ... now, if ... it didn't click, or if you say something which ... wasn't very flattering, I ... well, I'd just feel that ... I'd probably say that ... you just couldn't say that after ... such a short time like ... I'd feel that you wasn't competent to say it ... after such a short time, whereas, on the other hand, if it's something that (pause) I thought I could accept, I ... I wouldn't question it at all. (Pause.)
T.: The way you use the phrase "not flattering" there made me wonder ... if I said something about you ... and it was somehow ... rather deeply *disapproving* of you, then you could find a lot of reasons why ... it shouldn't be *accepted;* where if ... does the opposite hold true? Where if it was something that ... rather deeply *approved* of you ... then perhaps that would click with your own feelings. Is that ...?
C.: M-hm. Yeah. (Pause.)
T.: Is this going too far, then, to say that ... it looks as though your own feelings ... were looking for some basis on which they could really ... approve of you?
C.: Yes. That is ... I just want some sort (*sighs*) of ... verification ... And ... if it didn't coincide ... I'd just ... not accept it ... I mean, just reject it.
T.: M-hm. If you could find some *confirmation* ... something that would *support* you in feeling positively about yourself ... then you could accept that ... and if it was anything else you'd just ... toss it out.
C.: M-hm. (Pause.) Seems just that I feel uncertain ... of myself. But yet-yet I hope and I want (*sighs*) confirmation for ...
T.: M-hm. You have real hope in regard to yourself but you ... you doubt that hope, you wish that something could confirm it, could support it. Is that ...?
C.: Yeah. (Pause.) Since ... I mean, I want to ... I mean, rationally I feel that I have to ... accept myself ... for what ... competent people, who know me,

evaluate me to be. (Pause.) But sometimes if it . . . doesn't coincide with . . . what I hope . . . (*sighs*), I just feel that I wouldn't accept it. (Pause.)

T.: In other words, you know within yourself (pause) that your acceptance of yourself . . . would have to be in the terms that you . . . that you hope for yourself. Does that make sense?

C.: Yeah. I mean, I know . . . I mean, rationally, I know that . . . as I may say . . . I mean, I'm only what I am . . . I mean, I'm nothing more or nothing less than that. But I hope that what I am is . . . is something *good* rather than something *bad* . . . but if someone should come along and say that . . . tell me that it's something bad . . . I just wouldn't accept it, but then I feel . . . I'd just go elsewhere to seek some confirmation.

T.: Almost as though your feelings were pretty well convinced that what you are is basically good . . . and if someone says, "No, you're not; you're basically bad" . . . you just know that you couldn't and wouldn't accept *that*.

Fifth interview—In this interview he strikes a new note in this thinking about the evaluation of himself.

C.: Somehow I feel that . . . I never get . . . I mean, any real external proof of . . . of one's own . . . abilities or capacities for doing something well. Somehow it (*sighs*) . . . don't you think it all depends upon . . . an inner awareness or an inner . . . conscious feeling of one's own . . . abilities? Somehow I feel that even if I should get a degree, it would really mean nothing to me unless I felt convinced myself that I really had accomplished something and produced something . . . something good. And, well, in that case, a degree is never really any proof. I feel that there's inner awareness of, a feeling of . . . that what one does is *good,* and . . . is appreciated, I mean, has to be . . . judged just mostly by one's self.

It is in this interview, too, that he becomes more specific as to the reason why he feels insane.

C.: And I . . . sometimes I (*sighs*) sort of hear noises which I know they're not . . . I mean, I know they're not there. That, of course may just be . . . I don't know, it may just be different levels of consciousness, I don't know enough about it. But at that time . . . I mean at the times like . . . these, I just feel that, well, it's . . . I mean, it's just something which . . . which is there. Maybe I'm just (pause), just abnormal, I . . . mean . . . (*Sighs.*)

T.: M-hm. It's when you hear sounds that intellectually you know aren't there, then there's the feeling, "Oh, my gosh, I'm really abnormal." (Pause.)

C.: Well, I mean, at times like that I just feel like (*sighs*) I mean, just more or less like . . . just resigning to my fate or whatever you want to call it. Just accept whatever consequences are involved.

At the close of the interview he is discussing his feelings about abnormality, when there comes a segment which is of considerable interest from the point of view of therapist handling.

C.: Yeah, and then I feel that, well, I've tried, and I've, so to speak, just failed. Then . . . instances like that I'd just like for someone to sit before me just to give me the answers. And tell me just . . . what is up.

T.: And so you feel that the answers can't be . . . haven't been able to come from within you, and you'd like very much to . . . have someone else . . . put the answer before you.

C.: Yeah. That's right.

T.: Guess we'll have to call it quits for today. (Arrangements for next appointment.)

C.: Say ... I'd like to ... have some kind of an answer. Is there any reason to worry about it if you hear noises or could it just be levels of consciousness? (*Laughs.*) I know it's an unfair question. I know that ... and you don't have to answer it.

T.: But that doesn't mean that you wouldn't like an answer, I mean, you wish that you...

C.: Yes. But I mean, it's an unfair question, because it's against your ... You don't have to ...

T.: Well, you feel it's an unfair question because it's against my method. I would just feel that ... I don't know of any answer I can quite give, because the fact is, you *are* worried about it.

C.: Yeah.

T.: I mean, that's why you talked it over.

C.: Yeah.

T.: And I guess my feeling is that, as we explore your concern about it, then maybe we can find out whether there is anything there to be concerned about. I mean, as I look at it, take some of these other things. You felt first: "Here are a lot of *problems* that I want to get the answers to." Now today, you're saying: "No ... that isn't quite it. I want to see what I can do about *myself.*" Well, the thing looks differently to you perhaps than it did at first. Now ... that may be the kind of thing that would happen if we get down and talk of these other things.

C.: Yeah. M-hm.

Sixth interview—In this interview most of the time is spent in discussing the standards by which one should live with some reference to the question of how "abnormalities" are to be judged. Toward the end of the interview he explores his fear of insanity a bit more directly, though still cautiously and in the third person.

C.: And I feel that the thing which really brings about the conflict in a person is ... when he finds similarities between phenomena described and labeled in a ... in a scientific book perhaps and phenomena observed in himself. I mean it might not have seemed very significant to him. But then when he reads a book or maybe is lectured, given certain labeled phenomena, he ... I mean, he begins to ... think about it, and ... this ... well really like this, I think the conflict might arise. (*This last in almost a trembling voice.*)

T.: So it can really set up conflicts in a person to find that things that he has observed within himself ... are categorized and labeled ... by the ... experts ... as being this or that ... and then he may become concerned about it. Is that ...? (Pause.)

C.: That is why ... I mean, if you become completely yourself, I mean, or just accept yourself for what you are, I mean ... In that case, you just exclude any labeling or any ... any way of handling(?) things by words. But that I feel is impossible because of your ... of the way we live ... I mean, in reality (*tone more confident*).

T.: From your tone of voice it almost sounds as if you felt it might be desirable to simply be yourself and not be ... labeling all aspects of experience. But you feel that's just impossible in the present-day world.

C.: (*A few moments later in the interview.*) But maybe . . . I mean, even if you did label certain phenomena in your own personality, (pause) it might not make much difference . . . until you observed the same phenomena in other people just carried to a . . . more extreme, I mean to a larger degree like . . . you might find within yourself . . . sometimes that you might be somewhat neurotic or even somewhat psychotic which might not worry you, but then when you see . . . an extremely psychotic person, you know that they are insane and, I mean . . . by and large are beyond any help or any . . . repair, I mean, I feel that you become worried . . . maybe this will happen to me, and . . .

T.: Quite a frightening thing if some of the things that you observe within yourself . . . you see carried to a much greater extreme in others . . . and those others are psychotic.

C.: M-hm.

T.: Because then it seems to you they're hopeless and therefore . . . does it mean that . . . a—I harbor within me the beginnings of this hopeless . . . a . . .

C.: It might evolve to the same. (Pause.)

T.: That can really worry you.

C.: Yeah. I mean, if you just . . . so to speak . . . existed within yourself . . . and didn't have any contact with other people . . . that would be . . . I mean, would be fine . . . and might even be (*sighs*) an ideal, because you . . . I mean, you wouldn't be put in contrast with—to other people . . . but I mean your daily contact with other people . . . reveals these contrasts . . . makes them more apparent.

Seventh interview—Mr. Bebb opens the seventh interview with the feeling that his need for counseling is a sign of weakness.

C.: I've been thinking about this counseling service. And I've somewhat questioned my necessity for . . . for seeking . . . counseling help. Because it seems . . . well, maybe not quite apparent but it . . . just . . . seems to be a reasonable inference that (pause) the solution to any problem that you might find . . . more or less it lies . . . within the individual, I mean it . . . seems that . . . to me that he should be capable of reasoning and . . . reflecting about them himself. Thus . . . he might, arrive at some solution . . . since we'll agree that . . . I mean it's not the problems but . . . it's to look within the person. And . . . well . . . it's just . . . a little . . . sort of . . . well, ridiculous. I mean, seeking out . . . seems to me it's sort of a . . . manifestation of my own . . . inferiority in trying to solve my own problems. Well, I'm not . . .

T.: Seems like kind of a . . . weak and . . . ridiculous thing that . . .

C.: Yes, I feel . . .

T.: . . . that you feel that you have such a need. (Pause.)

C.: And . . . well, I'm not saying that I don't think it will help. But . . . well, I just feel that it's sorta just . . . declaring my own . . . incapability to solve my own problems. Well, I just don't know how to . . .

A bit later he goes further, saying that counseling thus far has been both discouraging and disturbing. He mentions the possibility of stopping.

C.: I also feel that this . . . introspection is . . . not necessary because it doesn't . . . seem to have taken anywhere, or lead anywhere. And I feel that . . . what I see within myself I should just . . . accept rather than asking how and why. But somehow that doesn't satisfy. (Pause.)

T.: But you feel as though looking within . . . hasn't led to any progress and . . . you think you have to just stop that and accept whatever is . . . within; then you can't quite let yourself do that either.

C.: No. (Pause.) But as I said, I mean . . . it seems that the more I try to look at myself, the more pecu-confused I become . . .

T.: And is what . . . is this part of what you're saying today, that as you look at yourself . . . it does seem more confusing . . . and that that confusion seems a little frightening? (Pause.)

C.: Well, it seems discouraging. . . . . And I feel that, rather than . . . *help* me, it disturbs me.

T.: M-hm. That by and large to discover . . . confusion within yourself . . . has been disturbing . . . rather than helping.

C.: Then I also think that . . . could be that I just want to . . . to know too much about myself, or maybe that I just indulged in too much introspection . . . Mean, it appears to me that . . . sometimes, that I should just stop where I am . . . and just, just stop there and don't . . . not speculate any more about it. But . . . well, I, again I don't.

T.: It looks kind of attractive to say . . . "Okay, I'll just shut the doors here. I won't look at myself any further and go on from here." . . . But somehow you don't find yourself . . . doing that.

C.: I don't . . . no.

Later in the interview he explores the possibility that his discouragement may be due to the fact that what he is finding within himself is not in accord with his hope and intuition. He tells how much he wishes to discover that he is a positive and worth-while person.

C.: Maybe the fact that it appears to me that I'm not getting anywhere . . . might be or might . . . yeah, might be indicative of (pause) the fact that what I find within myself is not in concord with my . . . intuitive or my . . . intuitive . . . knowledge of what I hope to find . . . But yet . . . seems that I don't want to abandon my intuition.

T.: M-hm. M-hm. M-hm.

C.: I mean, if there were any definite traces within myself . . . which might bear out the . . . intuition, then, I mean, I would know that I was getting somewhere, because I would know that I was getting closer to . . . my original . . . or . . . the things which I see verification for. But the fact that I don't seem to get anywhere might be . . . indication that it doesn't exist . . . I don't know if it's clear.

T.: I think it is. That perhaps the reason you feel . . . no progress and so on is that . . . perhaps in this exploration of yourself . . . you haven't yet, at least . . . well, I'll put it the other way around . . . that you have discovered things that aren't entirely in accordance with what . . . somehow basically . . . you feel you are . . . And perhaps that's a disturbing . . . thing. Is that . . . something of what you're saying?

C.: Yes. (Pause.) And I suppose it's because of this fact that the things which I find are not in accordance with my intuitive knowledge of myself, that I feel the need of some person whom I suppose . . . or hope, would feel the same way about it might guide me to what . . . I mean, I hope that his evaluation of me might coincide with my intuition about . . . what I . . . basically am.

T.: That almost sounds, and I'm not quite sure that I understand it, but that **almost sounds as though (pause) as though you feel concerned that what**

you're discovering within yourself ... may make you a less worth-while person than you had intuitively felt ... you were, and if you could find somebody who says, "But you are a worth-while person," and who would confirm that side of your self ... that that would have a good deal of meaning. Is that ... ?

C.: Yes. I was just going to say that. That what I've been saying here, I mean, would ... give the implication that (pause) what I ... intuitively feel that I am is something good ... and ... from what I've been saying it rather appears that ... what I *do* find is ... I mean, is not good. (Pause.) But, other times, I feel that I find something within myself which is good, but then that ... it doesn't develop far enough to ... I mean for me to be completely convinced of its validity. I mean, it just seems ... to stop, and you have ... sort of ... opposites ... just ... entering in, disturbing the ... distorting the picture, so to speak.

T.: M-hm. In other words ... in this exploration, it isn't just that you find bad things about yourself, but when you find things you *value* about yourself, they don't seem too *certain* or too sure, and there are often contradictions involved ... ?

C.: Yeah ... They just don't seem to be ... strongly enough set off ... to be convincing.

T.: M-hm. Sorta gives you kind of an ... *uncertain* feeling about that aspect of it. Is that ... ?

C.: Yes. In fact (pause) I mean, I feel that basically what it is, I mean what is troubling me about myself is that uncertainty as to, as to just what I am. And (pause) I feel that what I'm seeking *for* ... within myself is just ... a convincing ... verification of (pause) good qualities which I might discover. (Pause.)

At the close of this period he recognizes that perhaps he is trying to escape the effort which would be involved in becoming the person he wants to be. At this point he also reduces the number of interviews from two per week to one.

C.: I mean if that is the case, and I have to conclude that I consist ... of both good and evil, the only thing I can do is just ... work toward elimination of the ... I mean elimination of the evil (pause) by working for something good. (Pause.) That is to say, I mean to be truly good, just seems to be ... a process of just hard ... plain hard work rather than something which you ... you *are* ... inherently ... I mean that you are innately.

T.: That is, *possibly* it isn't the (pause) possibly being really good isn't a type of *description,* but a type of *effort.* Is that ... ?

C.: Yeah. (Pause.) Then maybe if that is the case the problems which I seem to encounter might just be (*sighs*) obstacles in my ... conscious effort to ... becoming good. (Pause.) Well, I might ... I mean, rather than trying to fight them (pause) just try to (pause) resign and try to rationalize, attempt to find some ... logical (pause)necessity for the existence. (Pause.)

T.: M-hm. That is, a part of what's going on in *you* may be a (pause) a need to kind of ... escape seeing them as obstacles which might yield to effort, and maybe it's just an attempt to see them in some more absolute light. Is that ... ?

C.: Yeah. Just try to become convinced of the ... necessary reason for their existence rather than try to eliminate them. (Pause.)

T.: Guess our time's about up.

C.: Yeah. (Arrangements for next appointment.) Really, only one meeting a week would be all right.

T.: All right. Want to make it a week from today?

Eighth interview—Our client opens the interview by considering further the process of effort which is necessary to become "good." He feels that one has to have incentive to work toward the goal of realizing one's potentialities. Very tentatively he concludes that even if one's potentialities are not great, but "sort of limited," it might still be some reason to work toward their realization.

He wishes very much that he knew whether he had potentialities. He explores this uncertainty further in the passage that follows:

C.: Sometimes I just feel that . . . personally I'm (pause) well, I'm (pause) well, I'm working or sort of . . . directing my life or my existence . . . on the basis of some sort of hypothesis which is really . . . there's no rational . . . a, basis for, for accepting it in the first place. I mean, sometimes I feel that I am worth while and other times . . . I feel that I'm not. Again . . . it's just this uncertainty.

T.: M-hm. (Pause.) Does that . . . does that feeling almost amount to being . . . very deep wish that . . . someone did regard you as worth while? . . . Or isn't it? I don't know.

C.: Yes. In a sense. But then (pause) if it does happen that . . . people should compliment me on something I've done . . . it just doesn't seem to be enough . . . and I just seem to want more . . . and that's . . .

T.: M-hm. You know very well . . . that praise for achievement . . . that isn't the thing that satisfies this need.

C.: No, it's . . . mean, it's . . . more or less boils down to what I said before. I mean, it has to be some sort of . . . an inner realization of your . . . I mean, of your own worth-whileness. (Pause.) But then again . . . I mean, it's a contradiction . . . because that may not at all be attained by (*sighs*) . . . even if someone . . . or if I should . . . should agree for someone to tell me what he . . . what he, what he thought. I mean, someone whom I considered . . . well, competent. That's why. (Pause.)

T.: That there is the feeling that you would so much like to regard yourself as a worth-while person . . . and it seems to you as though perhaps . . . someone else by some kind of evidence . . . could convince you that that's true. (Pause.)

C.: Ah, yes. (Pause.) I mean (*sighs*) there exist such . . . conflicting and contradictory . . . notions within myself that I just don't. (Pause.)

T.: You don't see *how* you can find the . . . sure sense of your own worth within yourself because there are such . . . contradictory feelings *in you.*

Later he discusses an intelligence test as a way of proving his worth to himself.

C.: (Long pause.) So I mean, the problem is really how to (pause) how to, to achieve some sort of stability within . . . I mean, some stable . . . belief . . . about myself . . . I'm just . . . not sure. (Long pause.)

T.: I can't help but wonder there . . . if what you are asking basically in your feelings . . . may not be this . . . ah, "Is there *anyone* . . . who really . . . deeply believes that . . . I'm worth while?"

C.: Yeah. I'm . . . I've been thinking about that. (Pause.) If that is so, I mean then it is . . . a more or less universal . . . problem for . . . the human. (Pause.) Like, I mean at times I've just felt . . . oh, it sounds silly, I mean . . .

T.: You were saying it seems kind of silly but . . .

C.: Yes. I mean . . . at least it does . . . to me . . . that it is silly because sometimes I do want it that way. Like . . . I mean, great many times I'm just sort of . . . obsessed with the idea . . . of having an intelligence . . . I mean, having an intelligence test made ... on me. (Pause.) In a way that seems sort of artificial, but, on the other hand, sometimes I feel it would serve a purpose. But here again I feel that ... if it didn't sort of mark up to the I.Q. of my friends, I just feel that I wouldn't accept it because ... I have this ... innate ... desire ... to try to be like my friends, at least ... meet their standards.

A long quotation from the end of this interview indicates something of the depth of his despair about himself and his doubt about continuing in the interviews.

C.: (Long pause.) Now, here again I just feel the need of some sort ... well, sort of universal standard by which to ... to measure myself, I mean (pause) attempt to get some sort of definite (pause) certain way ... or notion about myself.

T.: M-hm. (Pause.) This seems like such a strong desire to have someone say, or give you evidence that ... this is the way you should look at yourself, or this is why you do the things you do or ...

C.: Yes. I mean, sorta the key to myself. Key to my personality.

T.: M-hm. You'd like so much to get the key to yourself that would enable you to measure yourself and understand yourself. (Pause.)

C.: Just at least get ... get something which would explain ... my certain basic ... recurrent traits ... behavioristic traits. (Pause.)

T.: You'd like to know, "Why do I behave recurrently in this way?" (Long pause.)

C.: Mean, it's also a confusion, I mean, sometimes I just feel that I should have this, and other times I feel that I shouldn't. Mean, feel that I shouldn't because it's artificial. I should be able to discover those truths or these truths about myself and by my own efforts. And then when I feel that that's impossible, then I ... would like for someone else to do it.

T.: M-hm. When you feel a little bit hopeless about finding the answers to some of those things within yourself, then it just seems as though you've got to have someone else to provide that assurance. (Long pause.)

C.: But as I said ... I mean, deep within myself, I feel that it has to be. I mean, no external assurance would really alter anything or ... would make any modification or ... well, I mean, it has to be some sort of ... some inner realization or inner awareness or inner realization of just what I am. (Pause.)

T.: You're very sure that in the long run it's got to be that inner realization of what you are, or a realization that comes from within you. But still, that doesn't. ... And you realize that the other would be somewhat artificial, but still that doesn't stop you from feeling ... at times that, "By gosh, that's what I want." (Pause.)

C.: Yes. You're right. And also I feel that, at times, that this outside assurance or information about myself ... might work as a clue toward this ultimate self-realization.

T.: M-hm. You might sort of get some leads from an outside evaluation. (Long pause.)

C.: But here ... I mean, this desire, those doubts about myself (*sighs*) I mean, I've had them for years, and I sort of think about them perpetually, constantly, but (pause) I never reach any solution though. I feel that now, while I'm in here, I should attempt to talk more about them, sort of feel that maybe I'm just trying to shun away from them because they appear so futile.

T.: M-hm. Feel that you've struggled for so long with those feelings of worthlessness that ... well, that you just don't know what ... what you can hope for there. And I gather that you even ... even criticize yourself in the interview for not ... why don't you get at them more and so on. You're feeling somewhat critical toward yourself in that.

C.: Yeah. (Pause.)

T.: As though you (pause) can't quite accept yourself in the interview either. I mean, you should be doing something different and better. (Pause.)

C.: Yes. I mean, I feel that (pause) I don't think that I make enough of any personal effort ... I mean, somehow I just feel that I don't decide to tell about it or ... try to sort of shut it out.

T.: Seems to you that you can't ... or that you don't think well of yourself in the interview any more than you do outside. That you're just not making an adequate effort.

C.: M-hm. (Pause.) Mean, I sometimes feel that ... I really shouldn't be ... taking or undergoing these interviews, that I feel it's ... what I see within myself is just ... I mean, is just *me,* and it's ... it's unchangeable. And I feel that that is manifested in my desire sometimes ... my speaking language about it, and just trying to remain quiet.

T.: M-hm. Just sort of feel, "Look, all I get at in the interview is *me* ... and that's a pretty hopeless futile kind of ... thing. I can't change that worthless me. What right have I to take up anybody's time?" Is that putting it too strongly or is that ... ?

C.: No, that's ... I mean, that's pretty ...

T.: (*Very sympathetically.*) Maybe it doesn't quite seem to you that (pause) that anybody *could* feel it was worth while to spend time with you when you are only *you.* (Pause.)

Ninth interview—He opens this contact with the possibility of working things out entirely within himself.

C.: Well ... (*sighs*) I've been thinking about what I told you. And ... a ... I've concluded that (pause) that since (pause) if I (pause) achieve some inner realization ... that what I'm doing ... is right ... well, then everything, it appears, would ... would be all right ... and ... but then if that is the case ... I mean, there's no ... use ... I mean, for me ... to ... talk it over with other ... other people any more when, when I've ... if I've come to this realization.

T.: M-hm. That is, seems to you as though if the thing seems inwardly right to you ... then you really believe perhaps you can *trust* that ... that inner feeling. But if you have really and fully come to that conclusion ... then ... counseling wouldn't particularly be needed.

C.: No. Because (pause) I mean, since it all depends upon how I feel about myself, and ... because of the fact that ... now ... I've come to the belief that it all ... depends on my own attitude toward it ... then ... a ... I don't think ... I should take (*sighs*) any more of your time. I mean ... I feel that, I mean, that as of now it's more or less up to me ... That is, I ... I'll have to act in accordance with ... what I think is right, and then the rest will be trying to (*very softly*) eliminate whatever is troubling me. (Pause.) I may not always know when (*sighs*) I mean, I might set up problems but ... least I'll know what they are and then abandon whatever I'm doing and then go back and try to do it over. See if I'll be satisfied with that. (Pause.) Mean more or less the sensible ... thing ... I'll have to follow is just that (pause) if I feel bad about something, it is because it's not ... what I ... I mean, deep within me, I really want to do, but what I think that I *should* do. So ... the thing to do would just be to ... go back and then try to do it over. And it seems to me I have to ... work ... on the basis of that-that principle.

A little later he explores much more fully his growing confidence in his own capacity for self-evaluation. A lengthy quotation seems justified here to give the full flavor of his feeling.

C.: But I've come to believe that . . . whatever I do . . . I just will have to be the judge of it myself. I mean, at least . . . in important questions or personal questions maybe.

T.: You're the only one who can really . . . put the value . . . on what you do.

C.: Yeah. M-hm. (Pause.) And what I've wanted . . . I mean, having the . . . trying to get assurance or . . . sanction or confirmation or verification or whatever you want to call it, from other people . . . I mean, it's really no good unless . . . it agrees with what I . . . I myself want to do, or what I myself think of it. (Pause.)

T.: Are you sort of saying there that . . . since the opinion of others and the judgment of others about *you* . . . is only really of value to you when it . . . confirms your own . . . judgments, then it isn't really quite as important as . . . as . . . you had previously thought. Is that . . . ?

C.: Yes. M-hm. (Pause.) I mean it's part of what I feel that . . . if I think what I'm doing is good . . . and other people don't think it's good, I still give my . . . own judgment preference . . . And if other people think it is good . . . and I also think it is good, well, then I don't really care about . . . a . . . the other people's judgment because it just—fits in—it's according to my own, coincides with my own. (Pause.) But still it just (pause) just occurred to me that . . . I mean, I might have found a principle (pause) to, so to speak, work under . . . follow, but still if I have to . . . mean if I have to apply this principle very much, it would imply that there's still something, I mean . . . which must be bothering me, whatever it may be. Because of the fact that I have to apply the principle. I mean . . . the fact that I have found something . . . to . . . to work by, or to . . . yes, to work by . . . it doesn't mean that . . . whatever problems I think I have, or I thought I had, I mean, it doesn't mean they're eliminated. Just that I've found maybe some sort of a cure for them, or . . . I mean, it may eliminate them. But then again . . . it may not.

T.: Are you saying there that . . . as you think it over, you really feel . . . somewhat *uncertain* as to just . . . how much the . . . recognition of this principle or any use of this principle will do for you in terms of the problems that you feel. Is that . . . ?

C.: Yes. I mean, I feel that it may be . . . a good . . . therapy, I mean, for the elimination of them or . . . What I mean to say is that with this principle, or this . . . yeah, principle . . . I haven't found the, so to speak, the cause of the problem . . . But . . . what I mean is that I've found some sort of . . . medicine, or some sort of . . . thing which might help solve them or be superior to them . . . might even eliminate them.

T.: M-hm. You might have found a way . . . of dealing with your problems, but without ever being completely aware of what the causes of these problems were. Is that . . . ?

C.: M-hm. Yeah. (Pause.) Well, I also feel that . . . mean, I'll probably (*sighs*) continue having problems as long as I live, and . . . could be that . . . maybe I'm only overemphasizing them . . . And . . . if I just look at them possibly a little differently, I may get more confidence, might not think as much about them.

T.: These *problems* may be something that you'll always have with you, but if . . . if you found a *constructive* way of looking at them . . . that might be a very important . . . step . . . or very important thing. (Pause.)

C.: But I think that the most important thing . . . is the fact . . . I feel that . . .

well, that I realize that . . . in reality that . . . the people of . . . I mean, the judgment of other people . . . outside yourself is not really . . . important. And you can only realize your own value . . . I mean through some inner awareness of what you feel that you are. And no matter what other people think of it, it makes really no difference unless you . . . you yourself feel that way about it . . . if you don't agree with them, then you . . . it just won't (*sighs*) just won't help any.

T.: Feel that for you that's a pretty important . . . discovery that . . . the only values you can ever be sure of are the ones you actually *experience* within yourself.

C.: And the ones you really accept or believe in. (Pause.) I mean, someone might come along and pat you on the shoulder and say that . . . you're an excellent fellow, you're good, but . . . if you don't believe it in yourself I mean, it's just . . . doesn't help any. You might just think the person is insincere. (Pause.) So I'm just . . . convinced it all depends on me . . . or, least, depends on myself.

T.: And you feel, I gather, much more . . . *willing,* and perhaps much more able, to rely on yourself in that kind of thing. Is that right? Or am I . . .

C.: Yes. M-hm. I do, because . . . as I've said, I don't know . . . I just. (Pause.) My own . . . judgment is not absolute. At least it's . . . but . . . or my own judgment about myself anyway . . . may not be absolute, but . . . it's relatively higher than the . . . judgment which other people might pass upon me. (Pause.) I feel that if I ultimately should become (pause) convinced of the fact that . . . what I do or what I have done . . . is good, well, there's just . . . nothing that anyone ever could say about it that I think would change my mind.

T.: M-hm. (Pause.) If you have the *inner* conviction that what you've done is worth-while . . . then you doubt if a thousand people telling you the opposite could . . . change your mind.

C.: Yeah. M-hm. I feel that . . . I mean, previously, a great deal of my trouble has . . . stemmed from the fact that I've . . . I've sought too much the opinion of other people without relying too much on myself; and that . . . though I did rely a little on myself, I also relied on . . . other people; and that . . . brings up the uncertainty. But that was really what caused difficulties.

T.: M-hm. That actually you weren't quite relying on one or the other.

C.: M-hm.

T.: And . . . so never had a firm . . . basis.

C.: M-hm. That's right. And I feel now that . . . I'm much more certain about . . .

T.: You just feel more assurance about yourself, hm?

C.: Yeah. I think. (Long pause.) I mean, I feel that the thing to do is just to be . . . be honest with yourself and be sincere.

Toward the end of this interview comes a portion in which the therapist's handling is likely to be much questioned.

C.: (Long pause.) Well, I may be (*sighs*) repeating myself again. But (pause) I think it's a major . . . achievement or . . . a major step . . . in individual progress to come to realize . . . well, that you should . . . depend on your own judgment rather than the judgment of other people. I know I've said this before, but . . . the more I think about it, the more I realize how important it is. I just want to stress that . . . more important . . . I mean, I think . . .

T.: That's something that has a lot of meaning . . . for you.

C.: M-hm. I feel it has eliminated the uncertainty. (Pause.) I feel that participation and things like that would only be meant toward this end that ... coming to depend more upon yourself. (Pause.) Well, I mean, not depend on yourself to the extent that you exclude, I mean, human relations or anything like that. (Pause.) Just depend on yourself so that (pause) you realize that you (pause) do have the ... potentialities, I mean, of doing something, instead of having to ask people all the time whether they think it's right or not.

T.: M-hm. This isn't an independence that shuts other people out or anything like that. It sounds more as though ... it was an experience of trusting yourself more in ... in the directions that you're going.

C.: M-hm. (Long pause: 2 minutes). Well, I don't know if I can say more without just repeating myself.

T.: You really feel you've ... said almost what you have to say.

C.: Well, yeah, I feel that ... I just found the essentials, and (pause) I could ... probably talk more about it. I'd just ... be elaborating on details rather than ... I don't know just ...

T.: It just sorta seems to me that ... what you're saying in your feeling is, "I think I'm through" ...

C.: M-hm. Yeah.

T.: ... but that you're having kind of a hard time putting that in words. Is that right?

C.: Yeah. (*With relief.*) (Pause.) I mean, I don't want to imply that I have no use for you any more. (*Sighs.*) I mean ...

T.: Sort of fearful that if you said you think you're through, that would seem as though you were somehow ... ?

C.: It would be just sort of selfish, I mean. (Pause.) Just ... talk to clarify my own thoughts maybe. (Long pause.)

T.: Okay?

C.: Yes. I think I'm through. (*Sighs.*)

T.: Okay. And I'd just say that ... I think so too. But that if ... if, on the other hand, next week or next month or some time, you feel, well, "By gosh, I see more things that I want to work out or something," all right, I'll be very glad to see you.

A comment probably needs to be made here which would be unnecessary if we were presenting a recording rather than a transcript. When the counselor attempts to respond to the client's unspoken feeling, "I think I'm through," the relief in Mr. Bebb's voice is very obvious. It seems clear that this *is* his feeling and that he is greatly relieved to have it recognized. This comment is only a description of a fact which would be evident to anyone who listened to the recording. Whether the therapist was wise to respond in this way is an entirely separate question upon which the reader can form his own judgment.

A few minutes after this excerpt the client concluded his interviews, with thanks to the therapist and with the therapist's repetition that he should come back in if he wished to.

Follow-up interview—Six months later Mr. Bebb was asked to return to the Counseling Center for follow-up interviews. He was interviewed both by the psychologist who had administered the tests and by the therapist. The content of both interviews was very similar. An excerpt from the interview with the psychologist will illustrate the flavor of both interviews.

Test Administrator: Jim, I'm interested in . . . right now in your reaction to your counseling experience and whether it meant anything to you, then or during the last months. How do you feel about . . . ?

C.: Well. (Pause.) It . . . seems to me that, right after I completed it and even during the latter part of the counseling service . . . it meant a great deal more to me than . . . it does now.

T.A.: Some diminution in the benefits, sort of . . . as time has lapsed, it's become less beneficial or meaningful?

C.: Yeah. I wouldn't say *beneficial.* I mean, rather the, apparent value, uh, at least . . . for me, it's seemed to decrease. (Pause.) Let me explain it this way: I don't know if everyone who undergoes counseling feels this way or not, but I felt that . . . when I . . . went to counseling, went to my therapist about myself, I felt that the . . . the ultimate thing that I had to . . . do, I mean, effect by myself was . . . I mean, by my own efforts, was a change in *myself,* I mean a change in my way of doing things or in looking at myself or in looking at other people. Now . . . while undergoing counseling with the help of the thera- pist I . . . apparently . . . or I thought . . . seemed to me that I (pause) realized the value of a great many things and that's not . . . I mean, I was very sincere about certain resolutions that . . . was implicitly inferred by the . . . by . . . I mean, some of the answers I gave in the . . . in the counseling, and the answers I gave to myself. And . . . so, I mean, I was very sincere in my . . . in my hope of fulfilling these . . . resolutions and doing everything that I myself wanted to do about myself. However, as it is now, it seems that (pause) at that time, of course it only remains in theory, I mean, I don't think I ever sincerely tried to . . . *do* what I've talked about. I mean, I rather just talked about it, instead of doing it, although I did have the very sincere intention of . . . starting doing . . . starting to . . . I mean, starting to do what I . . . sincerely believed I should try to, about changing myself.

In these interviews Mr. Bebb also stated that he felt he gained more respect for his own individuality and that he came to recognize that it is a lifelong job to mold one's self. He wished the therapist had given his opinion, a "temporary answer," which might have helped to provide a tentative goal.

His major feeling, however, was that he had not put into action some of the things he had seen. In response to direct questions he said that his physical symptoms were pretty much unchanged, though he did not feel they were quite as alarming. He was also asked by the therapist, "You once mentioned that you were kinda concerned about some experiences that you'd had, sort of hallucinations. . . . Anything to say about that?" His response was: "I haven't had any for a long time. When I have them, I become concerned, but I haven't really any cause for concern."

IV: Global Personality Change

In the total research program one of the projects was concerned with measuring, on a continuum of adjustment and integration, the degree of general personality change. The TAT was the instrument used for this purpose. In this section the findings of this portion of the research in the case of Mr. Bebb will be presented.

The hypothesis for this project was that if a competent psychologist placed the TAT's in an order from most poorly integrated to best integrated, the pre- and post-therapy and follow-up tests would show increasing integration. This hypothesis was made, of course, in regard to all the cases in the study as one of the outcomes which could be expected from client-centered therapy. A special investigation was made of the TAT's available in the case of Mr. Bebb which was parallel to, but goes further than, the study thus far made of the whole group.

There were four TAT's available for analysis: from the pre-wait battery, the pre-therapy battery, the post-therapy test, and the follow-up. The respective intervals between tests were as follows: 60 days, 49 days, and 180 days. The stories as given by Mr. Bebb were electrically recorded and transcribed. A set of these four transcriptions, with the dates removed, and identified only by letter, were then given to a psychologist who was experienced in the interpretation of the TAT[3] but who had no knowledge of the case or its outcome and no knowledge of the order in which the TAT's had been given. She was asked to study each TAT and to summarize her impression of the individual and his psychological state. She was also asked to order the TAT's from least well adjusted and integrated to best adjusted and integrated.

The psychologist carried out this assignment but stated that the ordering of the tests was difficult in this case, since the differences in degree of integration seemed small, and hence the placements were made with considerable uncertainty. The order is, however, of considerable interest. They were rated as shown in Table 1. It is evident that the first, second, and third TAT's showed improvement in adjustment as predicted but that the fourth TAT, the follow-up, showed a regression toward the initial status.

Table 1

Ranking	TAT	Time of Administration
4. Least integrated and adjusted	Z	Pre-wait (1st TAT)
3.	W	Follow-up (4th TAT)
2.	Y	Pre-therapy (2d TAT)
1. Best integrated and adjusted	X	Post-therapy (3d TAT)

In order to give the reader somewhat more of an opportunity to make these judgments for himself, the summarized personality pictures, as written by the psychologist without knowledge of the case, are presented in the order in which the tests were administered.

First TAT: Code Letter Z[4]

This is a passive, dependent individual whose characteristic response to frustration is to withdraw, to retreat either by removing himself bodily or by becoming as inconspicuous as possible physically while withdrawing mentally and emotionally into a kind of passionless nirvana. He is strongly ambivalent but as strongly represses his own aggressiveness. A favorite retreat from too deeply experienced emotion is intellectualizing, a philosophical approach which makes discussion possible by making it impersonal. This is a highly complex and very intelligent individual who is very anxious, very insecure, and rather guilt-ridden. There are masochistic trends in his passivity, and, although he wishes to give the impression of being impervious to persuasion, to continue on his own chosen path "in spite of. . . . . pleading," he is very unsure of his own strength and ability to choose and hold to any goal requiring real effort for attainment. There is ambivalence expressed in both father-son and mother-son relationships, with a heightening of guilt feelings in these areas. The Freudian "death wish" is strongly expressed. A depression, a desire to quit the uneven struggle, a despair of ever being accepted as the noble creature he is in his secret heart—are all lying as an undercurrent in everything he thinks and says. The fairy-tale changeling prince, of finer clay than those about him but unacknowledged and unrecognized, he is desperately unhappy. His refusal to accept challenge and to be the aggressor is based upon a real fear of discovery that these delightful fantasies are far from reality—and because the lone dissenter *always* fails if he becomes aggressive. The only thing to do is to withdraw, in lofty superiority, to his ivory tower. Since warm human relationships can undermine even this security, they, too, are thrown aside with finality—"there can be no means of altering" the "facing in an opposite direction" from love and affection. Freedom is seen as the ability to do nothing. This individual may be rather too close to a real break with reality for comfort, having shut off all feeling, all desiring, all hoping, all struggle as too painful and too hopeless. It might be that he is a victim of an actual catastrophe which has actually overwhelmed and rather benumbed him; it might be a very deep feeling of inadequacy and impotence for physical reasons—or perhaps the whole depression is basically self-induced. *Something* is sensed as catastrophic, inescapable, and bearable only by complete passivity with an almost panic reaction when the possibility of being overcome by this "it" is faced. The individual holds himself in with a very tight rein indeed.

Second TAT: Code Letter Y[5]
This individual is torn by ambivalence but not to the extent of panic or complete dissolution. He feels impotent to utilize his own gifts, either because the world won't listen or outside forces prevent it or "things" are just too much for him. The ivory tower is still seen as desirable—contemplation of the conflict between good and evil, of strife versus inertia is still the safest way to handle himself. "Someone" will come along and fix everything—it will not need effort on his part. However, the eventuality of having to take an active part in effecting harmony is beginning to dawn upon him. There is a tentative facing of the problems which produce panic with almost immediate flight into "nirvana"—but with more and more cautious but continuing, positive steps toward action. There is realization of the need for love and support in a faint realization that rejection results in utter misery. He is afraid to allow himself to hope for happiness, and he refuses to admit to himself how strong his feelings of hostility and aggression are—especially toward men. He turns his back upon emotional involvement, refusing to admit how necessary love is to him and affirming stoutly that the conflict of intellect versus emotion must be won on the intellectual level.

Life and struggle seem empty, futile, and nonrewarding. He despairs of being recognized as the superior person he feels he is and is desperately lonely while at the same time denying the need for deference. There is a guilt about failing to come up to the expectations of the mother (or other women) in affectional responsiveness.

Outstanding in this record is the feeling of futility—struggles against terrific odds only to find the object, once gained, turning into dust. The individual is gravely ambivalent; he wants to be "above" or aloof from all feeling tone, but can't. Being aloof, refraining from aggressiveness is seen as "good"; displays of strength are "evil." The individual is so insecure, so unsure of his invulnerability, that he still runs—escapes into depersonalization. The unconscious desire to show great hostility in aggressive, almost antisocial, ways is very close to the surface but not quite—there is always the hasty interpolation of "This is only make-believe." Instead of overt aggressiveness, the individual prefers manipulation of others (power over others without resistance or competition) with a corresponding fear of being manipulated by others. His determination to ignore or minimize familial ties is a denial of deep dependency needs and may point toward a strong oedipal complex deeply buried. He is afraid and knows he is afraid—of people and contacts with people. Life is futile; therefore, one must acknowledge no needs, feel no emotion. He is afraid of the challenge of living, but cessation from struggle is not now seen as an end in itself; it is just a resting place. Inertia—nirvana—is a temporary withdrawal into a "secure" place, where strength may be gathered to go on from there. This is not the feeling of utter chaos and black despair; although the individual has a long way to go, he has seen that there is a way out and feels that it is available to him if and when he is ready for it.

Progress may be illusory—and the feeling of superiority may be hollow—but the converse *may* also be true.

There is a constant swing from feelings of desperate inadequacy to an almost equally desperate demand that everyone recognize his superior qualities; but gradually the value of some kind of compromise is making itself felt. Since this way of life has resulted in nothing but futility and loneliness, there is a need, not to negate life, but to seek a substitute for the present or established ways of meeting its challenge. The safety of the known—safe although unrewarding—is being sensed as an insufficient reason for clinging to it. The individual wants to protect himself from others—is highly suspicious of others—and his impulse to stand aside and observe life flow by is beginning to seem both impossible and undesirable in the long run. Dimly he senses that if enough of the facets of personality are integrated, the "strays" or "mavericks" may be ignored or may even be swept along with the rest—they are not necessarily potential shatter points.

Third TAT: Code Letter X[6]

The individual admits his own ineptitude in handling life. Passivity and dependency have not "worked"—rather sluggishly, some degree of activity is stirring. Action is seen as preferable to inaction, but the individual still cannot trust others or himself in relationship to others. There must be manipulation, and therefore there must be eternal vigilance. Emotions and frustrations are acknowledged—grudgingly—and the familiar cover-up ("This isn't real; this hasn't actually happened; it's a horrible nightmare, and I'll soon wake up") is readily assumed. The individual is now aware that his panicky flights into a nirvana state solve nothing; attempts to withdraw from reality have failed. The outlook is weakly positive, weakly optimistic, but dissolution of personality is no longer so frankly feared. Love, as a real, warm, living thing between two peers, is still a threat, and there are strong indications of almost overt homosexual activities (as the passive partner), which have caused grave concern. Love and affection are almost deliberately placed "in the background" for later fulfillment but are no longer ignored or blacked out completely. The alternative to giving up is to try again in a different direction. The patient feels lost; he doesn't know the terrain—but no longer utterly helpless. There is great guilt feeling with respect to the mother figure, with pronounced dependency needs almost desperately denied and defied. He is both drawn to and repelled by men—and has no real convictions as to which will predominate. There is an increased compulsivity, increased ambivalence, but *some* decrease in anxiety and insecurity. The preferred aloof, on-looker role is reluctantly given up; it is so safe, so Jovian! But man's attempts to alter the unalterable are futile; struggle is of no avail. The struggle between good and evil within himself is never going to be resolved "for keeps," and reinforcement of "good" relationships or a "split" may ensue. Aggressiveness is seen as "lurking in wait." Life is a monster, lying in wait to trap the unwary—which it always does. It is futile to try to escape. Hence nirvana is no answer. The individual still feels helpless in the influence of stronger forces than himself; he is weak and cannot overcome evil by himself. Masochistic trends are apparent, but there is the "maybe"—rather stronger than in any other record—that to struggle is really preferable. The possibility of finding a way out is seen as, *perhaps,* even pleasant. *Maybe* he will "enjoy the light"—*maybe* he will "return to the dark." The present sense of confusion and loss is here seen as, possibly, of his own doing; and therefore it can, maybe, be undone. This is tentative, but sensed for the first time. All is still "vanity," and the irrevocability of the way he has handled life can be borne only if it can be depersonalized. This takes real strength. Dependency is still highly necessary, but there is still, also, distrust of the stronger person and a need to find some *impersonal* support for the dependency. Some people, he feels, *like* dependent individuals and can help develop them into potential leaders. There is still much self-doubt—"Am I going anywhere or not?" Competition can still exist only where there is no question of his superiority—he is still sure that weakness is equivalent to death—but there is now the possibility of facing some of his fears; and the reassurance of being able to "see for a little way" helps.

Fourth TAT: Code Letter W[7]
This record seems to split into two distinct parts, as if given on separate occasions. The first ten responses delineate a very disturbed person indeed, so close to a schizoid break that one cannot be quite certain he has not slipped over the brink. The complete disorganization is focused around Cards I and II, which may indicate a despair so profound he cannot bear to remember it—a guilt so deep it throws him completely. He does not recover for the first ten cards. The sense of loss begun in Card I ("Outside forces have destroyed..... the thing they like"—note he does not say "love") reaches its culmination at Card III and results in utter chaos. The possibility of some crime of violence contemplated or actually performed should be considered, although the probability of actual performance by this patient is not too great. He is struggling very hard to fight through the chaotic currents, and throughout there is a general feeling of slight optimism—that having reached the "depths of dark despair" there's a possibility of ascent, that any descent implies an eventual ascent. The individual "prefers" the "dark," "fears" the "light"—yet struggles toward it. Withdrawal is futile even though comparatively safe, and, while the individual is passive, the flight into complete inactivity is less headlong—the tendency to overintellectualize is strong, and there is a determined effort to depersonalize all situations. This effort is not always successful; then the individual shows deep dependency needs and a sense of complete inadequacy. He is constantly asking, "Who am I? Where am I? Where do I go from here?" Almost in spite of himself a feeling of the necessity for compromise, for acceptance "both/and" rather than his desire for "either/or"

grows upon him. There is considerable guilt feeling centered around the mother figure. He fears aggressiveness and offers only passive resistance to frustration, at best; this easily breaks down into an almost overtly desired dependency. Panicky when activity seems to be forced upon him, he is equally panicky at the idea of uncertainty in the natural forces around him, and the real sense of his inadequacy to deal with reality. Escape would be a "miracle," yet he begins to hope for such a miracle, *very* tentatively. His attempts to face real emotional depths are extremely inadequate; he quietly retreats into an immature, unreal "Bang, bang, you're dead —now get up and shoot me" kind of wishful thinking. Yet he gropes toward a realization of the necessity for facing painful facts. He can't actually *do* so; but he sees, dimly, that some people can; maybe, someday, he can learn to do so. There is revealed for the first time a feeling of having been rejected, of being alone *not* of his own volition. The changeling prince may be a mortal among men—but still of somewhat finer clay . . . people should value him, and be willing to "carry" him even though he is dead weight. Passivity, dependency, competition only against nonexistent competitors—it is still the picture of inadequacy, although some beginnings of insight may be inferred, and fear of personal involvement is slowly losing its deep emotional loading enough to be faced—or at least talked about, in the latter half of the record. The complete breakdown in the first half and the consequent feeling of terrific and almost hopeless struggle smooth out to less desperation and to a clinging to abstraction as to a life-raft.

Comments

These TAT's indicate that this client was a rather deeply disturbed person, and it is quite clear that at no point does he approach a real resolution of his conflicts or a genuinely good adjustment. The range of change is narrow.

One point of interest is that some change is seen by the TAT analyst between the first and second TAT's. This would seem to indicate that in a person motivated for therapy, and looking forward to the beginning of therapy, some change may take place even in the absence of any interviews or other contacts.

It seems clear that some change occurred during the period of therapy. The post-therapy record seems well described as "weakly positive" and showing constructive indications not present in the other TAT's. It is also evident that in the ensuing six months Mr. Bebb dropped back to a state in which inner catastrophe or breakdown again seems very close.

V: Changes in Self-Perception

The General Findings

We may turn now to the process of change as reflected in the Q-sorts of self-referent items. The hypotheses of this portion of our study were these: (*a*) that the perceived self as measured by the Q-sort would become increasingly congruent with the self-ideal as therapy progressed; (*b*) that the perceived self would change more than the perceived self-ideal; (*c*) that the self as perceived at the end of therapy would be more confident, more self-directing, less divided, less inhibited than the self prior to therapy; and (*d*) that the changes in the perceived self would be greater during a period of therapy than during a period of no therapy. We will now have an opportunity to examine the data relevant to these hypotheses from the case of Mr. Bebb.

Table 2: Correlation Matrix of Q-Sortings*

	SBW	SB	S7	SA	SF	IBW	IB	I7	IA	IF	OBW	OB	O7	OA	OF	CS7	CI7	CO7
SBW																		
SB	63																	
S7	55	62																
SA	22	41	45															
SF	54	45	39	54														
IBW	−18	01	−06	35	10													
IB	−16	06	00	37	14	77												
I7	−25	−16	−29	02	−03	51	47											
IA	−13	−09	−13	26	13	70	67	49										
IF	−01	03	03	35	21	67	68	43	73									
OBW	−42	−38	−31	−28	−17	06	06	35	15	01								
OB	−38	−51	−42	−49	−47	−03	−12	20	04	13	65							
O7	−50	−48	−45	−44	−49	01	−08	16	−05	−14	43	10						
OA	−31	−29	−26	−20	−30	−07	−14	11	01	−06	28	52	39					
OF	−11	−25	−24	−16	02	−10	−10	15	05	04	31	37	25	24				
CS7	55	30	30	09	30	−38	−35	−28	−35	−22	−18	−19	−31	−11	11			
CI7	−23	−16	−29	17	01	68	71	54	69	64	29	19	13	11	05	−38		
CO7	−24	−25	−27	−25	−14	−03	−01	23	07	01	50	53	34	30	42	−03	20	

CODE

S = Self
I = Self-ideal or wanted self
O = Ordinary person
BW = Before waiting period
B = Before therapy
7 = Following the seventh interview
A = After the conclusion of therapy
F = Follow-up, six months after end of therapy
C = Counselor's prediction of client's sorting

* Decimal points omitted.

From the design of the research it will be shown that Mr. Bebb, on five different occasions, sorted the cards to represent his perception of himself, his perception of the self he desired to be, and his perception of others as he thinks they generally are. These fifteen sortings, together with the three made by the therapist at the end of the seventh interview, were correlated with each other, and all the intercorrelations are given in Table 2.

Two Significant Sortings
These are some of the very general results of the Q-sort study, and they add up to the statement that, in terms of the client's perceptions as revealed by his sortings, some change occurred, and to some degree tension was reduced. The more significant findings come, however, from a much more detailed scrutiny. A careful study of Table 2 will reveal that the self-ideal as perceived after the seventh interview is definitely distinct from the other ideal sortings. Likewise the self as perceived at the conclusion of therapy is much the most distinctive of the self-sorts. The following paragraphs will attempt to depict the facts in this connection, from which certain inferences will be drawn.

An examination of the items as they were sorted at the pre-wait point, the end of therapy, and the follow-up point justifies the following description. The self at the end of therapy was seen as being much less dependent on the opinions of others, and as being much more self-reliant and acceptable, than at the pre-wait point. In comparing the self as first perceived by Mr. Bebb with the self at the end of therapy, there are some sharp changes. The two items which show the most radical shift illustrate the above. "I am afraid of what other people think about me" shifts from

7 ("very characteristic of me") to 1 ("very unlike me"). (The maximum possible change is from 8 to 0.) The item "I take a positive attitude toward myself" shifts from 2 ("unlike me") to 8 ("most characteristic of me"). These are the most extreme changes in item placements, but others are in the same direction. The client pictures himself as less afraid of others' opinions; he feels himself to be more social in his behavior. He is less afraid of sex and more expressive of his emotions. He can admit that he is often lonely and often disliked by others and that he feels insecure and confused. He feels, however, that he understands himself much better, this item having changed from 2 to 7 in his placements. This sorting for the self at the end of therapy thus shows a very considerable amount of change in a constructive direction. It appears to be realistic rather than defensive. The direction of change appears very similar to the alterations which have occurred in cases where significant permanent change has taken place.

Let us leave this picture of the self at the end of therapy and turn to the self-ideal at the seventh interview, which also stands out as distinctive. Examining the item placements, and comparing the pre-wait self-ideal with this ideal at the seventh interview, gives us this description.

The changes in item placement are frequent but not extreme. The ideal at the seventh interview seems definitely more personalized, less stereotyped, than the first ideal. He places less stress on achieving social conformity, on being a good mixer, etc. There is less stress on being ambitious. There is more stress on understanding himself, being satisfied and content with himself, more value placed on being unafraid of sex and sexuality. His ideal now places more weight on being a person of worth, not helpless or hopeless. Greater value is given to tolerance, and one gains the impression that this is tolerance of himself. He is less inclined to wish for compulsive perfection, and his ideal seems somewhat closer to the person he may internally be. He wants very much to achieve a state where his hardest battles are not with himself.

The Dynamics of Failure as Seen in the Q-Sorts

Let us now try to draw the natural inferences and to interpret the dynamics of this failure in therapy as they are revealed by the Q-sorts. It would seem that by the time of the seventh interview Mr. Bebb had come to reperceive the self he wished to be, achieving a more uniquely personal goal. But this achievement increased the discrepancy between self and ideal and probably the internal tension.

In two more interviews he comes to perceive himself quite differently, in a way which marks the high point of self-reorganization. He is now closer than at any other time to his usual self-ideal and is making definite progress in the direction of his unique ideal as held at the seventh interview.

But already a regression process is at work, owing perhaps to fright or concern at the tension which existed at the seventh interview. The self-ideal has been sharply modified in a regressive direction. At this point he leaves therapy. During the follow-up period the self joins the self-ideal in regression, and, though not all the change is negated, he never comes near achieving the self-ideal which he glimpsed at the seventh interview.

It would appear to be true that in the waiting period both self and ideal changed in such a way as to reduce the extreme tension to some degree. The exploration of the therapeutic interviews increases this tension to its maximum by the seventh interview. This is unbearable, and, though a sharp and constructive change takes place immediately thereafter in self-perception, the self-ideal retreats to a more and more comfortable form, and the self later regresses too.

The Counselor's Perceptions

The only other portion of the matrix upon which specific comment will be made is the counselor's sortings at the seventh interview, which attempted to predict the sortings the client was doing at this same time. Unfortunately, these are the only counselor sortings we have, because, when therapy concluded two interviews later, and a post-therapy counselor sorting was called for, the therapist felt that it would be so similar to his previous sortings as to be of no value. In view of the changes occurring in the client sorts, it is quite unfortunate that we do not have this comparative picture.

The counselor's sorting for the client's self was much more predictive of an earlier sorting (SBW) than of the self at the seventh interview. It was not at all predictive of the self two interviews later. Likewise the counselor's sorting for the client's ideal was very much in line with any of the other ideals but is not so close to the more differentiated ideal at seven, which it was intended to predict. However, the counselor's ideal sort bears the expected relationship to the client's selves, being most discrepant from the self at seventh interview and most like the self two interviews later.

Evidently the therapist perceived the client more as he had been than as he was and perceived his self-ideal as it generally was rather than as it existed at the time of the interview.

Factor Analysis of the Matrix

Thus far all our analysis of the correlation matrix has been made by a logical and inspectional type of analysis. To check this and to see what additional information might be gained, the matrix was also subjected to factor analysis.[8] Table 3 presents the pertinent data from this analysis.

Factor A is clearly a self-factor. It is most strongly exemplified by the sorting for self at the seventh interview. It is to be noted that all self-sortings, those made by the client and the counselor's sort for the client's self, have significant loadings on this factor. Of the client's self-sorts, the one at the conclusion of therapy (SA) has the lowest loading.

Factor B is almost equally clearly interpretable as an "ideal" factor. All the client's sortings for the self he would like to be have heavy loadings on this factor, except the self-ideal following the seventh interview, which has a more modest loading. The counselor's sort for the client's ideal also has a heavy loading on this factor. The client's self, as the counselor sees it, has a significant negative loading.

Table 3: The Four Factors

	A (Self)	B (Ideal)	C (Ordinary)	D (Conventional)		A (Self)	B (Ideal)	C (Ordinary)	D (Conventional)
SBW	48	—	—	26	IF	—	78	—	—
SB	54	—	—	—	OBW	—	—	51	27
S7	62	—	—	−19	OB	—	—	70	—
SA	40	43	—	—	O7	—	—	50	−19
SF	45	—	—	36	OA	—	—	51	—
IBW	—	86	—	—	OF	—	—	40	38
IB	—	83	—	—	CS7	38	−41	—	32
I7	—	46	—	23	CI7	—	70	—	—
IA	—	73	—	—	CO7	—	—	54	34

Much the most interesting element in this second factor is the presence of the self at the conclusion of therapy. It would appear that the client came so much closer to being the self he wished to be that his picture of his self at the conclusion of therapy has approximately equal loadings on the self and wanted-self factors. However, by the follow-up period this is no longer true, and at follow-up time his self has a negligible weighting on the ideal factor.

Factor C is his concept of the ordinary person, and there is little that is remarkable about it except that it indicates a more stable picture of the ordinary person than is indicated by the correlation matrix itself. The correlation between the picture of the ordinary person before therapy and after the seventh interview is only .10—one of the sharpest changes in the matrix. The factor analysis indicates, however, that underlying such changes is a more stable element which runs through all the sortings for the ordinary person. The qualitative picture of this factor indicates that the ordinary person is regarded as one who lives by herd standards, is a good mixer, and is definitely not different from others.

The fourth factor is a more complex one, which, after examining all the data, it seems reasonable to label as the "conventional self" or the "social stereotype." It has modest loadings contributed by the self before therapy and at follow-up time, but a rather strong (though insignificant) negative loading from the self at the seventh interview. The ideal at the seventh interview contained something of this conventional person. It is natural that two of the sortings for the ordinary person also contribute. The counselor saw something of this in the client in his sort at the seventh interview.

The items which are characteristic of this factor show that this self is primarily formed to suit other people. It is intelligent, competitive, well liked, and not emotionally upset. Feelings of resentment are not too prominent.

The factor analysis confirms what we have seen previously from other sources in regard to Mr. Bebb. His self-picture changes quite markedly by the end of therapy, becoming more like his ideal, but drops back in the post-therapy period to something not unlike the self with which he started. The desired self changes considerably by the seventh interview but then changes back gradually to something much closer to his initial ideal. Running through all these facets of self is the fact that a conventional self, concerned primarily about what others think, is evident when he first comes in and at the follow-up time but not in between. His picture of the ordinary person is also weighted with this stereotype at the same points.

VI: The Relation of the Perceived Self to Diagnosis

It has been evident that the preceding section deals with the objective analysis of the client's self-perceptions, as made operationally available through the Q-sorts. But the psychologist who is accustomed to think of clients solely from an external or diagnostic frame of reference may continually be asking himself the question as to what is "really" happening, judged from the outside. Though the material from the TAT has been given, it is not directly relatable to the Q-sorts in the form in which it was given.

The present section deals with the relationship between these two ways of viewing an individual. The hypothesis was that in effective therapy the self as perceived by the client would become more similar to the client as perceived by the diagnostician. As denied material enters awareness, the client should view himself more realistically and hence in a manner more similar to that of the diagnostician.

The tool for this investigation was again the Q-sort. The four TAT's which had been given to Mr. Bebb—both the protocols and the summarized diagnosis—were given to a psychologist[9] who had no contact with any of the case material, knew nothing of the client, and did not know how the case was regarded or, indeed, whether the individual had been in therapy. Neither did he know the order in which the TAT's were administered. He was asked to take each TAT protocol and its summary, study it carefully, and then sort the Q-cards to represent this individual as he actually was, diagnostically, at that time. It was of course recognized that the cards were not ideal for this purpose, since they are self-referent rather than diagnostic statements. It was also learned that different diagnosticians do not sort the cards in any very similar fashion for the same TAT (two judges, sorting for two of these TAT's independently, had a mean correlation of .45), so that the results must be interpreted cautiously. Nevertheless, this method gives both the external and the internal frame of reference operationally expressed in a fashion which permits direct comparison.

The findings in this case are somewhat puzzling and not too easy to interpret. Table 4 contains the correlations between each of the four diagnostic sortings and all the sortings for self and ideal.

Comment

It is obvious that the findings are not clear cut and unambiguous in the foregoing section. Yet the basic finding of constructive change in this

Table 4: Correlation Matrix for Self, Ideal and Diagnosis*

	SBW	SB	S7	SA	SF	IBW	IB	I7	IA	IF	DBW	DB	DA
SBW													
SB	63												
S7	55	62											
SA	22	41	45										
SF	54	45	39	54									
IBW	–18	01	–06	35	10								
IB	–16	06	00	37	14	77							
I7	–25	–16	–29	02	–03	51	47						
IA	–13	–09	–13	26	13	70	67	49					
IF	–01	03	03	35	21	67	68	43	73				
DBW	38	38	32	01	00	–41	–41	–27	–49	–41			
DB	40	14	25	23	22	–13	–15	–09	–15	–02	39		
DA	20	06	02	11	23	03	02	10	01	10	15	49	
DF	29	28	16	–11	02	–44	–48	–29	–44	–36	54	35	30

Code
S = Self
I = Self-ideal
D = Diagnostic picture
BW = Before waiting period
B = Before therapy
7 = Following the seventh interview
A = After therapy
F = Follow-up, six months later

* Decimal points omitted.

client, followed by regression, is confirmed, and also the crucial importance of the self-ideal at the seventh interview. The other findings are sufficiently suggestive to warrant further use of the method in other "failure" cases, as well as those showing permanent change, in order to isolate out the necessary elements in effective therapy. Furthermore, if diagnosis proves, upon further study, to be as unstable as it is in this case and in the previously reported case of Mrs. Oak,[10] some drastic rethinking as to the place and function of diagnosis in clinical psychology will become necessary.

VII: Changes in Adjustment Score

Following the collection of the foregoing Q-sort data, a new method of looking at this material was devised by one of our staff. All the items of the Q-sort were submitted to a number of clinical psychologists with the instructions: "Place in one pile those items which a well-adjusted person would regard as characteristic of himself, and in another pile those which he would regard as not characteristic of himself." A very high degree of agreement was found on the placement of seventy-four of the one hundred items. These seventy-four were then used as a basis for a very crude score of adjustment. When the subject had sorted one of these items in that half of his sorting which would be predicted by this concept of "good adjustment," he was given a score of 1. Obviously the total possible score is 74.

Using this method gives us another way of examining the Q-sort data, this time in a normative way. It is of interest that the data provided by this approach confirm several of the findings already given. Again we find that it is the self after therapy which is best adjusted. Again we find evidence of the regression after therapy toward the initial status.

By calculating the degree of adjustment indicated by the sorting for the wanted self, we find confirmation of another finding already stated. All the ideals except the seventh are very similar. The ideal at the seventh interview is the least "adjusted" or stereotyped; it has the greatest negative correlation with the self-picture. It thus appears to be distinctive but less idealized and more achievable.

The "adjustment" score was also calculated for the diagnostic sortings described in the preceding section, based upon the four available TAT's. Several elements stand out. The first is that, as would be predicted, the total personality as seen by the diagnostician is scored as much more poorly adjusted than the self as seen by the client. This would be a crude measure of the degree of defensiveness. The improvement during the waiting period is given some additional (though not entirely independent) confirmation by the increase in "adjustment" score of the second diagnosis. The improvement during therapy likewise receives further confirmation. It is of some interest that the degree of adjustment as perceived by the client and as perceived by the diagnostician approach each other at the close of therapy and at this point only. Finally, of course, the evidence of regression in the follow-up period is very marked.

While providing us with little new information, this method of analyzing the Q-sort data tends to corroborate the findings previously described.

VIII: Change in Maturity of Behavior

As part of the general research design, the Willoughby Emotional-Maturity Scale was used to measure any alteration in the behavior of the individual as seen by himself and by his friends. Not only was the client to be rated by himself and two friends at four points during the entire period but, as a check on their reliability as raters, the two friends were each to rate some other individual well known to them, presumably not in therapy.

The hypothesis in this project, as applied to all the cases in the study, was that the client's behavior, as perceived by himself and by his friends, would change during therapy in a direction defined by experts as constituting greater emotional maturity. The behavior of control persons, rated by the same friends, would, it was hypothesized, show less change in the direction of maturity. The net result of this portion of the study is that there is little striking change in the quality of Mr. Bebb's behavior, except possibly a slight deterioration during therapy and a slight improvement during the follow-up period.

IX: Change in the Acceptance of Others

Still another project in the experimental design had to do with the changes in attitudes toward others. It was hypothesized that, when therapy was effective, a change would occur in the direction of greater acceptance of others, increased respect for the individual, the placing of greater values upon other individuals and their contribution, and a decrease in political and economic conservatism and in authoritarian beliefs. The instrument for the investigation of this hypothesis was the Self-Other

Attitude Scale, a compilation of items largely from scales developed else-where.

Comment

Here is a clear-cut reversal of one of the outcomes which has been hypothesized for client-centered therapy. It would appear that Mr. Bebb has moved away from, not toward, acceptance of others. It is barely possible that his increased scores are caused by an increased willingness to state his own authoritarian beliefs. Thus, a greater frankness in avowing beliefs unpopular in a democratic country would increase the score. The only evidence for this speculation is that he seems most consistent in his views on the first taking of this test. Later his views show definite internal contradiction at times, which might represent a more accurate portrayal of his real sentiments rather than an "official" ideology. While this possibility cannot be entirely discarded, there is little evidence to support it.

In general, then, it would seem that in the successive periods before, during, and after therapy Mr. Bebb became more authoritarian in his views, less acceptant of others, and more willing to use any means to reach a goal. The fact that this direction is most sharply seen during the waiting period before therapy indicates that it was not caused by therapy, but neither did therapy alter or stop this trend.

X: Discussion of Results

Extent to Which Hypotheses Were Upheld

Though Mr. Bebb has been referred to throughout as a "failure" case, the objective reasons for this have not been summarized. It may be well to take the hypotheses from each of the separate projects and draw them together, indicating the extent to which they were upheld or negated in this case. These hypotheses were initially drawn from the theory of client-centered therapy and were hypotheses as to the types of change predicted in client-centered therapy.

It was hypothesized that if a competent psychologist placed the TAT's in an order from most poorly integrated to best integrated, the pre- and post-therapy and the follow-up TAT's would show an increasing degree of integration. This hypothesis was not confirmed in the case of Mr. Bebb. The post-test showed more integration than the pretest, but the follow-up test showed regression.

It was hypothesized that the perceived self as measured by the Q-sort would become increasingly congruent with the perceived self-ideal during and after therapy. This hypothesis was upheld, although the process was irregular and the increase in congruence was slight.

Another hypothesis was that the perceived self would change more than the perceived self-ideal. This hypothesis was upheld.

It was predicted that the self as perceived at the end of therapy would be more confident, more self-directing, less divided, and less inhibited than the self prior to therapy. This hypothesis receives some qualitative confirmation at the end of therapy, but most of this confirmation had disappeared at the follow-up point.

Another hypothesis was that the changes in the perceived self would be greater during a period of therapy than during a period of no therapy. This hypothesis was upheld, whether the change in the therapy period was compared with the control period (the wait period) or with the follow-up period.

It was hypothesized that the self as perceived by the client would become more similar to the client as perceived by a diagnostician. The evidence proved the reverse of this hypothesis.

It was hypothesized that the client's behavior, as perceived by himself and by his friends, would change in the direction of emotional maturity. The evidence provided no confirmation of this.

It was hypothesized that the client's score on the S-O Scale would change in a direction indicating more acceptant and democratic attitudes toward others. The data show a steady decrease in democratic attitudes and acceptance of others from the first to the follow-up test.

With only three of these hypotheses clearly upheld, it seems fair to conclude that this is a failure in client-centered therapy, in which the predictions made by the theory of client-centered therapy are not confirmed.

Since the hypotheses of these studies had to do with the prediction of changes which were likely to occur in successful therapy, there are no specific hypotheses formulated in advance which were concerned with possible concomitants of failure. Hence we cannot prove or disprove hypotheses regarding the failure to change significantly. All we can do is to examine first the clinical data of the recorded interviews and then the objective data, to see if we can formulate objectively supported explanations of this failure and get leads which will provide hypotheses for future studies.

Inferences Drawn from the Clinical Data

If we examine the material from the interviews in the endeavor to understand why lasting personality changes did not occur in this case, two conclusions seem to this writer justified. In the first place, it is the client's fear of what he is finding within himself which tends to drive him from therapy in spite of the progress he is making. In the second place, the therapist makes at least two serious mistakes in handling the client's desire to leave therapy. Let us state the bases for these conclusions.

From the sixth interview onward Mr. Bebb is pulling away from therapy. In the sixth contact he voices his real fear of the psychotic phenomena within himself, which he regards as essentially beyond help. In the seventh interview he talks of his need for therapy as an evidence of weakness. He also feels that therapy has been confusing, discouraging, and disturbing, because what he is thus far finding within himself is not "in accordance with my intuitive knowledge of myself." It is at this point that he partly leaves therapy by reducing the number of interviews from two per week to one. In the eighth interview he feels that he is trying to "shun away" from dealing with his doubts about himself. He also expresses the feeling that he should not be undergoing these interviews because what he is discovering is just himself and hence unchangeable. In the ninth interview he begins by stating that he does not think he should take any more of the counselor's time. It seems clear that the underlying reason for pulling away from therapy is his fear of the unacceptable or abnormal aspects of himself which he is in the process of discovering.

This brings us to the therapist's handling of this material. Was the therapist partly responsible for the premature closure which occurred? Undoubtedly there will be as many opinions about the therapist's procedures as there are orientations, or possibly as many opinions as there are readers. In regard to the therapist's general handling of the material, some will feel that he should have given the client more reassurance. Others will feel that he should have interpreted to the client his fear and his desire to leave the relationship. Others will feel that he did not provide enough support for a dependent client. Others—and this opinion is shared by the writer—will feel that his two most serious mistakes occurred within one moment of time during the ninth interview. In this moment he voiced *for* the client the client's feeling that he was through and then added his own support to this, "I think so too." If one listens to the recording, there can be no doubt that Mr. Bebb was endeavoring to leave therapy. His voice shows great relief when the therapist recognizes this feeling and voices it. The therapist was not, it is clear, injecting this feeling into the situation. But by voicing it before the client could bring himself to voice it and then by supporting it, he helped to truncate therapy. Had he refrained from this response, Mr. Bebb might or might not have left therapy at this time. But if Mr. Bebb had voiced this feeling or this decision, and the therapist had accepted it, the client would still have been left with his own deep ambivalence about continuing and would have had to live with that ambivalence. As it was actually handled, it would seem that the therapist sided with one side of the ambivalence and thus helped to give the client a premature and defensive closure.

Another possible mistake of the therapist is that both in respect to leaving therapy and in respect to the client's desire for liking from another person, the therapist accepts feelings which have not yet been expressed. There is not much doubt as to the accuracy of the therapist's responses. The client did, at some level, wish love and approval from someone; he did wish to leave therapy. But to respond to these feelings prematurely may well have been frightening to an already frightened individual.

The Objective Findings
Let us now draw together the various findings of the objective studies so that we may see what they contribute to the understanding of a failure in therapy.

Mr. Bebb shows some personality change, in a favorable direction, during the sixty-day wait period (IV, V, VI, VII).[11]

He makes progress toward integration during the therapy period (IV, V, VI, VII).

Greater congruence of self and ideal is achieved, both during the waiting period and during therapy (V).

From the point before the wait period to the conclusion of therapy there is a decided and favorable change (IV, V, VI, VII).

During the follow-up period the client regresses toward his original status, whether the measure is the TAT, the Q-sort for self, or the "adjustment" score (IV, V, VI, VII).

Changes in both the perceived self and the self-ideal are sharper in the therapy period than in the waiting period or the follow-up period (V).

Changes in both the self and the ideal are at one point very sharp, as indicated by a correlation of only .45 between the self of the seventh interview and the self of the ninth interview, and a correlation of only .49 for the ideal during the same period (V).

The self-ideal moves from a rather stereotyped ideal before therapy to a more unique and more achievable ideal at the seventh interview and then regresses (V, VII).

The self at the conclusion of the interviews shows many characteristics of better adjustment but regresses (V, VII).

The self after therapy had a significant loading on the client's generalized ideal, but the self at follow-up time had no such loading (V).

The change in the diagnostic picture was as great as the change in the self-picture and showed a similar fluctuation (VI).

There is no significant trend in the maturity of behavior, as observed by self or others (VIII).

There is a trend toward a lessened acceptance of others throughout and after therapy (IX).

This change is sharpest in the waiting period prior to therapy (IX).

Inferences Drawn from the Objective Data

It may be helpful to sketch the dynamics of therapeutic failure in this case from the information provided by the objective data.

In the first place, a degree of therapeutic change appears to take place in this seriously disturbed person motivated for therapy, even in a period of no therapy. This change in the sixty-day period is supported by evidence from the TAT analysis, the diagnostic sorting based on the TAT, the Q-sort for self and ideal, and the behavior rating. The only contrary evidence is in the sharply lessened acceptance of others, which is difficult to explain.

In the second place, if this study had been concluded at the time of the ninth interview, the evidence indicates a definite amount of therapeutic progress in a person who was close to a psychological breakdown. The counselor rating, the TAT analysis, the diagnostic sorting based on the TAT, the Q-sort for self and ideal—all support this. The behavior ratings show some contrary trend, and there is a somewhat lessened acceptance of others. If the ninth interview had been merely a point *in* therapy, rather than the *end* of therapy, all the evidence would have fallen into line. It would have been interpretable as genuine progress in therapy, with a decreasing defensiveness helping to account for the lessened acceptance of others and the temporary deterioration of behavioral maturity.

From the objective point of view, the most likely influence in the client's leaving therapy is the increased tension indicated by the sharp and increased discrepancy between self and ideal as he moves forward in therapy. This point is also supported by the low loading of the seventh interview ideal on the ideal factor and the ninth interview self on the self factor, indicating that these particular perceptions are very different from those which precede or follow. They are thus likely to be tension-creating.

Finally, the objective evidence of regression is strong. It begins with a regression in the self-ideal between the seventh and ninth interviews and is evidenced by the TAT analysis, the diagnostic Q-sort, the "adjustment" score, and the self and ideal Q-sorts. The S-O Scale shows still further decrease of acceptance of others. Only the behavior rating shows an increase in maturity, back to approximately the pre-therapy state.

The over-all picture from the objective point of view is that the client was making progress—progress in which greater tension was being experienced—with some painful fluctuations in perception of self and ideal and perhaps some deterioration of behavior. These kinds of "constructive disorganization" are known to be often evident in successful cases. But at this point therapy was truncated, and thereafter regression toward the original status set in.

A Meaningful Parallelism

It will have been noted that all our data, clinical and objective, show in most respects a surprising degree of parallelism. An improvement during the therapy period is indicated whether we rely on the client's statements during the therapeutic and follow-up interviews, the objective analysis of the client's frame of reference through his Q-sorts, an adjustment score based on the Q-sorts, the counselor rating, the TAT analyzed in conventional fashion, or by means of an objective method. The later regression is equally well indicated by any of the above except the counselor rating, which was made only at the conclusion of therapy and hence offers no evidence on this issue.

This point in worth making, since some psychologists have been concerned about the objective analysis of material from within the client's phenomenological field. They are fearful that the client's desire "to impress the therapist" or the "hello-goodbye" effect will vitiate such material. Where a case is generally successful, it is difficult to refute such a view. In this case, however, the improvement and the later regression show up just as strikingly, and sometimes more meaningfully, from analysis of the internal frame of reference as from analysis of external observations such as the TAT.

Both this case and the previously reported case of Mrs. Oak show that diagnostic representations of the client reveal even greater variability than do self-representations. If then one is looking for some stable objective fashion of representing the individual through time, the suggestion is that such stability does not truly exist, either in the internally perceived picture of self or in the externally perceived picture of the personality.

"A Flight into Health?"

This phrase has not been used because its meaning is so ambiguous, but, since it is a term very commonly used by clinicians and therapists, it deserves comment. Is this case "a flight into health"? If the phrase is understood to mean a defensive pretense of therapeutic progress, when none in fact exists, then Mr. Bebb did not exhibit a flight into health. The picture of definite improvement seems real, whether judged by conscious or by projective material. But if "flight into health" is interpreted as leaving therapy because further progress appears very frightening, then Mr. Bebb would fall into that category.

Hypotheses for Future Study
Have we been able to achieve our goal of discovering fruitful hypotheses regarding failures in the therapeutic process? It would seem that from this exhaustive study of one unique failure have feelings was premature and frightening to the client. Perhaps two generalized hypotheses could be stated in these terms. Third hypothesis: Failure by the therapist to accept all aspects of a client's expressed feelings is associated with a lessened degree of change in the client or with a greater likelihood of premature closure. Fourth hypothesis: The therapist's expressed acceptance of feelings and meanings not expressed by the client is associated with a lessened degree of change in the client or with a greater likelihood of premature closure. There is little doubt but that reliable categorizations of client and counselor statements could be set up to test these hypotheses. It is less clear whether Hypotheses 3 and 4 are the most significant hypotheses to test.

To the writer, these are the only significant general questions which grow out of this analysis of Mr. Bebb's experience, but it is hoped that an examination of the data may provide others with additional issues for investigation.

XI: Summary

In this chapter an analysis has been presented of the data from the case of a seriously maladjusted young man undergoing client-centered therapy in which the hypothesized concomitants of such therapy did not occur. In addition to the counselor's ratings, extensive excerpts from the recorded interviews have been given to supply the clinical evidence for this failure. Data from the repeated administrations of the TAT, analyzed both by conventional and by objective methods, have been given. The data from repeated self-referent Q-sorts and their factor analysis have been presented. Information is also given from repeated ratings of the client's behavior by self and friends on the Willoughby Emotional-Maturity Scale and from repeated administrations of a test of attitudes toward others.

The findings from these data have been summarized, and the attempt has been made to formulate both a clinical and an objective picture of the reasons for the progress exhibited and the regression which followed. Some hypotheses have been developed from this analysis for testing in future studies.

FOOTNOTES

[1] Some readers may prefer to study the objective research evidence before forming a clinical impression. With this in mind, the present section has been prepared as a unit and can be read either before or after the sections which present the data (Sections IV through IX) without any loss of meaning.

[2] We shall attempt to indicate short pauses or hesitations by three-dot ellipses (...), while longer pauses are indicated in parentheses "(pause)." Where irrelevant material has been omitted in editing, the ommission is indicated by five-dot ellipses (.....). "**C.**" refers to the client; "**T.**" refers to the therapist.

[3] Thanks are due to Dr. Carol Bowie, at that time psychologist of the Municipal Court of Chicago, for her assistance in this task.

[4] Given prior to waiting period; ranked No. 4, least well adjusted.

[5] Given prior to therapy; ranked No. 2 in adjustment.

[6] Given after therapy; ranked No. 1, best adjusted.

[7] Given as follow-up point; ranked No. 3 in adjustment.

[8] Full credit for the factor analysis is due Miss Sarah Counts, who was responsible for this portion of the study.

[9] Thanks are due to Mr. Richard Farson for his help on this portion of the study.

[10] Carl R. Rogers and Rosalind F. Dymond, eds., *Psychotherapy and Personality Change.* (Chicago: University of Chicago Press, 1954), 287-295.

[11] Following each conclusion Roman numerals in parentheses indicate the section or sections of this chapter in which data are found to support the conclusions.

BIBLIOGRAPHY

Bartlett, Marion R. A Six Month Follow-up of the Effects of Personal Adjustment Counseling of Veterans. *Journal of Consulting Psychology* 14 (1950):393-394.

Fiedler, Fred E. A Comparison of Therapeutic Relationships in Psychoanalytic, Nondirective and Adlerian Therapy. *Journal of Consulting Psychology* 14 (1950):436-445.

Porter, E. H., Jr. Clients' Evaluations of Services at the University of Chicago Counseling Center. Unpublished manuscript.

Rogers, Carl R. *Client-centered Therapy.* Boston: Houghton Mifflin Co., 1951.

ROBERT F. MORGAN

15

Inside View: Max on Max

Following a short description of *Max,* this case history presents the verbatim self-described experience of an involuntary resident of a maximum security psychiatric ward. It is meant to share the perspective of a consumer of one of our most institutionalized services where the client is identified as *society* (and staff) while the patient is identified as *dangerous.* Most institutionalized patients are no longer on locked wards; very few are considered dangerous. Yet the use of this extreme case may illustrate some general principles more clearly by its very starkness. Thanks are due to *Max* for his participation, courage and candor. For *Max*'s protection, his real name has been withheld. He is, however, in all other ways an equal contributor to this handbook and may be contacted by mail through myself. **R.F.M.**

Normally less than one percent of any institutionalized mental patient population is considered so dangerous that they are involuntarily locked in maximum security. It would be a serious mistake to consider this minority as simply helpless victims of an oppressive treatment system since quite serious crimes often precede their incarceration. On the other hand, the hospital setting, unlike the jail, infers they are to be *treated* for the personality disorder leading to the violence. Too often staff do not know what treatment to give or, worse, assert there is no effective help possible. Further, who will take the responsibility to risk that someone, already having committed a serious crime, will never commit another?

Max is a pseudonym for a thirty-eight-year-old man incarcerated since the age of fourteen. Abandoned at the age of six months, he was reclaimed and abandoned again by his mother at six years. Receiving a blow to the head from a baseball bat at that age, he developed mild epileptic attacks, since treated effectively with moderate medication. At fourteen, after some *vandalism,* he was labeled a juvenile delinquent and found his new home to be a mental hospital. At eighteen, while on leave, he attacked a man who he insisted came at him with a knife. He was described at that time as having violent outbursts of temper and earned the diagnostic label still with him today: "anti-social personality, severe". Transferred to the penitentiary, he was charged with the murder of another inmate at age twenty-four. Max said the inmate attacked him and he held him at arm's length by the throat. Max has unusual strength and the other inmate's larynx was fatally crushed. Max was twenty-four. Max still has a temper and a reputation for regularly getting into "intense oppositional positions with authority figures." He has mellowed much over the years but has recently become more and more invested in beginning a life on the outside of the institution. He objects to a perceived lack of meaningful resocialization treatment and the omission of key behavioral signposts leading to an exit. To most residents of his ward, he is seen as congenial and positive. But, last year, he attempted an escape. In explaining his actions he said: "I need a resocialization program. I'm sane, competent, and not dangerous." The periodic fights he explained with "No matter what environment you're in, you have to adapt. If not, you're an outcast. I'm acting normally for this environment." The staff agree he is not psychotic, suicidal or homicidal. They don't agree, however, that he's not dangerous. They feel in a less-defined environment like the *"outside,"* his rage would be more likely to surface. Max asks what evidence will be accepted that he is safe . . . or is he a perpetual victim of his past? The staff reply that worse than he have been released (and this is true) but make no specific predictions. They, in my judgment, are sincere and, if they cover themselves, they also mean to protect people on the outside. Max wants to be one of those people on the outside.

Here is a letter from Max on "max" (maximum security), a stream of consciousness reflecting the range of his perspective and personality, verbatim et literatim.

Daily Life in Max

From the day the hospital was opened, it has been against the rules to have sexual relationships with women: visitors or female patients. But it is O.K. to have sex with someone of your own sex.

In the hospital's eyes, this is normal. If a man gets caught having sex with a woman, even if she is his own wife, he gets regressed back to rather medium or maximum security. And nothing is done to the female, other than maybe a week's restriction or if she is a visitor, restricted from the hospital grounds. There isn't a maximum security for women.

In order to have visitors, the patient must fill out a written request to the ward staff, and it has to be signed by the ward Doctor, ward charge and the track chief. This is done in prison the same way. Also, the visitors are *shuck down* before they can come in to visit. They are not allowed to bring in anything except a pack of smokes, no lighter or matches, to smoke while visiting the patient. Kissing and hugging is frowned upon and sometimes stopped.

Patients are not allowed to have homemade or store bought food or candy of any kind brought into them.

Patients are chained down to the bed with steel hand and leg cuffs, not leather cuffs, for reasons such as, defending themselves, for refusing to put up with verbal abuse from patients and staff, for trying to protect their personal property from thieves, for voicing their feeling or opinions about a wrong that is or has been done to a patient or patients or to themselves, for standing up for the rights of patients when they are being abused, being harmful to ourselves or others and sometimes just because a staff member doesn't like a certain patient.

The overall treatment of a patient, is that of a criminal in a prison, not as a patient in a hospital.

When a patient starts making waves, by filing writs and lawsuits against the hospital for a release hearing or to sue the hospital, the ward staff and professional staff do their best to make that patient blow up so they can rather regress him back to maximum security or chain him down. Then, when it's time for him to go to court, the hospital can say that he is dangerous. Therefore, they can prevent the patient from getting out.

The longer a patient is kept in confinement, the more money the hospital gets for his keep. How they do this is: they tell the government budget committees and the legislators that they need more money to treat you; they need more experienced doctors and a better treatment program for you in order to properly treat you so you can return to the street a cured man. The patients never receive any of this wonderful treatment that the hospital got the money for. Patients receive nothing in most cases but confinement, abusive treatment and never accepts any more of that. So what you have in most mental hospitals, mainly this one, is a warehouse of nothing but bodies. These are bodies that the outside world could care less about. So, they are warehoused and forgotten and the *big wheels* that run the regional government rake in the money that is supposed to go for the treatment of these patients or bodies.

In most cases, the hospital staff members make a patient sick or sicker and a lot of times cause nondangerous patients to rather act out in a dangerous manner or become dangerous. The reason for this is: the professional staff and ward staff are so incompetent that they can't diagnose a patient properly for his mental illness if he has any to begin with. But surely there will be more illnesses than he will know what to do with by the time these one-year wonders, crystal ball readers and miracle workers get through brainwashing him with their psychological warfare games. This means, that if the doctor keeps telling the patient that he has a mental illness, and after hearing this from him and ward staff over a period of time, the patient will start believing he has this mental illness, when in fact he hadn't, up until he was brainwashed. But now he becomes sick and becomes a mental illness unto himself. All because the professional staff are too incompetent to do their job efficiently. As for causing a nondangerous patient to become dangerous, the reason for this is: the staff force a patient into a prison-like setting, so that a patient can run but can't hide from trouble and abuse from patients and staff alike.

So, he is forced to act out in a violent manner even though he isn't violent by nature. But because staff will not aid him when he is being assaulted or abused, to the point that any normal person will fight back, by not doing anything when other patients steal or bulldog him out of his personal property, by chaining him down for defending himself or his property, for standing up for his rights, especially when it's an employee who is abusing his rights. These are just a few things the staff do to patients that make them act out in a violent manner. And when the patient does act out, the staff says he's dangerous.

Patients are not allowed to buy, sell or trade with other patients or employees. Patients are not even allowed to put what little they're allowed to make in a place where visitors can see them and buy them. So, patients without any money can't make money by selling the things that they make to visitors. Selling to visitors is even against the rules.

Patients on maximum security are not allowed to check out books from the library or the law library. Only patients from medium and open wards with privileges outside the fence can use these libraries. So, maximum security patients do without.

When a patient is put down in steels, hands and feet are chained to the bed, the ward staff gang up on him. Anywhere from six to ten employees jump on him before they put the steels on and hit, kick, twist legs and arms, neck to the point that they almost break and sometimes do. This isn't done in all cases, but most. Then, when they start chaining him down, they put the cuffs on tight, to where his wrists and ankles start to swell or the steel cuts into the skin. And then they pull the leather belt so tight around his arms and bed that he can hardly move. If he complains, the staff beat on him some more if they don't like him. And the only time you are allowed to use the "john" is when they let you up for your meals. So, if you have "to go" you either do it in your bed or try to lean over enough to do it on the floor.

Myself, I am a locksmith, so I take the chains off of me whenever I want up and then chain myself back down. This kind of treatment happens to those patients that the staff dislike or when a staff member comes to work with a hard on because his old lady refused to take care of it or when a female staff member comes to work pissed off because she couldn't get enough dick. So he or she takes it out on the patients and the first one that looks wrong or says something that the staff member doesn't like. A prime example is: "V. X.," ward charge. He comes to work mad at the whole world because his wife wears the pants in the house.

So, he comes to work and takes it out on every patient on the ward, but rather than locking them up in their rooms, he aggravates and agitates the patients until one of them can't take any more and voices his dislike about what he is doing. In some cases, it's up to five to six patients that get thrown in their rooms or chained down. You can tell when he is on the ward without even seeing or hearing him because the tension is so thick you can't cut it with a chain saw. When he is on duty, the whole ward is sitting on a case of TNT but when he leaves you can feel the tension go out with him. Then the ward is back to normal. Every ward he has been on, there has been nothing but trouble because of him.

He got stabbed one time by another patient whom he had been agitating for months *every day*. So the patient had as much as he could take and stabbed him with a piece of steel off a table. If he had had a handle on that shank, he would have killed him. But when he tried to stab him, it only went in a few inches and slipped out of his hand.

He threw me in *lock up* for saying "Hey guy." I didn't care because chains are like toys to me. I can take them off almost as fast as they can put them on me. A person that has been locked up as long as I have, things like chains, lock up and prison don't bother that person because he or she is used to it.

The staff have been trying to get me to *blow up* so they can say and prove that I'm dangerous because that is the only way I can lose the lawsuit I have against the hospital and the District Court approved my lawsuit to be heard. The federal courts don't usually approve a writ that is against the hospital unless that person has a damn good case against it. Most, if not all hospitals, are funded by the federal government so if I win, the federal government will stop funding this place until they get their act straightened out, where this will be a hospital, *Not* a prison as it is now.

Group therapy and one-to-one are nothing but a side show for the staff. Patients can't get any help out of these make-believe groups and one-to-ones because the staff only hold these therapies so they can write in the patient's chart that he has been receiving treatment. This is another way the hospital has of beating a patient in court. When a patient files for a release hearing or files a law suit on grounds of not receiving treatment, the hospital shows the court your chart which states that you have been receiving treatment in groups and one-to-one therapies.

So this circus-style side show therapy isn't doing the patients any good because it's nothing but a big joke and that joke is on the patients. They go to these groups and one-to-ones, looking for help and treatment for their problems. They go to them angry and come out angrier.

Patients on maximum security do not and cannot have occupational therapy to help them pass the time of day constructively. If a patient is on medium security he has to put in a written request to the ward staff to be approved. And then, he has to wait for an opening before he can participate in occupational therapy. This waiting more often than never takes weeks and sometimes months.

The reason for this is because the hospital only lets up to ten patients participate at a time, so the patient has to wait until a patient gets transferred to another ward.

The hospital has a gym with a swimming pool, bowling alley, basketball court, billiard room, exercise room with bar-bells, etc. and a library. But patients that do not have privileges outside of the fence are deprived of these things. These so-called privileges are therapy and good treatment for patients but a patient has to earn the right to treatment. So patients on maximum security never get to use these facilities. So, therefore, they are deprived of treatment because they are looked upon as convicts instead of patients.

Maximum security has a small basketball court and a yard of nothing but dirt. But, we are denied daily use of these. Patients are lucky to get outside once a year, and we're lucky to use the gym once a week. The reason for this is because the staff are too lazy to take us out or to the gym. And the recreational therapist is also too lazy. He spends most of his time in the South recreational hall playing pinball machines and other games with the other recreational men, to come over and take our ward, outside or to the gym.

The food is prepared so badly that most of the meals are thrown-up. Ninety percent of it is starch.

I'm five foot ten and weigh a hundred and forty-five pounds. I've never weighed over a hundred and forty-nine because the food is too bad for my stomach to hold down. The only times we get good meals are when a holiday comes around or when important visitors come around to inspect the hospital. Most of the ward staff won't eat it.

The ward staff and professional staff, which we don't have many of here, because they're all one-year wonders and incompetent to help themselves, let alone to help the patients. They can't control their emotions, like most people do. So they get a job here where they can take their frustrations, anger and any other problems they have out on the patients. Then they can go back out on the streets after they've put in their eight hours and be almost normal for another sixteen hours.

Patients on maximum and medium security are deprived of a proper educational program because education and vocational rehabilitation is a "privilege," *not* treatment or therapy, in the eyes of the hospital staff. So, therefore, patients have to earn the right or privilege of a proper education. Patients aren't allowed to attend Vocational rehabilitational or more commonly called Voc. rehab which is on the hospital grounds without privileges outside the fence.

These privileges can only be gotten on medium security to further the patient's education by taking a GED or a vocational training.

The ward staff can, and often or mostly do, use foul language when expressing themselves about their dislike about a patient or what he is doing that they don't like: whether it be to them or another patient. But let a patient do the same to the staff and down he goes in steels. It's okay for a staff member to verbalize his or her feelings in whatever way they feel like but not a patient. This also goes for threatening: staff can, but not a patient.

Staff can and often do, mentally and physically abuse patients for pushing the staff too far, but don't let a patient try it. He will not only be chained down, but also get the shit kicked or slapped out of him. In some cases, if the patient gets hurt, he won't get any medical care unless you're too badly hurt or someone feels sorry for you which is very unlikely.

Some patients can do almost anything and get away with it, but let another patient try it and he'll get chained down. Most of the patients here at the hospital get a screwing because of their past record. The hospital holds their past record against them. But let a patient keep bringing up a staff member's past, if he has one, and down he goes in chains.

Most of the staff don't want to do anything like open doors to patients' side rooms, clothes room doors or mop room floors, go to the canteen for the patients, have therapy with patients. All they do most of the time is sit in the office and gossip, play footsies with the female employees, read newspapers or books like *Playboy* and watch TV and sometimes *bulldog it* so they can see what they want to watch, play cards and other games with other patients. Things like this is what an employee does with his or her eight-hour shift. They do hold make-believe staff-ings to consider transfers, treatment programs for patients twice a week in which the patient has no say so on any of the planned treatment the staff have already set up for the patient.

But the staff demands the patients to jump when they say jump. Ward staff and professional staff expect and demand respect from the patients but they don't believe they have to earn it because they are the employees and we are patients which in their eyes makes us not equal to them as humans. And, therefore, we don't deserve the same respect. But let a patient or patients try and demand the respect that is due them and all the patients get is: ignored, told in not so good language to shut up. And if he still demands respect that is due him, he gets chained down.

Ward and professional staff want the patients to trust and believe them, but the staff won't trust and believe the patients. How can patients trust and believe in staff that live by a double standard and have proven time after time that they can't be trusted or believed? Not all mental hospital employees are this way but there are enough to make a patient afraid to trust even the nicest employees that work here. There are a few but not that many because they don't last long.

Most of the staff say all kinds of good things about you, to your face, but then they go and write in your chart just the opposite of what they said.

I learned along time ago, "that a man is only as good as his word." And I have lived by that almost to the tee. And because I have, I'm trusted and believed by those who are the same, and by most who aren't.

The hospital discharges the ones that they know can't make it, and have to return for more hospitalization. The staff makes this mistake because they don't have what it takes to be a competent person let alone a competent professional staff member in any hospital.

They think just because a patient does and says what they want him to say and do, that he is ready for the outside world. What these crystal ball readers won't accept is that school and book learning is good to a certain point. But after that you have to put aside the book and use common sense. There are things in life that all the schooling and book learning in the world won't teach you. And one of those things is how to read a human being and tell him what he is going to do in the foreseeable future. You can only guess, and in a lot of cases you will be wrong.

Life in an institution and life in the free world is like daylight and dark. So just because a patient acts like a model patient, or is a model patient in a institution like this hospital or a convict in prison doesn't mean he can or is going to be a model citizen. Because I have seen and did time with both, patients and convicts that were as much as a lamb in confinement, but went on a killing spree once they were released were model citizens. The only way to find out how a patient or convict is really going to be once he is released, is give him a chance to prove himself by putting him on an open ward with town passes so he can work and be with other citizens or to place him on an outpatient basis. The staff should do this to the patients that they can't prove one way or the other that they can or can't make it. This test should be for six months to a year. And if he can make it for a year, then he can make it for good. But the hospital won't do this to patients that could and can make it, because these are the kind of patients that scare the hell out of them.

Not because the patient is trying to but because the so-called professional staff don't know how to deal with a patient that can't and will not be intimidated, or turned into one of their brainwashed model nuts, that will kiss their ass and make them feel important. I am and always have been one of those patients that they don't know how (and are afraid) to deal with. I don't lie to them, or kiss their asses, and will never be intimidated by them with their chains, lock up, the threat of not getting a transfer or privileges outside the fence, etc. I am freer or should I say that I have more freedom than most people I have ever met. Freedom is a matter of mind, prison is also.

A man can lock another man's body up, but he can never lock his free will and mind up. So man makes his own prison and his own garden of Eden with his mind. So that's why these people will never intimidate me to becoming one of their brain washed nuts. "I'm free of mind and will."

These kind of patients are the ones that scare the hell out of them, and they don't know how to deal with them. Someone that tells them like it is, and hope they don't like it.

Most patients are intimidated by the hospital. The reason for this, is because the hospital threatens them with maximum security, chains, medication if they don't want treatment or refuse to participate in any of the therapy programs that have been forced on them. So patients are intimidated and they attend any and all the groups and one to one's they are told to attend. And does anything else that he is told to do, if they want to or not, just to get a transfer and privileges.

When this kind of forced treatment or therapy is applied the patient gains nothing if hardly anything, but a transfer and some privileges.

So what good is the hospital system doing for patients that need help, but feel too intimidated to open up to the ones that are hired to help them regain their sanity?

This kind of system is the cause of all the warehousing of patients in the hospital.

And because of this, the heads of the hospital administration and some of the heads of the local government get rich off of the overcrowded patient population. They're getting rich at the expense of patients that need help and can't get it, because of incompetent staff, and money hungry politicians.

The law states: The rights of patients in all mental hospitals are for all patients, whether they're on maximum security or not. But the real hospital policy has its own laws and rules, and disregards government laws in most cases.

There are too many patient rights to list, but the most important ones that the patients on maximum security have are:

Leather restraints are to be used; not steel restraints, *but* steel restraints (hand and leg cuffs) are always used on maximum.

Physical restraints are *only* to be used when a patient is an immediate danger to himself or others, *and* if *no* preventive measures are possible, without restraints.

Patients on Forensic don't have to do hardly anything to get *steels* put on them and tied to the bed, *even when seriously injured.*

Seclusion is *only* to be used when *leather* restraints are not necessary to keep patient from hurting himself or others. Maximum patients are locked in seclusion for as little as an employee's bad day or mood.

Restraints and seclusion are not to be used as a disciplinary use. Maximum patients are punished in this manner for little reason at all.

Medical treatment: patients are entitled to psychiatric and medical treatment and care appropriate to his individual needs, while in this facility. Maximum patients only receive medical and psychiatric treatment and care, if and when the ward doctor or staff feels like giving it to them, "even when everyone can clearly see that you need it."

Personal rights: patient has the right to be free from metal or physical abuse on the part of the staff members, other patients and visitors. Maximum patients have no way to protect themselves from abuse from others, staff or patients, because self-defence is against the rules.

Visiting rights: no visiting restrictions are to be put on either the patients or visitors, unless the patient becomes or is a danger to himself or others or to his visitor or the visitor becomes detrimental to the patient's well being. Maximum patients must fill out a visitor's list or request *like prisoners do in prison* in order to get a visit from anyone, other than immediate family, lawyers, doctors or religious counselors. In some cases, patients have to have their immediate family put on their visiting list before they can visit.

Recreational rights: All patients are to have at least one hour of fresh air and sunshine, if weather permits, *if not* one hour of recreation in the gym. This recreational right is to be at least once a day.

Maximum patients are deprived of this right because the recreational man and ward staff are too lazy to take us outside or to the gym.

Occupational therapy: patients are to have at least four to six hours of occupational therapy a day. So they will have something constructive to do during the waking hours of the day. Maximum patients aren't allowed to have any kind of occupational therapy for reasons of: a patient stole a hammer from the O.T. shop, and tried to knock the bricks out of the wall to escape. So everyone paid for it, *over two years ago* leaving us short of building space, and short of occupational therapists.

Social rights: insofar as possible, this facility shall attempt to maintain a normal social environment. Maximum patients are treated like convicts and are locked up with convicts. There is very little therapy if any and patients are forced to live in a prison-like setting, instead of a hospital or a normal social environment.

Ventilation, heating and lighting rights: patients are to be housed in a building that is adequately well ventilated, heated and well lighted. Maximum patients are deprived of these rights; the ventilation, heating have never worked. We freeze in the winter and roast in the summer. The lighting is very bad, our windows are eight feet high and three inches wide, this doesn't let much, if any sunlight in at all.

These are the most important patient rights that are being abused on maximum.

The things that happen to maximum patients which I have mentioned do not and would not happen outside maximum wards too much or too long, because the outside world, meaning the patients visitors, would put a stop to it. The reason for this is because non-maximum patients are allowed to have their visitors come on the wards, where they can see what goes on in the wards, and are allowed to talk to other patients on the ward, to see and find out how they are treated.

Also security police are not in charge of the housing of patients and the treatment programs and care of the patients on other wards "like they are on maximum: security first, treatment second!"

This goes for all treatment; medical care on surgery. Maximum patients are chained to the bed by a log chain around their leg while on surgery!

But since the patient's visitors do not see the wards, and how patients are treated, most all the people in the free world think we are treated with all the TLC in the world. Because they can't bring themselves to believe that people are treated like we are in this day and age.

The law states: that all patients, no matter what their commitment, are to be treated as civil commitments. The only exceptions are, transfers from penal institutions and those who have been found guilty of a crime, but not guilty by reason of insanity.

There is one problem the patients of this system have that seems to make our grievances even worse.

This problem is that, our patient representative works for the hospital system, *not for us.* So when ever we have a grievance about our rights or anything else that is against the hospital staff, we can't get anything done. Because we have to go through a person who has and always will back up the system.

Sexual relationships are not allowed with any women not even your own wife, anywhere on the hospital grounds. There isn't a ward on the whole maximum unit that has men and women on the same ward.

Psychological warfare: Harrassment; intentional and systematic efforts to elicit strong expression of emotion by means of various forms of provocation.

Frightening patients into conformity... "This is the number one treatment program."

Dual numbers: it is unlawful to try and convict and then send a mental patient to prison.

The hospital does this and has been getting away with it for God only knows how long. What the hospital does if a patient commits a crime while a patient here at the hospital in most cases is they find the patient sane and competent after he has been filed on. And if the court sends him to prison, the court has sent a mental patient to prison by law, because the hospital has not discharged the patient.

This is called a *dual number,* which by federal law is against the law. Because the patient is a mental patient until he is fully discharged. And you can't send a mental patient to prison, because mental patients and convicts can not be confined together.

Patients that have been found *not* guilty by reason of insanity are not allowed to be transferred out of maximum where all the civil commitments are housed, because we are labeled as criminal commitments by the law and therefore treated as criminals instead of mental patients.

Hospital police carry guns all over the hospital grounds. They carry them in their cars and are stored in their office, where any patient that really wanted a gun could steal one, right out of their car or out of their office. By law no weapons are allowed on State hospital grounds.

Patients who have been sent to the hospital for observation, confinement, treatment, and incompetency are also locked up with convicts from prison.

So to sum up the trouble with this system and what changes should be made to make it a system that could and would help those in need of help are as follows:

Stop the warehousing of patients to make money.

The only way to stop this abuse to patients, is to have a Federal investigation of how this hospital is run. And rather close it down or weed out the incompetent staff and the greedy heads of the government, and replace professional staff that will do the job that they are trained and paid for.

Cause so much trouble for the government and the hospital, through the press and other organizations that want and aren't afraid to help put so much heat on the politician and the hospital, that it will cause the concerned people of the outside world to demand a change and get it.

Talk to good and important lawyers, about how patients are deprived of their rights "which I have already mentioned most of these rights," and ask them even if you have to beg them to, to take on the government on behalf of the patients, by filing a class action law suit for as much money as they can get plus a reform of the hospital, so there won't be anymore abuse and mistreatment of patients like warehousing. They would have to take the case free, because we don't have the money that most lawyers want. But they would get paid out of the money they made off of the law suit.

These are the only ways that can be used to straighten this place up, so that patients in need of help can receive the proper treatment and care.

Max has learned the trades of locksmith, jeweler, watch repairman. He has ventilated much of his younger fury but rage remains. Is it inappropriate? He is seen as lacking insight into the things he does to provoke attack or confinement, but are his criticisms of the system off the mark? The work of Zimbardo, Milgram and others demonstrate the brutalizing effect on principled staff of an environment in which one group holds total power over another; in which both groups are confronted daily by their failures and inadequately rewarded for successes. There *are* some treatment programs (in my memory: Hamilton Psychiatric in Ontario and Lake's Crossing in Nevada) that seem to have more dynamic treatment programs with more effective placements; where, even in locked wards, growth conditions are maximized and placement development has great priority. Max has a complete new set of staff to deal with each time he progresses to a lower security ward. A long list of people must take responsibility for protecting their reputations by correctly predicting his future behavior. Only the mistakes of premature release make headlines; mistakes of overlong residence are less likely to be noticed.

Max is antisocial to the system and the system reacts in kind. Maybe he needs more attention, indeed certain kinds he asks for, but surely in twenty-four years, it would be reasonable to assume he has had adequate exposure to treatment, also assuming that the treatment is there to be had. Instead, Max has adapted his disorders to the system and the system feeds his expectations. Now Max is rocking the boat: he wants out but he also wants to keep his personality intact—antisocial and all. Is Max dangerous because of future actions or because of present attitudes? Max has the message quite clearly: conform to ward procedures and expectations, be less threatening and more humble, recognize publicly (insightfully?) his errors and rescind all blame from others. Taking full responsibility for oneself and avoiding all displacement mechanisms would be both admirable and healthy. Max wants out with the personality he has. How necessary is it he change? Another twenty-four years worth?

Without adequate help, some of Max's colleagues should not be released. Some have, and have repeatedly, raped or killed. A solution is to focus our most intense resources to *offer* adequate help, to build on the models that appear to be working for patients treated as hopeless elsewhere. Max has the motivation and intelligence to begin serious deinstitutionalization work, with the right support and candor, assuming we can allow ourselves to coexist with his personality and that Max's personality allows others to coexist with him. Max says yes, he has already changed his behavior, but no, he won't change his identity. Max will continue to gripe vehemently about life as he fights his way through it and, in some ways, he may have retained more of his health, humor, and vitality than the salaried staff surrounding him.

A paperback book I strongly recommend is *Frances Farmer: Shadowland* by William Arnold (New York: Jove Publications/McGraw-Hill, 1979) which details in moving journalistic style the incarceration and ultimate demise of a compelling screen personality through iatrogenic involuntary institutional care including a final lobotomy. To quote Arnold's final statement:

> The first thing an investigative reporter learns about the mental health industry is that it does not like to talk about its old psychiatric cases—*any* old psychiatric cases. This reticence is less a frightened cover-up than a painful memory: the victims of 40 years of radical shock treatments and some 50,000 lobotomies in state mental hospitals do not make for good public relations. When I tried to confront various psychiatric authorities with the story of Frances Farmer, for the most part they simply refused to discuss it. Many of them looked sympathetic and shrugged it off as a "terrible" thing that happened a long, long time ago. They all insisted that such a thing could never happen today.
>
> But the sad and appalling truth is that the Frances Farmer case is not merely an isolated incident dredged up from another era. It is extraordinary only in terms of the woman's fame and great visibility (and, indeed, there are many other examples of the negative effects of radical treatment on such celebrities as Ernest Hemingway, Judy Garland, and Vivien Leigh). The literature of psychiatric abuse chronicles thousands of more recent and equally disturbing cases—hyperactive nine-year-olds lobotomized in Mississippi, homosexuals shocked into insensibility in England, Steilacoom-like conditions in Massachusetts and Indiana and Virginia. While I was doing research in the Midwest, a Hungarian immigrant was arrested there and subjected to extensive shock therapy because he didn't speak English and his dialect had been diagnosed by a psychiatrist as the babblings of psychosis. In California, eight Stanford University researchers who had themselves admitted to a dozen different mental hospitals by pretending to be insane found they could not overcome the label "schizophrenic" no matter how normal they subsequently behaved. (They were finally released after outside intervention by the project director.) Similar stories abound.
>
> The fact is that surprisingly little has changed in the 35 years since Frances Farmer first came under the thumb of organized psychiatry. Many states—including Washington—have passed new laws which make involuntary commitment more difficult, but the potential for abuse remains enormous in a field where a mental patient's future may be decided on the most arbitrary and subjective grounds. Psychiatry has never been able to define precisely

what is normal (or abnormal) behavior, and thus it inevitably ends up enforcing conformity to whatever the current community and government standards happen to be—whether defined by Fascist Italy, National Socialist Germany, Soviet Russia or the State of Washington.

In the past decade, the tide of public opinion has swung heavily against traditional psychiatry. Recent research indicates that schizophrenia is attributable to an excess of receptors in the brain for a chemical messenger called dopamine, a condition which is probably related to heredity and nutrition. And this could conceivably make much of the practice of psychiatry obsolete. Laing, Szasz, and other radical therapists are still gunning away at their colleagues, and virtually every theory and treatment has been challenged by one eminent psychiatrist or another. An increasing number of studies made by psychiatry itself, in fact, confirms that suspicion that mental patients often get well faster when given no treatment than when given conventional psychiatric therapy.

And yet, despite this landslide of damning evidence and new information, institutional psychiatry has still managed to hang on to its extra-legal power and medieval treatments. Psychiatric associations have battled off attempts to outlaw shock therapy in numerous states. The big pharmaceutical companies continue recklessly to market the maze of mind controlling drugs before their side effects are thoroughly known. The population of the 337 public mental institutions—including Western State Hospital at Steilacoom—has swelled to nearly four times the prison population, and in the past decade more Americans died in mental hospitals than died in battle in all wars except World War II.

Even more ominous is the fact that, after a 15-year fallow period in which psychosurgery fell from fashion, it is now undergoing a world-wide resurgence. Various subtle and almost undetectable operations with names like "hypothalamotomy" and "amygdalotomy"—operations which largely grew out of the Freeman transorbital experiments of the late '40s—have been developed and widely performed in the '70s. According to some estimates, nearly 1,000 lobotomies a year take place and as the procedures become more simple and refined, the possibility of their use by a totalitarian government as a means of mass mind control becomes chillingly plausible.

The mentality of the system which deals with supposedly abnormal behavior is virtually unchanged since the 1940s. The chance of an individual like Frances Farmer being trapped and destroyed by this system is as real today as it was then. The bitter legacy of her story is not that such a fate could strike a public figure protected by the privileges of celebrity, but that it can happen to anyone (Arnold 1979, 188-190).

Epilogue

I asked a staff member, someone I like and respect, what Max's status really was. He responded: "It boils down to this: he says he's cured and he'll kill any son-of-a-bitch that says otherwise." I shared the quote (without attribution) with Max and he responded with a genuine belly laugh. "Well, it's even worse than that," he said, "the son-of-a-bitch I'm killing is *me!* They just won't let me out until I agree that I'm too dangerous to leave.... (laugh) and I'm too stubborn to lie. The most dangerous thing about me right now are my lawsuits! I hope they will be dangerous enough. No, wait a minute, more dangerous than the lawsuits is this: I won't give up on myself. As to the people here, some I care about and some I don't. I don't want to kill them, what I want to do is say *goodbye* to them. *I* understand the difference, I'm not sure they do."

BERTON ROUECHE

16

As Empty as Eve

Author of the epidemiological sleuth book *The Medical Detectives* (New York: Truman Talley/Times, 1981), widely acclaimed medical science writer Berton Roueché has had much experience unearthing iatrogenesis along with the pathogenesis. Perhaps his most quoted and controversial article is the classic "As empty as Eve" on the electroshock damage done to a professional woman in the course of her *treatment*. If Ernest Hemingway, himself an alleged victim of ECT, were still alive he might outdo Roueché with some autobiographical statements on the subject. Without that possibility, this article yet stands as the definitive case history on the liabilities of shock treatment. Thanks are due *The New Yorker* magazine for permission to reprint this September 9th, 1974 piece, and to courageous Marilyn Rice, former government economist, for serving as its model. **R.F.M.**

Natalie Parker, as I'll call her, is an attractive woman of medium height, with large gray eyes and light gray hair, but thin—still painfully thin. She is in her early fifties, and is an economist by profession. Her husband, Alan, is an artist and illustrator. The Parkers live in Washington, in an apartment on J Street that also includes Mr. Parker's studio. They have no children. Until September of 1973, when she retired for reasons of health, Mrs. Parker was employed—and had been for more than twenty years—at the Department of Commerce. Her work there involved certain aspects of the computation and analysis of the gross national product.

The misfortunes that led to Mrs. Parker's premature retirement began in the spring of 1972, when she learned from her dentist that she had a serious gum problem. He referred her to a periodontist of his acquaintance. In June, the periodontist, after a long and interested examination, referred her to an orthodontist for the realignment of several teeth affected by the condition of her gums. The orthodontic work was not a success. Indeed, as Mrs. Parker subsequently declared in an application for disability retirement, the results were both mechanically and cosmetically "disastrous." They were also emotionally daunting. As the summer passed and autumn came on, she began to despair, and fell into a deep depression. She was tired all day, she couldn't sleep at night, her teeth hurt, her appetite vanished. Her family physician prescribed a conventional tranquillizer. She continued to work, but with increasing difficulty. Her weight dropped from a normal hundred and eighteen pounds to a hundred and ten, and then to ninety-eight. By Christmas, it was down to eighty-nine. Her physician referred her to a consulting psychiatrist. The psychiatrist's prognosis was guardedly hopeful. He thought a period of rest in a relaxed environment would be a sufficient restorative. The environment he had in mind was that of a psychiatric hospital. Mrs. Parker was at first appalled. The idea was socially unacceptable. In time, however, her resistance weakened, and at last, too discouraged to care, she allowed herself to be admitted for observation to a well-appointed hospital with which the psychiatrist was associated. That, according to Mr. Parker, was on February 8, 1973, and his recollection is confirmed by the hospital records. Mrs. Parker herself has no recollection of that decisive event. She has, in fact, no recollection of any part of her hospital stay.

Mrs. Parker's stay in the hospital lasted about nine weeks. She was discharged around the middle of April. Nothing of that time remains in her memory but an occasional shifting shadow, a half-heard sound, an indefinable feeling. She has had to recover the nature of the experience from sources outside herself. One of these, of course, is her husband. Mr. Parker came to the hospital every day for a leisurely visit, often joining her for lunch or dinner, and he sometimes took her out for a drive or for an afternoon of shopping. Another source—an almost eerily definitive source—is a series of letters that she wrote to her parents, in Boonville, Missouri, nearly all of which they fortunately preserved. The first of these letters was written on February 16th, the ninth day of her hospitalization. It reads:

> Well, here I find myself in a totally new experience for me, and one I never expected to have—residing in a mental hospital. This place is a nice new building. The atmosphere and décor are those of a hotel. The patients, nurses, and other staff members all dress in casual clothes—no uniforms. There are two patients to a room. Most of the patients here are perfectly lucid, though some are kind of mixed up. One woman laments that she knows that she is going to live forever, whereas she would rather die. There is a cute young colored girl who worries because she thinks the Communists are taking over the world etc. But all perfectly harmless.
>
> [Alan] has been coming over to have lunch and dinner with me. I am a unique patient here. Some are on drugs, some are on electric shock, some are on individual psychotherapy, and some are on group therapy. I seem to be on a sort of do-it-yourself therapy—in other words a sort of rest cure. I had been assigned to the head doctor (I mean the chief doctor; I guess they are all "head doctors"), but I felt dubious about him. Also, one of the patients told me that he is noted for wanting to give all of his patients electric shock. I told him that I had the same kind of intuition about him that I had had about the orthodontist—namely: This man doesn't understand my case. I said that after being turned into a monster by the orthodontist, I didn't want to take any chances on being turned into a hopeless lunatic by him. So I lounged around for several days in nobody's charge, and then was assigned to a young fellow (thirtyish) named Dr. [Smith]. I told him my problem was that I have to get

adjusted to life as a damned ugly woman. He said, "You certainly have a gutsy way of putting it." Actually, the name of what ails me is depression. After fighting the battle of the hopeless dental work for so many months, I was so worn down that I lost all appetite for food, work, or anything else. Every little thing—even putting my clothes on—seemed as difficult as climbing Mt. Everest. I tried resting at home, and tried going back to work, but nothing got me into gear again. The medical doctor recommended that I talk to a "consulting psychiatrist," and the latter recommended that some time in the hospital—change of environment and no need to push myself—might get me going again. So here I am. I look at it philosophically, and when I get out I will tell people that it is "mod" to be "mad."

Don't worry about my being out of my head. It is not like that at all. I pulled myself together a few days before I came here and made out all the income-tax forms—federal and D.C. and estimated tax. I didn't want to leave poor [Alan] with that job because I have always done the household paperwork and he wouldn't know how.

The next letter in the series was written about a week later, on February 25th. It reads:

I continue taking it easy here—something like living in a college dorm. My main pals seem to be the girls in their twenties. Perhaps the teeth braces automatically identify me with the younger group. I had thought that I might get to tell my dreams and interesting life experiences. But instead I get a diet supplement and a laxative pill. There is quite a lot of humor around here of the type [Alan] calls gallows humor. One little girl is determined to commit suicide but can't figure out any way to do it here. I offered to save up a hundred laxative pills for her. She got the giggles. My case has been so mixed up that they only got around to giving me my entry exam a couple of days ago—two weeks after I had come here. Apparently I am O.K. except for being weak and run down. A nurse was doing something at her desk with rubber bands, and I told her in case I got violent, she could use one of those to restrain me.

A following letter in the series, written early in March, appears to have been lost. The next, and penultimate, letter is dated April 5th. It reads:

I certainly am in a strange state. Early last week I suddenly came to—so to speak—and wondered where I was and how I got here. I learned that I had had something called "electric-shock treatments" that had caused me to lose my memory. Now I know how Eve must have felt, having been created full grown out of somebody's rib without any past history. I feel as empty as Eve.

I can remember a few things. I know my phone number and who my relatives are. However, the letters from you all that I found in my dresser were completely new to me. I reread them without any recollection of having read them before. There were a number of get-well cards, and some were from names I didn't recognize. There were a couple from a [Margaret Davis], who [Alan] says lives on our floor, but I don't remember her. Also some from people in the office whose names sound familiar but whom I couldn't visualize.

A cute-looking young fellow with a turned-up nose came in to see me and was asking how I felt. I told him I felt all right except that I couldn't remember much of anything. I asked him who he was and he said he was my doctor. Then I asked him what kind of doctor he was. He looked surprised,

and said he was a psychiatrist. I said: "A psychiatrist! Then I must be crazy."
He said: "Oh, no, no!" However, I presume I must be off balance to some
extent or I wouldn't be in what turns out to be a mental institution.

Actually, the so-called patients here all seem to be in command of their
wits except for one—namely, the woman who has been my roommate for the
past couple of days. She is a nice-looking woman and about my age, but she
talks a blue streak, pure nonsense—on and on about the Pope and sex and
euthanasia and syphilis and strangers' toothbrushes and God knows what all.

This morning I went to the orthodontist and this afternoon I have an
appointment with the periodontist, Dr. [Brown]. [Alan] has kept track of my
appointments—otherwise I wouldn't know about them. Oddly, I can remember Dr. [Brown's] attractive red-and-black waiting room, but I can't remember
him—don't know whether he is young or old, short or tall. I haven't the
slightest idea what kind of dental work he is doing to me.

Mrs. Parker wrote her final hospital letter to her parents on the following
day, April 6th. She had learned by then that she had been given a total of
eight treatments. Her letter reads:

For the first several days after those electric-shock treatments were over—
possibly as long as a week—I felt just fine, perfectly relaxed and comfortable
and also very hungry, as if I were making up for lost time. However, beginning Monday night (today is Friday) I began feeling all churned up and
nervous and jittery and tense for no reason, and I have felt that way ever
since. [Alan] said that what I was describing was the way I have felt for a long
time. Then, beginning last night, in addition to feeling tense and agitated, I
also felt scared, also for no reason.

Somebody the other day asked me to make a fourth at bridge and I
refused, saying I hadn't played bridge for at least fifteen years. Then he said I
had been playing right along for the two months I had been at the hospital.
Also I was surprised to find a very pretty black-and-white checked raincoat in
my closet. [Alan] told me I had bought it one day soon after I came here
when we went out to get my hair fixed. They tell me that gradually I will get
my memory back. I hope so.

Electroconvulsive-shock therapy is a relatively recent refinement of a
primitive procedure that was first employed around the turn of the eigh-
teenth century. Johann Christian Reil (1759-1813), a German neurologist
and anatomist whose name distinguishes several structures of the human
body, is generally regarded as its pioneer proponent. Reil's curious contribution to psychiatry was a product of his interest in the then just forming
humanitarian opposition to the traditional chain-and-shackle treatment of
the mentally ill. Reil went further than most of his associates in the
movement. It was not enough, in his opinion, that the inmates of the
madhouse be merely freed of their fetters. They should also, he proposed,
be given some sort of restorative treatment, and after consideration he
came up with a plausible psychotherapeutic program. Its aim was to
frighten, or shock, the patient into rationality. Reil's regime could be
administered in many different ways. The unsuspecting patient might be
suddenly seized and flung into a pond. Or a cannon might be shot off
behind him. Or he might be wrenched from sleep to face a hovering

ghost. More heroic measures were prescribed for stubborn cases. Medical historians of the period have reported elaborate tableaux (with large casts drawn from the madhouse staff) that depicted such salubrious horrors as a resurrection of the dead, the Last Judgment, the yawning gates of Hell. Reil called his treatment "noninjurious torture."

If Reil was the first to attempt an instant psychotherapy, he was also (except for the perennial hypnotist) the last. Most subsequent attempts to achieve an immediate emotional rehabilitation by means of a cathartic shock have employed a chemotherapy. The renowned eighteenth-century American clinician Benjamin Rush was responsible for one of the earliest of these. Rush treated mental patients in his Philadelphia practice with a shock therapy that involved the induction of suppuration at the back of the neck to excite a tonic discharge "from the neighborhood of the brain." The triumphant confirmation in the late nineteenth century of the germ theory of disease provided a more convenient method of producing a chemotherapeutic shock. In 1890, the Austrian neuropsychiatrist Julius Wagner von Jauregg used an extract of the tubercle bacillus to ignite what he hoped would be an explosively curative fever in an insane patient. This early effort was not a success, but many years later, in 1914, he tried again, with the malaria organism, and this time achieved a distinct improvement in the condition of a group of men suffering from general paresis. The discovery of insulin, in 1921, made possible a variety of chemotherapeutic shock that remains the awesome ultimate in the pharmacopoeia of psychiatry. Another Austrian, a clinical investigator at Berlin's Lichterfelde Hospital named Manfred Sakel (1900-57), is recognized as the discoverer of insulin as a psychiatric tool. Insulin is distinguished for its power to reduce the sugar content of the blood, and it is this power, of course, that makes it a salvational drug in the treatment of diabetes. Its impact on a normal person is very different. A large injection will produce confusion, deep sleep, and, finally, coma. It was this capacity that interested Sakel. He first experimented with the induction of insulin shock, or hypoglycemic coma, as a means of calming morphine addicts during a withdrawal period. The results (when he learned to reverse the action with a timely does of glucose) were gratifying enough to encourage him to try the same treatment in other excited states, and in 1933 he reported its usefulness in the treatment of schizophrenia. Sakel's estimation of the value of his work was soon confirmed by other investigators, and insulin-shock therapy—though not without drawbacks, and even dangers—is still in widespread use. It is, however, most highly esteemed as the inspirational prototype of electroconvulsive therapy.

The principles of electroconvulsive therapy were developed by the Italian clinicians Ugo Cerletti and Lucio Bini, and first described by them in a report (entitled "L'Elettroshock") to the journal *Archivio Generale di Neurologìa, Psichiatrìa, e Psicanalisi* in 1938. Electric shock differs from other forms of shock therapy in that it involves the direct mechanical manipulation of the brain to produce a generalized convulsion, or epileptiform seizure. It is thus a physiotherapeutic treatment. Cerletti and Bini conceived electric-shock therapy as a treatment for schizophrenia—as an improvement on Sakel's insulin shock—but subsequent investigators have found it most effective in treating the depression of old age (involutional melancholia) and the depressive phase of manic-depressive psychosis. The procedure currently in vogue is as simple as it is direct. Electroconvulsive therapy is usually given in the morning, and the patient is prepared for it as if for surgery: he is allowed no breakfast, and false teeth, if any, are removed. He is positioned comfortably in bed on his back, and given an intravenous injection of a muscle-relaxant drug and a complementing injection of a hypnotic to maintain normal respiration. An electrode is then placed on each temple, and an alternating current of (usually) eighty or ninety volts is passed between the electrodes for a fraction of a fraction of a second. In that stupendous instant, the brain is so raced that the mind cannot function, and it is from this eerie quietus that the beneficial results of the treatment appear to spring. Just why a halt in cerebral function should be therapeutic is not, however, known. Most cases of depression require several such treatments, and the usual course is between eight and twelve convulsions. In the early days of electroconvulsive therapy, before the development of a satisfactory muscle relaxant, fractures or dislocations were frequent in the moment of violent seizure, but they are now relatively rare, and the patient passes from a brief (four or five minutes) unconsciousness into a peaceful sleep.

The states of mind of most patients emerging from the post-convulsion sleep are similar. There is a harrowing sense of confusion, and then a full awakening in the midnight dark of total amnesia. The patient has no idea who he is or where he is or what has happened to him. He is often a bit weak, unsteady, and dizzy. Nausea, sometimes with vomiting, and headache are not uncommon. Some sense of identity soon and spontaneously returns, and from the attending doctors and nurses the patient learns his whereabouts and the nature of his situation. At that point, reorientation slows, and the deepest amnesia remains. The distant past—the past of childhood and adolescence—is the first to gradually reappear. The middle past is more difficult to recover, and the immediate past—the weeks or months just preceding treatment—is almost always irretrievable.

Psychiatrists are generally inclined to regard electroconvulsive therapy as a useful psychiatric tool. Some are more enthusiastic than others. The late Arthur P. Noyes, director of psychiatric education at the Pennsylvania Department of Public Welfare, and Lawrence C. Kolb, chairman of the Department of Psychiatry at the Columbia University College of Physicians and Surgeons, who together wrote the standard text "Modern Clinical Psychiatry," observe, "In the depressions of involutional melancholia and of manic depressive psychosis, the improvement following electroconvulsive shock therapy is striking. In eighty per cent or more of these disorders, five to ten treatments are followed by full or social recovery." Justin Hope, clinical professor of psychiatry at the Tufts University Medical School, and Raymond I. Adams, Bullard Professor of Neuropathology at Harvard Medical School take a somewhat guarded position. In a collaborative contribution to "Principles of Internal Medicine" they note, "Although carefully controlled experiments cast some doubt upon the efficacy of electric-shock therapy in terminating an individual depressive episode or preventing recurrences, nevertheless it is the authors' clinical impression that it does indeed favorably influence the course of the individual depressive episode." Aubrey Lewis, professor of psychiatry at the Institute of Psychiatry of the University of London, has expressed what seems to be the opinion of a majority of clinicians. "Electric-convulsive therapy," he suggests in a current monograph on the psychoses, "has been over-used in the last twenty years, being applied in unsuitable cases or when less severe methods would have sufficed; but this reproach has been taken from it since the new drugs have superseded it as the easiest acceptable form of somatic treatment."

Most psychiatrists are satisfied that electroconvulsive therapy is as benign as it is beneficial. They are generally agreed (on the basis of numerous psychometric tests and other objective studies) that the patient undergoing such treatment runs no risk of basic intellectual impairment. There is less agreement on the question of memory impairment. Some investigators have recently suggested that the more or less permanent amnesia resulting from repeated electric-shock treatments may not be confined to the period immediately preceding treatment. Larry R. Squire, assistant professor of psychiatry at the University of California School of Medicine at La Jolla, reported to the third annual meeting of the Society for Neuroscience, in San Diego in 1973, that controlled tests involving memory of long-past events indicated that repeated electroconvulsive stimulation "apparently produces a defect in recall which can extend to memories that are some twenty years old, [but] it is not yet known how long this amnesia...persists." And J.-O. Ottoson, a participant in the 1967 International Congress of the Academy of Psychosomatic Medicine, observed in a paper entitled "Memory Disturbance After E.C.T.—A Major or a Minor Side Effect?" that while "in most cases memory impairment soon vanishes...some patients have prolonged, perhaps irreversible, disturbances." These, however, are minority cautions. The majority view would seem to be the one proclaimed by the editors of the 1973 edition of "The New Home Medical Encyclopedia." They conclude, "Memory may be somewhat impaired as a result of the treatment, but it returns when the full course of treatment is terminated." This is the reassurance that most patients are given as they prepare to leave the hospital after treatment. It is precisely the reassurance that Mrs. Parker received at the end of her hospital stay.

Mrs. Parker's return, on April 13th, to the apartment that had been her home for many years was something of a *déjà-vu* experience. She had an uncertain feeling that she had been there before. It was strange, and yet familiar.

> It was all very peculiar, Mrs. Parker told me shortly after her retirement. I was puzzled—but only vaguely. I really felt too vague to care. Nothing really bothered me. Not at first. I felt physically very well. I felt vegetablized and calm. I didn't have enough memory to think, or even worry, with. And then, because the apartment was so familiar, my mind seemed to open up a little.

and my memory began to come back. I mean my memory for where I was—
for simple, household things. Although there were odd gaps even there. I
remember my first morning at home. I thought of breakfast, and my mind
was a blank. I turned to Alan: 'What do I usually have for breakfast?' He
looked a little startled, but he told me—an egg and a cookie. Oh, yes. I
remembered. I was full of questions. It was like beginning life all over again.
I said something one day about the hospital, about the bills, and Alan said
Blue Cross was taking care of it. Blue Cross? I didn't know what he was
talking about. I'd never heard of it. And, of course, Watergate. I kept hearing
'Watergate' on the radio, and seeing it in the paper. It meant nothing to me.
So Alan had to explain. That was the way I remembered, the way things
came back, the way I relearned.

The hospital had told me to take it easy, to rest at home for a few weeks,
not to even think about my job. I had a general memory of my job. I knew
where I worked, and that I was an economist and analyst. But it was no
problem not to think about my work. Work was just something that drifted
across my mind from time to time. It didn't interest me. I was too comfortable doing nothing. I've always been a great reader, but even reading didn't
interest me now. I read a couple of novels, and the minute I put them down I
forgot everything about them. I read a book called 'Zelda,' but I don't
remember a single thing about it. Any more serious reading—a book that
required any background of general knowledge—I simply couldn't read. I
couldn't understand it. So I gave up trying and just let myself be comfortable.
And I was comfortable. I got to know our friends again. We went out to
dinner now and then. We went to the movies. I kept house. I functioned very
well.

I went back to work in July. The rest at home and some sessions with a
sympathetic psychotherapist had done me good, and I felt almost like my old
self again. My memory seemed to be coming back the way the hospital had
told me it would. I was eager to work, eager to put my mind to work again.
And I was curious. I wanted to find out what I had been working on before I
took my sick leave. So I went back to work one Monday morning and up to
my office and sat down at my desk, and my old associates flocked around.
Most of them looked familiar, and I was able to remember some of the
names. I was still feeling pretty good. Then I started going through my desk—
all the current papers and pamphlets and so on. I gathered that I'd been
working on the income of securities dealers—relating their earnings to the
gross national product. The papers were full of professional terms that
seemed familiar. I knew what they were, but I didn't know what they meant.
'Over-the-counter,' for example. It was a familiar term, but I didn't know—I
couldn't remember—exactly what it referred to. 'Mutual funds' was another.
And 'odd-lot dealers.' All blanks. But I had a vague idea that there was
something that might help, that might get me reoriented. I went to one of the
girls. I hemmed and hawed, and said I'd forgotten but wasn't there some
particular book that I had been using? 'Oh, sure,' she said. 'You mean that
book you got at the National Association of Securities Dealers meeting in
December.' I said I guessed that was it, but had I been at the meeting? She
almost laughed. She said, 'Were you there? Why, Natalie, you practically ran
it. It was you who asked most of the questions. It was you who got most of
the information we needed.' It was a terrible moment. I thought I was losing
my mind. I had no recollection of it at all. And then, like a shadowy film, I
got a dim sense of a man sitting on my left in a meeting room. But that was
all. Just the shadow of a presence. My friend just stared at me.

I came home from the office that first day feeling panicky. I didn't know where to turn. I didn't know what to do. I was terrified. I've never been a crying person, but all my beloved knowledge, everything I had learned in my field during twenty years or more, was gone. I'd lost the body of knowledge that constituted my professional skill. I'd lost everything that professionals take for granted. I'd lost my experience, my knowing. But it was worse than that. I felt that I'd lost myself. I fell on the bed and cried and cried and cried.

But you know how it is. One always hopes, or tries to hope. I told myself that maybe it was only a matter of time. If I was patient, maybe in time everything would come back to me. So I went back to the office determined to try. I was going to start all over again. I was going to relearn. I started looking everything up and making elaborate notes. It was like learning to walk—I started out taking little baby steps. The days and weeks went by, and everybody at the office was good and patient and helpful. Every now and then, I'd get a little glimmer. But mostly it was discouraging. There weren't just gaps in my memory. There were oceans and oceans of blankness. And yet there seemed to be a kind of pattern. My childhood recollections were as strong as ever. That, I've gathered from my reading about electric shock, is quite typical. The fog of amnesia increased as I came forward in time. The events of the past several years were the blurriest and the blankest. Another area that didn't seem to be affected was ingrained habits—repetitive acts and procedures. I mean, I hadn't lost my command of the English language, I still knew the multiplication tables, I could still do double-entry bookkeeping. And then there was an area that I call emotional. I could still remember experiences from any period of my life that had had a big emotional impact. Good *and* bad. I could remember pains and hurts. And I could also remember a trip we took to Spain only a few years ago. A wonderful trip.

But the worst of all my problems was that I couldn't seem to retain. I couldn't hang on to my relearning. Or only a part of it. The rest kept sliding away again. I think there was—and is—another factor involved in that. I mean my teeth. My ordeal at the orthodontist goes on and on. And it's a constant worry, a constant distraction. I think that stands partly in the way of my relearning. Anyway, sometime in August I was so discouraged that I had an idea. I was still seeing my psychiatrist—the psychotherapist. Well, one day I asked him about the possibility of recovering my memory through hypnosis. He said he didn't know but he would try to find out. The next time I saw him, he gave me the name of a professional hypnotist. I got in touch with the man and made an appointment. I told him my troubles, and I told him what I had in mind. My idea was to be put to sleep and then asked where I had bought the dress I had on. That was to sort of start my memory working. Then, if I remembered that, he was to ask me the meaning of a term we use at the office—a certain labelling of a concept on which I've written a dozen little treatises. But that wasn't what *he* wanted to do. He was a Freudian psychoanalyst at heart. He got me talking—to blubbering out a sort of intellectual life history. It began with how I could hardly wait to go to school when I was a little girl, and then on to how I never cared about amassing money but only about amassing mental capital—and now it's gone and I want it back. That was on my second visit. I saw him three times, but we never got together. All I wanted was a kind of parlor trick. I wanted him to pull my memory back. All he wanted was to analyze me. That was the end of it. He said he could help recover an emotional memory loss—but not a loss from brain damage. He didn't seem to know anything about electric-shock memory loss. He said he couldn't do much about that. So we both gave up.

I believe the electric-shock literature is right in one regard. My brain may be damaged insofar as part of my memory has been erased, but my mentality is certainly not impaired. I can still use my mind. And, except for that period of vegetating at home, I've never lost my intellectual curiosity. I was curious almost from the beginning to learn more about what had happened to me — about the whole idea of electric-shock therapy. So I began to look into the literature. I got a list of references from the National Institute of Mental Health. That was around mid-summer. I went through the list at one of the medical libraries — the George Washington University library. The result was almost nothing. The authorities all seemed to be parroting each other. I couldn't find a single study that tested the permanence of memory loss. Then, almost by accident, I got started on a little investigation of my own. Soon after I went back to work, I devised a routine to handle my inability to recognize the names and faces of people around the office. I would say, 'I'm sorry. I haven't any memory. You will have to tell me who you are and what you do.' I was going through this one day with a man from one of our coordinating sections when he stopped me. He said, 'You don't have to apologize to me. My wife had shock treatments a couple of years ago, and she hasn't any memory, either.' Well, you can imagine my interest in that. I got him to sit down and tell me all about it, and I made notes on it later. He told me, 'Within a few weeks after her discharge, my wife got reoriented to the main outlines of her life. After that, there was very little further spontaneous memory return. I'm a statistician, so I'll put it this way: maybe she improves three per cent a year. She gets by. For the life of a suburban housewife, she doesn't need much memory — the kaffeeklatsches and all that.'

That conversation was the beginning. I started bringing up the subject of electric shock whenever I met new people, and it's absolutely astonishing how many people have a relative or a friend or somebody who has had the treatment. I met a museum friend of Alan's at an art exhibition in Baltimore whose aunt had had the shock experience. He said her memory for the year that preceded treatment was a blank, but she could function. She has money, he said, and doesn't work — just lives quietly at home. I remembered an older woman from my home town who had had shock treatments maybe twenty years ago. She was a professional woman — a dietitian. I wrote and asked her about her experience. She told me, 'There was a lot of memory I never got back. But I did manage to relearn my work — all those recipes and things.' Another person I questioned was a man who had been at the hospital with me. He was a political analyst for the C.I.A., but he hadn't gone back to work. I talked to him at his home. He said he could remember the general type of work he had been doing but not the specifics. Then there was a lawyer I met. He had had shock therapy about four months before. He told me, 'I haven't any memory, but I have a book that I look things up in.' I questioned about a dozen people in all, and there really wasn't much difference in the answers. Their experience was pretty much mine. Oh, yes — I even wrote to Senator Thomas Eagleton. I thought his experience would be interesting. After all, it cost him the Democratic Vice-Presidential nomination. But he never acknowledged my letter.

All that while, of course, I was trying to work — desperately trying to relearn my job. But it was heartbreaking. It was so slow. I was relearning, but only a little, only after a fashion. It was like tunnel vision. I couldn't seem to see the whole panorama anymore. As far as my actual job went — the job I was being very well paid for — I was doing nothing. I was totally unproductive. I wasn't worth my salary, and I didn't see how I ever would be again. No one was pushing me. Everyone was wonderful. Still and all, the office isn't running a home for incurables. So I did what seemed to me the only sensible thing. I applied for disability retirement. I asked for one concession. I asked to be allowed to stay on—without pay—as what's called a 'guest employee.' They were kind enough to grant both of my requests. I have my retirement, and I also have a desk at the office. I go there almost every day. I can type. I can do low-level clerical work. And I'm trying, still trying, to rebuild my mental capital.

Mrs. Parker and I had our first conversations in the fall of 1973. We met again, by prearrangement, some four months later—early in 1974. She told me at once that there had been no appreciable progress in her efforts to recover her professional past.

But I don't want to sound like a pill, she said. I mean, I mustn't give the impression that my experience with electric shock was a total disaster. There have been some beneficial results. For one thing, my physical health has improved. I'm beginning to eat again, my digestion is much improved, and I have no trouble with sleep. I also feel emotionally relaxed. And I've lost a lot of bothersome inhibitions. I don't shrink the way I used to. I got in a cab the other day that had a big 'No Smoking' sign, and the driver was one of those know-it-all non-stop talkers. But I interrupted him. I said, 'I see you have a rule against smoking. Well, I've got a rule against talking.' He gave me a look, but he shut up.

I'm thankful for those little blessings. I'm thankful that I got something for the price I paid. Because my memory is still as blank in those certain areas as it was when I went back to work in July. I walked out of the office one evening last week with a man I'd worked with very closely for a number of years. He was saying something about his children, and I asked how many children he had. He looked surprised. 'Why, six,' he said. I said, 'Well, that's a statistic I would certainly think I'd have remembered.' He said, 'Yes—I would have thought so, too. You were always telling me that six was too many.' That's just one example. I could give you dozens more. It happens all the time, and it makes me feel so stupid. It keeps reminding me of how much of myself I've lost. There are times when I almost wish I were back in those weeks of resting and vegetating at home. When I didn't know what I know now. But that's a little frightening. If I hadn't been a professional woman—if I hadn't been a woman with a highly specialized and demanding job—I might never have realized the extent of my amnesia. I would have thought that I was still perfectly whole and complete.

PART FOUR

TREATMENT CONTEXT: CLINICAL APPLICATIONS

ROBERT F. MORGAN AND STANLEY K. FEVENS

17

The Iatrogenics of Retarded Attitudes on the Successful Treatment of the Retarded

Stanley K. Fevens is at present a government policy analyst and an instructor at Heritage Campus, Quebec. During his graduate training at Acadia University, Fevens worked with me on a variety of community change projects including the one illustrated in the following section. The subject matter itself is an area of much iatrogenesis. Clearly, the retarded are a group in which the opportunities and goals for change far underreach even the already existing technology. A chief psychologist at a home for the retarded, having defined his clients as *incurable,* was asked what could be done with a 10:1 staff/patient ratio: "Oh, well, *then* we could cure them!" he replied. Economics and politics too often hide behind pseudo-scientific defeatism: Most politicians would much rather pay the approximately one million dollars, spaced over a lifetime, needed to maintain a profoundly retarded person in custodial care (no immediate tax increase) than to secure less than half that sum over a few intensely concentrated treatment years toward returning the client to normal and independent functioning (immediate, if short term, tax increase). **R.F.M.**

Summary—Selected milestone and local programs from Canada and the United States of America are reviewed to illustrate the need to transcend the iatrogenic or socially harmful pseudo-scientific defeatism which often blocks meaningful investment by a community in efforts designed to return mentally impaired persons to normal functioning. The material presented attempts to bridge the gap between the specialized literature of psychological research and the very practical interpretations demanded of community psychologists in the field. Local context evaluations and replications are encouraged.

Recently the first author was treated to a colloquium presentation in which a psychologist presented his findings from a $200,000 program evaluation of an entire state's de-institutionalization of mentally retarded clients. The psychologist defined retardation as measured by substandard intelligence and social maturity scores. The study compared alternative treatment settings in the community on a cost-effective and perceived

Reprinted with permission from *Psychological Reports* 49 (1981):47-54. © *Psychological Reports.* 1981.

behavioral basis. No outcome measures relating to intelligence or social maturity were used.

In a brief discussion session following the presentation, the psychologist was asked why such outcome data were not tracked. His response was that such changes in intelligence or social maturity were "impossible," going on to cite the work of Arthur Jensen on genetic and racial effects (1977). In subsequent discussion, he denied the utility of research in the area and convinced us he was, like many of his colleagues, unaware of the decades of research demonstrating the effectiveness of methods for change of retarded and learning disabled persons. This otherwise knowledgeable social scientist had missed an opportunity to give crucial feedback to his state on the relative efficiency of community placement alternatives in resolving the disabling pathology by denying such resolution was possible.

This article reviews some of the encouraging breakthroughs in the field, and describes a demonstration local study performed by the second author in rural Canada.

Mental retardation has been defined by the American Association on Mental Deficiency as "subaverage general intellectual functioning existing concurrently with deficits in adaptive behavior and manifested during the developmental period (birth through eighteen years)" (Grossman 1973). Typical measures include the Vineland Social Maturity Scale (Doll 1965) and standardized intelligence tests such as the Wechsler Intelligence Scale for Children (WISC; Wechsler 1974). What can be measured can be changed, for better or for worse, and such information is imperative if progress is to be made.

In 1938 (*not* in 1981!) many psychologists felt intelligence to be a predetermined and fixed quantity. That was the year Harold Skeels began the apparently first recorded successful attempt to move retarded children to normal functioning (Skeels, *et al.* 1938; Skeels & Skodak 1965; Skeels, 1966). Skeels identified ten girls and three boys, all under three years old, whose tested intelligence averaged 64 (range 35 to 89) with the consequence being a planned transfer from their Iowa orphanage to an institution for the mentally retarded. Twelve children were selected from the orphanage as a control group: their average tested intelligence was 23 points higher (87; range 50 to 103). Each child in the experimental group was placed in his own ward of adult female retardates where they experienced considerable individual love and attention. The children were each bonded emotionally to an adult parent figure and to a nourishing ward 'family' who took pride in his individual successes. Before three years had passed, the experimental group had *gained* an average 28.5 IQ points per child while the control group, living in a more depersonalized institution, *lost* an average 26 points of measured intelligence per child. In a follow-up more than two decades later, all thirteen members of the experimental group were self-supporting, the median education was Grade 12 (four had gone to college; one had completed a BA with some graduate work), eleven were married, nine had children, and all were earning incomes within the normal range for the nation at

Attitudes on Treatment of the Retarded **223**

the time. Of the control group of twelve, one had died as an adolescent in an institution for the mentally retarded, three were still in the institution, one was in a mental hospital, and seven were out of the institution: of these last seven, two were married (one with a mentally retarded child). The median education for the control group was Grade 3. The eleven of the experimental group who were married had a total of twenty-eight children whose average IQ was 104, with none falling into the retarded range.

Another major series of studies demonstrating the impact of environment on tested intelligence took place in the early 1960s in a southeastern state in the U.S.A. In Prince Edward County, Virginia, the schools were closed for four years and 3000 children felt the impact: the average intelligence of children in the county fell into the retarded range, as much as a mean drop of 30 IQ points from pre-closing levels (Green, Hoffman, Morse, Hayes & Morgan 1964). We learned, dramatically, how much a child's expressed intelligence depends on the school (Green, Hoffman, Morse & Morgan 1965; Green, Hoffman & Morgan 1967; Green & Morgan 1969). A conservative estimate is that at least four of every five diagnosed cases of retardation are non-organic, that is, something went wrong in the child's environment. Since the mid-1960s, the literature has been overflowing with exciting new special or compensatory approaches to successful educational intervention with all children, including the retarded or disadvantaged (Pines 1966; Morgan 1969; Morgan & Toy 1970). Even more encouraging are the many viable prenatal and birthing interventions, nutritional to psychological, often classified as "wholistic health care" (Morgan 1977).

In 1971, the city and county of San Francisco's Department of Public Health distributed a weekly bulletin to the public on mental retardation which asserted: "Unlike mental disorders, mental retardation is an inevitable lifelong condition. Therefore, adjustment and acceptance rather than a return to normal functioning is the goal..." (Curry 1971). Was taxpayers' money being paid only to adjust people to their disorders rather than curing them? Actually, some of the psychologists working in the county system had some extremely effective programs going in which their clients did indeed reach normal functioning. Ultimately, the Department of Public Health retracted their statement of hopelessness. Unfortunately, many, if not most, structured public programs for mental retardation still set their goals only for clients' tranquility and behavioral adjustment while the very same disorder is often under successful attack only a county or a state or a province away.

Again, as long as the public is led to believe that progress is impossible, it becomes more difficult to bring the newest progress to them. The 1970s and 1980s have been times of increased efforts at primary prevention with, in addition, burgeoning local treatment programs in a variety of countries with varying cost. Probably the best publicized successful prevention project of recent years was the Milwaukee Project (Heber 1978) in which twenty high-risk (mothers' IQs less than 75) families received stimulation for newborn infants, as well as specialized training in child care and vocational rehabilitation for the mother. Infants received attention beginning in the first weeks of life, followed by a more formal intervention from three months of age until the beginning of public school. This program attempted to foster the "acquisition of cognitive skills and allow each child to develop socially, emotionally and physically . . . the program focused heavily on developing language and cognitive skills and on maintaining a positive and responsive learning environment . . . the social-emotional needs of the developing infant (were met) by providing a consistent one-to-one teacher/child relationship throughout the child's first year" (p. 49). By the mean age of five years, the tested intelligence of the experimental group's children averaged over 30 points ahead of the control group's children (121 vs 87). Language and behavioral skills also followed this differential pattern.

The first author has initiated and observed local programs designed to return the retarded and learning disabled to normal functioning throughout several countries. Communities often remain skeptical of new ideas until they can see the effects for themselves. Nova Scotia, for example, in its rural areas often had pockets of environmentally produced retardation: both parents would work during the day, leaving the infant in barren surroundings, physically safe but mentally unchallenged. Fresh information to parents went a long way toward correcting many of these consequent potential tragedies of environmental retardation.

The second author subsequently launched a pilot demonstration study for slower school-age children in Bridgewater, Nova Scotia, which is excerpted as follows.

The Bridgewater Project

A summer tutoring program for children with learning disabilities was evaluated using the Peabody Picture Vocabulary Test (Dunn 1965) for measured intelligence, the Vineland Social Maturity Scale (Doll 1965), and a school questionnaire. Pre- and post-testing of the Peabody Test used alternate Forms A and B. Initial testing took place at the program's beginning in the summer. Posttesting eight months later during the following April included interviews with both child and at least one parent.

The program dealt with eleven children chosen as those most needing immediate intervention to increase their probability of success in the coming school year. Some of the children chosen had clearly defined learning problems while others had been performing poorly in school. The eleven children were seven boys and four girls; age range six to fifteen years. Every child except one was behind in school at least one grade; several were behind three grades and one was behind five grades. Although not all the children in the program had other emotional problems, every child came from a home (and sometimes a school) in which the dynamics were clearly highly tension-ridden.

Shortly before the program began, the clinic social workers referred perspective tutors for interviews with the program coordinator. Seven tutors were chosen. Six of the seven were high school or college students while the seventh was a particularly capable parent. Six tutors were female and one male. Tutors were chosen on the basis of the following criteria: (1) display of patience and general relaxation, (2) some knowledge of school subjects with which children in the program were having difficulty, (3) interest and enjoyment of "Checkers" and "Snakes & Ladders."

Tutors were asked to meet with a child for two two-hour sessions per week for five weeks. Each tutor was encouraged to provide structure as required by the individual child. Sessions were held in private homes and community halls as well as at the local mental health centre. In every case tutors were encouraged to hold sessions outside the child's home.

Food treats were used to establish rapport and as a reward for successes. The importance of a low-tension environment was stressed for every tutoring situation. Perhaps somewhat in the spirit of A. S. Neill (1960), it was felt that for the short-term program sophisticated pedagogical methodology was of secondary importance compared to an atmosphere in which the child might enjoy learning. For example, an attempt was made to compensate for the lack of specialized reading equipment by developing a child's interest in being read to by the tutor. Extensive use was made of card games and other games which used mathematical concepts. Lastly, tutors used traditional methods of teaching and reviewing the regular grade school work of the children.

At the outset of the program contact was made with the Inspector of Schools of the area to involve the schools in the program. The intention of this activity was twofold: that the schools might be exposed to the goals and methods of the program and that the progress of the children in the program might be carried on into the school year with specific recommendations concerning each child communicated to the school principal and school teacher involved with each child. Both of these intentions were realized with the excellent cooperation of the school system.

Results

Ten of the eleven children in the program were available for evaluation. All but one showed an increase in tested intelligence: the median group IQ went from 76.5 ($\sigma = $ 12) to 97.0 ($\sigma = $ 14) in eight months. In the same time, the average gain in social maturity exceeded two years. The group went from dissatisfaction with school to enthusiastic satisfaction by the time of retesting. This summer program, which produced a median gain of 20 IQ points plus improved social and emotional well-being, cost a total of $1000 and conservatively saved the school system ten times that amount in unneeded extra grades and training. Parents and teachers all reported lasting improvements at home and at school.

For the purpose of this report two children are considered briefly. *Child Number one* was a sixteen-yr.-old male who showed a Social Maturity Development of 7.2 yr. in the eight months between program and evaluation. His tested IQ changed from 77 to 88. His attitude towards school was considerably more positive and his academic goals appeared to be considerably more realistic. It should be noted that in the case of this adolescent a central goal with which the program appeared to help was there were many areas in which he was quite adequate and he might relax about these. He is presently pursuing an academic program at the high school level with success whereas prior to his involvement in the eight-month program he was failing in a general program.

Child Number two was a twelve-year-old girl who had a specific learning problem in mathematics, as well as a particularly complicated and disturbed emotional background. Before the program her IQ was 76, and after the program 115. The first score is in the range of what would widely be considered retardation; the second score is in fact an above average IQ. Her social maturity development both before and after the program was reasonably consistent with her chronological age. In the evaluation interview as well as the post-test school questionnaire this child expressed enthusiasm both for school in general and for her mathematics class in particular. The child's mother reported that she is no longer a "loner," that she is mixing well with friends both at school and in the community and that relationships within the family have improved considerably. That this child was at great risk of having not only serious problems with school work but also serious personal emotional problems early last summer was very clear. At the moment this child is probably no longer at any risk; the rationale of the program was perhaps most successfully and most completely carried out between this child and her tutor, i.e., a relaxed tension-free learning experience based on a happy relationship between child and tutor, is most significant.

The second author's previously unpublished study was distributed locally and facilitated the upgrading of the self-fulfilling prophecies of the community, giving hope to the children not yet given access to any special programs. The study had no control group and followed a small number of children. But, for this community, it was more eloquent than any number of distinguished publications by Skeels, Green, Heber or others.

Returning now to the first author's colloquium experience, the discussion of what was possible takes on new meaning. In a recent study (Morgan 1978), it was demonstrated that half of a sample of psychologists polled (and 90% of the physicians) made the iatrogenic (harmful) error of asserting the null hypothesis, of insisting that something was impossible to cure. Not only, in this probabilistic world, is this a logical absurdity, but in the face of research and treatment advances, it is distinctly unfair and misleading to local cummunities. Lulled by unscientific experts promoting defeatism, the real issues of cost-effectiveness and program-effectiveness need not be faced.

Ironically, the move away from institutionalization may bypass a potential new role for previously custodial, largely counter-productive institutions for the mentally retarded. One survival role for institutional staff would be intense but short-term treatment (e.g., six months) with superb staffing ratios and high quality treatment methods. The initial expense would be more than counter-balanced by the funds saved through the return of the client to normal functioning. Of course, the non-institutional industry giving community treatment might suffer consequent unemployment for it depends on life-time clients. This seems a small and worthwhile price, obviously, to pay for the ending of a mentally disabled social class.

The colloquium speaker wound up his presentation by insisting that the retarded must always be with us since intelligence is normally distributed in the population and there will always be a bottom percentile. Here the relative was confused with the absolute: the bottom percentile need not be so dysfunctional as to be deserving of the 'retarded' label if the population improves its basic cognitive skills.

Postscript—The preceding material has emphasized the iatrogenic practices worthy of avoidance. For those more interested in delineation of positive treatment which involves effective strategies, the recent book by Feuerstein (1980) is one of the best examples. There are two new journals, *Applied Research in Mental Retardation* and *Analysis and Intervention in Developmental Disabilities,* which are contemporary sources for evidence of change and new techniques for bringing about intellectual change.

BIBLIOGRAPHY

Analysis and Intervention in Developmental Disabilities. New York: Pergamon, 1981.

Applied Research in Mental Retardation: A Multidisciplinary Journal. New York: Pergamon, 1981.

Curry, F. J. Mental retardation program. Weekly Bulletin, City and County of San Francisco, Department of Public Health. (December 27, 1971):1.

Doll, E. A. *Vineland Social Maturity Scale.* Circle Pines, MN: American Guidance Service, 1965.

Dunn, L. M. *Peabody Picture Vocabulary Test.* Circle Pines, MN: American Guidance Service, 1965.

Feuerstein, R. *Instrumental enrichment: an intervention program for cognitive modifiability.* Baltimore, MD: University Park Press, 1980.

Green, R. L., L. J. Hoffman and R. F. Morgan. The effects of deprivation on intelligence, achievement, and cognitive growth: a review. *Journal of Negro Education* 36 (1967):5-14.

Green, R. L., L. J. Hoffman, R. J. Morse, M. Hayes and R. F. Morgan. *The educational status of children in a district without public schools.* Washington, D.C.: United States Office of Education, 1964. (Cooperative Research Project 2321 Report.)

Green, R. L., L. J. Hoffman, R. J. Morse and R. F. Morgan. *The educational status of children during the first school year following four years of little or no schooling.* Washington, D.C.: United States Office of Education, 1965. (Cooperative Research Project 2498 Report.)

Green, R. L. and R. F. Morgan. The effects of resumed schooling on the measured intelligence of Prince Edward County's black children. *Journal of Negro Education* 38 (1969):147-155.

Grossman, H. J., ed. *Manual on terminology and classification in mental retardation.* Washington, D.C.:

American Association on Mental Deficiency, 1973. (Special Publication Series, No. 2.)

Heber, F. R. Socio-cultural mental retardation: a longitudinal study. In *Primary prevention of psychopathology.* Vol. II. *Environmental influences,* edited by D. G. Forgays, 39-62. Hanover, NH: University Press of New England, 1978.

Jensen, A. R. Cumulative deficit in IQ of blacks in the rural South. *Developmental Psychology* 13 (1977): 184-191.

Morgan, R. F. Compensatory education and educational growth. In *Racial crisis in American education,* edited by R. L. Green, 186-219. Chicago: Follett, 1969.

——. *Conquest of aging: modern measurement and intervention,* 2d ed. Pueblo, CO: Applied Gerontology Communications, 1977.

——. The iatrogenic psychology of practitioners' defeatism and other assertions of the null hypothesis. *Psychological Reports* 43 (1978):963-977.

Morgan, R. F. and T. B. Toy. Learning by teaching: a student-to-student compensatory tutoring program and the Educational Cooperative. *Psychological Record* 20 (1970): 159-169.

Neill, A. S. *Summerhill: a radical approach to child rearing.* New York: Hart, 1960.

Pines, M. *Revolution in learning: the years from birth to six.* New York: Harper & Row, 1966.

Skeels, H. M. Adult status of children with contrasting early life experiences. *Monograph of the Society for Research in Child Development* 31, no. 3 (1966).

Skeels, H. M. and M. Skodak. Techniques for a high yield follow-up in the field. *Public Health Reports* 80 (1965):249-257.

Skeels, H. M., R. Updegraff, B. L. Wellman and H. M. Williams. A study of environmental stimulation: an orphanage preschool project. *University of Iowa Studies in Child Welfare* 15, no. 4 (1938).

Wechsler, D. *Wechsler Intelligence Scale for Children,* revised. New York: Psychological Corp., 1974.

KENNETH WALKER

18

The Doctor Game: Reflections of a Canadian Physician

Kenneth Walker is a gynecologist and surgeon in private practice in Niagara Falls, Ontario, and the much acclaimed author of *What Every Woman Should Know About Hysterectomy* (New York: Harper & Row, 1977), *The Doctor Game* (Toronto: McClelland & Stewart, 1975), *On Being a Woman: The Modern Woman's Guide to Gynecology* (Toronto: Macmillan/McClelland & Stewart, 1969) and magazine articles in *Maclean's*, *Chatelaine* and others. His most prominent input to the public is via a weekly syndicated newspaper column *The Doctor Game*, under the pseudonym "W. Gifford-Jones." Only the name is pseudo: for years now, Walker has candidly and informatively given the medical consumers reading his column valuable inside information and cautions. The column itself has become a widely respected hedge against iatrogenesis, a prevention effort of some probable national impact. With Dr. Walker's permission, we have chosen two of his recent articles on representative iatrogenic issues. The point that I hope is made by Walker's approach goes beyond the specific content of the articles but rather is the power of his particular methodology and style: such media communiques can potentially (given sufficient courage, candor and data) be a powerful anti-iatrogenic technique. **R.F.M.**

Modern medical treatment can be worse than ailment

Which would be easier? Peddling refrigerators to Eskimos? Or selling a medical column to the Christian Science Monitor? This idea tickled me during a recent visit to Boston. Since my days as a student at the Harvard Medical School I've had great respect for this newspaper. Regrettably it doesn't share my enthusiasm for modern medicine. But medical consumers can learn something from my visit to this Boston newspaper.

I may be burned at the stake by my colleagues for saying so. But my office tells me daily that over-medicated Canadians need an injection of this faith. That the scale is presently tipping in favor of the positive thinking of Christian Science. That, in fact, Christian Scientists may have better solutions for some contemporary medical problems.

The medicine you don't get these days is often more beneficial than the drugs you receive. In 1673 J. B. Moliere, writing in *Le Malade Imaginaire*, said, "Nearly all men die of their medicines, not of their diseases." And Napoleon, talking to his physician at St. Helena in 1817 remarked, "Take a dose of medicine once and in all probability you will be obliged to take an additional hundred afterwards."

What problems do Christian Scientists avoid? Sometimes they're life-saving situations. For instance, several years ago three healthy students in the U.S. were given antibiotics. They subsequently developed a virulent form of anemia and died.

One was given the drug for a simple acne. Another for an infected mosquito bite. The third for a sore throat. What a tragedy when all three could have survived without any medication at all.

Consider that between 200 and 300 people die every year in the U.S. from penicillin reaction. Many are needless deaths and probably few are Christian Scientists. Most infected throats are the result of a virus and antibiotics won't kill viruses. But today about one-third of patients who visit a doctor for a cold or sore throat leave the office with an antibiotic prescription.

Christian Scientists don't fall prey to questionable surgery. I'd prefer to adopt this faith rather than have a scalpel needlessly remove my gallbladder, uterus or tonsils.

Some questionable surgery results in death. Or complications and prolonged hospital stay.

Members of the faith will surely avoid the hazards of a recent surgical fad. Betty Ford, wife of the former U.S. President, acquired a new face through cosmetic surgery about a year ago. Her publicized facelift prompted many other women to undergo similar treatment.

No doubt some were pleased with the immediate results. Others suffered unforeseen complications. A few were probably shocked at the sight of their new aquiline nose. Later, the cruel truth will become apparent slowly. Such new faces last only four to eight years.

But how should medical consumers interpret these remarks? Should you toss your pills down the drain? Politely tell the doctor to go fishing? Convert to Christian Science? Or is there a better way?

Consumers might take a lesson from the business world. We know that amalgamation can make companies stronger and more competitive. Why shouldn't the same concept work in medical care? Some of the Christian Science determination to avoid our medical cures is sound. We should incorporate this benefit into conventional medicine. It would give everyone a more realistic view of disease.

Consumers must first lower expectations about medications. There may be miracles in Heaven but none on earth. So don't count on miracle drugs for every ailment. Don't judge your doctor by the number of tests and X-rays he orders. Swallow instead some of the Christian Science philosophy of positive thinking.

Did the newspaper agree to publish the column? I'd have been wiser to try selling refrigerators to the Eskimos. But it helped to get me into shape for my next column. Trying to alert Canadians to the dangers of overmedication.

Barnum often remarked, "There's a sucker born every minute."

Hundreds of useless over-the-counter medical products purchased every day attest to this fact.

Many provide no beneficial results at all. Some are even hazardous to health or cause unrelated complications. Nevertheless, people are convinced that popping a pill of some sort will solve their problems.

Next week I'll discuss how some unconscionable pharmaceutical companies are publicly preaching hazardous medical nonsense. And why your entire family should laugh the newest advertising gimmick off the TV screen.

TV, radio ads could kill your kidneys

What will happen if Canadians allow the TV tube to become their doctor? Today pharmaceutical companies are selling hazardous medical nonsense on TV. They're urging the public, young and old, to take extra-strength painkillers for everyday use.

But they never mention the terrifying complications of this habit for human kidneys.

Consumers should laugh dangerous commercials off the TV screen. And the Canadian Medical Association should mount a massive protest against such unconscionable advertising.

The CMA might emphasize a major discrepancy. Physicians are required to caution patients of possible complications during medical treatment. But TV and radio commercials never warn the public that painkillers can cause severe kidney damage.

No mention is made of the Australian disaster. Statistics show the Aussies to be the greatest pill poppers in the world. Now many are paying a terrible price for their folly. Twenty-five per cent of patients on renal dialysis machines in Australia are there for one reason. Painkillers damaged their kidneys.

Renal failure in the past was usually due to generalized disease. For example, diabetes often accelerates atherosclerosis which gradually destroys kidney function. It's still a major health problem.

But in 1953 Drs. Spuhler and Zollinger made a startling discovery. They observed that many middle-aged women were developing renal failure. Yet these patients didn't have an underlying medical disease.

There was just one clue. They had all consumed excessive amounts of painkillers.

It was initially believed that phenacetin was the culprit. This drug was removed from all products in Australia in 1967. Canada followed suit in 1971. It's still available in parts of the U.S. without a prescription. But taking phenacetin off the market in Australia didn't stop kidney damage.

It left doctors with one conclusion. Any common painkiller taken in excess is bad for kidneys.

How many painkillers do Canadians consume? We know that North Americans gulped down several thousand tons in 1979. But individual

Reprinted with permission of the author.

consumption is hard to calculate. Like alcohol consumption, it is underestimated by most people.

The wily Swiss dreamed up a clever scheme to evaluate usage. They refused to believe the answers of female factory workers. So each day they searched company garbage cans for empty wrappers. Their survey concluded that 30 per cent of working women took more than five tablets a day.

How many 300 milligram (mg) tablets are needed to produce renal damage? Dr. Priscilla Kincaid-Smith is an authority on kidney disease. She noted that Australians on dialysis machines have taken painkillers for three or more years.

Extra-strength tablets contain 500 mg and the latest advertised on TV contain 800 mg. Taking two tablets of the strongest dosages every four hours adds up to 9600 mg. Doctors know that 20,000 can be a fatal dose.

Can you protect yourself and your family from the perils of over-the-counter painkillers? First ask yourself what you would do if you were an advertiser with a captive TV audience and a huge budget to hire professionals. As well as a gullible public which wants to believe that aspirin, entrophen, anacin and instantine are all different when they all contain acetylacedic acid.

Today's naive consumer even accepts the theory that one brand is better than another because it dissolves a few seconds faster.

Businessmen don't moralize when the marketplace offers such a profitable return. It's much easier to retor, "You can't be your brother's keeper. The nation is full of assorted pains and people seek help." Currently, there's only one response to this. Decline that kind of "help."

Don't let TV ads insult your intelligence. Who cares how fast a painkiller dissolves? Never purchase a product just because it has extra strength. The greater the potency the more the risk of renal damage.

Don't buy painkillers in bottles of 500 unless you have a chronic arthritic problem. The larger bottle and the ability to purchase it anywhere is a hazardous trend. It gives the impression that painkillers are like peppermint candy.

The Canadian Medical Association should inform the government of its concern. But consumers should help themselves by making it a national pastime to laugh at pill pushing TV commercials. A big laugh would save some small kidneys.

ROBERT F. MORGAN

19

Shock Treatment I: Resistance in the 1960s

During the 1940s, shock treatment was regularly used, often en masse, in the majority of North American psychiatric institutions. Throughout the 1950s, this inexpensive and dramatic treatment bridged the gap between dwindling lobotomies and the armament from pharmacology. In the 1960s, alternate drug treatments, behavioral treatments and even humanistic approaches allowed the resistance to shock treatment to grow. By the end of the 1960s, psychiatry was evenly split, psychology largely opposed and even proponents of ECT were largely confining their usage to specified problems (e.g., depression). In practice, however, the treatment was often used punitively, generating predictable resistance from fresh quarters.

The first article to follow was a research proposal, never funded, used as discussion material for the staff of Hawaii State Hospital. It stakes out an extreme position but one that data over the years has increasingly supported: short-term benefits of ECT, even properly applied, are outweighed by side effects and long-term disability risks.

Not that ECT was often properly applied. In my first week at the hospital a genuinely dedicated ward nurse asked my consent to have a patient shocked for failing to mow the lawns three days running. He sought my backup for what to him was disciplinary parenting. I asked him why he didn't punch the patient in the nose. "That wouldn't be ethical!" he said. I responded that using the treatment for punishment wasn't ethical either (not knowing until after some study that it was probably unethical under *any* conditions). The staff supported this point of view and ECT was abandoned during my year on that ward, with no apparent harm to the residents. When I left, however, the administrative psychiatrist brought it right back. Obviously rhetoric fluctuated with the presence or absence of the debators: data was needed. The second study reflects more of the pilot data approach often used in the 1960s. We learned ECT was given primarily to those most unlike the givers, and to those who hit the staff; it was not given to the suicidal depressives in any consistent pattern. The 1960s, known for struggle and social change, included ECT as a battleground.   **R.F.M.**

The Isolation, Description, and Treatment of the Pathological Behavior of ECT-Damaged Patients

Introduction

As clinical treatment of mental illness has steadily evolved in the direction of therapy and rehabilitation, it has necessarily moved away from the destructive tools and practices of custodial imprisonment. It is somewhat of a paradox then that many widely publicized therapeutic tools of the first *non*custodial hospitals have turned out to be powerful instruments of custody rather than cure. Lobotomies, for example, were once hailed as the Treatment which would empty mental hospitals. Lobotomized patients remained aware of their pain and anxieties but no longer cared about them. They were able to return to society much calmer than when they had left it. The general public readily accepted such brain surgery since mental illness was obviously a malfunction of the head and should be cut away. Soon, however, lobotomized patients began returning to the hospitals. Their concentration, memory, comprehension, all seemed to be impaired. Embarrassingly, many had retained their delusions and obsessions even at their surgically reduced intellectual and emotional levels. When it was generally realized that lobotomies changed curable acutes to uncurable chronics, this surgical tool passed from use as therapy to use as an emergency control. A patient suspected of suicidal intentions might be lobotomized "for his own good" while a psychotic patient attacking the staff or continually escaping would be lobotomized for the "greater good of others." The advent of effective tranquilizers and more enlightened staff attitudes coupled with the rise of psychotherapy and the vocational therapies eventually led the lobotomy to pass into oblivion. In the light of clinical history it stands out more as a cause of pathological behavior than a cure.

It remains today as a treatment of choice for none but a few surviving senior citizens of psychiatry. Like euthanasia or mercy killing, the solution offered to custodial problems by lobotomy was at too high a human cost.

The Rise and Fall of ECT

From Cure to Control to Cause of Mental Illness

When electro-convulsive therapy (ECT) was introduced several decades ago, it too took the psychiatric world by storm. Unlike lobotomy, no complex brain surgery was required, the cost was minimal, the administration so simple that any competent staff member could be trained to administer it. Furthermore, the behavioral results were every bit as promising as those of lobotomy. Violent patients, severely depressed patients, paranoid schizophrenics . . . all responded to shock with varying degrees of calmness and manageability. In relatively short periods of time, patients were on their feet again and a good many returned to function on the outside. And, although there were initial signs of confusion and memory loss, there was no obvious mental impairment such as had been seen with lobotomies. Electric shock worked side by side with insulin shock and drug therapy to clear the hospitals of most of their *"problem"* patients. Yet, today, a review of ECT's therapeutic effectiveness begins with:

> A recent review of shock therapy in the United States since its introduction in 1937 until 1956 leads the authors to conclude that the era of shock therapy is fast drawing to a close. (Riddell 1963)

Research in the last decade since 1956 has hastened that close. What went wrong?

When ECT patients began to filter back to the hospitals, psychiatric research devoted itself to investigating the question of therapeutic effectiveness. Riddell (1963) discusses these studies which were experimentally sound. The results included:

1. ECT was often found insignificant in effect even for immediate improvement in behavior. D. Miller et al. (1953) compared ECT with pentothal anesthetic. The psychoses remained, the incidence of hallucinations increased, but staff-rated ward behavior improved with both treatments. D. Naidoo (1956) compared ECT with placebo (phony) shock for chronic schizophrenics. There was no significant difference in weekly psychiatric assessment of improvement. N. Brill et al. (1959) compared ECT with anesthetic for ninety-seven schizophrenics and depressives. There were no significant differences in rated improvement. E. Goller (1960) compared ECT with non-ECT group for chronic schizophrenics. Psychiatric assessed improvement showed no significant differences.

2. ECT appeared immediately effective, when effective at all, only for depressives and not for schizophrenics. M. Shapiro et al. (1958) showed significantly better improvement on rated behavior for depressives having ECT as opposed to those depressives not having ECT. Psychomotor speed of the ECT group, however, was retarded. D. Langsley et al. (1959) found schizophrenics having ECT to show no better improvement than those having drugs. The ECT group remained in the hospital longer. L. Kiloh et al. (1960) found reactive depressives to show more immediate improvement with ECT than a control group without it. S. Riddell (1963) summarized the literature and decided the evidence was that ECT was not therapeutic for schizophrenics but did offer immediate relief for depressives.

3. ECT seemed immediately therapeutic only for a certain type of depressive. B. Ackner and O. Grant (1960) found ECT effective only for clear-cut endogenous depressives showing depersonalization.

4. Drug therapy appeared to be just as therapeutic as ECT without ECT's side effects. G. Ulett et al. (1956) found secobarbital patients showed significantly less confusion than ECT patients after a six-month follow up although both treatments had been initially effective. L. Ciulla (1960) found Tofranil, an anti-depressant drug, to be equally as effective as ECT in pulling depressives out of serious melancholia. H. Delgade (1960) found both Tofranil and ECT to be 50% effective in reducing melancholia in depressives with no apparent side effects from Tofranil.

Thus ECT seemed therapeutically effective only as an immediate agent for dealing with melancholia in depersonalized depressives, i.e., a suicide preventer. Although certain drugs could give the same results, ECT was generally preferred due to its ease of application and its calming effect on violent behavior.

Side effects of ECT
It would still be a treatment of choice for melancholia, if nothing else, if it hadn't been for the *side effects* mentioned previously. We will now turn to these. The following studies used a total of from one to fifteen shocks per patient.

Non-ECT seizures (spontaneous convulsions) become more likely. French et al. (1956) found ECT to selectively depress threshold for seizures in the central nervous system.

Death from stress ulcers and renal disease. Selzer (1963) lost a thirty-year-old schizophrenic to a hemorrhaging ulcer after the third ECT treatment.

Speed and coordination become retarded. Shapiro (1958) and Hardi (1958) found handwriting of ECT patients more primitive and uncoordinated after a single ECT treatment.

Retrograde amnesia (Lewis & Adams 1963; McGaugh & Madsen 1964; Lewis & Maher 1965).

Reduced concentration and attention span (Tecce & Tarrell 1965).

Impaired learning from damage to limbic centers of brain (Hudspeth & Gerbrandt 1965).

Impaired response flexibility and retention (Williams 1960; Cronholm & Ortoson 1961; Cronholm & Molander 1961).

Eventual ablation of the limbic system in the brain. Flynn, MacLean & Kim (1961) found ECT with repetition becomes in effect a limbic *lobotomy*.

Generalized fear of the hospital setting ECT given in Lewis & Adams (1963) found may be covert but effectively blocks most psychotherapy.

Confusion lasting at least six months following ECT (Ulett et al. 1956).

A significantly longer stay in the hospital (Langsley et al. 1959).

Lack of immediate response to re-educative therapy (Mitsos 1960).

Lack of immediate response to psychotherapy was due to all of these but especially reduced concentration and attention span; impaired learning; impaired response flexibility and retention; fear of hospital setting; and confusion lasting at least six months.

In summary, even one or two ECT treatments risk limbic damage in the brain leading to retarded speed, coordination, handwriting, concentration, attention span, memory, response flexibility, retention and re-education. On the psychological side, fear of ECT has produced stress ulcers, renal disease, confusion, amnesic withdrawal and resistance to re-educative or psychological therapy. The research thus indicated that ECT was a slower acting lobotomy with the added complications of shock-induced terror. As with lobotomy, to use it facilitated custody, but damaged therapy. For the sake of the patient's present (or the staff's), his future was sacrificed.

Reasons for maintaining ECT

ECT has not yet vanished from the picture. If it does risk serious brain damage and psychological damage, there must be powerful reasons for maintaining it. Let's look at some of them.

Professional investment—Many psychiatrists spent years of practice administering ECT: some psychiatric interns learned little else. As with those now aged practitioners still clinging to lobotomies, there is a natural reluctance to face the research data suggesting that their therapy has been destructive.

ECT as punishment—We have already discussed the fact that most patients fear ECT (Crumpton et al. 1963). Hospital staffs have not been lax in making the most use of this fear to motivate desired behavior. In other terms, it's like whipping a child for disobedience. The results are the same. Immediate compliance but big trouble in the long run. Apart from the efficacy of severe punishment as a motivator, the serious danger of brain damage has diminished the realization of use of ECT as a maintenance tool in the more progressive hospitals. On the basis of the research cited so far, it would seem the problem child is being more than whipped; he's being crippled.

ECT as retribution—Rabiner *et al.* (1961) found that those patients chosen for ECT were highest on a doctor-patient, tension-level scale given the administering psychiatrist. In other words, patients liked the least by the doctor are most likely to get ECT. It is also common knowledge in many hospitals that any patient who physically damages an aide or other staff member is typically on the ECT table within a week or two.

ECT as suicide prevention—In a drastically understaffed, underspaced hospital with insufficient psychotherapy or drug therapy programs to deal effectively with suicide risks, ECT is typically still a well-used weapon in the ward arsenal. The understanding is that hitting the patient over the head with the ECT club confuses him so much so that he forgets to do away with himself. This frequently works. However, most hospitals are now exploring other less damaging ways of dealing with suicide attempts; ones that don't sacrifice the mind to save the body. The use of seclusion rooms, immediate one-to-one psychotherapy, a special attention ward for such patients, a single staff member trained in suicide prevention to take on all such cases, etc., are some of these avenues.

ECT as treatment in the absence of knowledge of its side effects—It is sometimes true that important research takes a lot of time to filter down to the action levels of treatment. ECT and lobotomy never had to survive the rigorous checks most drugs must pass before use. Even in the latter case, it is sometimes too tragically long between administration of a drug and knowledge of the damaging side effects. A hospital staff using ECT in the absence of knowledge of its side effects is much in the position of those doctors who prescribed Thalidomide as a tranquilizer for pregnant women before the first malformed babies were born. As the ECT research becomes more widely disseminated it should continue to decrease the frequency of use. A doctor now giving Thalidomide to a pregnant patient would be hard pressed to justify himself on the grounds that its the most effective tranquilizer available and besides, she was keeping everyone up at night.

Where to from here?

Impistate 1962 tells us that while drug therapy has to a large extent replaced ECT, the latter has not been completely replaced. Thus, for the near future anyway, there will be some continued use of shock therapy for the patient population. The recipients of this treatment, as we've seen, undergo as a direct result a variety of tissue and behavioral disorders. Often these specific effects of ECT are confused with the behavior complexes of already established mental illnesses. It is suggested by the literature and by observation that ECT-damaged patients exhibit unique behavior disorders which should not be diagnosed as schizophrenic, psychoneurotic, etc. For example, a common complaint among ECT-damaged patients is one of inability to remember *or* relearn material from the classroom that, prior to treatment, had been well mastered. Three other common complaints are the inability to concentrate on the job, amnesia and convulsive fits. Observers often view these patients as flighty, undependable and angry without apparent reason. It is suggested here that ECT damage be investigated and treated in its own right as an important mental impairment.

Method

Before adequate treatment methods are to be explored, a more systematic collection of the behaviors associated with ECT-damage will be undertaken. While there is an almost unlimited number of psychological assessment measures which could be administered, it would be best to begin with observational accounts of patient behaviors and to draw which tests would be appropriate from these. Accordingly, the following four groups of ten patients each will be described as to daily ward behavior by two staff members who have been in a position to observe them:

Group I: Patients who have had less than ten ECT treatments with none in the last year.

Group II: Patients who have had more than ten ECT treatments with none in the last year.

Group III: Patients who have never had ECT (or lobotomy) but have the same diagnosis as patients in Group I.

Group IV: Patients who have never had ECT (or lobotomy) but have the same diagnosis as patients in Group II.

The latter two groups, of course, are control groups to separate the effects of the diagnosed illness from ECT damage. Comparing groups I and II separates the excessively shocked from normally shocked patients. Instruments will then be constructed around the behavioral observations seemingly unique to the ECT groups. Should these be validated on a fresh four groups, we would then have isolated the undesirable behaviors which the proper therapy would be expected to alter. It is assumed that some form of psychotherapy or re-educative therapy, perhaps built upon radically new lines, will significantly aid the ECT-damaged patients to deal with life more successfully despite their handicap. It is also possible that neuro-surgery and neurological psychiatry may one day be able to restore the damaged sections of the limbic system and undo the pathological effects of the once well-intentioned electro-convulsive therapy.

BIBLIOGRAPHY

Ackner, B. and O. Grant. The prognostic significance of depersonalization in depressive illnesses treated with ECT. *J. neurol. neurosurg. Psychiat.* 23 (1960):242-246.

Brill, N., E. Crumpton, S. Eiduson, H. Grayson, L. Hillman and R. Richards. Relative effectiveness of various components of ECT. *Arch. neurol. Psychiat.* 81 (1959):627-635.

Cronholm, B. and L. Molander. Memory disturbances after ECT. *Acta psychiat., neurol. Scand.* 36 (1961):83-90.

Cronholm, B. and J. Ottoson. Memory functions in endogenous depression: before and after ECT. *Arch. gen. Psychiat.* 1961 5 193-199.

Crumpton, E., N. Brill, S. Eiduron and E. Galler. The role of fear in electroconvulsive treatment. *J. nerv. ment. Dis.* 136 (1963):29-33.

Ciulla, L. Roundtable contribution on treatment with Tofranil. *J. Brasil Psiquist.* 9 (1960):70-99.

Delgado, H. The treatment of melancholia. *Rev. Neuro-Psiquist,* Lima 23 (1960):291-300.

Flynn, MacLean and Kim. Effects of hippocampal after discharges on conditioned response. In *Electric stimulation of the brain,* edited by D. Sheer. Austin: University of Texas Press, 1961.

French, J., B. Gernandt and R. Livingston. Regional differences in seizures susceptibility in monkey cortex. *AMA Arch. neurol. Psychiat.* 75 (1956):260-274.

Goller, E. A controlled trial of Reserpine in chronic schizophrenia. *J. Ment. Sci.* 106 (1960):1408-1412.

Hardi, I. Handwriting observations after EST. *Przichol. Taynlmanyok* 1 (1958):303-309.

Hudspeth, W. and L. Gerbrandt. Electro-convulsive shock: conflict, competition, consolidation and neuro-anatomical functions. *Psychol. Bull.* 63 (1965):377-383.

Impistato, D. Effects of drug therapy on the frequency of ECT. *Amer. J. Psychother.* 16 (1962):387-396.

Kiloh, L. G., J. Child and G. Latney. Controlled trial of Ipronionizid in the treatment of endogenous depression. *J. ment. Sci.* 106 (1960):1139-1144.

Langsley, D., J. Enterline and G. Hickerson. A comparison of chlorpromazine and EST in treatment of acute schizophrenic and manic reactions. *Arch. neurol. Psychiat.* 81 (1959):384-391.

Lewis, D. and H. Adams. Retrograde amnesia from conditional competing response. *Science* 141 (1963):516-517.

Lewis, D. and B. Maher. Neural consolidation and electroconvulsive shock. *Psychol. Rev.* 72 (1965):225-239.

McGaugh, J. and M. Madsen. Amnesic and punishing effects of ECT. *Science* 144 (1964):182-183.

Miller, D. J. Clancy and E. Cumming. A comparison between unidirectional current nonconvulsive electrical stimulation given with Reiter's machine, standard alternating current electroshock (Ecletti method) and pentothal in chronic schizophrenia. *Amer. J. Psychiat.* 109 (1953):617-620.

Mitsos, S. Learning in the post-ECT period. *J. Clin. Psychol.* 16 (1960):187-189.

Naidoo, D. The effects of Reserpine on the chronic disturbed schizophrenic: a comparative study of alkaloids and ECT. *J nerv. ment. Dis.* 123 (1956):1-13.

Pronko, N., R. Sitterly and K. Berg. Twenty years of shock therapy in America, 1937-1956: an annotated bibliography. *Genet. Psychol. Monogr.* 62 (1960):233-329.

Rabiner, E., M. Reiser, J. Silverburg and L. Schacht. Method of assaying doctor-patient tensions: its application in assessing the role of tensions in the choice of electroshock. *Arch. gen. Psychiat.* 4 (1961):533-560.

Riddell, S. The therapeutic efficacy of ECT: a review of literature. *Arch. Gen. Psychiat.* 8 (1963):546-556.

Selzer, M. Stress ulcers and Renal disease following ECT. *Psychiat. Quarterly* 37 (1963):509-517.

Shapiro, M., D. Campbell, A. Harier and J. Deursberg. Effects of ECT on psychomotor speed and the distraction effect in depressed psychotic patients. *J. Ment. Sci.* 104 (1958):681-695.

Tecce, J. and M. Tarrell. Focal and incidental movement time as a function of shock-arousal in humans. *J. Psychol.* 59 (1965):155-158.

Ulett, G., K. Smith and G. Gleser. Evaluation of convulsive and subconvulsive shock therapies utilizing a control group. *Amer. J. Psychiat.* 112 (1956):795-802.

Williams, L. N. The effect of ECT on response flexibility and retention. *Diss. Abstr.* 20 (1960):4734.

Relationship of Ethnic Background, Religion, Diagnosis, Memory and Other Variables to Presence of Shock Therapy
History for a Sample of Hospitalized Mental Patients: Preliminary Investigation of the Lasting Effects of Shock Treatment on Behavior[1]

Abstract—One hundred twenty seven male hospitalized mental patients, aged twenty to fifty, were compared on the basis of prior shock treatment experience. None were brain damaged, lobotomized or had had shock within a year (since lasting effects of shock were the focus of interest). The data suggest *S*s were significantly less likely to have had a shock treatment history if they were nonschizophrenic, Catholic, under thirty years and employed prior to hospital admission; *S*s were significantly more likely to have had shock if they were diagnosed schizophrenics (particularly catatonics), without religion, over thirty-five, unemployed prior to hospital admission and of Japanese ethnic background (Filipino, Hawaiian, Chinese, Korean, U.S. Caucasian ethnic groups showed no significant differences). Marital status, educational level, history of severe depression or suicide attempts were not significantly related to presence or absence of shock. A miniature experiment on Digit Span memory, tested and retested, showed for four matched pairs of *S*s drawn from the sample, greater mean gains for *S*s without shock history. Seemingly fruitful measures and procedures for further research are discussed.

Although a recent review of shock treatment or ECT[2] in the United States from 1937 to 1956 led the author to conclude "the era of shock therapy is fast coming to a close" (Riddell 1963), such an end has yet to arrive. Nor is the field of mental health free of its past influence. Morgan (1966) felt ECT leads to permanent neurological and psychological damage with resultant behavior change that is potentially detectable by established psychological measures. Mednick (1955), Flynn, MacLean and Kim (1961), among many others (Geller 1965), have progressed toward validating and identifying this neurological damage, much of which centers on the limbic system. Since this latter area is associated with memory function, behavior checks and observations have typically dealt with immediate memory impairment following ECT. However, Morgan (1966) suggests that the *permanent* effects of ECT be investigated with populations having at least one year between them and their last ECT. Despite the evidence for permanent brain damage as a result of ECT, permanent behavioral consequences have yet to be adequately explored, although generally they are categorically denied by ECT practitioners.

This preliminary study is a first step towards such an investigation.

Sample and Procedure

In July of 1966, the active files of patients currently admitted to Hawaii State Hospital were examined for the following criteria: males between the ages of twenty to fifty who were not diagnosed as brain damaged (nor lobotomized) *nor had had ECT within the last year.* In addition, the records on prior ECT history had to have been available. A total of 127 patients fit this description.

Of these, eighty-three had a history of at least one shock treatment (group median was twenty treatments) and forty-four had no previous history of ECT. Both groups were examined by variables of age, number of treatments, marital status, education, ethnic background, religion, diagnosis, evidence of severe depression and/or suicide attempts and employment prior to admission.

Of the 127 patient sample, thirty-five had been interviewed on a wide variety of behavioral measures for an ongoing research venture at Hawaii State Hospital (Katz, Gudeman and Sanborn 1966). It was decided to investigate patients tested on these measures to take advantage of the substantial amount of additional data that will therefore eventually be available on these Ss. (These data have, at this time, not yet become available.) Of the tested sub-sample of thirty-five, admitted from 10/65 to 6/66, by July of 1966 the number of patients without a history of ECT had dropped from thirteen to four (a drop due both to discharge and to newly innovated exposure to ECT). The four patients without a history of ECT were matched as closely as possible on education and age with four members of the ECT group having a number of treatments within the modal range of their group (ten to eighteen treatments). It was hoped that matching for education and age would help control their influence on the cognitive measures to be made. (Mean sub-group ages were twenty-nine and thirty; mean education levels were 10.1 years and 10.6 years; the latter figure is that of the ECT sub-group.) The four members of the ECT sub-group averaged a history of thirteen shock treatments and a range of ten to eighteen treatments.

Using the Peabody Vocabulary Test (PPVT), IQ was tested on the eight Ss on July 26 and retested on July 28, two days later. Tests used were PPVT Form B and Retest Form A. A mean IQ of eighty-three for the No ECT sub-group and seventy-four for the ECT sub-group (medians were just the opposite at seventy-four and eighty-two respectively). Thus the two sub-groups seemed relatively close in average IQ performance. On July 26, following the IQ test, the Digit Span Test of the Wechsler Adult Intelligence Scale was administered to the four pairs of patients. The same test was readministered on July 28 following the alternate form of the IQ test.

Results

Results of the analysis of records for the full sample:

1. Members of the ECT group averaged 5½ years older (a statistically significant difference) despite the restricted age range of the full sample (ages twenty to fifty). Shock treatment may actually be a fading phenomenon.

2. Of the full sample, the median number of shock treatments was eleven; for only those patients receiving ECT, the median dosage was twenty treatments (range was 1 to 293).

3. Of the full sample, 87% were not and had never been married. This percentage did not differ significantly between ECT and No ECT groups.

4. Of the full sample, the average education was 10.9 years. This average did not differ significantly between ECT and No ECT groups.

5. Of the full sample, the largest ethnic minority was the Japanese at 43%. Percentage-wise, twice as many Japanese were in the ECT group as those in the No ECT group. This was the only statistically significant finding along ethnic lines. It is tempting to speculate that some connection exists between this finding and the significant hospital-specific belligerence of the Japanese patients discussed in the paper by Katz et al. (1966).

6. The religious categories of Catholic, Protestant, Buddhist and No Religion account for 96% of the sample. Significantly more Catholics fail to be in the ECT group than those patients of the No Religion group.

7. Schizophrenics, 91% of the full sample, were significantly more often found in the ECT group than non-schizophrenics. Within schizophrenic diagnostic categories, there were three times more catatonics shocked than any other brand (paranoid, hebephrenic, etc.).

8. Of the full sample, only one patient was diagnosed as a depressive. Therefore, the records of all 127 patients were checked for evidence of severe depression and/or attempted suicide (these being among the few remaining reasons for ECT typically verbalized by psychiatrists still using it: Geller 1965). While 48% of the patients in the full sample had such histories, their membership in the ECT versus No ECT group was not significantly different.

9. Two-thirds (66%) of the No ECT group were able to list employment prior to hospitalization whereas less than half (52%) of the ECT group had done so. This difference was statistically significant.

Summary of the analysis of the sample:
Of hospitalized non-brain damaged males age twenty to fifty, those most likely to have avoided ECT at Hawaii State Hospital were: nonschizophrenic, catholic, under thirty and employed prior to admission.

Of the same group, those most likely to have already received ECT at Hawaii State Hospital were: schizophrenic (particularly catatonics), no religion, over thirty five, unemployed prior to admission and Japanese.

The following factors were not significantly related to either presence or absence of ECT: marital status, education, severe depression and/or attempted suicide.

Results of the miniature experiment on Digit Span memory, tested and retested, for the four ECT-No ECT matched pairs of *S*s. There was a net gain in favor of those patients without a history of ECT and a smaller net loss for those with a past history of ECT. The discrepancy between the mean scores of the No ECT and ECT groups was three times as large on day two as it was on day one and in favor of the No ECT group. These data suggest that memory of day one testing may not have been as helpful to ECT groups *S*s two days later to overcome on their initial learning disadvantage and catch up to the No ECT group.

Discussion: Where to From Here?

The data suggest further experiments with larger samples, better controlled, should be done with learning and relearning over varying time periods. It seems a possibility that patients who have experienced ECT would do more poorly at this than those who have not.

Other measures that seem fruitful for research on the permanent effects of ECT are those used by deMille (1962) to differentiate matched subgroups of fifty lobotomized schizophrenics from fifty non-lobotomized schizophrenics (*S*s were matched for age, education, duration of illness, sex, race, diagnosis, veteran status, hospital and tranquilizer). deMille found the following to be most sensitive to lobotomy-generated intellectual deficit:

a. Numerical Operations Test (Guilford-Zimmerman Aptitude Survey, Part III, Form A—eight minutes)
b. Ship Destination Test (Christenson & Guilford, fifteen minutes)
c. Letter Series (adaptation of Thurstone's PMA Reasoning subtest, twelve minutes)
d. Social Situations (consequences of actions, Guilford & Merrifred, EPO 3A, ten minutes)
e. Digit Span (on the Wechsler-Bellevue, Form I)
f. Similarities (on the Wechsler-Bellevue, Form I)
g. Verbal, Performance, and Full Scale IQ (on Wechsler-Bellevue, Form I)

In a study of the permanent ECT effects on intellect and memory, these measures should be made at intervals of say one day, one week, one month and one year. The same sample should be tested on the measures used by Katz et al. (1966) to more fully investigate the personality changes associated with a given number of ECT.

deMille found lobotomies did wipe out some schizophrenic behavior but while the patient was less characteristically psychotic, it was achieved "at a cost of impairment of a number of factor-defined intellectual abilities" (p. 171) and with a 20% probability of epilepsy following the lobotomy.

Like lobotomy, ECT damage must be investigated and treated in its own right as an important mental impairment. To do this we must better define the consequences of X treatments on behavior as well as develop reliably sensitive measures for this behavior change. With enough data, it may some day be possible to deal therapeutically with ECT damaged patients, perhaps with some radically new approach to psychotherapy or direct re-education and modification of behavior. Optimistically, Morgan (1966) has suggested that "neurosurgery and neurological psychiatry may one day be able to restore the damaged sections of the limbic system and undo the pathological effects of the once well-intentioned electro-convulsive therapy."

FOOTNOTES

[1] This paper would not have been possible without the careful, continuous and conscientious data collection and discussion provided by Alberta Ing, Barbara Lam and Mark Ames, WICHE students affiliating with Hawaii State Hospital for the summer of 1966 under Dr. Robert Hunt. Drs. Howard Gudeman and Kenneth Sanborn also were especially helpful in making data available and discussing its meaning.

[2] The 'T' in ECT is more often used to signify "therapy" than "treatment." That this electric form of limbic lobotomy is therapeutic is an assumption this author will not take for granted by giving it semantic validity.

[3] A particular thank you is due Michael "O," a resident with the diagnostic label *paranoid schizophrenic* who, despite his periodic visits to an alternate perception of reality, managed to help tremendously in combing the literature toward a more scientific understanding of the pluses and liabilities of ECT. While an out-patient on conditional discharge, Michael came to see me one day while I was away and was assigned to my former administrative supervisor, an ECT-advocate. He was involuntarily given a *maintenance dose* of ECT to *bolster his success* in adjusting to the outside. This despite his paranoia and his known research into ECT. Michael became a living example of impaired *savings* or the inability to retain new material: it adversely affected his night studies in college. Due to some very creative relearning techniques, Michael managed to bypass his disability and ultimately completed a graduate degree in another state. ECT was never just a conceptual or scientific focus; it was always, at least to its recipient, a very personal debate.

BIBLIOGRAPHY

deMille, R. Intellect after lobotomy in schizophrenia: a factor analytic study. *Psychol. Monographico* 76, no. 16 (1962):1-18.

Flynn, MacLean and Kim. Effects of hippocampal after discharge on conditional response. In *Electric stimulation of the brain*, edited by

D. Sheer. Austin: University of Texas Press, 1961.

Geller, M. R. *Studies on electroconvulsive therapy, 1939-1963: a selected annotated bibliography.* National Clearinghouse for Mental Health Information (NIMH): Public Health Service Publication No. 1447, Public Health Bibliography Series No. 64 (1965):413 pages.

Katz, M., H. Gudeman and K. Sanborn. Characterizing the differences in psychopathology among several ethnic groups: preliminary report on a comparison of Japanese and American schizophrenics. Paper presented at the Conference on Mental Health in Asia and the Pacific (March 1966) Honolulu, Hawaii.

Mednick, S. A. Distortions in the gradient of stimulus generalization related to cortical brain damages and schizophrenia. *J. Abnorm. Soc. Psychol.* 51 (1955):536-542.

Morgan, R. F. The isolation, description and treatment of the pathological behavior of ECT damaged patients. Unpublished review and proposal (1966). Hawaii State Hospital, Kaneohe.

Riddell, S. The therapeutic efficacy of ECT: a review of literature. *Arch. Gen. Psychiat.* 8 (1963):546-556.

JOHN M. FRIEDBERG

20
Shock Treatment II: Resistance in the 1970s

By the mid-1970s, the tide had turned against ECT. States and provinces had passed or were considering legislation limiting its use and banning involuntary use altogether. At the beginning of the decade, I had managed to secure cooperation in a Nova Scotian hospital to evaluate ECT given its clients: the psychiatrist in charge was a *believer* and I a *sceptic,* so, as you might imagine, there was some negotiating. He wanted behavioral ward compliance measures while I wanted tests of memory, personality and brain damage. We did finally agree to use all these measures. Then came the procedure: for ethical reasons (believing the treatment damaging) I requested he withhold ECT from half those scheduled for it, randomly, as a control; for ethical reasons he (believing the treatment of significant value) wanted to randomly assign ECT to patients who otherwise wouldn't have received it (not wishing to deprive any patients of their treatment). We never agreed on method and the evaluation never took place at that hospital.

But elsewhere evaluation *was taking* place and events with it. The ex-patient organization NAPA (Network Against Psychiatric Assault, San Francisco) produced the still available *History of Shock Treatment* (1975) which I highly recommend. Feminist organizations were beginning to realize that, at least in California, women (especially gay women) received a disproportionately large amount of ECT from their male doctors. For reasons only indirectly related to scientific data and carefully controlled studies, ECT was being edged out of use as a little too controversial. Hemingway's death, following ECT treatments for depression, drew much notice as did Roueché's classic "As Empty As Eve" case history published in the *New Yorker* (*see* chapter 16). Powerful fiction like Kesey's *One Flew Over the Cuckoo's Nest* and Brand's *Savage Sleep* (1968) influenced the decade at its inception; by its end, more scholarly volumes were also available—Fink's *Convulsive Therapy: Theory & Practice* (1979), identifying permanent brain damage. Much of the criticism had come from outside medicine: patients, psychologists, authors, activists. Physicians resented nonphysicians criticizing a certified medical-only tool. Yet, when a physician became the most outspoken and best documented scientifically in opposition to the use of ECT, he was hardly met with welcome. John Friedberg, MD, Berkeley practitioner in general medicine and neurology, combined principle with scientific method, carefully organized facts with courage and drive. His work led the resistance to ECT in the 1970s and led it to its near demise. In 1976 he appeared at the 129th annual meeting of the

Revised version of a paper presented at the 129th annual meeting of the American Psychiatric Association. May 10-14, 1976, Miami Beach, Fla. Reprinted with permission of the author who thanks Mrs. Marilyn Rice for her assistance in assembling references.

American Psychiatric Association and delivered a paper well representing his efforts, a revision of which follows. Mrs. Marilyn Rice who is given credit for assisting in assembling the references, was the model for Roueché's "As Empty As Eve" case history. **R.F.M.**

Shock Treatment, Brain Damage and Memory Loss: A Neurological Perspective

Summary—The author reviews reports of neuropathology resulting from electroconvulsive therapy in experimental animals and humans. Although findings of petechial hemorrhage, gliosis and neuronal loss were well established in the decade following the introduction of ECT, they have been generally ignored since then. ECT produces characteristic EEG changes and severe retrograde amnesia, as well as other more subtle effects on memory and learning. The author concludes that ECT results in brain disease and questions whether doctors should offer brain damage to their patients.

A thirty-two-year-old woman who had received twenty-one ECT treatments stated five years later:

One of the results of the whole thing is that I have no memory of what happened in the year to year and a half prior to my shock treatments. The doctor assured me that it was going to come back and it never has. I don't remember a bloody thing. I couldn't even find my way around the town I lived in for three years. If I walked into a building I didn't even know where I was. I could barely find my way around my own house. I could sew and knit before, but afterward I could no more comprehend a pattern to sew than the man in the moon (*see* References, no. 1).

By 1928, ten years before the introduction of electroconvulsive therapy, it was known that accidental death by cardiac arrest could result from as little as seventy to eighty milliamperes in the human (2). It was also known in this early period that voltage applied to the head, as in legal electrocution, produced hemorrhage and rupture of cranial contents. Ugo Cerletti (3) demonstrated that electricity in the range of 100 volts and 200 milliamperes is rarely fatal when the current path is confined to the head, but does evoke a grand mal seizure marked by a stereotyped succession of events. A tetanic muscular contraction, the "electric spasm," is followed after a latency of seconds by unconsciousness, a high voltage paroxysmal spike and sharp-wave discharge, and a clonic convulsion. Upon recovery of consciousness the subject is left with a transient acute brain syndrome, a high likelihood of permanent brain damage, and greater retrograde amnesia than is seen in any other form of head injury.

Brain Damage in Experimental Animals

Before examining the premise that ECT damages human brains, a brief discussion of the lesions produced in animals by electrically induced convulsions is worthwhile. The many reports on this subject indicate that petechial hemorrhages scattered throughout both white and gray matter and concentrated in the path of the current are the most consistent finding. If animals are sacrificed after a delay of days or weeks following a convulsive series, hemosiderin pigment in phagocytes remains as evidence of vascular insult. Proliferation of glial cells, neuronal changes and dropout are also commonly reported.

In 1938, the year of the first use of ECT on a human being, Lucio Bini, Cerletti's collaborator, reported "widespread and severe" brain damage in dogs with mouth to rectum electrode placement (4). At least seven subsequent animal studies employing conventional cranial electrodes supported his findings (5-11). These culminated in the exhaustive controlled experiment by Hans Hartelius in 1952 (12). This researcher found discernible vascular, glial, and neuronal changes in cats subjected to a maximum of sixteen shocks. The animals were not paralyzed but were protected from physical injury during the seizure. Damage was slight but consistent, and the author concluded: "The question of whether or not irreversible damage to the nerve cells may occur in association with ECT must therefore be answered in the affirmative." Furthermore, by examination of unlabeled slides alone Hartelius was able to correctly recognize eight of eight slides from shocked animals as well as eight of eight controls. Although he considered many of the vascular and glial changes to be reversible, there was no mistaking the brain of a shocked animal for that of a control.

Since that time, ECT in humans has been modified through the use of oxygen and muscle paralysis to reduce the incidence of bone fractures. Although it is believed that these modifications also reduce brain damage, there are no animal studies to support this idea. On the contrary, recent work in England by Meldrum and associates (13, 14) on status epilepticus in primates suggests that the overexcited neuron by itself may be an important factor in seizure damage, especially in the hippocampus.

Human Brain Damage

Let us turn now to the neuropathological findings in humans who died during or shortly after ECT. As in lower animals, bleeding is the most frequent non-specific tissue response to injury and the one seen most often after electric shock. The first autopsy study in this country revealed brain damage identical to that seen in experimental animals. Alpers and Hughes (15) described the brains of two women who had received sixty-two and six shocks, respectively. The first woman's seizures had been suppressed by curare. Both brains showed hemorrhagic lesions around small blood vessels, rarefaction of tissue, and gliosis.

Throughout the 1940s similar reports continued to call attention to brain changes after ECT, including cases in which oxygen and curare had been administered (16). In 1948 Riese (17) added two more autopsy studies to the growing list and commented, "In all observations of sudden death after electric shock reported so far, petechial hemorrhages, cellular changes and some glial proliferation stand out prominently, as an almost constant whole."

Pathologists were especially interested in cases that discriminated between the direct effect of electricity and the mechanical and hypoxic effects secondary to convulsive motor activity. In 1953 Larsen reported on a forty-five-year-old man who had been given four electroshocks in the course of five days. The ECT did not induce any convulsions. The subject died from pneumonia thirty-six hours after the fourth electroshock. At autopsy fresh subarachnoid hemorrhage was found in the upper part of the left motor region—"at the site where an electrode had been applied" (18).

In 1957 Impastato summarized 254 electroshock fatalities. Brain damage was the leading cause of death in persons under forty years of age, and nearly one-fifth of all cerebral deaths were hemorrhagic (19).

Some physicians were alarmed by the evidence of human brain damage. In 1959 Allen reported eighteen cases in which he had found signs and symptoms of neurological sequelae following ECT. He concluded, "It is probable that some damage, which may be reversible but is often irreversible, is inseparable from this form of treatment," and called for "more serious consideration" of the entire procedure (20).

In 1963 McKegney and associates (21) reported the case of a twenty-three-year-old man who became comatose fifteen minutes after a single shock. The significance of this case was twofold: first, a complete physical and neurological examination was reportedly normal prior to ECT, and second, the ECT technique was contemporary and impeccable. The patient had received .6 mg of atropine, 16 mg of succinylcholine (Anectine), and forced oxygenation pre- and post-shock. ECT parameters were conventional, i.e., 130 volts for .3 seconds. Four days later a brain biopsy showed diffuse degeneration of neurons with hyperplasia of astrocytes. The young man never regained consciousness and at autopsy two months later evidence of old hemorrhage was found in the brain. This was the last detailed report in the English-language literature.

The damaging effects of ECT on the brain are thoroughly documented. All told, there have been twenty-one reports of neuropathology in humans (22-36). It is interesting that, despite the importance of a negative finding, there has not been a single detailed report of a normal human brain after shock.

Electroencephalographic Effects of ECT

Like other insults to the brain, ECT produces EEG abnormalities. Diffuse slowing in the delta and theta range, increased voltage, and dysrhythmic activity are seen in all patients immediately following a series of bilateral ECT and, according to Blaurock and associates (37), may persist more than six months in 30% of the cases. Such slowing suggests damage to the thalamus.

Sutherland and associates (38) showed that the side of the brain shocked with unilateral ECT could be predicted by double-blind assessment of EEG tracings.

The seizure thresholds of the hippocampus and other temporal lobe structures are the lowest in the brain; considerable interest has centered recently around "kindling," or seizure induction by subthreshold stimulation of these areas in animals (39). The induction of a permanent epileptic disorder following ECT in humans was first reported in 1942 and other reports followed (40).

Memory Loss

ECT is a common cause of severe retrograde amnesia, i.e., destruction of memories of events prior to an injury. The potency of ECT as an amnestic exceeds that of severe closed head injury with coma. It is surpassed only by prolonged deficiency of thiamine pyrophosphate, bilateral temporal lobectomy, and the accelerated dementias, such as Alzheimer's.

After ECT it takes five to ten minutes just to remember who you are, where you are and what day it is. In the first weeks after a full course, retrograde and, to a lesser extent, anterograde amnesia are evident to the casual observer. But as time passes compensation occurs. As in other forms of brain injury, the subject is often oblivious to the residual deficit. Unless specific memories essential to daily living are discovered to be unavailable the victim may never know for sure the extent of memory loss. Unless sensitive tests for spontaneous recall of personal preshock data are employed, no one else will know either.

The memory loss following ECT generally follows Ribot's law for all pathological amnesias: the new dies before the old. This, of course, is the opposite of normal forgetting. Squire, however, has shown that the loss may extend to items learned more than thirty years before (41).

The effect of ECT on memory was common knowledge within a few years of its introduction. There were reports of persons who forgot they had children (42, 43), although most amnesias involved humbler matters, such as the woman who forgot how to cook familiar dishes (44) and another who couldn't remember her own clothing and demanded to know who had put the unfamiliar dresses in her closet (45). Some doctors dismissed these sequelae as trivial or transient, although one psychiatrist remarked that psychotherapy was useless in patients undergoing ECT because they couldn't remember "either the analyst or the content of the analytic sessions from one day to the next" (46).

Numerous such case reports finally led to a definitive study of the effects of ECT on memory by Irving Janis in 1950 (47). He found that all nineteen subjects in a controlled prospective investigation had significant memory loss four weeks after ECT, compared to negligible losses among control subjects. He also noted that these losses may involve events of early childhood dating back twenty to forty years, with the more recently encoded memories being the most vulnerable. Patient E, for example, a thirty-eight-year-old woman, had told Janis in an interview prior to ECT that thyroid medication had caused heart palpitations and panic which led to her admission to the psychiatric hospital. When asked after a course of ten shocks if she had ever taken thyroid she responded: "I don't think so."

In the late 1950s, when the enthusiasm for ECT seemed to have passed its peak (48), Lancaster and associates (49) advocated the use of unilateral nondominant ECT in treating patients who earn their livelihood with retained knowledge. In this variant the current path and most of the damage is confined to the nonverbal side of the brain, usually the right hemisphere. This exploits the well-known neurological phenomenon of anosognosia, or denial, that is associated with right-hemisphere lesions—victims can't verbalize their difficulties. They complain less. Cohen and associates (50), however, using design-completion tests, proved that shock to the right hemisphere produces its own kind of memory loss—visual and spatial. Inglis found in 1970 (51) that the effects of unilateral ECT were comparable to those of right and left temporal lobectomy, with identical impairment of memory and learning.

Recently there has been a good deal of human experimentation in a futile effort to find electrode placements that eliminate amnesia. As the use of ECT has shifted from state hospitals to private practice, the literature has focused more and more on memory loss. Although some studies have purported to show improvement of learning ability after ECT, not one used sham ECT as a control and few used any controls at all.[1]

In regard to more general intellectual ability, a study in 1973 (54) showed that the performance on the Bender Gestalt perceptual motor test of twenty institutionalized subjects who had received fifty or more ECT treatments ten to fifteen years before testing was significantly impaired compared to the performance of twenty carefully matched control subjects who had not received ECT. The authors inferred that ECT had caused permanent brain damage.

Mechanism of Action of ECT

The mechanism of action of ECT can now be summarized on the basis of evidence accumulated since its introduction. Penfield and Perot showed in the 1950s that memory traces may be evoked by direct electrical stimulation of the temporal lobe cortex, and nowhere else (55). Scoville and Milner (56) discovered that bilateral hippocampal resection utterly abolished the ability to remember any new material, resulting in a catastrophic inability to learn. From numerous studies of the neuropathology of the amnestic-confabulatory syndrome of Korsakoff it is known that the mammillary bodies, the dorsal median nuclei of the thalamus, and the gray matter surrounding the third ventricle and aqueduct are essential to the general memory process. All of these critical brain structures are just beneath the thin squamous plate of the temporal bone, within seven centimeters of the electrodes, in the direct path and highest density of the current during ECT.

Conclusions

From a neurological point of view ECT is a method of producing amnesia by selectively damaging the temporal lobes and the structures within them. When it was first introduced it was only one of several methods of producing brain damage employed in psychiatry, including insulin coma (1927), camphor and pentylenetetrazol (Metrazol) injections (1933), and prefrontal lobotomy (1935). It is the only such method from that era still used on a large scale. It is highly unlikely that ECT, if critically examined, would be found acceptable by today's standards of safety.

From a neurological point of view ECT produces a form of brain disease, with an estimated incidence of new cases in the range of 100,000 per year (57). Many psychiatrists are unaware that ECT causes brain damage and memory loss because numerous authorities and a leading psychiatric textbook (58) deny these facts. Others, who know of its effects, argue that the interruption of unpleasant states of mind is worth the damage. Some are beginning to give the client a truly informed choice, although most state laws still allow ECT to be imposed if the doctor feels that "good cause" exists.

Assuming free and fully informed consent, it is well to reaffirm the individual's right to pursue happiness through brain damage if he or she so chooses. But we might ask ourselves whether we, as doctors sworn to the Hippocratic Oath, should be offering it.

FOOTNOTE

[1] Sham ECT, an essential control technique, has been employed in only two studies, which were tests of efficacy, not tests of memory loss. Neither study showed any superiority of ECT over the control treatment (52, 53).

REFERENCES

1. Friedberg, J. 1976. *Shock Treatment Is Not Good For Your Brain.* San Francisco: Glide Publications.
2. Jaffe, R. 1928. Electropathology: a review of the pathologic changes produced by electric current. *Arch. Neurol. Psychiatry* 5:838-864.
3. Cerletti, U. 1956. Electroshock therapy. In *The Great Physiodynamic Therapies in Psychiatry,* edited by A. Sackler et al., 91-120. New York: Hoeber-Harper.
4. Bini, L. 1938. Experimental researches on epileptic attacks induced by the electric current. *Am. J. Psychiatry* 94:172-174.
5. Heilbrunn, G. and E. Liebert. 1941. Biopsies on the brain following artificially produced convulsions. *Arch. Neurol. Psychiatry* 46:548-552.
6. Neubuerger, K. T., R. W. Whitehead, R. K. Rutledge et al. 1942. Pathologic changes in the brains of dogs given repeated electric shocks. *Am. J. Med. Sci.* 204:381-387.
7. Heilbrunn, G. and A. Weil. 1942.

Pathologic changes in the central nervous system in experimental electric shock. *Arch. Neurol. Psychiatry* 47:918.

8. Alpers, B. J. and J. Hughes. 1942. Changes in the brain after electrically induced convulsions in cats. *Arch. Neurol. Psychiatry* 47:385.

9. Alexander, L. and H. Lowenbach. 1944. Experimental studies on electroshock treatment: the intracerebral vascular reaction as an indicator of the path of the current and the threshold of early changes within the brain tissue. *J. Neuropathol. Exp. Neurol.* 3:139.

10. Ferraro, A., L. Roizin and M. Helfand. 1946. Morphologic changes in the brain of monkeys following convulsions electrically induced. *J. Neuropathol. Exp. Neurol.* 5:285.

11. Ferraro, A. and L. Roizin. 1949. Cerebral morphologic changes in monkeys subjected to a large number of electrically induced convulsions (32-100). *Am. J. Psychiatry* 106:278.

12. Hartelius, H. 1952. Cerebral changes following electrically induced convulsions. *Acta. Psychiat. et Neurol. Scand.* Supplement 77.

13. Meldrum, B., V. Roger and J. Brierley. 1973. Systemic factors and epileptic brain damage. *Arch. Neurol.* 29:82-87.

14. Meldrum B., R. Herton and J. Brierley. 1974. Epileptic brain damage in adolescent baboons following seizures induced by allylglycine. *Brain* 97:407-418.

15. Alpers, B. J. and J. Hughes. 1942. The brain changes in electrically induced convulsions in the human. *J. Neuropathol. Exp. Neurol.* 1:173.

16. Ebaugh, E. G., C. H. Barnacle and K. T. Neubuerger. 1943. Fatalities following electric convulsive therapy: report of two cases, with autopsy. *Arch. Neurol. Psychiatry* 49:107.

17. Riese, W. 1948. Report of two new cases of sudden death after electric shock treatment with histopathol-

ogical findings in the central nervous system. *J. Neuropathol. Exp. Neurol.* 7:98-100.

18. Larsen, E. G. and G. Vraa-Jansen. 1953. Ischaemic changes in the brain following electroshock therapy. *Acta. Psychiat. et Neurol. Scand.* 28:75-80.

19. Impastato, D. 1957. Prevention of fatalities in electroshock therapy. *Dis. Nerv. Syst.* 18:34-75.

20. Allen, I. 1959. Cerebral lesions from electric shock treatment. *NZ Med. J.* 58:369.

21. McKegney, F. P. and A. F. Panzella. 1963. An unusual fatal outcome of electro-convulsive therapy. *Am. J. Psychiatry* 120:398-400.

22. Ebaugh, F. G., C. H. Barnacle and K. T. Neubuerger. June 1942. Fatalities following electric convulsive therapy. A report of 2 cases with autopsy findings. *Trans. Am. Neurol. Assoc.*: 36.

23. Gralnick, A. 1944. Fatalities associated with electric shock treatment of psychoses: report of two cases, with autopsy observations in one of them. *Arch. Neurol. Psychiatry* 51:397.

24. Jetter, W. W. 1944. Fatal circulatory failure caused by electric shock therapy. *Arch. Neurol. Psychiatry* 51:557.

25. Meyer, A. and D. Teare. 1945. Cerebral fat embolism after electrical convulsion therapy. *Br. Med. J.* 2:42.

26. Sprague, D. W. and R. C. Taylor. 1948. The complications of electric shock therapy with a case study. *Ohio State Med. J.* 44:51-54.

27. Will, O. A. Jr. and F. C. Rehfeldt. 1948. A fatality in electroshock therapy: report of a case and review of certain previously described cases. *J. Nerv. Ment. Dis.* 107:105-126.

28. Martin, P. A. 1949. Convulsive therapies: review of 511 cases at Pontiac State Hospital. *J. Nerv. Ment. Dis.* 109:142-157.

29. Riese, W. and G. S. Fultz. 1949. Electric shock treatment succeeded by complete flaccid paralysis, hallucinations, and sudden death: case report with anatomical findings in the central nervous system. *Am. J. Psychiatry* 106:206-211.

30. Liban, E., L. Halpern and J. Rozanski. 1951. Vascular changes in the brain in a fatality following electroshock. *J. Neuropathol. Exp. Neurol.* 10:309-318.

31. Corsellis, J. and A. Meyer. 1954. Histological changes in the brain after uncomplicated electro-convulsant treatment. *J. Ment. Sci.* 100:375-383.

32. Madow, L. 1956. Brain changes in electroshock therapy. *Am. J. Psychiatry* 113:337-347.

33. Faurbye, A. 1942. Death under electroshock treatment. *Acta. Psychiat. et Neurologica* 17:39.

34. Maclay, W. S. 1953. Death due to treatment. *Proc. Soc. Med.* 46:13-20.

35. Matthew, J. R. and E. Constan. 1964. Complications following ECT over a three-year period in a state institution. *Am. J. Psychiatry* 120:1119-1120.

36. Barker, J. and A. Barker. 1959. Deaths associated with electroplexy. *J. Ment. Sci.* 105:339-348.

37. Blaurock, M., F. Lorimer, M. Segal et al. 1950. Focal electroencephalographic changes in unilateral electric convulsion therapy. *Arch. Neurol. Psychiatry* 64:220-226.

38. Sutherland, E., J. Oliver and D. Knight. 1969. EEG, memory and confusion in dominant, non-dominant and bi-temporal ECT. *Br. J. Psychiatry* 115:1059-1064.

39. Wada, J. and T. Osawa. 1976. Spontaneous recurrent seizure state induced by daily electric amygdaloid stimulation in senegalese baboons (papio papio). *Neurology* 26:273-286.

40. Parfitt, D. 1942. Persisting epilepsy following shock therapy. *Br. Med. J.* 2:514.

41. Squire, L. 1973. A thirty-year retrograde amnesia following electroconvulsive therapy in depressed patients. Presented at the 3rd annual meeting of the Society for Neuroscience, San Diego, Calif.

42. Tyler B. and H. Lowenbach. 1947. Polydiurnal electric shock treatment in mental disorders. *NC Med. J.* 8:577-582.

43. Medlicott, R. 1948. Convulsive therapy. Results and complications in four hundred cases. *NZ Med. J.* 47:338.

44. Brody, M. 1944. Prolonged memory defects following electro-therapy. *J. Ment. Sci.* 90:777-779.

45. Zubin, J. 1948. Objective studies of disordered persons. In *Methods of Psychology,* edited by T. Andrews 595-623. New York: John Wiley & Sons.

46. Stainbrook, E. 1956. Shock therapy: psychologic theory and research. *Psychol. Bull.* 43:21-60.

47. Janis I. 1950. Psychologic effects of electric convulsive treatments. Part 1: post-treatment amnesias. *J. Nerv. Ment. Dis.* 3:359-382.

48. Spiegel, E., ed. 1957. *Progress In Neurology and Psychiatry: An Annual Review.* New York: Grune & Stratton.

49. Lancaster, N., R. Steinert and I. Frost. 1958. Unilateral electro-convulsive therapy. *J. Ment. Sci.* 104:221-227.

50. Cohen, B., C. Noblin and A. Silverman. 1968. Functional asymmetry of the human brain. *Science* 162:475-477.

51. Inglis, J. 1970. Shock, surgery and cerebral assymmetry. *Br. J. Psychiatry* 117:143-148.

52. Miller, D., J. Clancy and E. Cummings. 1953. A comparison between unidirectional current non-convulsive electrical stimulation given with Reiter's machine, standard alternating current electroshock (Cerletti method), and pento-

thal in chronic schizophrenia. *Am. J. Psychiatry* 109:617-620.

53. Brill H., E. Crumpton, S. Eiduson et al. 1959. Relative effectiveness of various components of electroconvulsive therapy. *Arch. Neurol. Psychiatry* 81:627-635.

54. Templer, D., C. Ruff and G. Armstrong. 1973. Cognitive functioning and degree of psychosis in schizophrenics given many electro-convulsive treatments. *Br. J. Psychiatry* 123:441-443.

55. Penfield, W. and P. Perot. 1963. The brain's record of auditory and visual experience. *Brain* 86, Part 4.

56. Scoville, W. and B. Milner. 1957. Loss of recent memory after bilateral hippocampal lesions. *J. Neurol. Neurosurg. Psychiatry* 20:11-21.

57. Friedberg, J. 1975. Electroshock therapy: let's stop blasting the brain. *Psychology Today* 9(8):18-23.

58. Kalinowsky, I. B. 1975. The convulsive therapies. In *Comprehensive Textbook of Psychiatry*, 2d ed. Vol. 2, edited by A. M. Freedman, H. I. Kaplan and B. J. Sadock, 1972-73. Baltimore: Williams & Wilkins Co.

PETER R. BREGGIN

21

Shock Treatment III: Resistance in the 1980s

As the 1970s ebbed, the economy ebbed with it. Inflation and unemployment impacted on national and world economies. Insurance companies and governments began to look at medical costs. Malpractice insurance rose as consumers became more aware of personal iatrogenic effects. Reimbursement decreased for less than major diagnoses or recognized major treatments. ECT was discussed for a comeback strictly for economic reasons. Psychologists objected, presented their data and were laid off. ECT is a big moneymaker and a dramatic hedge against inflation for entrepreneurial physicians: it is cheap, easily administered and 100 percent reimbursable. *Time Magazine* (November 19, 1979) ran a story entitled "Comeback for shock therapy?: It's unsavory reputation may be changing." In the article no new ideas or data were introduced to change that reputation, however, and it was acknowledged that ECT was well on its way to becoming obsolete (e.g., in New York State, a bastion of ECT practice, use of ECT dropped 38 percent between 1972 and 1977). Similar articles followed in *Newsweek, Your Health* and other national magazines. An aggressive customer campaign by a California hospital included a community fair, balloons and a pamphlet recommending ECT for "pregnant women, patients in their nineties and even patients who had recently undergone heart surgery." "If given early in the day," the pamphlet stated "ECT does not prevent the patient from going to work an hour or two afterwards." Side effects? "Much research has been done over the last thirty-five years to investigate the possibility of permanent memory changes occurring with ECT. Research now suggests that such changes are not likely regardless of the number of treatments given." No research is specifically cited.

The national and international campaign for a renaissance of ECT and psychosurgery generally may be a cynical grab for money or it may reflect the reactionary political turn of events marking the beginning of the decade. However, the resistance has reformed as well. Legislation guarding informed consent and limiting abuses continues to accumulate. My own preferred model code would guarantee an independent assessment of any patient before and after treatment in any facility. Such a code, some colleagues fear, would push malpractice insurance higher. In the long run, I think it would lower it by putting malpracticers out of business. And, on the way, we might learn something about the effects of varying treatments: successes as well as iatrogenic failures.

The leader of the resistance for the 1980s will probably be Peter Breggin. An articulate physician, careful scholar and forceful tactician, he has written *Electroshock: Its Brain-Disabling Effects* (1979) to launch the decade's ECT debate. The following chapter is from his significant and controversial book.   **R.F.M.**

Are the Patients Lying?

Pro-ECT articles and books often acknowledge frequent complaints about memory loss from their patients, but they dismiss or rationalize them as manifestations of "mental illness" and especially "neuroticism." As in so many other aspects of justifying ECT, Kalinowsky has led the way in dismissing patient complaints about the treatment. In 1959 he wrote:

> More insistent complaints of memory impairment are sometimes heard from neurotic patients who are overconcerned with all side effects of the treatment, and many complain of forgetfulness long after tests have shown a return to normal memory function.

Kalinowsky has repeated this viewpoint throughout the era of modified ECT (see Kalinowsky & Hoch 1961; Kalinowsky & Hippius 1969). In the 1975 edition of *The American Handbook of Psychiatry* he again called the complainers "neurotics" and said, "Many complain of forgetfulness long after tests have shown a return of normal memory function." In the same year in the *Comprehensive Textbook of Psychiatry,* he took the position that "Some patients complain more than others, and neurotics are often overconcerned with these temporary memory difficulties."

Perhaps the most revealing statement in all the electroshock literature was made by Kalinowsky and Hoch in the 1952 edition of their textbook when they wrote, "All patients who remain unimproved after ECT are inclined to complain bitterly about their memory difficulties" (p. 139). The sentence (one of the few edited out of later editions) merits careful reading. The authors said that *all* patients who remain unimproved complain about amnesia and, furthermore, they admitted that these people complain *bitterly.* How then could Kalinowsky and Hoch argue, on the same page, "No evidence has been brought forward to indicate that permanent mental sequelae are caused by the treatment"? In order to make this claim they must disregard the report of *every patient* who does not respond to ECT in their prescribed manner. These patients are "unimproved" or "neurotic" and therefore cannot be trusted. Why *all* such patients complain *bitterly* about memory loss is left to the imagination. Is there some inexplicable ECT effect that always brings about a subjective feeling of memory loss in patients whom it fails to help, although it never does so in the patients whom it succeeds in helping? Instead, could it be that those patients who complain about memory loss are labeled "unimproved" or "neurotic" in order to invalidate their opinions, while all those patients who make no complaints are labeled "improved" or "cured"?

Refusing to accept that so many consistent complaints must be taken seriously, other apologists for ECT have suggested variations on the theme that patients who complain about memory loss are irresponsible and "mentally ill," whereas patients who don't complain are "trustworthy" and "improved." Schwartzman and Termansen (1967) concluded from their research that patients are so upset about "subjective" memory loss that intensive ECT should be largely abandoned, yet they raised the possibility that these complaints have no basis in reality. Squire (1977) concluded from his own systematic follow-up studies that, "it seems quite clear that individuals judged clinically appropriate for bilateral ECT do have memory complaints long after ECT"; then he went on to suggest that memory loss is an "illusion."

Faced with insurmountable evidence that patients complain about memory loss years after ECT, the American Psychiatric Association Task Force on ECT (1978), with Squire as its research consultant, rallied around the suggestion that former ECT patients are suffering a "persistent illusion of memory impairment" (p. 68). The theory states that bilateral modified ECT (but not unilateral, nondominant ECT) does produce a "lingering sense of memory impairment," which then causes "some individuals to be more sensitive to subsequent failures in recall, even if they occur at a normal frequency." This is not ascribed to neuroticism in the patients, but to the treatment itself, so that the "illusion" of memory loss can occur "with or without psychiatric illness." This is the final suggestion made by the Task Force at the conclusion of its skimpy review of the literature on mental dysfunction following ECT.

But why would patients experience this illusion following bilateral modified ECT but not following nondominant unilateral ECT? The advocates of this theory must claim that nondominant unilateral ECT does not produce an acute organic brain syndrome and acute memory loss, a position wholly at odds with the literature and clinical observation. The position also seems faulty as a defense against liability; should not a patient be able to sue a psychiatrist for using a treatment that commonly produces an emotionally upsetting and disabling "illusion"? The advocates of the illusion theory seem to be hoping for a switch from bilateral to unilateral ECT, accompanied by a new cycle of claims that this form of ECT is harmless.

The illusion theory was stated in a less elaborated form by Noyes and Kolb (1973) and by Kolb (1977) in recent editions of *Modern Clinical Psychiatry*. The patients, they said, cannot be "trusted" in evaluating their own memory loss. Their thrust was clear: the patients unaccountably *exaggerate* their losses. Noyes and Kolb cited a study by Cronholm and Ottosson (1963a) to support their assertion that the patients cannot be trusted. But, on reading the Cronholm and Ottosson study, we find to the contrary that the patients who have the *most memory loss tend to complain the least.* This is why they cannot be trusted—they tend to *deny* the degree of damage they have suffered. Gomez (1975) found in regard to the treatment period that "those who remembered least of this period complained least of memory loss."

This denial of mental impairment is exactly what can be expected and what typically is found after brain damage. Instead of exaggerating their mental defects after brain damage, patients *almost always* tend to deny or to downplay them. They do this out of fear and shame over their mental condition (Goldstein 1975). The phenomenon of denying mental dysfunction after brain damage is so commonplace that it has a name: confabulation. If post-ECT patients cannot be trusted in evaluating their mental function, it is because they do not wish to acknowledge their impairments. Confabulation is such a well-known phenomenon in clinical neurology and psychiatry that it is usually discussed, in separate chapters, in the very books in which it is claimed that ECT patients, for some unaccountable reason, *like to exaggerate* their mental losses and dysfunction.

In the 1959 edition of the *American Handbook of Psychiatry,* in which Kalinowsky claimed that patients who complain about memory defects after ECT are "neurotic," two excellent discussions of confabulation were presented in other chapters (Brosin; Weinstein & Kahn). Both chapters made clear that patients with brain trauma, including ECT, tend to deny or hide the extent of their brain dysfunction. As Weinstein and Kahn put it, the confabulations are "seemingly designed to amplify the denial, minimize the traumatic implications of the illness, and explain away the manifestations." Weinstein and Kahn went so far as to relate the confabulations and euphoria to the alleged "improvement" seen in post-ECT patients—a subject that will receive further attention in regard to the brain-disabling hypothesis.

Weinstein and Kahn made clear the difference between retrograde amnesia based on brain disease and fake or neurotic amnesia. Retrograde amnesia following brain trauma is general and rubs out a broad spectrum of memories, both trivial and significant, without regard for their symbolic importance to the individual. Fake amnesia is usually highly symbolic. Typically, a painful loss or traumatic event is forgotten, such as the death of a comrade in battle. Global memory will be unaffected and the amnesia will not be retrograde. The patient forgets what he *wishes* to forget. But in memory loss following damage to the brain, the person cannot remember things he wishes to remember. As described in my six cases and in the psychiatric literature, post-ECT patients have very global losses that follow the classic pattern of true retrograde amnesia, with the greatest losses occurring nearest to the trauma. Rarely if ever do such patients report symbolic losses.

Weinstein and Kahn also described another well-known diagnostic difference between real, or retrograde, amnesias and fake, or neurotic, amnesias. The patient who is consciously or unconsciously faking wishes to forget his forgotten memories, so he rarely displays eagerness to recover them. When he is reminded of his forgotten memories, he is rather indifferent to the revelation. By contrast, the individual with retrograde amnesia is very upset about his losses and often works very hard, much as my cases, in order to recover them. When Kalinowsky admits that his patients complain "bitterly" about their losses, he adds validity to their complaints.

Brosin's chapter (1959) confirms the observations of Weinstein and Kahn. He described the Korsakoff-like syndrome that develops after trauma to the brain, pointed out that it can occur after lobotomy and electroshock, and emphasized the confabulation and euphoria with which patients try to cover up or to deny their defects.

Questions designed to reveal the functions of mental status, such as perception, recent memory, orientation, attention, ability to handle abstractions, arithmetic, and proverbs, will usually reveal marked defects. This may be true in other acute brain disorders, including patients operated on for brain tumor, lobotomy, and post-electric shock. In the Korsakoff syndrome we often have the opportunity to see many of the psychodynamic defenses described by Goldstein and some of the psychoanalysts. As in other organic cerebral disorders, the patient is unconsciously, if not consciously, aware of many of his defects and tries to overcome them, compensate for them, or avoid them in many ways. . . . Some patients are placid and even euphoric, but the delicately defensive nature of this facade can usually be quickly proved by questions.

Brosin's observations help destroy the hypothesis that the patients are exaggerating their defects.

The reality that most brain-damaged people cannot bear to acknowledge or face their deficits was portrayed in various ways by each of my six patients. Their losses were almost always greater than they were willing to admit. While all acknowledged some degree of retrograde amnesia, they were especially reluctant to talk about any ongoing mental disabilities, such as difficulties remembering new material or a lack of mental dexterity. One patient denied any ongoing mental defects despite a long course of ECT treatment, until I mentioned his good fortune offhandedly a year after we had gotten to know each other. Only then did he confess with great shame that he felt less able to think and learn. He was very guarded and very embarrassed about this, and I chose for lack of information or confirmation not to include him in the group of four of six patients having anterograde defects. He is listed in my study as suffering from retrograde amnesia alone. In long-term relationships with three of the six post-ECT patients I had begun to assume that their lack of complaints about ongoing dsyfunction meant a full recovery, only to realize from the expressions on their faces and from subsequent discussions that they were hiding their dysfunctions out of shame and frustration. As further confirmation of the confabulation in the six cases, the two most obviously damaged individuals were the ones who most adamantly and strenuously denied any losses other than retrograde amnesia. In one case I too was misled, and only realized the degree of confabulation when the neurologic tests and psychological tests were returned with significant defects.

I am not the only investigator who has discovered that ECT patients, however much they complain of memory loss, are nonetheless hiding many of their deficits. In his painstaking and elegant research, Janis (1948) came to the same conclusion. Here is his classic illustration of confabulation in a post-ECT patient:

Sometimes a patient will deny that a given event or series of events has occurred, and he will fill in the amnesic gap, as in the following example. The patient, a 37-year-old borderline schizophrenic, reported in the pretreatment interview that he had been unable to work for several months before coming to the hospital, during which period he would spend his time riding around in subways, wandering about the city, sitting in churches, etc. (These facts were confirmed by information from members of the family in the patient's case history record.) Four weeks after a series of 12 electroshock treatments, the patient was unable to recall this period of unemployment and claimed: "I worked right up till I came to this hospital." After many detailed questions, the patient was finally told about his former statement and he replied: "I don't recall that. My wife would know because she has to take care of the bills. You could ask her. It might have been for a few days . . . There are some things I can't remember. But I think I did support the family right up till I came to this hospital" (elipses in original).

Other clinicians have made similar observations. Dedichen (1946) was aware that patients "often do not spontaneously complain" of amnesia. He believed the complaint is withheld because the patient "interprets this defect as an aftermath of the psychosis from which he has just suffered and not as a sequel to the treatment." Indeed, as Kalinowsky exemplifies, the *doctor* is likely to attribute any such complaint to mental illness, or to a failure to improve. The complaining patient may be forced to receive more treatment because her complaints "show" she is unimproved. This could very well encourage a patient to withhold complaints out of fear.

To whatever degree patients do confuse their ECT brain-damage with psychosis, they are most likely to make this error in regard to anterograde dysfunction, such as difficulties in thinking rapidly, concentrating, or learning. Similarly, their physicians will more easily dismiss these ongoing symptoms as manifestations of "mental illness" rather than consider them organic illness. This may be the main reason why clinical reports concerning post-ECT effects rarely mention continuing mental dysfunction. Even "Practising Psychiatrist" (1965) had difficulty in interpreting his own post-ECT dysfunction. He described unpleasant olfactory sensations and could not determine if they were caused by his depression or by ECT.

Addressing himself to "the marked impairment of memory in a large number of patients after shock treatment," Braatoy (1948) summed up the problem accurately:

> It seems to be generally agreed that this deficiency can be detected in ordinary clinical examination in some patients for a couple of months after the conclusion of the treatment. (N.B.: The examination must then be made with a special view to this matter. Many of these patients will, like other persons with impaired memory, be somewhat reserved in conversation and therefore the defect may easily be overlooked on cursory inspection, just as all psychiatrists and neurologists know that presenile dementia may advance remarkably far without any changes being noted by the patient's associates—precisely because the person affected seeks to evade test situations.)

Fink (1957, 1958), Fink, Kahn & Green (1958), and others have described the frequency with which post-ECT patients use denial as a mechanism of defense. This further verifies the probability that these patients are denying their brain damage as well as their psychological problems. The euphoria described by Fink, Kalinowsky, and dozens of others as a frequent sequela of the treatment is in itself a form of denial. It is entirely consistent with a refusal to admit mental defects of any kind. Euphoria is most common in the face of catastrophic losses, such as severe, general central nervous system disease, or lobotomy and ECT. As already noted, euphoria is defined in medical dictionaries and medical usage as an abnormal state in which the individual exaggerates his state of well being, or conversely, denies his state of ill health. In the earlier electroshock literature (see for example, Levy et al. 1942), it was openly recognized that euphoria was a serious indication of brain damage and dysfunction. Only in the hands of modern advocates of ECT has an abnormal reaction been redefined as an indicator of improvement (see Chapters 11 and 12).

Because detailed case reports are rarely presented in the ECT literature, it is usually impossible to judge for oneself the actual losses of patients presented as proof of the harmlessness of ECT. One especially detailed self-report was offered anonymously by "Practising Psychiatrist" (1965) and, as already described, his claim to no significant memory loss was in sharp contrast to his actual description of labored attempts to relearn the subway system and his filing cabinets, despite years of familiarity with them before ECT. Similarly, Watkins, Stainbrook, and Lowenbach (1941) described the disastrous reaction of another physician to one subconvulsive ECT and reported that those who knew him were largely unaware of his impairment. As Dedichen (1946) originally observed, it is not only easy for the patient to hide his defects, it is easy for others to overlook them.

ECT and Psychological Testing

I have already noted that no reputable neurologist would rule out the existence of brain damage, even *severe* brain damage, on the grounds that psychological tests failed to detect any objective evidence. Because this question is so crucial, I want to return to it again. The question is this: If post-ECT patients report classic symptoms of permanent retrograde amnesia, can negative psychological tests be used to invalidate their claims or even to cast doubt about them?

As in one of my six cases, psychological tests are occasionally useful in documenting serious organic defects, especially in the presence of more objective physical findings. But they are not reliable or sensitive enough to rule out serious organic defects. In other words, the tests are useful when they find something definitive, but they are not meaningful when they fail in this task. In his discussion of trauma to the brain Brosin (1959) addressed himself to the question of psychological testing, noting that a great deal of evidence had been generated pertaining to its usefulness in regard to measuring organic brain damage. He observed that "the high hopes which existed from 1920 to 1945" concerning the development of reliable and sensitive objective tests had failed to materialize. He affirmed the position taken by all experts on psychological testing—the objective psychological tests "have not provided the clinician with readily available, reliable measures of loss of cortical function owing to brain-tissue damage." In his own detailed analysis of the mental effects of brain damage, Brosin relied almost wholly on clinical evaluations of the patient's subjective reports.

Neurologist Robert Grimm (1978) has addressed himself specifically to the matter of psychological testing for amnesia following electroshock therapy.

> Experimentalists who find no significant lasting changes in ECT memory studies must be concerned with the question of whether or not their measures are sensitive enough or aimed in the right direction. . . . In addition to losses of familiar recall items, it is the small, intermittent, or subtle changes in memory or its processes that may be at risk, intrinsic events which go undetected to external observers or formal testing. . . . In personal matters, small lacunae in memory can be very consequential. After the fact, recalling a missed appointment ordinarily engenders elaborate social responses to repair the situation. But not to know that a memory has been dropped is infinitely more troublesome to those embarrassed by the event and puzzled as how to respond.
>
> In memory as in intellect, it is the "little things" that count. Given the current lack of data, it is inappropriate to be blithe or argumentative about a patient's concern over alleged memory troubles or to be too comfortable with experimental findings that fail to reveal losses.

In the light of these generally accepted medical truths, it is dismaying that advocates of ECT use negative psychological tests to invalidate the patient's symptoms, and even more dismaying that they often use tests of their own creation with no known relevance to any clinical manifestations of brain disease.

The Lessons of Lobotomy

In animal studies, human autopsies, and EEG reports, the frontal lobes take the brunt of the damage inflicted by ECT. This is consistent with the placement of the electrodes and the flow of electric current. We have noted comparisons between ECT and lobotomy effects in the clinical literature, and in the following chapters we will find this comparison made more systematically, especially in regard to intensive ECT. We can therefore gain further insight into the question "Are the patients lying?" by examining the reaction of lobotomy patients to their deficits.

All lobotomized patients tend to underestimate their losses; none tends to exaggerate them. Lobotomy patients do distort a great deal, but wholly in the interest of denying their massive, overwhelming psychological deficits. Though obviously damaged, they often label themselves "better than ever," and frequently deny that they have been operated on, even when confronted with their surgical scars (Freeman & Watts 1950; Tow 1954).

A clinical experience cruelly illustrates both the losses and the process of denial. A man in his 30s had been lobotomized in the 1950s at the age of 20 and twice again in the mid-1960s. He and his mother brought a malpractice suit against the surgeon, not only because of the patient's mental deficits, but because of a partial paralysis following the third operation. He denied any impairment of intellectual function and believed that his IQ was higher than ever. He confabulated about reading the newspapers and staying abreast of current events. On clinical examination he had massive losses in abstract reasoning, judgment, insight, and planning for the future. He could not initiate simple activities and had to be supervised in his self-care, such as dressing and eating. He was apathetic and his emotions were shallow and almost nonexistent, except for occasional displays of inappropriate levity. However, after hearing me testify in court about his psychological deficits, he approached me during recess and in hesitant, broken sentences thanked me for my efforts. He agreed for the first time that his mind had been impaired by the surgery and he reported that he felt very sad, although his face remained stiff and emotionless. I asked him if he felt like crying, and he said with unusual firmness, "I am crying," though his eyes remained dry and his face masklike. After this very short exchange, he retreated again into apathy and denial.

The lobotomy studies not only confirm the denial and confabulation typical of individuals with frontal lobe damage, but they also suggest the direction in which to search for post-ECT mental deficits. The most comprehensive clinical analyses of postlobotomy patients were reported by Freeman (Freeman & Watts 1944, 1950), and the most thorough psychological studies were provided by Tow (1954). The two reports are wholly in agreement. The patients suffer global psychological losses in all the higher human functions: abstract reasoning, judgment, insight, imagination, creativity, emotional sensitivity, moral awareness. The losses are not always obvious on a standard IQ test, which may show an artifactual improvement when previously rebellious and unruly patients become more willing to sit down and to follow instructions following lobotomy. But the losses will show up grossly when the patients are asked to demonstrate initiative, autonomy, or spontaneously generated activity. When the patients are asked to perform fully unstructured and self-determined tasks, such as writing a brief autobiography, a rich and sensitive prelobotomy production will be replaced by a sterile, mechanical, and sometimes more grossly psychotic postlobotomy production (Tow 1954). Freeman & Watts, and Tow, strong advocates of the treatment, reported that the patients do best in structured, supervised and simplified environments after surgery. Tow (1954) observed, "One generalization which is fairly consistently true is that his performance is considerably better in a structured situation." He elaborated:

> Where the test is completely unstructured for him as in the autobiographies, the verbal fluency tests and abstract words, the deterioration in performance of the frontal subject was so gross as to be obvious without quantitative comparison. Where the situation is structured for him so that he only has to perform to a certain set pattern, within certain narrow limits, his performance approximates more nearly to his pre-operative.

Similar observations were made in the modern era of psychosurgery by

Andersen (1972), who found that amygdalotomy[1] produced more docile, tractable individuals requiring a supervised environment:

> Typically the patient tends to become more inert, and shows less zest and intensity of emotions. His spontaneous activity appears to be reduced, and he becomes less capable of creative productivity, which is independent of the intelligence level. . . . With these changes in initiative and control of behavior, our patients resemble those with frontal lesions. . . . Presumably he will make the most of this gain in well-structured situations of a somewhat monotonous and simple character.

A similar lack of self-determination, initiative, and spontaneity becomes grossly apparent during the acute brain syndrome that develops routinely after three or four ECT. This phenomenon is usually called apathy. That this reaction can last for months was demonstrated by the extensive use of ECT to subdue or quiet difficult, unruly, or uncooperative mental patients on a large scale in the state mental hospitals in the 1940s and 1950s (see Chapter 10). Two of my six cases, one in the short-course group, described a permanent loss of initiative, spontaneity, and overall energy years after ECT. A third was unsure if ECT caused this same feeling, since he had suffered a similar psychological reaction prior to ECT. A fourth felt he had more energy than ever, but he had a long course of ECT, showed clinical signs of an organic brain syndrome, and confabulated. His energy level seemed to reflect an ineffective, irrational euphoria. Finally, two patients in the short-course group felt and displayed no loss in this area, although one did have demonstrable brain damage.

The typical ECT patient suffers less damage to the frontal lobes than the typical lobotomy patient, and so we would expect to find a less severe clinical reaction. But any loss of self-determination, initiative, or spontaneity in a human being is a significant loss. Difficult to define subjectively and almost impossible to measure objectively except in grossly disordered cases, this loss is nonetheless of very great importance. It is therefore surprising that no ECT research study or textbook has raised the possibility of such a defect following ECT, even though many clinical studies indirectly describe the defect when reporting on the use of ECT to pacify or calm state mental hospital wards.

Throughout the United States and around the world today, former psychiatric patients have begun to organize to publicize their concern about the damaging and humiliating treatment they have received in psychiatric hospitals (Frank, 1978). Much of their energy has been devoted to describing the devastating effects of electroconvulsive therapy. What they have to say about the treatment corresponds exactly to the cases I have reported and to the many clinical and research studies in the literature. Are we to believe with Kalinowsky that these people—one and all—are "neurotics" who have not been helped by their ECT? Because the existence of brain damage following ECT is also confirmed through animal research, autopsy reports, brain-wave studies, neurological examinations, and systematic psychological research, it is both rational and imperative to acknowledge that ECT frequently produces severe mental dysfunction in the form of both retrograde amnesia and ongoing mental disabilities.

FOOTNOTE

[1] *Amygdalotomy* is a psychosurgical operation that damages or destroys the amygdala, a portion of the temporal lobe which plays a key role in the regulation of emotion. It lies close to the heaviest concentration of electric current during ECT.

BIBLIOGRAPHY

American Psychiatric Association. *Task Force Report 14: Electroconvulsive Therapy.* Washington, D.C.: American Psychiatric Association, September, 1978.

Andersen, R. Differences in the course of learning as measured by various memory tasks after amygdalotomy in man. In *Psychosurgery,* edited by E. Hitchcock, L. Laitinen and K. Vaernet. Springfield, Ill.: Charles C. Thomas, 1972.

Braatoy, T. Indications for shock treatment in psychiatry. *Am. J. Psychiatry* 104 (1948):573-575.

Breggin, P. R. Coercion of voluntary patients in an open hospital. *Arch. Gen. Psychiatry* 10 (1964):173-181.

——. *The Crazy From The Sane.* New York: Lyle Stuart, 1971a.

——. Psychotherapy as applied ethics. *Psychiatry* 34 (1971b):59-75.

——. Lobotomy is still bad medicine. *Medical Opinion* 8 (1972a):32-36.

——. The politics of therapy. *Mental Health* 56 (1972b):9-13.

——. The return of lobotomy and psychosurgery. *Congressional Record.* E1602-E1612, February 24, 1972. Reprinted in *Quality of Health Care—Human Experimentation.* Hearings before Senator Edward Kennedy's Subcommittee on Health, US Senate. Washington, D.C.: US Government Printing Office, 1973a.

——. Testimony given in *Kaimowitz v Department of Mental Health.* Civil No. 73-19, 434-AW (Cir. Ct. Wayne Co., Michigan, July 10, 1973b).

——. The second wave of psychosurgery. *Mental Health* 57 (1973c):10-13.

——. Therapy as applied utopian politics. *Ment. Health Soc.* 1 (1974):129-146.

——. Psychosurgery for political purposes. *Duquesne Law Rev.* 13 (1975a):841-862.

——. Psychosurgery for the control of violence: A critical review. In *Neural Bases of Violence and Aggression,* edited by W. Fields and W. Sweet. St. Louis: Warren H. Green, 1975b.

——. Psychiatry and psychotherapy as political processes. *Am. J. Psychother.* 29 (1975c):369-382.

——. Needed: voluntaristic psychiatry. *Reason* (September, 1975d):7.

——. Why we consent to oppression. *Reason* (September, 1977a):28.

——. If psychosurgery is wrong in principle? *Psychiatric Opinion* 14 (Nov./Dec. 1977b):23.

——. Madness is a failure of free will; therapy too often encourages it. In *La Folie Dans La Psychanalyse,* edited by A. Verdiglione. Paris: Payot, 1977c.

——. Mind-disabling therapy: The

common effects of the major tranquilizers, ECT and psychosurgery. In *The Psychosurgery Debate: A Model for Policy Makers in Mental Health,* edited by E. Valenstein. New York: W. H. Freeman, 1979.

Brosin, H. W. Psychiatric conditions following head injuries. In *American Handbook of Psychiatry.* Vol. 2, edited by S. Arieti. New York: Basic Books, 1959.

Cronholm, B. and J. O. Ottosson. The experience of memory function after electroconvulsive therapy. *Br. J. Psychiatry* 109 (1963a):251-258.

Dedichen, H. H. A comparison of 1459 shock-treated and 969 non-shock-treated psychoses in Norwegian hospitals. *Acta. Psychiatr. Neurol. Scand.* (supp) 37 (1946).

Fink, M. A unified theory of the action of the physiodynamic therapies. *J. Hillside Hosp.* 6 (1957):197-206.

——. Effect of anticholinergic agent, diethazine, on EEG and behavior: Significance for theory of convulsive therapy. *Arch. Neurol. Psychiatry* 80 (1958):380-386.

Fink, M., R. L. Kahn and M. Green. Experimental studies of the electroshock process. *Dis. Nerv. System* 19 (1958):113-118.

Frank L. R., ed. *The History of Shock Treatment.* San Francisco: Network Against Psychiatric Assault (NAPA), 1975. Revised and expanded edition, San Francisco: L. R. Frank, 1978.

Freeman, W. and J. W. Watts. Physiological psychology. *Annu. Rev. Psychol.* 6 (1944): 517-542.

——. *Psychosurgery.* Springfield, Ill.: Charles C. Thomas, 1950.

Goldstein, K. Functional disturbances in brain damage. In *American Handbook of Psychiatry,* 2d ed. Vol. 3, edited by S. Arieti. New York: Basic Books, 1975.

Gomez, J. Subjective side-effects of ECT. *Br. J. Psychiatry* 127 (1975): 609-611.

Grimm, R. J. Convulsions as therapy:

The outer shadows. *Psychiatric Opinion* (January, 1978):30.

Janis, I. L. Memory loss following electric convulsive treatments. *J. Pers.* 17 (1948):29-32.

Kalinowsky, L. Convulsive shock treatment. In *American Handbook of Psychiatry.* Vol. 2, edited by S. Arieti. New York: Basic Books, 1959.

——. Electric and other convulsive treatments. In *American Handbook of Psychiatry.* Vol. 5, edited by S. Arieti. New York: Basic Books, 1975a.

——. The convulsive therapies. In *Comprehensive Textbook of Psychiatry,* edited by A. M. Freedman, H. I. Kaplan and B. J. Sadock. Baltimore: Williams & Wilkins, 1975b.

Kalinowsky, L. and H. Hippius. *Pharmacological, Convulsive and Other Somatic Treatments in Psychiatry.* New York: Grune & Stratton, 1969.

Kalinowsky, L. and P. Hoch. *Somatic Treatments in Psychiatry.* New York: Grune & Stratton, 1952, 1961.

Kolb, L. *Modern Clinical Psychiatry,* 9th ed. Philadelphia: Saunders, 1977.

Levy, N. A., H. M. Serota and R. R. Grinker. Disturbances in brain function following convulsive shock therapy. *Arch. Neurol. Psychiatry* 47 (1942):1009-1029.

Noyes, A. and L. Kolb. *Modern Clinical Psychiatry,* 8th ed. Philadelphia: Saunders, 1973.

Practising Psychiatrist: The experience of electroconvulsive therapy. *Br. J. Psychiatry* 111 (1965):365-367.

Schwartzman, A. E. and P. E. Termansen. Intensive electroconvulsive therapy: A follow-up study. *Can. Psychiatr. Assoc. J.* 12 (1967): 217-218.

Squire, L. R. ECT and memory loss. *Am. J. Psychiatry* 134 (1977): 997-1001.

Tow, P. M. *Personality Changes Follow-*

ing Frontal Leucotomy. London: Oxford University Press, 1954.

Watkins, C., E. J. Stainbrook and H. Lowenbach. Report on subconvulsive reaction to electric shock and its sequelae in normal subject. *Psychiatr. Q.* 15 (1941):724-729.

Weinstein, E. A. and R. L. Kahn. Symbolic reorganization in brain injuries. In *American Handbook of Psychiatry.* Vol. 1, edited by S. Arieti. New York: Basic Books, 1959.

ROBERT F. MORGAN

22

The Commercial Pre-empted the Program: A Book Review

In the campaign to reduce iatrogenic impact, one finds a variety of campaigners. A few, in their zeal to reform, go beyond any data base and lose sight of progressive objectives, defining themselves only by what is attacked. Others may use an attack on one abuse to promote another, even more iatrogenic than the first. Others may be solely invested in the superiority of one discipline or approach over others. When books emerge designed to expose and confront iatrogenic abuses, such criticism has the potential to improve the system and deserves undefensive attention. Such books also deserve critical scrutiny themselves: is the anti-iatrogenic criticism a program that has been pre-empted by an underlying commercial? For this handbook, an attempt has been made to draw from a variety of disciplines and points of view, hopefully diffusing any personalized biases beyond the desire to criticize meaningfully held in common by all our authors. Following, however, a book is reviewed which exemplifies the commercialization of the obsolete model of medical supremacy at the cost of its promised program to combat iatrogenesis. Thanks are due the *Kitchener-Waterloo Record* for calling the book to my attention, and to *Canadian Psychology* (1981, 22:207-209) for encouraging and including this review.   **R.F.M.**

A Book Review:
Psychobattery: A Chronicle of Psychotherapeutic Abuse
written by educational psychologist Therese Spitzer
with medical discussion by husband Ralph Spitzer, M.D.

This book is iatrogenic. If the doctor tells you that you have an *iatrogenic* complication, he means that the medical staff made a mistake at your expense. This impressive sounding label often protects the clinician from having to explain that a sponge was left inside you, you were overdosed on medication, the wrong organ was removed or worse.

Well, clinicians, being human, make mistakes. Mature professionals acknowledge that and cooperate with fair and systematic evaluations of their work.

Reprinted with permission from *Canadian Psychology* 22 (1981):207-209. Author's rejoinder and reviewer's responses are in *Canadian Psychology* 23 (1982):48-50.

I suggested to the American Psychiatric Association some years back that they include an iatrogenic category in their diagnostic lists: they didn't answer formally but many individuals in the association told me there was fear such a diagnosis would lead to automatic malpractice prosecution. None argued that clinical mistakes did not lead to the problems diagnosed.

In recent years, I and others have moved toward encouraging an international study of Iatrogenics by an ombudsman group working to improve professional practice and protect the consumer. Using scientific and legal methods, some of the more drastic and hazardous techniques have already been curtailed (e.g., lobotomies, shock treatment, institutionalization). Ultimately, my hope would be that anyone treated for a serious condition would have access to independent before-and-after testing to determine the results of that treatment.

Given this point of view, I looked forward to reading the Spitzer book in hope of finding Canadian compadres, fresh recruits, for our efforts. *Psychobattery* promised a critical comprehensive review of psychotherapeutic techniques and, for this, there is certainly a need.

Those hopes weren't realized. This is basically a political book, promoting the partisan point of view that one discipline, medicine, is better than all the rest; that drug prescription works and psychotherapy does not; that medical supremacy, much as it was practised before World War II, is our only hope.

This is a book similar in pattern to the controversial American predecessor *The Psychological Society* by Martin Gross (New York: Random House, 1978) used by the American Medical Association lobby in the congressional effort to gain back ground lost to competing disciplines. Spitzer says quite clearly, and often, there is danger from "the growing power of psychologists, nurses and counsellors" (p. 202). Danger to whom? The patient? Or to medical monopolies on health insurance?

The book's argument rests primarily on anonymous case histories selected to put any approach but medical ones in their worst light. There is occasional passing reference to research, but none seems to have been done in any systematic way to shed light on the book's key issues. The result is diatribe without information.

Nothing short of scorn greets those who would prefer to learn more about themselves: "When I told an internationally famous physicist at Cambridge University that people in North America often got together for two or three days at a time to spend fifteen hours a day in such groups, his question was, 'What business are they transacting? Are they trying to stop nuclear armament, solve the genetic recombination problem or perhaps come to grips with the energy crisis?' When told there was no objective problem to consider, but simply exploration of the participants' psyches, he was completely incredulous and believed I was putting him on."

Are we really wrong to spend some time on subjective matters? Marathon groups can be done well or poorly, fittingly or inappropriately, but there have been controlled studies showing that *some* create useful human change. More basically, must we abandon *all* self-reflection to solve the energy crisis?

Clearly, the Vancouver author has: (without solving the energy crisis, either!) ... witness the confused thinking that denies mental disease can be treated by psychological means because "mental phenomenon is a function of the brain, a biochemical system" (p. 206, 207). This takes us back a century or more to the days when people separated thinking from brain activity. We have long since realized that thinking is in fact a biochemical activity based in the brain and the rest of the body's nervous system. *Because* the mind and the body are not separate, psychological techniques can bring about impressive changes in the body. Today, we see biofeedback, hypnosis and even guided imagery for fighting cancer available as never before. Remove the brain and thinking becomes exceedingly difficult! (The author, however, tries.)

Ernest Jones, Freud's biographer, remarked that at the turn of the century, Freud's greatest impact on the public was his ability to cure problems like hysterical paralysis without medicine or surgery, just by *talking* to the patient. Yes, talking has electro-chemical impact on the brain and, therefore, on behaviour. The Spitzers would have us turn the clock back more than eighty years, making scientific progress a casualty in the battle for patient dollars.

On the plus side, there is a brief but critical section on some risky procedures such as lithium overdosing (Ch. 4) and electro-convulsive shock (pp. 66-68). Even here, however, the criticism seems based more on the fact that physicians themselves have questioned the techniques than on any scientific findings from other disciplines.

Medical doctors belong on the team of problem solvers in resolving and preventing human problems. Many, perhaps most, physicians welcome common cause with other disciplines in this effort. This book will embarrass such clinicians.

The strong push Spitzer gives drugs over counselling in virtually any human crisis brings us to the logical conclusion that vocational counselling, marriage counselling, and even family therapy (p. 138) are best performed by drug prescription. How similar this thought is, come to think of it, to the Haight-Ashbury days of the sixties. . . .

I recommend this book only to those who are angry at their therapist: it may be therapeutic to read its pseudoscientific ventilation. But, then again, if the author is right, you might do better to save $12, skip the book and take a Tylenol.

S. JALAL SHAMSIE

23

Antisocial Adolescents: Our Treatments Do Not Work. Where Do We Go From Here?

Jalal Shamsie is a Professor of Psychiatry at the University of Toronto and Director of Research and Education at the Thistletown Regional Centre for Children and Adolescents. On October 13, 1980, the Toronto *Globe and Mail* ran an editorial referring to Dr. Shamsie's work: with much fanfare, the "Failed Techniques" feature shared his conclusion from program evaluation research that many professional approaches to treating juvenile delinquents were either ineffective or worse than no treatment at all. For example, adolescents seeing social workers for 2.5 hours of weekly counseling had, after eighteen months, worse police records and discipline problems than those having no counseling at all. The feature, appropriately, endorsed Shamsie's honesty although the community of helpers was far from unanimous in this applause. Willing to weather any storm of defensive professionals, Shamsie has modified and updated his original paper (presented at the Canadian Psychiatric Association's 30th annual meeting in Toronto, 1980) for this handbook. **R.F.M.**

Summary—This paper provides a review of studies conducted to determine the effectiveness of various techniques employed in the treatment of antisocial adolescents. The impact of such studies on clinical practice is examined. An explanation is provided to account for the poor results obtained. New approaches which have more promise are indicated.

For our purposes, antisocial adolescents will include all adolescents whose behavior shows evidence of a repetitive and persistent pattern of conduct through which either the basic rights of others or major age-appropriate societal norms are violated. The above definition is taken from the criteria laid down in DSM III (7) for conduct disorders in children and adolescents. The critical part of this definition is the persistent and repetitive aspect, which implies a long-standing disturbance. However, all antisocial adolescents are not necessarily repetitive and persistent offenders as required for the definition of conduct disorders. A number of adolescents who commit antisocial acts never appear before the family court, and

Reprinted with permission of the *Canadian Journal of Psychiatry* 26 (1981):357-364.

therefore are not included in any delinquent statistics or only commit one or two delinquent acts. Those antisocial adolescents therefore do not meet the criteria of a persistent and repetitive pattern of conduct disorder. Most of these adolescents fall into the group of emotional disorders as described in DSM III. In this group are included adolescents exhibiting a variety of neurotic disorders, exhibiting anxiety and depression as their main manifestations where the antisocial act is simply a cry for help or an act of desperation. These adolescents are disturbed and only become disturbing to draw attention to their condition. They generally are reasonably motivated to seeking a solution to their problem and respond well to traditional psychotherapeutic methods such as psychotherapy and case work.

These antisocial adolescents are different in their psychopathology and makeup from persistent and repetitious conduct disorders, who seldom show anxiety or depression as marked features. Their main, sometimes only, presenting problem is their antisocial behavior and therefore are more disturbing than disturbed. Most adolescents therefore who commit antisocial acts fall into two major categories: adolescents who exhibit a variety of neurotic symptoms, are more disturbed than disturbing, who commit an occasional antisocial act; and adolescents with conduct disorders who are persistent, repetitive offenders and are more disturbing than disturbed.

This presentation is mostly concerned about the latter group. It is the adolescents with conduct disorders who form the large portion of correctional school population, and appear again and again at the family court.

Incidence

Statistics referring to criminal acts of antisocial adolescents are based on legal definitions and out of necessity include some one-time offenders who do not fit our criteria of persistent antisocial adolescents. Statistics also neglect to include many adolescents who have committed antisocial acts but who for one reason or another have not come before the courts. Therefore, it must be remembered that statistics presented may include adolescents who do not meet our definition of antisocial adolescents.

There has been an alarming increase in juvenile crime in recent years. In Canada, between 1962 and 1975, juvenile arrests show an increase of 186.4 percent for violent crimes and 185.5 percent for property crimes (32). The Federal Bureau of Investigations of the United States has reported that the national increase in arrests for juveniles, between seven and seventeen years of age, has tripled for violent crimes climbing 293.4 percent and increased 131.9 percent for property crimes between 1960 and 1974 (35). Statistics for violent crimes in the United States include arrests for robbery 375 percent increase; aggravated assault 240 percent; homicide 211 percent and rape 102 percent.

This increase in juvenile crime is not only a North American phenomenon but is more widespread as indicated by the figures available for the

United Kingdom (26). Arrests for indictable offences, per 100,000 population, increased by 116 percent to 120 percent for juveniles between the ages of fourteen to seventeen and seventeen to twenty-one years respectively. American arrest rates per 100,000 population show an increase in juvenile arrests of 231.5 percent for violent crimes, 164.9 percent for property crimes and 170.8 percent for all serious crimes.

There are two significant facts about these figures. First the total increase cannot be explained by an increase in population. Both the United Kingdom and the American figures referred to above are based on arrests rates per 100,000 population. Although the Canadian figures are based on the national population figures, we find that the juvenile population, ages seven to seventeen years, has increased only 15 percent (33) while the crime rate has escalated dramatically.

The second fact is that although there has been an overall increase in crime affecting all ages, the increase in crime for the juvenile population is much larger than for the adult population. In Canada, violent crimes showed an increase of 186 percent for juveniles as compared to 128 percent for adults. In the United States, comparable figures are 293 percent (juveniles) and 130 percent (adults) and in the United Kingdom, 120 percent (juveniles) and 83 percent (adults). Therefore, the increase in the crime rate for the juvenile population cannot be explained by an increase in the population or an overall increase in crime. This is a significant increase which is confined to the juvenile population.

Our Treatments Do Not Work

The majority of antisocial adolescents are either treated in some correctional setting, such as a training school or in a mental health setting. A number of studies (20, 3, 34) have indicated that aggression and acting out behavior is a predominant symptom and possibly the largest single basis for clinical referral of children to mental health centers.

At Thistletown Regional Centre for Children and Adolescents, located in northwestern Toronto, out of a total of 3274 referrals between 1977 and 1979, 2380 (72.69 percent) had disruptive behavior as one of the major presenting problems. Naomi Rae-Grant (20) described aggression as a major problem in 53 percent of 119 boys from eight different settings in the Province of Ontario. In girls aggression was less common, but still present in 40 percent of the girls treated. These studies indicate the possibility that between one-half and two-thirds of all referrals, of children and adolescents to mental health centers, show antisocial behavior as a predominant symptom. In correctional settings and training schools, the figure is considerably larger and a vast majority of children and adolescents are there because of their antisocial behavior. Most of these children have had treatment in community mental health centers without success and were later placed in the correctional system.

The treatments carried out at mental health centers or correctional centers use similar approaches. In this paper the following treatment approaches will be examined: case work, individual psychotherapy, behavior therapy, group counseling and family therapy. From institutional programs two approaches will be examined: milieu therapy and therapeutic community.

Romig (23) carried out an extensive review of the literature on the rehabilitation of juvenile delinquents covering 829 studies. For detailed examination, he included only those studies which had controls and used behavioral criteria for improvement. One hundred and twenty studies met the above criteria. All studies reported in this paper also meet this criteria and most of them are taken from the review conducted by Romig. In most studies, the improvement criteria is the recidivism rate (i.e., a measure of whether released youth are reinstitutionalized after treatment). Although there are arguments both for and against using the recidivism rate as the only criteria for effectiveness (31, 8), it is a reliable and readily available measure.

Another possible critical observation might be that most of the evidence referred to in this paper is based on evaluative outcome studies. The question could be raised as to the merits of evaluative program processes as opposed to program outcomes. This question is discussed extensively in a study by Chommie et al. (6). Their paper raises some concerns as to whether complex clinical and social programs can best be evaluated by experimental designs focusing on program outcome alone without the usefulness of evaluating program processes. While program process may explain the program outcome, make goals more specific and improve delivery of services; the outcome must finally determine whether the programs should be continued, modified or discarded. Finally Elliott (9) has suggested that Romig's conclusions regarding the effectiveness of specific treatments appear premature, he suggests this on the basis of what he deems to be the poor quality of delinquency evaluation studies. The question is when should one draw any conclusions? If after close to one thousand studies in a decade and a half, nothing worthwhile can be said to the clinician in the field, then it is questionable whether the effort and the expense of evaluative research is justifiable. Robins (22) has suggested that conclusions drawn from two imperfect studies are more persuasive than a single elegant study. It seems that Romig's (23) conclusions, based on many controlled studies including thousands of subjects, are hardly premature, but it is about time that some guidance was provided to clinicians by the evaluative research.

Case Work

In most studies using case work as the main approach to treatment, the case work consisted of a definition of the problem, recommendations and direct service. It is the direct service which has been emphasized in this approach. This service was client system oriented; that meant that the problems of the adolescent were seen as influenced not only by his personality but equally or more by the pathological experiences encountered in relationships with significant others. Thus, any individual or combination of members of each client system could be indicated as the primary recipient of service. In most cases, clients were seen two to three hours a week in individual or group sessions, aimed at dealing with disturbed behavior, at times providing insight-oriented discussions.

Careful studies such as that conducted by Berleman et al. (4) show no differences between the experimental and control group. In this study fifty-two boys were placed in the treatment group and fifty boys were in the control group. The ages ranged between twelve to fourteen years. The treatment consisted of intensive case work and social services over a one-to-two-year period. The boys also participated in 2½ hours of group counseling each week and they were seen at home or at school for crisis intervention. At an eighteen-month follow up, the school discipline and police records were found to be significantly worse for the treatment group as compared with the control group. While this study reported negative results, nine others reviewed by Romig (23) involving 5356 adolescents all showed no significant difference at the end of treatment (table 1). All had controls and in all studies case work constituted the dominant program ingredient. Berleman et al. (4) concluded their study with the following:

> To have this effort fail and to have this failure so well documented that few rationalizations can be made to mitigate the outcome, inevitably raises the question whether such intervention efforts should continue.

Individual Psychotherapy

A major review in this area has been carried out by Levitt (12). After evaluating eighteen studies, he reported that much improvement and partial improvement was reported in 67.05 percent of cases across the studies. Cases with no improvement were found to be 32.51 percent. Therefore roughly one-third of the cases improved much, one-third partially and one-third not at all. On follow-up, the much or partial improvement rate increased a little further from 67 percent to 78 percent. However, the effectiveness of psychotherapy becomes very questionable when Levitt (12) reported 72.5 percent improvement in children who received no treatment at all. Therefore, if the success of psychotherapy as a treatment approach is to be established, the success rate has to be better than 72.5 percent. Another interesting finding reported by Levitt (13) was that success with psychotherapy varied depending upon the diagnosis. In this review (13), based on twenty-two evaluation studies, he found that the success rate with psychotherapy was lowest for the acting out children, 55 percent as compared to over 65.2 percent for the children as a whole. This finding is not surprising as psychotherapy is a mode of treatment where the motivation and cooperation of the patient is an essential element. As antisocial adolescents generally suffer from disorders which do not cause much anxiety or *disease* to themselves, there is little motivation for change. However those antisocial adolescents who are amenable and motivated do well in psychotherapy. This was borne out in a study by Adams (1). Each youth on entry to the training school was diagnosed as amenable or not amenable to psychotherapy. After determining the amenableness, they were randomly assigned to treatment or control groups. Altogether there were four groups with 100 youths per group: treatment amenable; treatment nonamenable; control amenable and control nonamenable. The length of treatment averaged nine months. Individual therapy was found to result in a significant difference in parole performance in favor of amenable youths who received individual psychotherapy. Nonamenable youths did no better than controls. Thus psychotherapy, if applied indiscriminately as a treatment of delinquents, is no better than no treatment, but if cases are selected there is at least evidence in one study that it works.

Table 1: Summary of Individual Interventions

Intervention Technique	No. of Studies	Cases	Results Positive	No Difference	Negative
Case Work	10	5356	0	9	1
Individual Psychotherapy	10	1648	2	6	2
Behavior Modification	14	1918	8	6	0

Romig (23) in his review of ten studies, using individual psychotherapy as the treatment, reported that only two of these studies showed positive results, six of the studies reported no significant difference and two were negative (table 1). Out of the two which had positive results one is Adam's (1) study referred to above and the other is a study by Thomas (37) who used some procedures which are more akin to a behavioral approach than psychodynamic.

Behavior Modification

The results of the application of this approach are variable. Romig (23) reviewed fourteen studies involving about 2000 youths (table I). He draws one firm conclusion at the end of his study, that behavior modification will work only when the behavior to be changed is specific and behaviorally simple. Therefore, it may be possible to modify a target behavior, but this may not effect the recidivism rate or overall delinquency.

This is illustrated in the study by Jesness et al. (10). He evaluated the effects of behavior modification contingency contracting on youth. Two hundred and fifty-four male and female youths on probation were randomly assigned to treatment or control groups. The control group had 158 youths. The probation case workers and their supervisors were given several days of training in contingency contracting and other behavior modification techniques. They were then required to develop contingency contracts for targeted behaviors. Contingency contracting involved written agreements with the youths through which they would receive certain rewards for improved behavior. The short range results were positive. Fifty-nine percent of the experimental group's target behaviors were eliminated as compared to 43 percent of the control group's target behaviors. The results were statistically significant. At the six-month follow up however, there were no significant differences between the two groups in terms of number and severity of offences.

This study illustrates that although behavior modification techniques can modify or reduce targeted antisocial behavior, it appears that on long-term basis it may not improve the chances of a youth successfully rehabilitating in the community.

There are a number of studies in the literature indicating that given a targeted behavior, a behavior modification program can be successfully applied which will alter the behavior so that it becomes more socially acceptable. However, this may simply make it easier for the staff to handle the adolescent while he is in the residential facility. The pertinent question is, does behavior modification as a treatment technique, go beyond the target behavior and generalize so as to improve the chances of the youth remaining in the community after his discharge from the institution? A large number of studies as documented by Romig (23) provide the answer in negative.

Group Counseling

Included here are group counseling, group therapy and group discussions. This probably is the single most frequently used method of treatment with delinquents both inside and outside the correctional institutions. Romig (23) reviewed twenty-seven studies involving over 1800 youths (table 2). Of these twenty-seven studies, nine showed positive results, one negative results and seventeen studies showed no difference from controls. Two examples of these studies will be cited, one with positive and one with negative results.

Table 2: Summary of Group Interventions

| Intervention Technique | No. of Studies | Cases | Results | | |
			Positive	No Difference	Negative
Group Counseling	27	1867	9	17	1
Family Therapy	12	2184	4	6	2

The study with positive results was carried out by O'Brien (15) on delinquent boys who were on probation or parole. All the youths were attending public high school. Most of the boys came from low socioeconomic groups. Before starting group therapy they were given eighteen hours of didactic pretherapy training. This was a unique feature of the study. This training involved teaching such concepts as the importance of interpersonal relationships to facilitate group psychotherapy. This teaching was done through lectures, films and field trips. Eighty-two hours of group psychotherapy was given to the experimental group, while the control group participated in a regular public school program. The results showed that the experimental group had a significantly lower number of boys dropping out of school and significantly fewer had to be returned to confinement.

In another study, O'Brien (16) evaluated the results of psychoanalytically oriented group therapy given once a week for seven months. The study involved thirty-two youths between the ages of sixteen to eighteen. Half were placed in the experimental and the other half in the control group. The youths in the control group received regular parole supervision. The results of the California Psychological Inventory Personality Test showed that the control group improved while the experimental group deteriorated. On follow up after seven months, there was no significant difference between the two groups in the recidivism rate.

Group counseling does not appear to be a very effective treatment approach as is evident by the fact that only one-third (nine out of twenty-seven) of the studies (23) reported positive results. Although some studies reported improvement for the time the youth was in treatment, this improvement did not carry over upon release. It appears that the improvement may have been due to the opportunity for the youths to express their feelings in a group, while in treatment, but made no significant difference in the recidivism rate.

Family Therapy

The characteristic of this approach is the involvement of the family as an essential element of the treatment. Unlike case work, group and individual therapy, family therapy is one of the newer treatment techniques to be used with delinquents. This may account for the fewer number of studies available for review. As there is no one or correct way of involving the family, therefore, almost every study has a slightly different slant. Three studies were found (5, 29, 36) where short-term family crisis counseling was utilized. The results of two studies (29, 36) were positive and in one (5) there was no difference between the control and the experimental group. In all studies, the family was involved at the time of arrest. Romig (23) reports two studies involving family counseling and case work where the results were negative in reducing subsequent delinquent behavior, six which showed no significant difference and four which were positive (table 2).

The study by Alexander and Parsons (2) deserves some detail as it is interesting in its design and results. Three approaches were tried in this study. First was a short-term behavioral family intervention with system theory providing the foundation. Deviant behavior was seen as a function of the entire system in which the individual was embedded. Second was a didactic group discussion on attitudes and feelings about family relationships and adolescent problems. The third group received psychodynamic insight-oriented family therapy. The control group received no therapeutic attention or contact. The treatment period ranged from four to six weeks.

The group which received the short-term behavioral family intervention program did best. There was an improvement in family communication skills as well as less recidivism, for such offences as runaway and truancy. There was no difference between the client-centered family discussion group and control, and the psychodynamic insight-oriented family program did worse on recidivism (73 percent) than the control group (50 percent).

The most significant finding of this study appears to be that the three types of family therapy produced three different results. Even the one type, behavioral, which was successful, the success was related to only behavioral offences such as running away and truancy. These offences by their nature may be more related to family problems and therefore, more amenable to family therapy, while criminal offences such as shoplifting and drug abuse were unaffected. To conclude, family therapy of a certain type is successful with certain problems of antisocial adolescents. It is also significant when it is applied, it appears to be more successful in a crisis situation such as at the time of arrest.

Institutional Programs

A child in most cases is sent to an institution such as a training school only after efforts to help him within the community have failed. Romig (24) reported that in one training school in Texas ninety-four percent of the youths in residence had received some form of community program before being placed in the training school. As we have indicated, the adequacy ad effectiveness of such community programs providing case work, individual and group therapy remain in question.

The percentage of adolescents however who appear before the family courts and end up in a correctional institution is very small. Romig & Seddler (25) estimated it to be 3 percent for Texas for the years 1972-1974. The number of children being sent to training schools is constantly dropping as the ineffectiveness and harmful effects of institutional treatments are being recognized. In Ontario, the number of children in training schools has decreased from 1389 in 1970, to 773 in 1979.

The institutional approaches reviewed for this paper include milieu therapy and therapeutic community. For our purposes, programs included under milieu therapy are those in which a more democratic and limited self-government was allowed and where some emphasis was placed on individual and group psychotherapy. The control groups generally participated in an authoritarian-disciplinary program. Eight studies were reviewed by Romig (23), which provided milieu therapy with proper control groups (table 3). These studies also provided follow-up reports. The results of six of the eight studies reported no significant difference, one was positive and one reported negative results.

Table 3: Summary of Institutional Interventions

Intervention Technique	No. of Studies	Cases	Positive	No Difference	Negative
				Results	
Milieu Therapy	8	2399	1	6	1
Therapeutic Community	4	867	0	3	1

An example of milieu therapy as defined in this paper is a study by Levinson et al. (11). In this study, 225 boys were randomly divided into either the treatment or control group. The treatment group received group and individual counseling as well as more informal and therapeutic staff-inmate contacts than the control group. A fifteen-month follow-up reported no significant difference in community adjustment as measured by parole failure.

Therapeutic Community

Four studies were reviewed by Romig (23), which used therapeutic community as the principal treatment approach (table 3). The key element of this approach was that the youths shared and were involved in the responsibility and decision-making regarding their own treatment. The program included counseling meetings, community meetings and group meetings. Out of the four studies, three found no significant difference and the fourth study showed negative results for the experimental group.

Seckel's study (30) is an example of therapeutic community as defined here. In this study, there was a random assignment of seventy-five boys to the treatment group and fifty-four boys to the control group. The three main components of the treatment group were five months determinant length of stay, self-government and more intensive individual and group therapy. The control group received the regular California training school program. Contrary to expectations of the staff, there was no significant difference in the follow-up performance of the two groups.

The inability to find a single study to establish the usefulness of the therapeutic community approach with antisocial adolescents is astonishing. For many years, there has been a belief among mental health professionals that therapeutic community is a uniquely effective treatment for antisocial adolescents. Yet, there is not a single study with proper controls and follow-up which proves that it is any more effective than the programs regularly provided in training schools.

Conclusions

Three facts clearly emerge from what has been presented here. First, there has been a considerable increase in the crime rate for the juvenile population, much larger than the increase in the rate for adults. The factor which makes this increase especially worrisome is that the increase is most significant in violent crimes.

The second fact is that the treatments available to help antisocial adolescents are remarkably unsuccessful. It does not appear to make any difference whether the adolescents are placed in the correctional stream or directed towards the more expensive mental health centers, the results are equally poor. Therefore, we are faced on the one hand with an increase in the number of adolescents involved in crime and on the other with the lack of success in treatment. There is one additional factor which makes this situation more critical. Unlike other psychiatric disorders (e.g., neurosis where there is a high rate of spontaneous recovery), it has been clearly shown that this is not so in conduct disorders (21, 28). Therefore, it cannot be hoped that with the passage of time most of these adolescents will grow out of their problems and join the ranks of law abiding, taxpaying adults. Robins (21) has shown that most adolescents with conduct disorders become adults who either end up in the correctional system or remain dependent on the welfare system.

The problems as outlined clearly point out two areas for possible attack. First steps must be taken to reduce the rate of increasing juvenile crimes and second, the effectiveness of treatment techniques must be improved. To achieve the first, there has to be an understanding of the causes of the significant increase in juvenile crime. Crime prevention is a complex subject and deserves a separate study aimed at understanding the sociocultural, economic and political factors which could be involved. The thrust of this paper however, is towards finding ways of improving the effectiveness of treatment techniques.

Where Do We Go From Here?

In light of this information, it seems worthwhile to ask the following questions. Why have such an array of treatment approaches produced unsatisfactory results? What new approaches, or concepts, show promise? How have evaluative studies affected clinical practice with adolescents?

The unsatisfactory results with the present prevalent approaches may be due to our perception of antisocial behavior as a sickness rather than a lack of socialization. The treatment model assumes a patient with a sickness or a problem which the therapist is going to cure or at least reduce the suffering. These adolescents do not profess to be suffering from any discomfort or desire a solution to any intrapsychic problem. When they do ask for help it is to get a job, money, or freedom from their families, family courts or the police. Most of the treatments discussed aim to help the adolescent understand the reasons for and the nature of his problem. The assumption being that if he understands why he is in his present predicament, then it will be easier for him to get out of it. However as the results show, it does not seem to work that way. The treatment model may not be the most appropriate conceptual model, as it assumes that there is someone who is willing to play or at least fits the patient's role. It may make more sense to visualize antisocial behavior in adolescents as a problem arising from the lack of socialization, which was caused by inadequate attempts to teach socialization at an early age, or by a defect in learning ability of social norms.

If the problem has arisen because of lack of proper teaching of social norms at an early age, then we should act as educators and develop programs of socialization. If, on the other hand, the problem has arisen because of a defect in learning ability, in spite of adequate teaching, then we should attempt to rehabilitate the adolescent in spite of his defect. This may mean teaching the adolescent to live with his handicap and adjusting the environment as far as possible.

There is some evidence that programs developed along the above lines are more successful. There are a number of studies showing the effectiveness of social learning programs, which are really concentrated efforts toward teaching social norms (17, 18, 19, 38, 39).

In one study, Patterson (18) working with the parents and teachers of aggressive children, has reported a success rate of roughly 70 percent which persisted during the twelve-month follow-up period. Yet, the problem of a lack of generalization remains as with other behavior modification techniques. It has been shown that reducing deviant child behavior in the home did not lessen disruptive behavior in the classroom (38). As the results indicate the success even in social learning is not universal. Patterson (18) admits that a welfare mother, living alone with her children, who is unable to cope with the myriad of crises, is the type of parent with whom success is hard to achieve. Yet, in spite of professional help and a behavioristic approach, one of the encouraging outcomes of this treatment is that the parent's and teacher's authority is not undermined but reinstated. Probably the essence of this approach is to teach parents and teachers how to use their authority effectively to bring about desired changes in the child's behavior. Wolf et al. (39), have shown that principles of social learning can be successfully applied with good results in an institutional setting.

The effectiveness of these programs may support the concept that the majority of children behave according to social norms because some person or persons took the trouble to teach the social norms, in a consistent and affectionate manner, at an early age. If this learning did not take place, for whatever reason, an asocial or antisocial adolescent may be the result. He can be taught social norms when he is older but like other learning it may take more time and effort.

Beside social learning, one more approach seems to hold promise, Mills et al. (14) have shown that getting a job and holding it, per se, prevents the adolescent from further antisocial acts. The authors explain the success of the program as due to recruiting and training employers and in shaping proemployment behavior in the adolescents. The positive results obtained could also have been affected by the fear of returning to the court's jurisdiction in case of failure. Another important factor may have been the reaction of peers, which was negative initially, but as the economic circumstances of these adolescents improved the opposition turned to envy and many of these peers requested to join the program. One additional factor, not mentioned by the authors, could be that besides the financial rewards, a job provides a status and a place in society which may satisfy a critical need for security and stability in these adolescents who mostly come from broken homes (27).

In answer to the last question, the impact of evaluative studies on clinical practice has been minimal. In many centers, case work, individual therapy and group therapy remain the main thrust of therapeutic armamentarium. In some centers, behavior therapy has taken root replacing milieu therapy with improved results, but even there the limitations of behavior therapy are not fully understood. How does one explain this lack of impact of evaluative studies on clinical practice? There are two obvious explanations. First, that the program managers, program directors and front-line workers are either not aware of the studies, and if they are they do not place much faith in the reliability of the results. Therefore, they continue to practice what they believe and what they have been trained to practice. The second possibility is that they are aware of the studies and do trust the results but are reluctant to follow through. This reluctance may be due to very practical, emotional and professional reasons. It is not easy to admit that one's therapy had little impact on patients in the long run. It also implies that one has to stop practicing what one is trained for and has become very good at after years of practice. It is not easy to give up the status of an expert, even though it has been shown that what one is expert at has no therapeutic validity. The reluctance to give up the status of an expert and accept the career of a novice is easy to understand, however this is what is involved for many professionals if the implications of the above studies are to affect clinical practice.

There may be other reasons why the evaluative studies had little effect, yet this situation must alter. There will be little use of continuing to do evaluative studies if treatment programs are not affected by the results. There will be little motivation for seeking new approaches if there is no dissatisfaction with the present practice. However it is achieved, practitioners should be encouraged to learn what works with whom and when. It is clear that antisocial adolescents are not a single diagnostic category. Their behaviors encompass at least all conduct disorders as described in DSM III (7). Any single approach is unlikely to work equally well with different types of conduct disorders. Through careful evaluative studies, the limitations and effectiveness of different approaches with different types of adolescents must be determined. Some of this has already been accomplished but more studies are needed to be carried out, what does not work must be discarded, what does work must be made more specific and finely tuned to further improve the effectiveness.

Finally, as a child psychiatrist who has treated antisocial adolescents for a number of years, I ask what role, if any, child psychiatrists should play with this population? Given the state of the art and very few child psychiatrists who work with this population, this requires some serious consideration. Besides helping in diagnosis, my bias would be that psychiatrists could contribute most by teaching and research. Teaching, so that up-to-date knowledge in the field is available to front-line workers and research not only to improve the effectiveness of treatment but also to determine what makes the child antisocial and what can be done to prevent this. Though traditionally, mental health professionals had been more concerned with the disturbed child than the disturbing, the increasing violence and decreasing resources in the family may finally force us to take note of the antisocial adolescent. He stands there, defying the law and violating the societal norms. It is unlikely that he will improve if we ignore him. The community has to create conditions so we do not force children to resort to violence, and when they do become violent we as professionals will have to find better and more effective ways of helping them.

REFERENCES

1. Adams, E. Effectiveness of interview therapy with older youth authority wards: an interim evaluation of the PICO project. Research Report No. 20. California Youth Authority, 1961.

2. Alexander, J. F. and B. V. Parsons. Short-term behavioral intervention with delinquent families: impact on family process and recidivism. *J. Abnorm. Psychol.* 81 (1973):219-225.

3. Anderson, F. N. and H. C. Dean. Some aspects of child guidance clinic intake policy and practice. *U.S. Department of Health, Education & Welfare, Public Health Monogram*, no. 42 (1956).

4. Berleman, W. C., J. R. Seaberg and T. Steinburg. Delinquency prevention of the Seattle Atlantic Street Centre—a final evaluation. *Social Science Review* 46 (1972):323-346.

5. Byles, J. A. and A. Maurice. The juvenile services project: an experiment in delinquency control. *Can. J. Criminology* 21, no. 2 (1979):155-164.

6. Chommie, P. W. and J. Hudson. Evaluation of outcome and process. *Social Work* (Nov. 1974):682-687.

7. Diagnostic and Statistical Manual of Mental Disorders, 3d ed. *The Am. Psychiatr. Assoc.* (1980).

8. Dincin, J. Reassessing recidivism rates. *Am. J. Orthopsychiatry* 50, no. 1 (Jan. 1980):181-182.

9. Elliott, D. S. Recurring issues in the evaluation of delinquency prevention and treatment programs. In *Critical Issues in Juvenile Delinquency*, edited by D. Shichor and D. Kelly. Lexington, Mass.: Lexington Books, 1980.

10. Jesness, C., T. Allison, P. McCormick, R. Wedge and M. Young. Cooperative behaviour demonstration project. Sacramento, Calif.: Youth Authority, 1975.

11. Levinson, R. B. and H. L. Kitchener. Demonstration Counselling project. Washington, D.C.: National Training School for Boys, 1964.

12. Levitt, E. E. Psychotherapy with children: a further evaluation. *Behav. Res. Ther.* 1 (1963):45-51.

13. ———. The results of psychotherapy with children: an evaluation. *J. Consult. Psychol.* 21, no. 3 (1957):189-196.

14. Mills, C. M. and T. L. Walker. Reducing juvenile delinquency: a be-

havioral-employment intervention program. In *Progress in Behavior Therapy with Delinquents,* edited by J. S. Stumphauzer, 287-301. Springfield, Il.: C. C. Thomas, 1979.

15. O'Brien, W. J. An experimental use of modified group therapy in a public school setting with delinquent adolescent males. Ph.D. dissertation. University of California. Berkeley, 1963.

16. ——. Personality assessment as a measure of change resulting from group psychotherapy with male juvenile delinquents. Sacramento, Calif.: Youth Authority, 1961.

17. Patterson, G. R. Multiple evaluation of a parent training program. In *Applications of Behavior Modification,* edited by T. Thompson and W. S. Dockens. New York: Appleton-Century-Crofts, 1975.

18. ——. Interventions for boys with conduct problems: multiple settings, treatments and criteria. *J. Consult. Clin. Psychol.* 42 (1974a): 471-481.

19. ——. Retraining of aggressive boys by their parents: review of recent literature and follow-up evaluation. *Canad. Psychiat. Assoc. J.* 19 (1974b):142-161.

20. Rae-Grant, N. I. Arresting the vicious cycle: care and treatment of adolescents displaying the Ovinnik Syndrome. *Can. Psychiatr. Assoc. J.* 23 (1978):ss22-ss40.

21. Robins, L. N. *Deviant Children Grow Up.* Baltimore: Williams & Wilkins, 1966.

22. ——. Sturdy childhood predictors of adult antisocial behaviour: Replications from Longitudinal Studies. *Psychological Medicine* 8, no. 4 (1978):611-622.

23. Romig, D. A. *Justice for Our Children,* Lexington, Mass.: D. C. Heath and Company, 1978.

24. ——. Use of Community Services Prior to Commitment. Brown-wood, Tex.: Brownwood State Home and School, 1973.

25. Romig, D. A. and C. Saddler. Texas Juvenile Court Statistics for 1974. Austin, Tex.: Texas Youth Council, 1976.

26. Rutter, M. *Changing Youth in a Changing Society.* London, England: The Nuffield Provincial Hospital Trust, 1979.

27. Rutter, M. and L. Hersov. *Child Psychiatry: Modern Approaches.* Toronto: J. B. Lippincott Company, 1977.

28. Rutter, M., J. Tizard, W. Yule, P. Graham and K. Whitmore. Research report: Isle of Wight Studies, 1964-1974. *Psychol. Med.* 6 (1976):313-332.

29. Sacramento County: Preventing delinquency through diversion. In Berkowitz, F., *Evaluation of Crime Control Programs in California: A Review.* Sacramento: California Council on Criminal Justice, 1973.

30. Seckel, J. The Fremont experiment: assessment of residential treatment at a youth authority reception centre. Research Report No. 50, Sacramento: California Youth Authority, 1967.

31. Soloman, P. and W. Doll. The varieties of readmission: the case against the use of recidivism rates as a measure of program effectiveness. *Am. J. Orthopsychiatry* 49, no. 2 (April 1979):230-238.

32. Statistics Canada. Justice Statistics Division. Ottawa, Ontario, 1980.

33. Statistics Canada. Population Estimates and Projections Division. Ottawa, Ontario, 1980.

34. Stevens, S. An ecological study of a child guidance clinic intake. *Smith College Student Social Work* 25 (1954):73-84.

35. Strasburg, P. A. *Violent Delinquents: A Report to the Ford Foundation from the Vera Institute of Justice.* New York: Monarch, 1978.

36. Stratton, J. G. Effects of crisis intervention counselling on predelinquent and misdemeanor juvenile offenders. *Juvenile Justice* 26 (1975):7-18.
37. Thomas, E. S. Effects of experimental school counselling of delinquency-prone adolescents. *Dissertation Abstracts* 28 (7-A), (1968):2572.
38. Wahler, R. G. Setting generally, some specific and general effects of child behavior therapy. *J. Appl. Behav. Anal.* 2 (1969):239-246.
39. Wolf, M. M., E. L. Phillips and D. L. Fixsen. *Achievement Place Phase II: Final Report.* Wichita: University of Kansas, 1975.

ROBERT F. MORGAN

24

Balloon Therapy

The balloon therapy technique described in the following chapter should only be done under medical supervision. **R.F.M.**

There are some excellent paperback guides available these days to catalogue the many therapeutic techniques available to a growth-oriented public. Chris Popenoe's *Wellness* (me-ness, you-ness, we-ness), (1977) includes hundreds of pages of brief descriptions of healing techniques from "Flower Remedies" to "Cold Sheet Treatments," from "Psychodietetics" to "Tibetan Medicine." Richie Herink has edited *The Psychotherapy Handbook* (1980) which lists and describes over 250 psychotherapeutic systems and techniques from "Creative Aggression" to "Vector" therapies, with an introductory caution that the list is likely far from complete.

Now, many of these techniques may well be quite effective, particularly when applied systematically, with ongoing feedback, to disorders that have been scientifically determined to best fit the approach. Further, careful reading shows that the general approaches (with the underlying theories) may be distilled down to but a very few unifying perspectives. Most of these fit well, in turn, into recognizable views giving differential priority to *thoughts* or *feelings* or *choice* or an *eclectic blend.* Why then, such variety of title, such smorgasbords of technique?

One must realize that often a professional career rests on such personalized labeling of generalized phenomenon. To attempt to unify and integrate a system is to risk de-individuation of one's reputational self-actualization (i.e., the big bucks follow they who stand out from the crowd).

Since everyone must individualize their own system, I choose to call my own world view "Contemporary Pragmatism" and, within that title, I have evolved a hypothetical technique neither Popenoe nor Herink have catalogued yet: Balloon Therapy.

Method

Client has two large helium-filled balloons fastened on, one to an ear (in the event of only one ear, use only one balloon). The shape, filling, color

Reprinted with permission from *Canadian Psychology* 23 (1982):45-46.

and design of balloon will vary with the judgment of the therapist (messages of client scripts might conceivably be purchased from transactional analysts or psychodramatists; the message must be securely fastened to the balloon and should not exceed the vocabulary of the people likely to be encountered). Client wears these fastened balloons twenty-four hours per day for an entire week. At the end of the week, the client returns to the therapist and the balloons are removed.

Benefits

1. Relief of depression: client feels elation at no longer having balloons on the ears.
2. Bolstering of self confidence: client, having survived this, can survive anything.
3. Advertising: few clients completing this procedure will fail to rationalize it as extremely beneficial (the alternative to be defended against is that they are, to some infinite extent, gullible) and the technique itself draws notice.
4. Reducing social isolation and withdrawal: not only are balloons a conversation piece but there would be immediate identity with anyone else undergoing this therapy (without breaching confidentiality, clients would be able to recognize each other anywhere).
5. Relieves anxiety neuroses: everything relieves anxiety neuroses.
6. Particularly suited to autistic and catatonic disorders: these clients immediately adjust to the unusual balloon presence, never once objecting or complaining. In several years, only one catatonic asked us to get the balloons the hell off his ears and we responded by certifying him cured.
7. Sexual dysfunction: relieves obsessional performance orientation or, in fact, performance.
8. Alcohol abuse and dependence: clients are refused service.
9. Significantly reduces discomfort from any disorder reimbursable by insurance or directly payable by client.

Points of Therapeutic Expertise

1. Deciding on characteristics of balloon (*see* Method).
2. Choosing between glue, clip, tape, magnetic or natural honey fastenings.
3. Selecting the best point of attachment for the balloons—using body parts other than the ears may be appropriate with several types of client.
4. Matching length of strings to client characteristics.
5. Fee structure.

Contra-indications:

This technique is not recommended when the client:
1. Has a poor sense of humor, combat experience or an attorney.
2. Has not had EST training.
3. Is financially insolvent.
4. Can spell iatrogenic.

BIBLIOGRAPHY

Herink, R., ed. *The Psychotherapy Handbook.* New York: Meridian/ New American Library, 1980.

Popenoe, C. *Wellness.* Washington, D.C.: Yes! Inc., 1977.

DAVID B. CHEEK

25

Hypnotic Techniques and Their Noniatrogenic Use

With the passing of Milton Erickson, it is quite possible that the greatest living clinical hypnotist might reasonably be considered to be Dr. David Cheek. Decades past it was he who, as a young obstetrician, demonstrated that patients under general anaesthetic were able to recall (under hypnosis) what was said during the operation and, even more important, to uncritically respond to suggestions made by medical staff during the procedure. Identifying high-stress states as times of great suggestibility (and undergoing anaesthetized surgical procedures qualifies as stressful), Cheek was able to reduce much iatrogenic postoperative morbidity. His concepts and their applications led to identifying effective accident-scene psychological first aid, more humanistic and effective birthings (pre-dating LeBoyer), and the potentially iatrogenic role of suggestion to preverbal (even prenatal) children. The following articles illustrate the two-sided nature of a representative, if powerful, technique: hypnosis. Knowledge of its workings can avoid iatrogenesis, or be used directly as a constructive intervention in its own right, ultimately even for comatose or profoundly withdrawn patients. **R.F.M.**

The Anesthetized Patient Can Hear and Can Remember

Anesthetized human beings maintain their hearing sense throughout the deepest planes of chemical anesthesia. Their physiologic adaptations to the stress of surgery may be profoundly disturbed by what they hear. Medicolegal implications are obvious even if we do not care about the patient. A charge of frightening conversation was made by a patient against a physician in Idaho in 1961. It was set aside by the court but other suits will follow as the facts become more widely known.

Arguments based on the assumption that patients cannot hear because they have conscious amnesia reflects careless thinking. Origins of most neurotic disabilities are unknown to the patient at the level of conscious thinking. Newer techniques of hypnoanalysis have revealed verifiable recollections which have been reported in detail. The side of the table from which the voice comes and the attitude of the speaker are always distinct. The understandings of an anesthetized patient are literal and childlike.

Reprinted with permission from *American Journal of Proctology* 13, no. 5 (October 1962):287-290.

Statements which would otherwise be innocuous may become powerfully dangerous to the anesthetized patient. The remark, "This thing isn't working" may apply to the suction apparatus but may fill the anesthetized patient with fears about his anatomy.

The late George Crile and W. E. Lower pointed out, in 1914 (9), the importance of emotional factors in the production of surgical shock. Crile believed that "anoci-association" depended upon all the details of an optimistic preoperative environment. He believed that nerve impulses to the brain from traumatized tissues could register in the subconscious mind even when the patient is under the influence of a general anesthetic. He added the use of local anesthesia for blocking the impulses along peripheral nerve pathways. A part of his very effective regimen depended upon protecting the patient from unnecessary noises. Crile recognized the fact that a rare patient could hear during anesthesia. One was able to give a complete report of her history which had been presented after she supposedly was anesthetized and ready for surgery(8). He believed, however, that general anesthesia usually protected the patient from careless conversation. He was concerned more with the conversation in scrub rooms, the noises of instruments being moved, the smell of the anesthetic. With attention to such details he lowered the mortality rate for surgery on patients with Graves' disease from approximately 50% down to less than 5%. Observation of average 5:00 PM pulse rate during the first four days after surgery with various operations performed under ether anesthesia was 102 beats per minute. With anoci-association techniques it was 83 per minute. The total Lakeside surgical mortality for all operations by the authors and their resident staff was 4.4%, in 1908, the year before adoption of the principles of anoci-association. This figure was reduced to 1.8% by 1913 (Crile 1914).

Crile was doing far more than add local nerve-blocking agents to his care of the unconscious, anesthetized patient. He was protecting the patient as much as possible from frightening external stimuli, visual, auditory and tactual.

The brilliant contributions of the late Harold Wolff and his associates, Loring Chapman and Helen Goodell (1, 2), suggest the possibility that Crile's general principles are correct, that hyperawareness of damaged tissue produced by anticipation and fear may increase inflammatory response to damage and interfere with healing. The group at Cornell have established the fact that damaged skin and subcutaneous tissues release an inflammatory enzyme, "neurokinin," when the brain knows damage has been done. Enzyme rlease is reduced by hypnotic suggestions permitting the brain to reject the awareness of damage; it is increased when suggestions are given to make the subject more apprehensive about the degree of injury which is to be done. We are coming to recognize, with the help of hypnotic questioning methods (6), that the subconscious brain may be aware damage is being done to tissues even though the patient is unconscious under the influence of general anesthesia. How much the fears of the preoperative period may influence irritability of the heart, increased coagulation qualities of the blood or rebound increased fibrinolytic activity remains to be seen (11, 12, 14). Requests for immediate voiding on awakening from anesthesia may be made during induction of anesthesia and will work like a posthypnotic suggestion on awakening. This means that the brain has been able to carry the imagery through the operative period in spite of chemical anesthesia. Wolfe and Millet (15) have shown that loudly given suggestions during surgical plane anesthesia will influence the post-operative behavior of patients. This work has been repeated by Hutchings (10) and explored experimentally by Pearson (13).

Since presentation of the first report on what surgically-anesthetized patients are able to hear (3, 4), the author has explored more than 500 surgical experiences. Some patients believe their untoward reactions to anesthesia, their hemorrhage and their postoperative disturbances of healing, nutrition and elimination are influenced by what they hear during the anesthetic experience. Methods of protecting the patients by training them to listen only when spoken to by name (5) and for making a "jumble of noises" out of all conversation in the operating room (7) have been described. It is possible for an anesthetist to give helpful suggestions to patients as they go to sleep with a pentothal induction. All surgical patients seem to be in a hypnoidal, hypersuggestible state before and during anesthesia. Patients may be more frightened than helped by having their ears stuffed with cotton or tape recordings played in their ear during surgery. They all want to know what is being done and the surgeon should respect their need by explaining steps of the procedure directly to them or indirectly to his assistant. The surgeon should compliment the patient on good behavior and give him helpful suggestions about relaxing and controlling physiologic responses when things go wrong. It is difficult for surgeons and anesthetists to bring themselves to the point of talking to a seemingly insensate patient, but the results will more than repay all members of the operating group for the effort. The occasional ribbing they will get from unenlightened colleagues will soon stop when results are tabulated.

Preoperative Fear of Cancer

No technique I have devised for preventing patients from listening during surgery has worked when the patient has a preoperative fear that cancer will be found. Particularly vulnerable are those awaiting cholecystectomy, gastric resection and abdominal gynecologic operations. It has been my experience that these patients are apprehensive even when they have been told before surgery that there is no possibility of cancer being found. Thirty-two cancer patients have strongly resented the lack of information given them about this possibility before surgery, and all of them who were not told the truth after surgery assumed their condition must be hopeless because otherwise the surgeon would have been willing to discuss the future with them. A nurse misunderstood the intended meaning of "five-year survival" after mastectomy for breast cancer and died of a bowel obstruction on the fifth anniversary of her operation. Autopsy showed no evidence of recurrence of her cancer. Her sister was a nurse and had repeatedly tried to change the conviction of this patient but conscious-level explanations could not alter the subconsciously fixed impression. There are many examples of this type of subconsciously powerful misunderstandings.

Cancer Can Be Discussed

We are now able to discuss cancer overtly at the operating table. We can honestly put the matter up to the patient now that we know the battle depends more on immune mechanisms than we used to think. We can explain to the assistant that we are removing the majority of the cancer cells to allow the maximum chance of killing off any stragglers just as we give the patient the tools for winning the combat against organisms in an abscess by draining the abscess. Not all organisms are removed but the course of battle between host and invaders is changed by what we do. I have yet to find a patient who was harmed by open and sincerely optimistic discussion about cancer. The harm from telling the truth is done by the way truth is told when it is offered with facial expressions and voice tones which take away hope. I have yet to find a patient who has failed to perceive subconsciously the discrepancy between words and music when a lie has been told.

We are on the threshold of a better understanding of reactions to surgery and anesthesia. We will know more when the medical schools permit wider education regarding ways in which the subconscious minds of patients can be explored and aided in their struggle with the stresses of life. Hypnosis is a psychiatric tool but clinicians who are not psychiatrists should know how to use it for it is a quick, safe and powerful adjunct when treated with the same respect we show for the ordinary needs of our patients.

REFERENCES

1. Chapman, L. et al. 1959. Changes in tissue vulnerability induced during hypnotic suggestion. *J. Psycho. Res.* 44:99-105.

2. Chapman, L. 1959. Augmentation of the inflammatory reaction by activity of the central nervous system. *Arch. Neurol.* 1:557-572.

3. Cheek, D. B. 1959. Unconscious perception of meaningful sounds during surgical anesthesia as revealed under hypnosis. *Am. J. Clin. Hypnosis* 1:101-113.

4. ———. 1960. What does the surgically anesthetized patient hear? *Rocky Mountain Med. J.* 57:49-53.

5. ———. 1960. Use of preoperative hypnosis for protection of surgical patients from careless conversation. *Am. J. Clin. Hypnosis* 3: 101-102.

6. ———. 1961. Unconscious reactions and surgical risk. *Western J. of Surg., Obs. & Gynec.* 69:325-328.

7. ———. 1962. Importance of recognizing that surgical patients behave as though hypnotized. *Am. J. Clin. Hypnosis* 4:227-236.

8. Crile, George. 1947. *George Crile, an autobiography.* Philadelphia: Lippincott.
9. Crile, George and W. E. Lower. 1914. *Anoci-association.* Philadelphia: Saunders.
10. Hutchings, D. 1961. The value of suggestion given under anesthesia. *Am. J. Clin. Hypnosis* 4:26-29.
11. MacFarlane, R. G. and R. Biggs. 1946. Observations on fibrinolysis, spontaneous activity associated with surgical operations, trauma. *Lancet* 2:862.
12. MacFarlane, R. G. 1961. The reaction of the blood to injury. In *Functions of the Blood,* edited by R. G. MacFarlane and A. H. T. Robb-Smith. New York: Academic Press.
13. Pearson, R. E. 1961. Response to suggestions given under general anesthesia. *Am. J. Clin. Hypnosis* 4:106-114.
14. Phillips, L. L., P. T. Rowley and D. V. Habif. 1956. Hypofibrinogenemia in surgical patients. *Surg., Gyn., Obst.* 103:433.
15. Wolfe, L. S. and J. B. Millet. 1960. Control of post-operative pain by suggestion under general anesthesia. *Am. J. Clin. Hypnosis* 3:109-112.

Significance of Dreams in Initiating Premature Labor

Summary—Thoughts and dreams during natural sleep may greatly exaggerate the impact of daytime experiences and, with vulnerable women, may be the major factor in causing fetal wastage through premature delivery. Criteria for differentiating good from poor-risk patients are indicated and methods of exploration are discussed.

Prematurity causes 45,000 deaths each year among the 4.5 million live-born babies in this country. This equals the number of humans killed annually on our highways. About 300,000 babies are born prematurely each year and 45,000 are dead within the first month of life. Many who survive will suffer from mental retardation, allergies and problems with skin, lungs, kidneys and gastrointestinal tract because of factors related to their prematurity. Enormous amounts of money and effort have been spent searching for ways to improve the care of these babies after they are born. This is too late. The problems of prematurity begin long before marriage and should be treated by obstetricians.

Twenty years of interest in this problem with babies weighing less than five and one half pounds at birth suggest to the author that statistics might improve if obstetricians and generalists could separate good-risk patients, who meet their stresses adequately, from the poor-risk patients who need plenty of attention early in pregnancy. Probably all women are fearful in their first pregnancy, and many are worried in successive pregnancies, but most women and their babies can compensate well for stresses. Can we recognize the ones whose backgrounds and conditionings

Presented at the Ninth Annual Scientific Meeting of the American Society of Clinical Hypnosis, October, 1966. Reprinted with permission from *American Journal of Clinical Hypnosis* 12 (1969):5-15.

make them vulnerable? Can we help them carry their babies to term? We should start before pregnancy begins, but we can also help during the first few critical weeks while the growing embryo is sensitive to changes in circulation and oxygen supply. Attention to the dreams of vulnerable patients must continue throughout pregnancy. The most casual and seemingly innocuous daytime experiences may evolve into potentially lethal dreams. We have not recognized the significance of dreams because patients usually consider their remembered dreams too ridiculous for reporting. Only 10% of damaging dreams are recalled on awakening; the rest are repressed. Dreams are real until they can be exposed to conscious reason. Repressed dreams, however, tend to recur. They change form with new daytime experiences and continue to affect physiological reactions. Repressed dreams can be discovered easily and quickly with a combination of ideomotor questioning methods and light hypnosis. We can help patients stop hemorrhaging during telephone conversations in emergencies. We can help check the progress of toxemia long enough to assure birth of a term-sized child.

How Can We Recognize Poor-Risk Patients?

The author's initial efforts to separate good-risk from bad-risk patients were started in a small community where he was the only physician with special training in obstetrics. Patients who seemed happily married, happy over the prospect of having a child, and those who had already delivered normal children were referred elsewhere as "good-risk" patients. Some of these good-risk patients miscarried and some delivered prematurely. Review of their histories often showed they had come from broken homes, or a mother had been seriously ill or had died when the patient was very young. Some had previously been divorced after delivery and were superstitiously afraid that another child would lead to a second divorce. Frigidity and early-life sexual worries took on increasing importance as the author learned to take better sexual histories. Frigidity, acne, childhood obesity, dysmenorrhea and infertility were more commonly found in histories of girls whose pregnancies got into trouble. Some had no siblings. Some had names like Jacqueline, Harriet, Henrietta or Carla, suggesting that their parents may have wanted a boy. An only child wonders why there were no siblings; the others feel they should have been boys. It did not seem to matter that such women consciously knew their parents appreciated them as female babies, that they were recognized for their beauty as adult women, that their husbands adored them. The power of early-life imprinting was becoming apparent.

The author learned that perspiration, tachycardia, initial elevation of blood pressure or an unexpected trace of blood in the cervical canal during initial examination seemed important warnings with the women who got into trouble. This fear sign was used as a criterion. About five years of private practice taught the author that males are basically more frightened by pregnancy than are their wives. It seemed wise to ask what reaction a husband showed to the first report of pregnancy. Sometimes it was a look of silent anguish, sometimes a groan, sometimes an angry-sounding "Oh, my God!" Such reactions can shatter the beliefs and ideals of a wife. Though jokingly offered, they may be responsible for continued, unrecognized hostility on the part of an otherwise loving wife. The shocks are even greater when pregnancy occurs before marriage, or so soon after marriage that relatives and friends might raise their eyebrows. It seemed these factors were important, but they were not always important to all women.

With continued probing and sorting out of results it was possible to set down some criteria which help separate the good from the bad-risk obstetrical patients.

Good-Risk Patients, Not Vulnerable
1. Happily adjusted family background, no divorce or death.
2. Happy marriage, patient looking forward to delivery.
3. Happy marriage and uncomplicated previous pregnancies.

Poor-Risk Patients To Be Followed Closely
A. Serious Primary Factors. (One of these is enough.)
  1. Death or divorce of parent before patient was age 10.
  2. Serious illness or death of mother at birth.
  3. Serious illness of patient during childhood (RHD, polio, etc.)
  4. Gynecological operation prior to pregnancy.
  5. Infertility for more than four years.
  6. Previous abortion, stillbirth, abnormal or premature baby.
  7. History of serious complication in earlier pregnancy.
B. Milder Criteria. (Must have two or more of these.)
  1. First born child, or child with only female older siblings and carrying "warmed-over boy's name" (Jacqueline, Harriet, Henrietta, Carla, etc.)
  2. Only child or only surviving child, and wondering why.
  3. Acne during adolescence. (Always found when child thought she should have been a boy.)
  4. Tall and "skinny" or short and fat during teens. (Feeling unloved.)
  5. History of severe dysmenorrhea. (Nearly always resenting being a girl.)
  6. Hostile-overprotective mother or "alcoholic" father. (Maternal frigidity.)
  7. Previous divorce when this had been requested by husband. (Blow to self-respect not suffered when patient asks for divorce.)

Comparative Results

When the author moved from the small community to San Francisco it was necessary to accept all obstetrical patients. Now it was possible to compare results in both groups. Naturally, an objection to this type of comparison is that patients quickly pick up the worries of their doctors and it is possible that the author's concerns over the poor-risk patients might have created the problems he wished to avoid. If this were entirely true, there should have been more premature babies and a greater fetal loss in this group. This was not the case. Blind and double-blind studies might be more acceptable for statistical evaluation, but the author has directed his interest toward letting women discover their problems in order to find ways of correcting them. This seems reasonable, perhaps defensible. The forewarning of vulnerable patients permitted them a chance to notify the author at the time complications were occurring. When these occur at night it is necessary for patients to know their call for help will not be considered an imposition. All vulnerable patients were trained early to use autohypnosis for relaxation. Trained patients will go immediately into hypnosis during a telephone conversation when request is made for ideomotor answers to questions. A state of hypnosis is often enough to permit termination of bleeding or premature labor, as has been shown by Logan (1963), Schwartz (1963), and Hartman and Rawling (1960). With repetition of abortion and with complications occurring in the second and third trimester it is increasingly hard to control the physiological effects of emotional stresses with ordinary, reassuring conscious communications. Stallworthy (1959) has shown that 80% of threatened abortions can be carried to successful delivery by any kind of optimistic therapy. This cannot be said when there have been four or more consecutive abortions, or when the complications have occurred late in pregnancy. Standard therapy with drugs and "reassurance" has failed consistently under such circumstances.

We need quick, accurate ways of discovering and correcting subconscious fears, guilt feelings and identifications. We need to know all about the thoughts of pregnant women while they are asleep. We need to include husbands in our therapy.

Results 1946-1955 in Small Community

There were 527 deliveries, not counting consultation or Cesarean sections done for other physicians. Of these, 34 were premature, a rate of 6.5%. One living premature baby was a Harlequin (massive scleroderma), and this died, as did two sets of twins delivered prematurely by another mother. There were three stillborn babies, one before labor and two at term during labor. Four patients had moderately severe toxemia but went on to deliver normal babies. One patient was first seen in eclampsia at term and was delivered of a normal infant by Cesarean section. Premature mortality was 15%, approximately the same as is found elsewhere. Two patients with incipient toxemia reduced their blood pressure to normal and lost their edema when they discovered relatively transparent fears. The author could not stop premature labor after the cervix had started to dilate. All patients hemorrhaging in the second and third trimester were admitted to the hospital. They seldom went home undelivered.

Results 1955-1966 in San Francisco

Of 231 cases there were 215 live births with six premature babies, a rate of 2.8%. Four of the six premature babies came in the good-risk group of 169 women. All of these were over four pounds three ounces and their mothers were free of complications before labor. There were no deaths of premature or mature liveborn infants in the two groups.

Table 1: Personal Experience Fetal Wastage 1955-1966

Class	Number	Abortion	Stillborn	Premature	Dead
Good-risk	169	3 (1.8%)	0	4 (2.4%)	0
Poor-risk	62	8 (13%)	5 (8%)	2 (3.2%)	5

Total liveborn incidence of prematurity = 2.8%
(Total including stillbirths = 5%)

There was a significant difference between the 2 groups on the basis of numbers who hemorrhaged on one or more occasions or threatened labor.

There were 17 times as many patients who threatened trouble in the poor-risk group, and there were nearly 10 times as many who threatened seriously. All of the 11 serious threats in the poor-risk group had the typical picture of threatened abortion in the first trimester and threatened again later. Four of these had aborted consecutively six or more times before and might have been expected to abort again. Two others would probably have aborted, according to criteria used by many obstetricians (ruptured membranes at 11 weeks and excessive hemorrhage). This leaves eight possible premature deliveries for both groups which could have changed the premature total to 7.4%.

Table 2: Personal Experience Threatened Fetal Wastage 1955-1966

Class	Number	Mild Threat	Serious Threat	Carried On
Good-risk	169	6 (3.6%)	3 (1.8%)	6
Poor-risk	62	37 (59.7%)	11 (17.7%)	37

It is fruitless to wonder what would have happened under other circumstances. The facts are that there were six premature babies in 215 deliveries of living babies and all of these lived. One patient who had delivered a stillborn at seven months in her first pregnancy and whose next child was delivered by Cesarean section had profuse bleeding after a disturbing dream. This episode occurred two weeks before delivery and was terminated by conversation and understanding of the dream. At operation the female baby weighing six pounds was initially in good condition, but developed the typical picture of hyaline membrane disease and was in critical condition for five days. It was the belief of the pediatrician that this baby would not have had strength to survive, if it had been delivered two weeks earlier, when it seemed there could be placental separation. At operation there was no evidence of placental separation; the bleeding was unexplained on any organic basis. Total blood lost with the first gush was estimated at 100 cc.

Concepts and Methods of Dream Exploration

Nathaniel Kleitman (1963) and his associates, Aserinsky and Dement (1953, 1957) have shown that an average of eight hours of sleep is broken into four or five cycles of light and deep sleep with approximately 90 minutes between peaks. Some years ago, the author began asking patients to spend a minimum of six hours in hypnosis instead of ordinary sleep in order to control damage to skin from unconscious scratching. In 1957 the author happened to ask such a patient whether or not she had followed directions. She was not sure. She was asked to put her hands on her lap and let her subconscious mind go over the night of sleep and signal with one finger for ordinary sleep and one finger for hypnosis sleep. Her responses were alternating between the fingers as though she spent a little time in hypnosis and a little time in ordinary sleep. There were four alternations. She was asked to go through the night again. The same thing happened. After this, a subconscious review of the preceding night was used as a rapid way of inducing hypnosis as well as setting up a means of communicating with ideomotor signals. The patient was asked to signal as she went to sleep and to signal when she knew she was dreaming. A third signal was requested to indicate final awakening in the morning. Worried patients often mobilize important thoughts on the eve of going to a doctor. It was found helpful to ask if there had been a frightening or disturbing dream that night. From this investigation came several results that seemed significant.

Signals for beginning of a dream always coincided with beginning of rapid lid movements and the kind of roving eyeball movements seen when patients are experiencing an age regression. Often the patient would lift the going-to-sleep finger at the end of the dream period; thereafter the eyes would remain immobile until the next dream period. There were four or five episodes of dreaming in an eight hour night. Intervals were regular and it was often possible to know how long patients had been asleep, or that her dreams had been disturbing according to the number of dreaming signals and quality of facial expressions.

A survey of abortion sequences with hypnotic age regression to the moment of onset of bleeding showed that 54% of 125 instances began while the patients believed they were sleeping. This was more than would have been expected. The author was busy with exploration of surgical anesthesia experiences. It was a short step to use of the same technique in exploring the night before onset of various complications in pregnancy. A number of patients were very much surprised to find they were aware of vaginal bleeding during the night several hours before awakening. Several patients who had been diagnosed as having "incompetent cervix" because they had delivered immature babies in the second trimester found they had been having frightening thoughts about their baby on successive nights, and about the same time of night before the physical problem was apparent. They reviewed their sleep experiences repeatedly and noticed that they knew the quality of the normal uterine contractions changed, became more rapid and more forceful during their unpleasant dreams. None of these women knew they had been dreaming, and none had been aware of being in painless labor with expulsive, rather than concentric, uterine contractions.

Obstetrical patients often report headaches, onset of nausea or facial edema on waking from sleep. Many frightened obstetrical patients find their legs going into spasms of cramps during the night after disturbing dreams. Scanning the night before these symptoms occur yields interesting information about sleep patterns, and further underlines the fact that daytime stresses may be troublesome, but they are not as troublesome as what the subconscious mind does with these experiences at night. Hyperventilation is frequently observed during reviews of disturbed sleep sequences. Over and over again, with slowly developing complications and with the urgent problems of hemorrhage and onset of premature labor, it was emphasized by patients that the few remembered dreams were only superficial reflections of much deeper ideation usually described as "a thought" or "an experience." Reason for differentiating was usually explained on the basis that dreams are filled with symbols. Dreams may be troublesome and alarming, but the real physiological disturbances occur with the other kind of thought sequences. These must be comparable to the experiences known as "night terrors" occurring with children who do not remember what has happened and whose physiological disturbance continues long after awakening. The physiologically dangerous experiences at night seem very real, they incorporate actions of the day preceding, and they seem to be repeated on successive cycles of sleep. The great majority of emergencies originating at night are allocated by patients to the time between midnight and 4:00 a.m.

Having learned that dreams, or something like dreams, could be dangerous to unborn babies, it was necessary to protect mothers from their dreams. This can be done in two ways. We can train the mother to awaken and understand her dream, and we can train her not to have troublesome dreams. It is usually necessary to teach her to awaken from the dream before she can learn to substitute pleasant thoughts for the bad ones. Poor-risk patients are told about dreams at the first or second visit. Frightened mothers cannot hallucinate the birth of their child. They are seen at least once a week until they are able to hallucinate a comfortable delivery at term with a living, healthy baby. They are told that 30% of women bleed during the first three months of pregnancy, that this does not mean there is anything wrong with the baby. Great care is used with the choice of words in communicating with these patients. They are told to expect moments of fear when friends tell them about women having complications of pregnancy. They are told about the superstitious fears that follow "showers" given by friends. These are very real threats, but the aftermath of these threats can be inactivated.

Once patients have been told about their dreams and how to manage their reactions to dreams, it is not necessary to quiz them on subsequent visits unless they show sudden weight gain or begin complaining of insomnia. Since sexual inhibitions are frequently found in the poor-risk group, I make a point of telling them that intercourse is not dangerous and can continue through pregnancy, but it is important to know if it ever causes bleeding. Coital bleeding is usually caused by trauma to the delicate mucosa of the cervix. All obstetrical patients, good- and poor-risk, are told to continue with work or sports for as long as they feel comfortable doing them. They may take trips of any sort in any type of vehicle *when they want to go on such trips.* Patients are told to use their obstetrician whenever they need support in stopping work, intercourse or trips. They are to say, "My doctor does not want me to _____".

Steps of Training

These are described in detail in an earlier paper (Cheek 1965). An extended discussion of ideomotor questioning techniques may be found in LeCron's book, *Techniques of Hypnotherapy* (1961).

1. Demonstrate postural suggestion.
2. Demonstrate difficulty in overcoming effect of word "try."
3. Demonstrate effect of hallucinating a goal of imagining the arms pulling together with the force of a stretched rubber band around wrists.
4. Show patient how to develop a subjective hypesthesia of one arm.
5. Demonstrate difference in response of skin scratches when one arm is "numb."
6. Explain value of ideomotor responses in revealing information which is not consciously recognized.
7. Set up ideomotor symbol movements.
8. Review entire sleep period of previous night and check to see if any thoughts or dreams were disturbing.
9. Demonstrate method of inducing self-hypnosis for brief periods of rest.
10. Explain conditioning of brain, making pain equate with muscle tension, and comfort equate with muscle relaxation. This allows a rationale for purposefully relaxing muscles and using suggestions of peace and calm at a time of stress.
11. Project forward to time of "easy delivery" and obtain hallucinated commitment on the date, weight and sex of the baby.

Pseudo-orientation to time of delivery is helpful in differentiating good-risk patients from those who must be watched. The hallucinated information may be wrong in every respect, but women who are happy at the prospect of delivering normal children will commit themselves on date, sex and weight. Some women initially appear calm and well-adjusted, but later reveal that they should be shifted from the good-risk category to a poor-risk classification on the basis of mounting fears as they approach term. By the same token, it has been repeatedly demonstrated that the real problems are over when a patient who blocks initially on any sort of commitment, or hallucinates an abnormal baby or no baby at all, changes to an optimistic hallucinated commitment.

Therapy at Time of Emergency

An example will be given. It is 3:00 a.m. and a patient is in bed or in the bathroom while her worried husband is reporting that his wife awakened from sleep to find she is hemorrhaging. The husband is asked to take the telephone to his wife or bring her to the telephone.

> **Patient:** "Oh, doctor, I feel terrible. I woke up a few minutes ago and I am really bleeding."
> **Doctor:** "Have you been mad at anybody recently?"
> **Patient:** (Laughing) "No, not really." (Purpose of the question has been accomplished, to take the attention away from bleeding momentarily and make the patient aware that emotional factors are thought to be the cause of bleeding.)
> **Doctor:** "Let's see what has been going on while you were asleep. Let your thoughts go back to the moment you fell asleep. When you are there your 'yes' finger will lift. Tell me when it goes up."
> **Patient:** (Lapse of 20 seconds. She is now in hypnosis.) "Now."
> **Doctor:** "Come forward now to the moment just before bleeding starts and, as your 'yes' finger lifts, bring that thought up to where you can tell me about it."
> **Patient:** (After 15 seconds.) "That's really crazy. My mother-in-law really wants me to have this baby now. She didn't at first, but that was six years ago when Bill was in school. I was dreaming that Mother was scolding Bill for getting me pregnant, and Bill was just standing there saying nothing. I was mad at *him,* too (laughing)."
> **Doctor:** "Let me ask your fingers now, 'Will you stop this bleeding and get back to sleep with pleasant dreams?'"
> **Patient:** (Laughing). "My 'yes' finger is going up."
> **Doctor:** "Okay then. Give me a call about two o-clock tomorrow." Care is taken to avoid suggesting an expectation of further bleeding. One should not say, "Let me know if you have any more bleeding."

Brief Clinical Reports

Helen R., aet. 26, gravida 3, para 2, with estimated blood loss of 1200 cc. during first trimester hemorrhages. This patient was bleeding so profusely with an 8.7 gm. hemoglobin that 1 cc. of pitocin was placed in the first of two units of blood in order to expedite abortion. The patient had loudly stated that she did not want this baby. Her behavior contradicted her words. Under anesthesia the following morning the cervix was tightly closed. The uterus seemed to be enlarging normally on schedule. I told the nurse at the operating table that I did not feel justified in terminating the life of this little baby. I did not then know that anesthetized patients can hear. There was no further bleeding. The patient delivered a seven pound nine ounce male at term, and her term hemoglobin was 12.4 gm. Subsequent investigation revealed cumulative disturbing dreams during four nights preceding profuse hemorrhage in the daytime at work.

Sonia W., aet. 34, gravida 10, para 0, with nine previous spontaneous abortions. Her first abortion had been induced surgically by Nazi physicians at four months of gestation, while she was interned in a Russian prison farm. She had been made to sign a statement that she would permit this abortion and would further permit surgical sterilization if she again became pregnant before the end of the war. Her next pregnancy came after termination of World War II, but she began bleeding during a dream that her baby would be taken from her by the Nazis. She had amnesia for the dream. Doctors in Italy "completed the abortion" because of profuse bleeding. This was the story of her next seven pregnancies. She lost her ninth pregnancy at 10 weeks the day after I left town for a vacation.

The first of six major emergencies occurred at eight weeks. A profuse hemorrhage began on a Saturday, when she thought no doctor would be available. I answered her call and told her to stop the bleeding, and that I was coming out to give her a shot. She was told that we simply were not going to let her waste another pregnancy. The bleeding, an estimated 400 cc., had stopped before I arrived. She announced that it had stopped as soon as she hung up the receiver. Spotting occurred at intervals until the sixth month when she had rhythmic, bearing-down contractions. She had tried to reach me to ask about some medicine. I had asked my answering service to announce that I was out of town, but had not yet gone. By the time I contacted the patient, her cervix was six cm. in diameter and a foot was visible through the delicate membranes protruding into the vagina. She was taken home and kept in hypnosis for 24 hours, after suturing the cervix together with chromic catgut, which was all I had available in the office. Four more episodes of profuse bleeding occurred and it was necessary to re-suture the cervix two more times before she ruptured her membranes. A four pound three ounce female infant was delivered by Cesarean section, after she had shown indications of fetal distress during 15 hours of labor. This child survived.

The next pregnancy was totally without complications other than one brief period of painful uterine contractions occurring after a frightening dream about losing the baby. I was away at the time. The patient reported later that she knew there had been a bad dream and that Dr. Cheek would be angry, if she did not stop the labor at this stage of seven months because the baby would be too small. The contractions stopped, and she delivered a boy weighing seven pounds seven ounces at term.

Her final pregnancy was not planned, and she had some conflict about this. There were numerous episodes of hemorrhage during this pregnancy, but her confidence was great by this time, and she usually would telephone to say, "Well, I had a bad dream again. Tell me to stop." I would reply, "Ask your fingers if it will be all right for you to stop bleeding," and always obtained a "yes" answer. She was delivered of a normal female, weighing six pounds two ounces, by Cesarean section.

Mrs. M., aet 26, gravida 3, para 0. This attractive and feminine Catholic girl had been infertile for six years when first seen in my office, and this was her reason for consultation. She had felt unwanted and less attractive than her younger and older brothers. At age 11 she had engaged in mutual sexual investigation with a girl friend and began worrying about being sexually abnormal after her first spontaneous abortion. She had intercourse with her husband before marriage, and was pregnant at the time of her marriage. Her father-in-law was violently opposed to their marriage because plans had been made for her husband's further education. She aborted after bleeding had started in the night in relation to a dream about her husband dying. The Korean War had finished, but her husband was scheduled for service in Korea. Her second abortion also followed a dream that she either had to abort this baby or her husband would be killed. Subconsciously she recognized her role in aborting both babies and she felt guilty, even though she had no conscious knowledge then of the dreams.

Her six years of infertility ended when she could tell me about the "homosexual experience" which had popped into her mind during each of the 16 office visits. She was relieved to know that such explorations were common and had nothing to do with homosexuality.

Her third pregnancy was complicated by many fears, many recognized disturbing dreams, and three unrecognized dreams, each of which produced hemorrhage and uterine contractions. The first serious threat occurred at 11:45 p.m. during her seventh month. She awakened from deep sleep with profuse bleeding. During the telephone call her fingers denied there had been a disturbing dream. It was not until I changed the question to "Has there been any disturbing thought?" that the answer was "I do not want to answer that question." She indicated a desire to be admitted to the hospital and promptly stopped bleeding as she got ready.

At office examination one month later her blood pressure was 160/94 and she had gained three and one half pounds since the week before. Dreams were searched, and again her subconscious mind refused to reveal the content of a repeated and very disturbing set of "thoughts." A 10-year-old child with congenitally absent hands had been visiting with her since the day her blood pressure went up and she had begun to develop edema. The dreams, however, continued to escape detection until the third day, when I insisted that her husband take a week off and stay with her in a motel near my office. I did not want her in the hospital where nurses and house officers might increase her apprehension with their frequent checking of her blood pressure. She was more than five weeks from her expected due date and I was afraid of being forced to terminate the pregnancy with a premature baby delivered by Cesarean section.

On this third day, while her husband was out getting a lunch tray, she told me she had discovered the reason for her anxiety and wanted to tell me before her husband returned. Her boss, a good friend of the family, had often dropped by her house for a cup of coffee. She knew he had been much attracted to her physically, but had kept him at a distance until one night during a party at the house of friends he got her into a room and very nearly had intercourse with her. She had missed her next period, and with her hypersensitive conscience had worried about whether the boss could be the father of her child. Her fears and consequent dreams had been intensified by the boss's repeated joking question, "Well, how's my baby getting along?"

We agreed to keep this information to ourselves providing she got her blood pressure down and would let this baby have the best possible blood supply. Pressure came down from the high point of 156/110 with 3.8 gm. of albumen per liter of urine to 138/92. She was unable to rid her urine of albumen, but she lost her edema with the help of diuretics and continued bed rest at home until a gush of blood awakened her at 3:30 a.m., four weeks from her due date. Again it was not a dream. She had noticed some blood on a handkerchief when she blew her nose before going to bed, and said to her husband, "Wouldn't it be nice if I hemorrhaged now and Dr. Cheek had to take the baby?" Bleeding stopped after uncovering the thought of hemorrhaging and my having to deliver a baby that was too small.

Fortunately the date of her last menstrual period had been incorrect. When another repressed "thought" occurred about the baby not looking like her husband, her blood pressure shot up and she had facial edema on awakening. She had a bloody show and some cramps at 8:30 a.m. Her blood pressure was 150/110. Her fibrinogen level was normal. I ruptured the membranes and she delivered a six pound one ounce healthy girl three hours and 15 minutes later. She let out a whoop of glee when she saw her husband's markings—a light streak of hair over the occiput.

Her second full-term pregnancy was complicated by uterine bleeding at eight months for which she was admitted, at her request, to the hospital. Investigation revealed that the moans of her daughter during a nightmare had stimulated a fear reaction that the child, who had been exposed to chicken pox, might become ill. There was a loss of 75 cc. of blood as she turned to go to the bathroom after covering her daughter up. She had gone to bed the night before with some feelings of apprehension but without knowing the cause. When asked to orient back to the time of falling asleep, she found herself concerned because I would be away at a convention for a few days. She lost her fears when she recognized them, and a month later delivered a normal male weighing six pounds three ounces. Her blood pressure rose briefly but there was no albuminuria.

Conclusions and Summary

Complications of pregnancy are not always directly caused by dreams. Great emotional stress or great physical trauma from infection or injuries can certainly cause intravascular clotting, followed by rebound fibrinolytic-type bleeding and expulsive contractions of the uterus. There is one constant feature of retrograde explorations of sequences leading to complications responsible for premature labor. Thoughts and dreams during natural sleep may greatly exaggerate the impact of daytime experiences and, with vulnerable women, may be the major factor in causing fetal wastage through premature delivery. The author's premature rate has dropped from 6.5% to 2.8% since paying attention to the nocturnal fears of pregnant women. Criteria of differentiating good, from poor-risk patients are indicated and methods of exploration are discussed.

BIBLIOGRAPHY

Aserinsky, E. and N. Kleitman. Regularly occurring periods of eye motility and concomitant phenomena during sleep. *Science* 118 (1953):273-274.

Cheek, D. B. Some newer understandings of dreams in relation to threatened abortion and premature labor. *Pacific Medicine and Surgery* 73 (1965):379-384.

Dement, W. and N. Kleitman. Cyclic variations in EEG during sleep and their relation to eye movement, body motility and dreaming. *Electroencephalography Clinical Neurophysiology* 9 (1957):673-690.

Hartman, W. and C. M. Rawling. Hypnosis in management of a case of abruptio placenta. *International Journal of Clinical and Experimental Hypnosis* 8 (1960):103-107.

Kleitman, N. *Sleep and Wakefulness.* Chicago: University of Chicago Press, 1963.

Logan, W. G. Delay of premature labor by the use of hypnosis. *American Journal of Clinical Hypnosis* 5 (1963):209-211.

LeCron, L. M. *Techniques of Hypnotherapy.* New York: Julian Press, 1961.

Schwartz, M. The cessation of labor using hypnotic techniques. *American Journal of Clinical Hypnosis* 5 (1963):211-213.

Stallworthy, J. Habitual abortion. *International Journal of Fertility* 4 (1959):237-241.

Ideomotor Questioning for Investigation of Subconscious "Pain" and Target Organ Vulnerability

The combination of ideomotor questioning methods with rapid scanning of subconscious experience makes possible some tentative explorations into areas of disturbed adaptation which have so far been closed to all but the most superficial of surveys. Work along these lines may be castigated by the organicists of medical research who say psychological factors are too hard to evaluate. The skeptics could be reminded that no objective study of human behavior in health or disease can be acceptable if the personal "weltanschauung" and the subjective responses of the individual are excluded from consideration.

The organicists will point out that exclusion of this factor is necessary because there is no way of communicating with the levels of subjective reaction relating directly with physiological adaptation. If we counter by saying that the nearest thing to this level can be reached by combining

Reprinted with permission from *American Journal of Clinical Hypnosis* 5 (1962):30-41.

ideomotor questioning methods with hypnosis, the organicists may say that is possible but it is a waste of time because only a small fraction of human beings can be deeply hypnotized. This is what Freud said in his widely publicized lectures at Clark University in 1909.

The objection that few can be deeply hypnotized is untrue but it is not important anyway. The 20% figure usually quoted applies to volunteers and is not valid for those who are highly motivated by fear or severe illness (4). Ideomotor questioning can be used for the induction of hypnosis and it can be used to uncover unconscious ideation with nearly all people who have the capacity for understanding and communicating thoughts. Unconscious resistance to entering a hypnotic state or cooperating with investigation can be circumvented (8).

Although most of us would agree that the brain has evolved as a central clearing house for the scanning of incoming sensations and the selection of appropriate outgoing messages directed toward adaptation we have been handicapped in our search for knowledge about these adaptations. Environmental threats mean different things to each individual. Conscious understandings of a threat may be greatly deranged by unconscious feelings about the significance of a stress. Let us consider the areas of human adaptation which seem most in need of clarification.

Immune Responses

These are most complex and seem to have evolved with the increasing complexities of vertebrate life. In mammals, they develop after birth although some of the mother's immune antibodies may get into the baby through the placenta or the amniotic membranes. Human beings may develop immune responses against the homotransplants of their husband's genetic characteristics to cause habitual abortion in some women. Erythroblastosis occurring with Rh incompatibility or AB-O incompatibility is of this type. The problem of the individual developing an immune reaction to his own tissues is also hard to comprehend unless it relates in some way to self-destructive forces centering on target organs. Hashimoto disease of the thyroid reflects this type of autoimmune response directed against thyroid tissue. All of the collagen diseases seem to relate in some way to autoimmune processes. We have learned that homologous tissue grafts from adult human mammals of the same species are rejected after a time and that repeat grafting from the same individual causes an accelerated rejection because of reinforced immune reactions to the foreign tissue. Only recently have we discovered that the grafted tissues themselves are competent to develop immune responses against the tissues of the host. We are now in a general way beginning to realize that some of the factors bearing on the abnormal growth characteristics of cancer cells and the capacity of the host to recover from cancer depend on which way the battle is turned. Removal of a majority of the cancer cells by surgery may throw the battle in favor of the host. Irradiation and the effect of radio-mimetic drugs may favor the host by interfering more with the immune responses of the cancer cells than with those of the mature host cells in the area of cancer growth. We have no knowledge of how despair and passive acceptance of cancer can shape the battle.

Since we know there have been verified spontaneous cures without treatment in a variety of malignancies including neuroblastoma, chorio-carcinoma, carcinoma of the kidney, malignant melanoma, cancer of the bladder, breast, stomach, lower bowel and uterus (13) we might wonder whether the victors could help us understand more about possible subjective attitudes and the course of battle.

We know that a shift from despair to hope may bring about an amazing shift from illness to health under many circumstances, but we have not explored the subconscious mechanisms responsible for this. There is evidence that some oriental people can decide to die and may do so at an appointed time in the absence of disease. We have known that death may occur unreasonably soon in the aged after a stroke or disabling injury. Only since the Korean War have we realized that American prisoners in their teens and early twenties could lose the will to live, enter a comatose state and be dead within 48 hours if left alone by their associates. We do not know how these things happen but we do know that all of the Turkish soldiers exposed to the same stresses in captivity which killed 50% of our boys in Korea came through their trials without loss of a single soldier (21).

Acute Emergencies of Hemorrhage in Surgical Patients and Pregnant Women

In 1794 the great John Hunter made the following significant observation:

> In many modes of destroying life, the blood is deprived of its power of coagulation, as happens in sudden death produced by many kinds of fits, by anger, electricity or lightning; or by a blow on the stomach, etc. In these cases we find the blood after death, not only in the fluid state as in the living vessels, but it does not even coagulate when taken out of them.

In Russia this quality of continued fluidity of blood after sudden great stress associated with death has been put to use. We now know that the blood coagulates initially but the production of plasmin or fibrinolysin is so great that the coagulated blood is quickly made fluid again. Such blood removed from the body may be very helpful in sustaining the lives of human beings of compatible blood type.

Turning now to the hemorrhagic emergencies of surgery and obstetrics we should not be surprised to discover that more than half of both types of serious bleeding cannot be explained on any physical or chemical basis yet devised. Hemorrhage is at the top of causes for maternal death today. This is not strange if we consider the classes of women most vulnerable to this threat. They are as follows: Women having had illegal abortions, those whose babies have died in utero, those having hypertensive renal disease, severe preeclampsia, abruptio placentae and overwhelming infection. Only the last of these might possibly be free of disturbed subconscious attitudes.

Obstetrical Problems Awaiting Investigation

Approximately 10% of desired pregnancies in human beings are aborted spontaneously and approximately 6% of all live births are premature. Prematurity accounts for approximately 60% of neonatal mortality. How many thousands or millions of lives are cut short by abortion or premature delivery is not as important here as the fact that individual mothers are being confronted by the threat of abortion or premature labor and there is nothing constructive that obstetricians have been able to do for these individual problems. A personal survey of the sequence of events in spontaneous abortions has shown that 80% of these start with bleeding. Fear and the misunderstandings created by this bleeding seem to lead to the beginning of expulsive uterine contractions. Conversely, a use of rapid subconscious review at levels of thinking reflected by ideomotor signals has permitted subconsciously willing mothers to pinpoint subjective reasons for their bleeding and to develop heightened awareness for uterine contractions. Normally these go on without causing distress. Some of my patients desiring their pregnancy seem to have been able to terminate bleeding and stop feeling their contractions on the basis of this type of investigation or procedure. It merits further exploration by those whose obstetrical practice is larger than mine.

Assumed guilt, self-punishment, identifications and conditioned pessimism are forces militating against the successful continuation of pregnancy (10).

All of the patients who have developed an antepartum incipient toxemia while under my direct care have been subjectively sure they knew what emotional factors were causing their subconscious anxiety which they relate to the toxemia. None has become worse after discussing the factors, and 50% have returned to normal physiological balance thereafter. Although few of the obstetrical authorities will consider seriously the possibility that all toxemia of pregnancy may be on the basis of emotional stress, consciously unrecognized, there are a number of fragments of evidence which point in that direction. The organicists argue that this is ridiculous because severe toxemias have occurred with women who had hydatidiform moles and chorioepitheliomas in the absence of a pregnancy. It would be hard to generalize on this matter or to exclude the possibility that women with hormone producing tumors could be wondering what is wrong. Failure to recognize the cause and effect relationships between unresolved continued stresses and the evidences of eclamptogenic toxemia apparently stems from the inadequate means of subsconscious evaluation so far developed. The stresses which may be powerfully destructive to an individual patient if consciously unrecognized may seem laughable to the patient when they emerge into conscious-level awareness. If it seems ridiculous to the patient it will naturally be given little attention by the average physician who depends on conscious communication about psycho-physiological relationships.

Cardiac Arrest Occurring in and About Surgical Operating Rooms

The incidence of cardiac arrest directly related to surgical experience is not readily available because there is understandable reluctance on the part of surgeons in accepting responsibility for the death of human beings on their way to the operating room, during induction of aesthesia or on being removed from the table to a carriage after surgery. A psychiatrist would have no difficulty understanding the possibility that a patient could die of fright in anticipation of surgery. He could also understand why the surgeon feels as he seems to feel. Similarly we find that cardiac arrest occurring on the eve of surgery or on the carriage taking a patient to surgery is likely to be looked at with a jaundiced eye by the anesthesiologists when they attempt to evaluate their responsibilities in surgical mortality. A fair number of cardiac arrest cases drop into the category of medical difficulties and are honestly enough classified under coronary artery disease or spasm. This is probably fair but it weakens the incentive of those who might be interested in learning what subjective factors may cause cardiac arrest before, during or after surgery. It is estimated that approximately 10,000 deaths a year are of this category and about half of them occur in human beings who are generally in reasonably good health and undergoing interval surgery of very moderate proportions (9).

Feelings of guilt, identifications with unfortunate people, dramatizations of self-pity and a host of possibilities present themselves as theoretical factors in the production of cardiac arrest but we have absolutely no information available on the subject. It is easier to get it now because long-range survival has advanced to approximately 35% in place of the 10% of 1956 when we were not so well prepared to deal with calamity.

Death and Destruction on Our Highways

In the last 3,652 days, representing ten years, there have been approximately three days when less than 100 human beings have met their death on highways of the United States. The annual mortality figure is fairly stable at 36,000 to 42,000 but there is a shocking part of the picture which does not readily come to our attention. Swifter action and better facilities are saving more lives. The proportion of injured to dead was 30:1 ten years ago; it is now nearly 50:1. An unknown number of these casualties may be attributed to the diminished fields of vision and slower muscular reactions which accompany spontaneously occurring hypnotic states. A casual survey of the subjective attitudes of twenty-four individuals who had been involved as drivers in automobile accidents suggested that more than half of them knew they could have avoided the accident but were powerless to react physically to the needs of the moment. Each realized in reviewing the accident that he or she had been in a state of heightened perception but diminished ability to move for several minutes to several hours before the accident occurred. The significant impression volunteered by several of these individuals was that they either did not care that they were heading into possible death or they momentarily welcomed the feeling. Since both of these attitudes were quite foreign to their normal conscious philosophy it seemed worthy of note. There is a great need for investigation into the subjective reactions of drivers at the time of accident. There is also a great need for restructuring the attitudes of those drivers who have contributed to the death or permanent injuries of others involved in the accident. Both investigation and therapy could be greatly and helpfully extended beyond the efforts presently possible with ordinary psychiatric methods.

Hypesthesia and Tissue Reaction with Scratches

Let us consider some of the possibilities for control of physiologic mechanisms of adaptation. Do we know anything about the relationship between perception and tissue reaction? The evidence is scanty but stimulating.

In 1952, while attempting to prove to an obstetrical patient that she was better able to anesthetize her arm hypnotically than she thought possible, I ran the point of a hypodermic needle upward from the supposedly anesthetized lower forearm to a point several inches above the antecubital space. The patient winced as the needle reached the antecubital space. The same linear scratch was made along the ventral surface of the sensitive opposite arm. The patient was convinced that there was a difference between the feeling of the arms with this stimulus. Normal sensation was suggested then and the patient discharged. When she was seen a week later at a regular prenatal visit there was a scratch still visible along the entire length of the arm used as a control but only the skin above the sensitive antecubital space of the previously anesthetized arm showed a scratch mark comparable to that of the unanesthetized arm. I did not then know anything about the inflammatory enzyme "neurokinin" but the accidental discovery that tissues which were even partially anesthetized seemed to heal more quickly and show less immediate edema and wheal formation proved to be an asset in convincing patients that hypnosis was worthy of investigation.

At first it seemed to me that the difference in tissue behavior might simply be due to the increased elasticity of the skin on the "numb" side making it yield more readily before the needle and thereby suffering less injury. There certainly was a demonstrable tensing of the muscles during injury to the sensitive skin. This could expose the skin to more trauma; the needle would have a more resistant bed under the skin. It was probable too that the dermal myofibrils contract reflexly when pain is experienced. I could devise no satisfactory way of proving to myself that tissues anesthetized by suggestion reacted less energetically than sensitive tissues. In the meantime, it was interesting and encouraging for surgical, obstetrical and cancer therapy patients to discover that their mind in some way could alter tissue reactions to injury. I have repeated the test with better than 99% positive response in more than 1,000 personal patients since then.

Some Possibilities for Clinical Investigation: Pain Perception and Abdominal Rigidity

Use of these theoretical principles derived from accidental observation made it possible in 1953 for me to speak with enough confidence to a discouraged obstetrical patient to help her change her behavior dramatically in the course of an overwhelming puerperal sepsis. The patient had been doing well after delivery of a Mongoloid child. She hemorrhaged profusely on the third day postpartum immediately after being told she could go home but would have to leave her baby at the hospital for a few days. Her temperature jumped from 98 to 105 degrees after a transfusion. There was a pure growth of E. coli on urine culture and a continued septic course. Pyelitis was ruled out by absence of microscopic evidence of infection in the urine. In spite of adequate doses of penicillin and gantrisin initially, followed by chloromycetin, she went on to develop abdominal rigidity and rebound tenderness on the third day of her illness. This patient, reported elsewhere (4), had been a non-responsive subject for hypnosis. Under the circumstances of her downhill course she either had an increased motivation for responding or else she was already in hypnosis when I began talking to her about hypnosis. I said that muscle spasm was interfering with blood supply in the uterus, that the drugs were fine drugs but that they were useless if they could not get into the area where the bacteria were causing trouble. Evidence to corroborate my fabricated theory was demonstrated to her by pressing again on her rigid abdomen. I said that the pain was tightening all the muscles in that area and blocking off the blood supply.

Within the space of time that it took to explain these things it became apparent that she was already in hypnosis without a formal induction. I asked her to press on her abdomen when she knew that all the pain was gone. After she carried out this suggestion, with the usual slow motion of a hypnotized subject, I asked her to go even deeper and stay in hypnosis just as she was for the next 24 hours in order to let her body best use the medication and best use the rest to rebuild her resistance to infection.

Her pulse rate, temperature and respiration remained normal after the initial 24 hours of continued hypnotic state. It seemed noteworthy that she had lost the rigidity and rebound tenderness within five minutes of signalling that the pain was gone. Rebound tenderness and reflex abdominal rigidity are supposedly controlled through sympathetic innervation from the peritoneum through the spinal cord. I decided that I must learn more about the mediating factors in pain perception and physiological response.

Three years after this experience it was possible to obtain a subjective report from this patient in a medium-trance state. Asked to orient to the time of the hospitalization and signal if she recognized some factor that might have been responsible for the bleeding, she gave a signal and said,

> You did not tell me, but I knew something was wrong with my baby by the way you said you wanted to keep her for a few days until she could gain a little weight. I did not want to leave her alone there.

The patient went on to teach me a lesson about ideomotor communication by saying,

> When you did not tell me the truth about my little girl I knew there must be something very seriously wrong.

I asked the patient then to call to mind something that might have helped her make the dramatic improvement in her condition. She said, after giving an ideomotor signal from her designated finger.

> I could tell by your face that you meant what you said about my being very sick and that you wanted me to use hypnosis to let the medicine start working. I had not wanted to live because I had done so much vomiting. I thought that must have made my baby not be normal. Then I realized she would need me to take care of her. I had to get well.

What is the Physiological Meaning of Pain?

These observations and others which have been reported elsewhere (7, 9) have suggested that our concepts of pain must be altered to fit the evidence. By definition, pain is usually defined as a consciously perceived sensation in response to a noxious stimulus, but this sort of definition seems worthless. George Crile has pointed out (11) that we cannot feel damaging stimuli in parts of the body which have not been phylogenetically conditioned for expectancy of potentially pain-producing damage. We feel pain with slow, tearing forces on the bowel or mesentery but we do not feel slow, cutting trauma with a scalpel. Attention to the stimulus, expectancy of pain, speed of initial trauma all play a part in what we call pain. Authorities on pain such as Judovich and Bates (18), Wolff and Wolf (24) and Thomas Lewis (19), make no mention of the spontaneous loss of pain perception in time of great danger or on entering a deep hypnotic state. Authorities writing on the subject of obstetrical analgesia have been unable to correlate the evaluations of patients. They have all been forced to lean on such artificial structures as the capacity of the patient to remember furniture in the labor or delivery room. We have seen that the capacity for consciously remembering something has no relationship to the fact.

Use of amnesia to measure the quality or intensity of pain is scientifically disrespectful to the truth. We should have some other way of recognizing the effects of trauma and inflammation. We should have some way also of understanding how these effects can be altered by expectancy, recognition and emotion. Each of these may have conscious and unconscious components. Perhaps we should consider the unconscious as well as the conscious perceptions of pain. This will require a change in definition and some definite changes in scientific thought. Damaging stimuli of surgery may be painless by virtue of the chemical anesthesia. Preoperative anticipations of great pain, however, might lead a well-anesthetized patient to develop the same postoperative edema, vascular stasis and muscular guarding that would have occurred in the old-fashioned way without anesthesia. A surgical team talking in an alarming way over a previously calm, sleeping patient might produce results which are even worse than those which could have been produced with anticipation and no general anesthesia (5, 6).

What then is pain and how can we learn more about it? For answers to these questions we must turn to the best authorities, patients. We must ask each individual patient about expectancy, about the feeling and about what that feeling means. Conscious reporting is useless. We need to know more.

Thermal Burns and Tissue Reaction in Relation to Pain

During preliminary discussion of hypnosis prior to a demonstration of phenomena a subject was asked whether the blister on her finger was painful. She immediately said "No" as she reached over with the other hand to rub it. After pressing on it she corroborated the initial statement. A few minutes later she was learning how to give symbol answers with her fingers. I touched the blister and asked, "Does the subconscious part of your mind feel any discomfort as I rub this blister?" Verbally she repeated the "No" answer but her "Yes" finger was slowly rising in the typical trembling response of an unconscious answer. The subject was then asked to make the blister area numb as though novocaine had been injected into it. An ideomotor signal was requested for this recognition and for the promise that the anesthetic would continue during the next twelve hours. At the end of two hours the blister exudate had resorbed. What was responsible for this? Could it be better circulation or something else?

Serious Burns

In 1959 I was asked to see the wife of a physician for the purpose of using hypnosis to relieve the pain of second and third degree burns extending from her buttocks to her neck. There were large keloids encircling most of the second degree burns. Although five weeks had elapsed since her accident she was requiring demerol every two hours. There had been very little spontaneous epithelialization. The patient had been adamant in prohibiting attempts at skin grafting because she could not stand the thought of adding to her pain by trimming donor sites. She was afraid to take an anesthetic. It took twenty minutes to discover, with the help of a Chevreul pendulum initially, and then finger signals as she went more deeply into hypnosis, that she had been punishing herself severely. When she was 17 her mother had caught her smoking a cigarette. Pointing a finger at her, the mother had exclaimed, "Some day God will punish you for this, you are not a good Mormon." The patient came out of hypnosis to tell me the burns had occurred while she was resting on a sofa in front of the television. She had finished a highball and had taken a sleeping pill to relax her after a strenuous day helping her husband in the office. She had fallen asleep. The cigarette in the ashtray on her lap had rolled down behind her nylon dressing gown. The smoldering heat awakened her with a start. As she pulled away from the sofa, the air rushed in exploding the robe. Her back was burned as she ran along the hall to her husband. Recovery of the memory about her mother came as a surprise. I had asked her "to orient to some reason for feeling so guilty as to suffer for five weeks like this." The thought entered her mind a few seconds after the signalling finger lifted.

After superimposing her conscious reasoning upon the unconscious one, that God was punishing her for being a bad Mormon, she was able to accept a feeling of coolness and numbness of all burned areas and acknowledged the promise to keep the anesthesia for 24 hours. A second session reinforced and continued the anesthesia. Seventy-two hours after the initial interview there was an interesting change in the appearance of the lesions. Where there had been keloids elevated 6 to 10 millimeters above the level of the surrounding skin there were now depressions. This is the type of reaction which one finds after injecting cortisol derivatives beneath keloids. The response must be different in some way from the cortisol anti-inflammatory effect, however, because I have never seen spread of infection after this type of anti-inflammatory pseudo-cortisol response (7). We know that cortisol derivatives allow the spread of infections when the fibrin and vascular barriers are broken down. This patient needed no demerol after the first interview. She permitted skin grafting a few days later. She even did better than heal. Three years after the injury there are only two small patches of scarred skin under each axilla. All the rest of her back is of uniform color and the skin is of uniform texture and mobility! This was her doing. She had sufficient pride to work at maintaining the imagery of normal skin on her back. This result is not supposed to happen after skin grafting for third-degree burns. It would be helpful to know just why guilt interfered with healing. We could reason that guilt feelings intensified the awareness of supposedly just punishment, that pain led to spasm of local muscles and stasis of blood. These are suppositions. It makes me wonder if more effort should be made to search out fears and guilt feelings with all human beings who are victims of trauma.

Body Image and Body Awareness

Patients in hypnosis give vivid and often helpful verbal impressions of what their body looks like and how it feels. Their subconscious idea of anatomy may be childlike and very different from the idea they render on awakening from hypnosis. Their impressions may give valuable clues to target organ vulnerability to stress. While watching a demonstration of a method for teaching a child how to imagine an electric wire running from a part of his body up to the brain and then turning off a light that represented the feeling from that part, I was amused at the choice of colors used by the youngster. The color of the light was so emphatically and quickly stated that it seemed meaningful to the child. I wondered if this dissociative method of inquiry might be helpful for understanding body image and awareness in adults. It seemed reasonable to ask the subject to hallucinate a sort of telephone switchboard in the shape of a body with Christmas tree lights to symbolize the feelings from whatever organs or extremities seemed appropriate in each case.

I tried it out during a symposium on medical hypnosis in the fall of 1959. It proved most interesting. The physician acting as a subject was in a medium state of hypnosis. He showed a lag of time between "seeing" the light in each area and being able to see it at whatever level is represented by the "mind's eye" where he could tell us the color and intensity of light. The head was represented by a yellow light, the arms by green lights of the same shade and intensity, but he had a great big red light above the knee in his right leg. I asked him to let his fingers answer the question, "Do you have any pain in that leg?" The answer was "No." I asked him to orient back through the years of his life experience to the time when a big red light was put in for that right leg. There was a pause and then the designated finger indicated he had arrived in his thinking at that time.

A few seconds later he started to chuckle as he said, "That is the darndest thing! I played football in high school and I had a charley-horse all through school because I kept bumping that leg." Here was an apparent carry-over of an unconsciously perceived hyperawareness, conditioned by multiple injuries many years ago. Was this a key to more knowledge that might help us understand target organ vulnerability to stress?

This hallucinated switchboard body has been most useful in my practice of gynecology and obstetrics because it has revealed just that type of information. Frigid patients have reported "black lights" representing rejection of feeling from genital areas. Some have actually stated that they could see a light socket but a piece of adhesive tape was covering it. When these subjects are asked to orient back to a time when "there is a light there" or when something happens to "make the tape be placed there" there have been helpful bits of information which were readily explained by the patient in the light of later understandings at the time of interview.

Increasingly I have been impressed by the conviction of many patients that very powerful forces have influenced their attitudes toward themselves as women according to what they think they experienced before, during and after birth. There have been many lights which have been changed by conversations in operating rooms while patients have been anesthetized. There have been strong hyperawarenesses for various organs because of identifications, because of material absorbed in the reading of semi-scientific reports in magazines, and because of conditioning.

Imprinting

In my experience the most common examples of misdirected sexual development and physiological performance seem to relate to what Herbert Spiegel might call "imprinting" (23). Adult females who have suffered from acne and dysmenorrhea have observed a change in their skin and have rid themselves of dysmenorrhea on realizing that there had been early rejection of them because of a parental wish for a boy, and that this did not really mean they were expected to become boys. Clinically the matter of fact seems not as important as the apparent fact that the patient believed it to be fact at the ideational horizon of thinking reflected by ideomotor symbol responses. Spiegel has likened the neurotic behavior of human beings who are disturbed by single episode experiences to the very powerful impact of some single episodes with lower animals. Lorenz (20) in 1935 found that mallard ducklings exposed to a wooden decoy duck during the first day of life would select and relate to that duck in preference to their own mother thereafter. Hess (16) is exploring this matter of single, significant experiences compared to the repeated conditioned types of learning in some birds and mammals. Spiegel has compared the "compulsive triad" of post-hypnotic behavior to this phenomenon of apparent "imprinting" in human compulsive neurotic behavior. An understanding linked with a powerful emotional stress such as birth, general anesthesia, serious illness, coma or frightening labor may be repressed into unconscious zones of mentation, may produce disturbed compulsive behavior which then has to be rationalized in some way by the patient. This is what happens with a suggestion for unusual post-hypnotic behavior. There may be no amnesia for the suggestion. In this case the subject may decide intellectually to discard the suggestion. If there is post-hypnotic amnesia for the suggestion then, as Spiegel points out, there is amnesia, compulsive behavior, dictated by the suggestion and conscious rationalization for the behavior.

Continuation of the process of post-hypnotic behavior varies with a number of factors, the most significant of which probably is the subconscious pre-hypnotic understanding that this is an experimental situation which is not expected to continue. Such a censoring mechanism may not be available for protection during great emotional stress.

Let us explore some of the reasons we may hope to advance in our understanding and therapy for psychosomatic disease. First we must know why an organ or system becomes susceptible to damage, then we must understand how damage occurs.

Research on Tissue Trauma, Pain and Inflammation

We have seen Esdaile in 1845 observing that "mesmeric" relief of pain diminished the inflammatory reactions of trauma and infection (14). The rush of enthusiasm about chemical anesthesia and what Huxley has called the "voluntary ignorance" (17) of the medical profession held up the investigation of just what happens to make this possible. Thirty-two years went by.

In 1877 Delboeuf, Professor of Psychology at Liege (12) did some experiments with hypnosis in an effort to understand the reasons for apparent rapid healing and the failure of blisters to form when hypnotically anesthetized parts of the body were traumatized or burned. He hypnotized two volunteers and burned both arms of each subject as nearly equally as possible. Each subject had one arm normally sensitive and the other "anesthetized" by suggestion. Blisters did not form on the insensitive arms. Healing was more rapid on the insensitive arms. Reversal of the experiment using the opposite arm for control gave the same results. Seventy-three years of voluntary blindness elapsed before the next progress.

In 1950 Graham (15) showed that reactions and permeability of minute vessels in the skin could be altered in situations perceived by the individual as threatening. The general principles of this type of reaction might be expected. We see it with the ideo-vascular reactions of blanching or blushing with emotion. Graham used conversational methods of interview.

Armstrong, Jepson, Keele and Stewart (1) in 1957 found pain producing substances in blister exudate. In the same year, Ostfield and a group at Cornell (22) found pain producing polypeptides in the scalp exudates of patients suffering from migraine headaches.

The first major contribution to our knowledge of subconsciously controllable tissue reactions came from Cornell Medical Center in New York. In 1959 Chapman, Goodell and Harold Wolff reported their findings with what appears to have been an independent repetition of Delboeuf's experiment (2, 3). Harold Wolff had not mentioned hypnosis in his 1948 book *Pain,* published in collaboration with Stewart Wolf of the University of Oklahoma School of Medicine.

Results were not particularly remarkable when one arm was normally sensitive and the other "anesthetized." They added another step which is of utmost importance. They suggested to the hypnotized volunteers that something very uncomfortable would be happening to the normal arm. Anticipation of an unknown painful stimulus brought about a marked difference in tissue reaction between the insensitive arm and the perceptive arm to which the subject was giving increased attentiveness. Now when the same stimulus was applied to both arms there was a marked inflammatory reaction in the sensitive skin and very little reaction in the insensitive skin.

Perfusates were collected from both traumatized areas of each subject by running physiological saline into the subcutaneous tissues at the upper edge of the injured skin and collecting it by gravity through another needle at the lower margin. It was possible for them to demonstrate the presence of an enzyme released by efferent nerves at the site of injury. The perfusate from the consciously painful skin area contained much of this substance but the amount of enzyme was diminished or absent on the anesthetized side. The enzyme has specific, reproducible qualities. It produced signs of inflammation when injected into normal skin elsewhere in the body. The perfusate from the "anesthetized" skin did not cause an inflammatory reaction.

These investigators state, in reference to the meaning of their work, that release of this enzyme which they have called "neurokinin" probably represents an adaptive mechanism for protection of the organism. They say,

> Such adaptive reactions at times may be essential to survival, but if evoked inappropriately or excessively may contribute to disease since non-noxious stimulation becomes noxious and mildly damaging stimuli result in greater injury.

The work has so far been restricted to observations of the skin in its response to stress. Harold Wolff acknowledged in a personal communication that, although the biological evidence cannot be extrapolated as yet to their consideration of target organ vulnerability in psychosomatic illness, this is the direction of their thinking at the moment.

Conclusion

We have discussed some techniques of ideomotor questioning and their values for communication with levels of awareness approximating those where perception and attitude govern physiologic adaptations. Consideration has been given to some applications of hypnosis and ideomotor techniques of analysis in areas of medicine where we need to understand better the emotional forces and their influence. Hypnosis is not a panacea. It cannot be used with all human beings. Not all professional persons are emotionally capable of using hypnosis productively and with adequate respect for the needs of their patients. Not all evidence derived from the use of ideomotor questioning methods and hypnosis is valid. It is increasingly evident, however, that hypnosis is a natural phenomenon occurring spontaneously and often helpfully during times of emotional and physical stress. It is a phenomenon relating to self-protection for the individual through camouflage and restriction of energy waste. In the hypnotic state, imagery and tissue memory can be mobilized for immediate use just as they are in times of stress. For this reason the combination of hypnosis with ideomotor means of communication permits more rapid and complete access to associations of imagery and physiologic response to stress than any other means so far available. Hypnosis can be used for analysis and psychotherapy quickly, safely and in a very high percentage of human beings who recognize their need for help. Arguments about the relationship between therapist and patient being autocratic and abnormal, as being one of dominance and submissiveness, only preserve the rigidities of those who have not had a chance to understand hypnotism. There is much to discover. We must not be afraid to look.

REFERENCES

1. Armstrong, D., J. B. Jepson, C. A. Keele and J. W. Stewart. 1957. Pain producing substance in human inflammatory exudates and plasma. *J. Physiol.* 135:350.
2. Chapman, L. F., H. Goodell and H. Wolff. 1959. Changes in tissue vulnerability during hypnotic suggestion. *J. Psychosom. Res.* 4:99-105.
3. ——. 1959. Augmentation of the inflammatory reaction by activity of the central nervous system. *Am. Med. Assn. Arch. Neurol.* 1:557-572.
4. Cheek, D. B. 1957. Effectiveness of incentive in clinical hypnosis. *Obs. Gynec.* 9:720-724.
5. ——. 1959. Unconscious perception of meaningful sounds during surgical anesthesia as revealed under hypnosis. *Am. J. Clin. Hypnosis* 1:101-113.
6. ——. 1960. What does the surgically anesthetized patient hear? *Rocky Mt. Med. J.* 57:49-53.
7. ——. 1960. Removal of subconscious resistance to hypnosis using ideomotor techniques. *Am. J. Clin. Hypnosis* 3:103-107.
8. ——. 1961. Possible uses of hypnosis in dermatology. *Med. Times* 39:76-82.
9. ——. 1961. Unconscious reactions and surgical risk. *Western J. Surg. Obs. Gynec.* 69:325-328.
10. ——. 1961. Value of ideomotor sex-determination technique of LeCron for uncovering subconscious fear in obstetric patients. *Int. J. Clin. Exper. Hyp.* 9:249-259.
11. Crile, G. and W. E. Lower. 1914. The clinical pathology of shock. In *Anoci-Association,* 80-93. Philadelphia: W. B. Saunders.
12. Delboeuf, J. 1877. De L'origine des effets curatifs de l'hypnotisme. *Bull. Acad. Royale Belgique.* In Bernheim, H. 1947. *Suggestive Therapeutics,* 411. New York: London Book Co.
13. Everson, T. and W. H. Cole. 1959. Spontaneous regression of malignant disease. (Guest editorial) *J. Am. Med. Assn.* 169:1758-1759.
14. Esdaile, J. 1957. *Hypnosis in Medicine and Surgery.* New York: Julian Press. (Originally titled *Mesmerism in India,* 1856).
15. Graham, D. T. 1950. The pathogenesis of hives. *Assn. Res. Nerv. Ment. Dis. Proc.* 29:987.
16. Hess, E. H. 1959. Imprinting. *Science* 130:3368.
17. Huxley, Aldous. 1956. A case of voluntary ignorance. *Esquire* (Oct.):47.
18. Judovich, B. and W. Bates. 1949. *Pain Syndromes.* Philadelphia: F. A. Davis.
19. Lewis, T. 1942. *Pain.* New York: Macmillan Co.
20. Lorenz, K. 1935. Reference to *Imprinting* by Hess. *J. Ornithol.* 83:137.
21. Mayer, Major Wm. E., U.S.A.M.C. *Report on Korean War Prisoners.* Freedom Foundation Lecture, Searcy, Arkansas.
22. Ostfield, A. M., L. F. Chapman, H. Goodell and H. Wolff. 1957. *Studies in Headache.* Summary of evidence concerning a noxious agent active locally during migraine headache. *Psychosom. Med.* 19:199.
23. Spiegel, H. 1960. Hypnosis and the psychotherapeutic process. *Comp. Psychiat.* 1:174-185.
24. Wolff, H. and S. Wolf. 1948. *Pain.* Springfield: Charles C. Thomas.

Therapy of Persistent Pain States: Part I, Neck and Shoulder Pain of Five Years' Duration

The author's description of general analysis and therapy for persistent pain states has been presented in the October issue of this Journal (1). From time to time significant cases will be presented when the evidence seems clear enough for exposition of factors responsible for success or failure of the therapy. The first case is submitted because it correlates with a paper on the meaning of persistent hearing under general chemo-anesthesia. Continuing and increasing pain after an operation seemed due to misunderstandings of expressed and implied ideas while the patient was in a presumed surgical plane of chemo-anesthesia. These misunderstandings were responsible for repeated, consciously unrecognized dreams. Symptomatic and physiologic relief followed the correction of these misunderstandings.

Case history—Miss C. M., a 27-year-old, single, white woman working as bank secretary under great pressure, was first seen on August 12, 1965, complaining of almost constant occipital headache with pain through her shoulders and the back of her neck. She was desperate because she had undergone a laminectomy for removal of a cervical disc in October, 1963, followed by a fixation of the neck vertebrae in April, 1964, and a second attempt at fixation in August of 1964. All the surgeries had been done by an eminent orthopedic surgeon. She hoped hypnosis might help control the pain which had persisted for 5 years since her automobile accident in July, 1960.

The patient, a tall, attractive woman, came in with and maintained a constant frown. She kept her head in a fixed position, turning her body and shoulders in order to turn her head. To look down she would bend her body rather than tip her head forward. Clearly there were physical habit patterns of posture that needed correction. She presented an appearance of constant alertness, reflected in posture and facial expression.

Patients with persistent pain states often give important clues at the first interview while they are explaining their trouble. This patient stated that it all began as she, her *married older* sister and the sister's daughter were on their way to a drive-in theater. (She emphasized the fact that her sister was married and had a daughter.) A car in her lane stopped abruptly to make a turn-off. The next car stopped in time to avoid collision, as did the patient's car. They were struck by the following car. There resulted a jolting-backward and rebound-forward thrust effect on the heads of the passengers. No one seemed injured. The patient added that the woman *causing the accident kept right on driving and was never apprehended. The owner of the other car had no insurance.* Immediate notes were made that the patient, who was driving the car, might have been jealous of her older, married sister, or may have felt guilty over hostility for her sister. It was also noted that she might have harbored resentments toward the unfair-

Reprinted with permission from *American Journal of Clinical Hypnosis* 8 (1966):281-286.

ness of the situation allowing escape for the woman who caused the accident and for the man who carried no insurance. (It was later found that these were unimportant factors.)

They decided to go on with their plan to see the movie, and did so in comfort. A highway patrol officer told them at the scene of collision that they were lucky to have stopped in time to avoid collision with the car in front. He said that she and her sister in the front seat might have been thrown through the windshield and then thrown backward as they were hit from behind. (Influence of this suggestion was greater than I first suspected.)

The next day the sister complained of pain in her neck but the patient had no distress of any sort. She drove her sister to the orthopedist who examined both of them. He explained that the sister had a slight whiplash injury, but that nothing was wrong with the patient. (At this point it was decided to interrupt conscious history-telling in order to combine hypnosis with a review of events at a subconscious level.)

After demonstrating postural suggestion and setting up ideomotor finger signals, the patient was asked to orient to the very first moment she was aware of pain "in her neck, shoulders or head." A signal of accomplishment occurred within 30 seconds. It surprised her to learn that the onset of pain was a few minutes after a dream about being in a very serious accident. The dream was at 3 a.m., she believed, on the second day after the accident. Now, circumstances were changed. Instead of a repetition of the real incident, this was the accident as suggested by the patrol officer. The patient had been unable to stop in time. Her sister and niece were uninjured, but she had been thrown forward with such force that her chest broke the steering wheel and her head smashed into the windshield. A few minutes later she awakened with severe head and neck pain, but she had no conscious recollection of the dream. (This phenomenon of traumatic dream repression is frequent following accidents of all sorts; it is an important factor in the complications of pregnancy.) (2, 3).

Later that second day the patient accompanied her sister to consult the orthopedst who now showed concern over the new symptoms after 36 hours of comfort. This delayed onset of pain meant that there had been some injury to the cord or to the nerve roots. Simple neck strain would have been reflected by immediate muscle guarding and rigidity, as was shown by her sister. She did not help his diagnosis because she could not associate the dream with pain. Her sister recovered swiftly, but the patient continued with pain in spite of traction and medication. After 3 years it was discovered that she had a herniated disc in the cervical region. The surgeon, in explaining the situation, told her that an incision would be made anteriorly in order to approach the trouble in the most direct and safe manner. The patient did not recall being told that constant pain and muscle guarding could have caused the degeneration of the annulus of the disc. She assumed the herniation had been there for 3 years. When she asked him why he would not go in from the back of the neck, which seemed the logical place, he explained that the best approach was anteriorly where there *could be no possible damage to the spinal cord.* Entry from behind *could risk paralysis if blood vessels supplying the cord were accidentally injured.*

The surgery of October, 1963, was "successful," but the pain persisted, as might have been expected. In April, 1964, an anterior procedure was again done under general anesthesia in order to place bone chips between the transverse processes *to limit motion of the neck.* The surgery was again considered a success, but there was no diminution in the pain. X-rays eventually showed that there had not been a satisfactory fusion. The orthopedist then decided on an immediate revision of the surgery. The abruptness of his decision alarmed the patient. She felt that if he decided so quickly on surgery there must be something more seriously wrong than he was willing to admit. When she asked him what would be done, he answered that he would go in from the back of the neck this time. When she asked him if this would be dangerous to the nerve roots or the spinal cord, as intimated in his first explanation, he answered that he would be nowhere near the nerve roots or the cord this time. He would simply be putting some more bone chips around the vertebrae, and would use wire to support them further. This was consciously acceptable, but subconsciously alarming in view of her general understanding of the first discussion in 1963.

Forty-five minutes had elapsed at this point. Time did not permit further analysis of the history. As the interview was concluded she was asked to have an ideomotor response to the question, "Will it be all right for me to help you be relieved of this pain?" The "yes" finger lifted immediately in response. (Indication that the pain was apparently not being used in self-punishment.) She was then asked to turn off the pain completely at a subconscious level, to notify me with an ideomotor signal when this was accomplished, and to tell me verbally when she felt comfortable. The ideomotor response came after 2 minutes. A change in posture and smoothing of her brow occurred during the next 90 seconds. Her verbal report of comfort came 5 minutes after the ideomotor signal. (This is the usual sequence of events and about average for time lapse between unconscious gesture, change in muscle tension and conscious awareness that pain has been blocked.) As the patient got up from her chair she moved her head from side to side, forward and back, stroked the back of her neck with her right hand. She looked somewhat surprised and then added the following note as she started for the door: "You know, when I woke up after that third operation I was horribly upset and remained upset for a week." This suggested the possibility that something could have occurred during the period of unconsciousness with the anesthetic. These last-minute bonanzas cannot safely be ignored. She was asked to sit down again for a moment to answer the question, "While you were under the anesthetic in the third operation was there anything said or done that could have been disturbing to you?" There was an immediate answer with the "yes" finger, and an appearance of agitation in her posture and facial expression. Her neck muscles tightened as she said, "The pain is starting again." Again I asked if it would be all right to turn off the pain and remain free of pain until her next appointment. The finger signal indicated a "yes." Twenty seconds later she appeared comfortable and reported that the pain had disappeared. I commented on this rapid shift back to pain on the basis of a recollection, and pointed out that this is the history of conditioned pain, that she must learn about the unconscious triggers responsible for onset of pain in order to learn how to remain comfortable. An appointment was given for 5 days from this first visit, but she was instructed to let me know at once in case she could not handle the next recurrence of pain.

Second visit, 8/18/65—At the second visit she reported great improvement. She recalled awakening in the early morning of the day after her first office visit with pain in her neck and head. She knew there must have been a dream, but she could not identify the dream. Realization that pain was due to an undetermined dream, however, permitted her to stop the pain as she moved about the house.

This visit was started with a review of that night from the moment of falling asleep until the awakening with pain. There was a dream which she was able to report in detail after 2 subconscious reviews from beginning to end at an ideomotor level of recollection. It was a reliving of the traumatic experiences in the third operation.

Operation #3—She has been placed on her abdomen prior to induction of anesthesia with sodium pentothal. The anesthesiologist is having much difficulty getting a tracheal catheter into position. (This is a difficult task. Usually patients are anesthetized in recumbent position, intubated and then placed in a prone position.) Asked what makes this important, she answers that this is an inauspicious beginning for the operation, and indicates that the operation will probably be a failure too. Her next signal of an important incident during the operation relates to difficulties a few minutes later. The surgeon is struggling to get a wire in place. He does not say anything, but she knows by his breathing and the way he is using his hands that things are not going the way he wanted them to. The assistant comments on the difficulty but gets no response, indicating that there really is some trouble. By the time the incision is made over the crest of the ilium to obtain bone fragments she is greatly agitated.

Bleeding from the tissues in this secondary site of operation further delays the progress of surgery. Asked if she knows why she is bleeding so profusely she gives a "yes" answer, followed by the verbal comment, "I'm bleeding because I'm afraid this operation will not work and there will be no hope for me." All during the operation she says, "I have been waiting for the surgeon to slip to cause a paralyzing injury to my cord, because he is working in the back of my neck where he once said the surgery could be dangerous." Review of this operative experience points up the fact that nothing really has been said by the surgeon to cause worry. It is difficulty of the anesthesiologist and the comment of the assistant which add to pre-existing subconscious alarm. Surgeons and anesthesiologists must constantly be alert to the semantics of the subconscious mind.

Her postoperative course was troubled by her constant headache and shoulder pain. During the interview the patient recognized that this pain was caused by fear that any movement would result in irreparable damage to her spinal cord. The fears were augmented by troubled dreams which were not consciously remembered. Such dreams are too threatening; they had been repressed. This phylogenetically adequate but humanly damaging defense mechanism of repression shows up frequently, and lends itself nicely to correction with ideomotor questioning techniques. It is with the help of subconscious review and ideomotor signalling devices that it is now possible to contradict the famous Freudian dictum of 1909:

> It is only if you exclude hypnosis that you can observe resistances and repressions and form an adequate idea of the *truly pathogenic* (sic) course of events. (4)

Third visit, 8/19/65—The patient had intermittent episodes of neck and shoulder pain after the second hour of therapy. At the third visit she was asked to rehearse putting herself into hypnosis, turning on and turning off the recollection of pain at an ideomotor level of awareness. She managed to keep within the 2 minute time limit from beginning of hypnosis (dropping a pencil) to the moment she felt like opening her eyes. This took 10 minutes of the hour.

Next she was asked to review all three of her operations to make sure there were not alarming incidents which had not yet been discovered. There seemed to be none. The third operation again appeared as the important one. During the review of this it was pointed out that both her anesthesiologist and her surgeon had shown concern and interest for her well-being. She was asked to go over the operation in detail and signal with her "yes" finger each time she came to something troublesome. She was asked to substitute the right action or the right saying to assure that Carol *there on the table* would have the smoothest recovery with the best results.

Hallucinated revision of third surgery—The anesthesiologist explained that it was hard to stand on your head to get an airway in, but that it was working all right now. The assistant commented on the difficulty the surgeon was having with the wire for fixation, but the surgeon just explained that he wanted to do an especially neat job this time to make sure this girl would be free of her pain. This very important phase of any review of surgical experiences took only 5 minutes. It is an important step because it permits us to learn the semantics of the anesthetized, unconscious brain. It is important because it permits the patient to forgive mistakes by substituting helpful suggestions to improve the behavior of other people under similar circumstances. It is an important step in obviating possible malpractice suits as long as the investigating patient can maintain personal humility in recognition of the doctor's mistakes. It can be potentially dangerous in the hands of a pusillanimous doctor anxious to "stand taller by chopping off the heads of his comrades."

The patient was next asked to review all the things that we had discussed so far during the three visits. She was asked to do this at an ideomotor level of thought, giving signals each time she came to something she thought important. Significant was the fact that there had been many frightening dreams during the first weeks after her third surgery. Always they were about the operation, that the neck "was all messed up," that they cannot do much with it because it has "all grown together with bone." This was interesting because it was volunteered as a substitute for my request to "go over the things we had talked about." I should have asked simply for her to consider "everything that was important since the first visit." No mention had been made of the postoperative bad dreams stimulated by the difficulties in moving her head to permit intubation, trouble with the wire or concern about the hemorrhage at the donor site for the bone chips.

At the conclusion of the hour she was asked to give a signal of acceptance when she knew that these dreams and fears had been completely resolved and she knew that she could move her head with progressively greater "freedom and comfort."

Fourth visit, 8/27/65 (3 hours used to this point)—At this time the patient was able to report that she had completely lost the feeling of occipital tension that used to come with situation pressures at work with a demanding boss. Whenever she felt the tension occurring she would tell herself to relax, or, in special instances, she would go to the bathroom and go through the 2-minute steps of autosuggestion.

I wanted to clear other possible sources of self-punishment. Her birth was unimportant. She knew that her birth did not trouble her mother, that she was perfectly acceptable although she heard her father make a remark about preferring to have a boy "this time." She indicated that her father had subsequently shown ample indications of loving her. There had been tensions in the family, mostly over her mother's alcoholism. These problems had been greater during the 5 years of the patient's illness, but the patient could discover no possible wish to assume any pain in the subconscious hope of sparing either her mother or father. She felt sure there had been no problems between herself and her sister. There were no concerns about her sexual adjustments and experiences. She was subconsciously sure of "cure" now.

Follow-up

The patient was asked to attend an advanced course on hypnotherapeutic methods. She willingly told the doctors about her experience, and was able to recognize the value of her contribution to our knowledge of subconscious ideation during natural sleep and the unconsciousness of general anesthesia. She demonstrated her method of brief autohypnosis for relaxation. Pain returned briefly during a time of stress in the office on September 29, but she indicated over the telephone that "her fingers knew" why she was uncomfortable, and they indicated that she could turn off this pain and remain well.

Summary

This patient is apparently cured of severe, disabling head and neck pain lasting for 5 years and through 3 surgical attempts to relieve pain with usual orthopedic methods. Initial pain seems clearly the result of a fabricated dream suggested by a well-meaning highway patrolman, and augmented by misunderstanding on the part of the orthopedist. Assumption that the injury had been more serious than first appeared reinforced the patient's unconscious alarm, and increased the painful muscle guarding which eventually led to herniation of the disc and surgical intervention. The explanation for anterior surgical approach set up reinforcing fears because he had initially told her there must be damage to the spinal cord and the nerve roots. Fear of disturbing the results of surgery maintained the painful muscle guarding and interfered with solidification of the implanted bone fragments after the second operation. Again reinforcement of the fears came with sudden decision to operate for the third time, and from a posterior approach to the neck with all its unreal but previously implied dangers of paralysis.

Therapy consisted primarily of an optimistic general approach aimed at excluding factors of guilt and self-punishment. These were not important. The information misunderstood during general anesthesia of the third operation was of utmost significance. Correction of these misunderstandings and reinforcement of her self-confidence in controlling pain seemed to be the chief factors in permitting total relief of symptoms.

REFERENCES

1. Cheek, D. B. 1965. Emotional factors in persistent pain states *Am. J. Clin. Hypnosis* 8:100-110.
2. ———. 1965. Some newer understandings of dreams in relation to threatened abortion. *Pacific Med. & Surg.* 73:379-384.
3. ———. 1963. Physiological impact of fear in dreams, post-operative hemorrhage. *Am. J. Clin. Hypnosis* 5:206-208.
4. Freud, S. 1909. *Complete Psychiatric Works* 11. Hogarth Press.

Maladjustment Patterns Apparently Related to Imprinting at Birth

Summary—Through use of ideomotor responses combined with light hypnosis it is possible to review birth memory when it is associated with maternal stress. The effect of maternal pain and emotional distress on the baby may cause conditioned problems that are evoked as patterned responses in later life. The quality of these patterned responses is comparable to the imprinting of lower animals but they may be changed as the initial memory is exposed to conscious reasoning and later perspective during age-regression.

Presented at 17th Annual Scientific Meeting of the American Society of Clinical Hypnosis, New Orleans, La., November, 1974. Reprinted with permission from *American Journal of Clinical Hypnosis* 18 (1975):75-82.

There is no single path to our understanding and correction of disease origins. We keep moving in our medical attitudes. Even the computer cannot diminish the humility we are forced to maintain as we consider various fancies of bygone years, the amputations of breasts to mitigate the effects of eclampsia, the marching of tuberculous patients up mountains to enlarge their hearts, the enthusiasm on finding "laudable pus" in a surgical incision.

The author offers the following paper with full respect for the possibility that the ideas here presented may now seem or will eventually be as wrong as these examples of our past ignorance. It has long been my belief that the basic factors in healing include willingness on the part of a sick person and optimism in the end result as communicated by the "healer." Sometimes the optimism springs up from within in rebellion to depressing medical opinion and the healer is the patient. Most of the time the potentiating forces for healing come from faith shown by the doctor either in a mode of treatment or in the deep subconscious drive for survival that can be released by a doctor who recognizes this force.

The matter of disturbed response to environmental stimuli has been my concern since interning in obstetrics at Johns Hopkins Hospital in 1942. There I witnessed an exsanguinating hemorrhage at delivery of a red-headed Irish woman who had been prepared for this trouble by our concern over her history of a "bleeding tendency." Subsequently I learned that bleeding tendencies are created by the alarms of doctors and can be prevented or terminated in midstream by attendants who believe in the capacity of people to conserve blood with delivery or injury.

After joining the panel of instructors in "Hypnosis Symposiums" formed by the late Leslie M. LeCron in September 1956 I learned that unconscious symbol movements of a Chevreul pendulum could indicate information about the beginnings of an illness (LeCron 1954). This could occur while the patient was consciously wondering why the pendulum was apparently swinging to give answers that were not expected. Fascination with the ideomotor responses permitted rapid entrance of the subject into hypnosis, if there were a need. If this happened LeCron switched to using unconscious movements of designated fingers for "yes," "no" and "I don't want to answer."

LeCron was of the opinion that most physical illnesses stemmed from some sort of initial preparation associated with a dramatic aura or with great emotional stress. His "twenty questions" method of approach to a problem would go something like this:

Q. "Does the inner part of your mind feel your trouble came from some past experience?"
A. "Yes" (given by the pendulum).
Q. "Was this before you were twenty years old?"
A. "Yes."
Q. "Was it before you were ten years old?"

The questions and affirmative answers would continue until the answer was a "No." Knowing that hypnotized people are economical in energy output and will try to stop an inquisitor from going too close to a troublesome event LeCron would then ask, "Is there a deeper part of your mind that knows about something earlier than this age?"

Sometimes it would not be necessary to narrow the site of origin beyond the initial bracketing. The patient might suddenly look surprised, put the pendulum down and say something like, "I know what it was!" Then he would explain some early life experience. When he was finished LeCron would ask, "Is there some event before this that might have prepared the way for your trouble to begin?" Frequently, this revealed an otherwise suppressed birth experience.

This apparent nagging the hypnotized subject into admitting something earlier bothered me very much at first. My training from the authorities on neurological development made the idea of a birth trauma unacceptable. I already knew from prior biased explorations with hypnosis that patients under general anesthesia could not hear or be troubled by noises in the operating room. LeCron and Milton Erickson had both told me they knew that anesthetized patients can hear and be harmfully affected but one was a psychologist and the other a psychiatrist. They seemed pretty bold to make such ridiculous assertions.

At a symposium in Houston in October 1957 a hypnotized doctor proved to me that he had heard his surgeons talking (1959). Two months later during a cruise back from a workshop in Honolulu LeCron was investigating the origins of severe headache with one of our group. In the course of pursuing the "past event" that might have some bearing on the headache the physician recalled a severe eye infection caused by some dirt accidentally kicked into his eye by playmates. When asked if there might be some earlier related event he went into a deep trance and described his very difficult delivery. He could hear his mother's cries and in addition to feeling very nervous he was aware also of head pain as forceps were being applied to his head. The blades were not applied to the sides of his face as is usual with a low forceps delivery but were misplaced as might have been the case with a high forceps delivery. One blade pressed very hard just above the eye that had later been infected, the other blade pressed against his occiput.

LeCron now asked the doctor to review some of his headaches to see what connection there might be between these two events. The eye infection was not important beyond the fact that this eye perhaps had a heightened vulnerability to injury or infection. What was immediately clear was that headaches always occurred when this very conscientious doctor became worried about a patient or felt upset over some personal trouble. It seemed that this might be a conditioned type of response associating his head pain at birth with the influence of his mother's adrenal hormones passing through the placenta into his circulation. Any doubts I had about the validity of traumatic birth memory were dispersed on our arrival at San Pedro. The physician was met at the dock by his mother. She verified the difficulty of his birth and the fact that high forceps had been applied in an effort to preserve his life. That the search was productive was established by the doctor's subsequent relief from headaches. When one would start at a time of pressure he would recognize the cause and stop the headache.

Further investigations by LeCron and me established, to our satisfaction, that migraine and ordinary tension headaches related to pain experienced by the baby at birth in the majority of instances. When we observed that a handclasp with interdigitated fingers revealed primal handedness in relation to which thumb was uppermost, there was an interesting byproduct of research that seemed to warrant mention. In testing more than 2,000 individuals in groups ranging from 50 to 500 people we found that an average of 50% would find their left thumb uppermost. Of these roughly 7% remained left handed. The remaining 43% were functionally right handed and usually did not know when they had converted. About 1% found their right thumb uppermost but were functionally left handed. When age regressed to about six months of age, I found a consistent correlation between the thumb-uppermost test and the hand that wants to reach out for a coveted object when the child is remembering sitting up and is able to use either hand in grasping. This is a matter needing careful research with consideration of factors we could not study. The feature of interest to me was that patients with true migraine or one-sided headache often change sides. When reliving a headache they indicate awareness of subconscious pain on the consciously painless side. Better than 90% of patients I have studied have been converted left-handers. The obvious possibility here might be that converted left-handers are more vulnerable to insult and might be more sensitive to laterality than a child maintaining its original laterality.

Another possible area for research would be the significance of early conversion from left- to right-handedness in terms of learning ability. Converted males seem to have trouble with spelling and reading which I have not found in girls, probably because girls are more readily able in grade school to make the adjustment in recognizing differences between printed "b" and "d," "p" and "q," "m" and "w." Freeway intersection dividers frequently attest to confusions some drivers experience on suddenly being told a direction to follow at the last moment. At a time of crisis there is spontaneous regression to the earlier dominant heandedness.

Search for earlier and earlier experiences relating to maladjustment problems often leads to birth as the causal stimulus in the following classes of problems.

Peptic Ulcer, Oesophageal Spasm, Spastic Colon

Here there is a frequent history of the mother having a painful and difficult delivery. She may be so heavily drugged that she is unable to speak to the baby. The assumed responsibility for maternal difficulty in labor may be immediate but usually is accumulated later from hearsay or when punished by mother for misdeeds. There is a tremendous feeling of rejection that occurs when a newborn baby is not able to hear its mother talk. This is variously described as "lost," "I feel confused," "everything seems dead."

In every instance of gastrointestinal pathology that I have explored the mother has either been unwilling or unable to nurse her baby at her breast. This seems to be the steering factor that makes the gastrointestinal tract vulnerable to subsequent emotional stress effects.

Case Example: Gastric Ulcer

A physician who was consciously aware of a deepseated resentment for all women had suffered from gastrointestinal upsets since childhood. He was operated upon for gastric ulcer shortly after learning that his wife was interested in another man. Without any request to do so he spontaneously regressed to his premature birth on a farm. His mother was very ill during the first weeks of his life and was unable to nurse him. He felt not only very hungry during this time, but resentful of the fact that his grandmother was the one trying to get him to nurse a bottle. Although there were many demonstrations of love when his mother was able to care for him he refused to believe her sincerity. During his adult life he recognized his need for attracting pretty women, but he could not allow himself any firm attachment to a woman he believed could be loving and loyal to him. It was better not to reach out for something lest he be hurt again.

Asthma, Emphysema, Thoracic Pain States, Hyperventilation Syndrome

The feeling of physiological alarm involving a sense of not getting enough air combined with a feeling of being responsible for maternal difficulty are augmented when the mother has been put to sleep for the actual delivery. A woman who has been worried about the outcome of her pregnancy will mobilize all her fears, if she is rendered unconscious before she has had a chance to see her baby. Her catecholamines profoundly affect the baby. Long ago Joseph DeLee pointed out that general anesthesia for delivery of a baby carries the highest morbidity and mortality for both mother and baby. I am sure the reason relates to the emotional stress added to the physical pain that is always greatest when a mother has been unhappily pregnant or has had fears that her child will be abnormal.

Rehearsal of the original stress coupled with explanations about the right of babies to be born with a feeling of freedom from guilt are very helpful in the corrective training program.

Case Example: Severe Angina Pectoris of Three Months' Duration

An executive for a large producer of farm seed sat next to me on a flight from Omaha to Denver. He announced to the stewardess that he could not eat the cheese sandwich because he was on special medicine for his heart. He had looked uncomfortable and pale as he got into his seat. Shortly after the sandwich exchange, the pilot announced that the weather in Denver was bad and we would have to hold a while. I learned that this gentleman was on his way to tell a subordinate that his field of sales activity would have to be shared with another man because results had not been up to expectations. He was troubled over the way this man would take the news. Chest pain with radiation down his left arm had been getting worse since he had been out of bed that morning.

Although I do not usually hypnotize people on airplane trips, this seemed an appropriate moment to do so, particularly after the gentleman had reported to me that his cardiologist had found nothing wrong with his heart but had prophesied that he would be dead within six months. I prepared the way by saying I had had the opportunity of working one time with a man who had been discharged from the navy as a cardiac cripple and was confined to his house until a friend brought him to a course we were giving in Carmel. After learning that a "silly" early life experience was a reason for his heart trouble, this man had been hiking several miles a day and was free of angina three years later when I met him at a wedding.

I showed my plane mate how to get his fingers moving to answer questions and then asked if he might be using the chest pain in some way to punish himself or someone else. He was surprised that self-punishment was involved, that it involved concern over hurting other people and that the origin of the angina was long before he was consciously aware of the chest pain and dyspnea. The real symptoms began a short time after his mother had died but the conditioning for this was his birth. He could feel the tight constriction of his chest before he was born. He could hear the screams and protestations of his mother. There was the typical hierarchy of response as he relived this event giving signals of beginning labor, hearing voices and ending with the comfort of a warm blanket after birth. First he began breathing more rapidly, neck pulsations became faster, perspiration appeared on the fingertips of the designated fingers. The physiological expression of stress came before the finger signals and both occurred before he was able to tell me what he was recalling.

He observed that the feeling he had with his recently acquired angina was exactly the same feeling he had experienced during the birth and that it had become sharper when he could hear his mother crying out. After coming out of hypnosis he recalled that his mother had always been an emotional and very verbal person. I asked his fingers to answer the question, "Would you agree that a mother's trouble in labor is related to her attitudes and her choice of an obstetrician who does not help her to have an easy labor?" His finger answered "Yes." I asked, "Wouldn't your mother want you to be well and comfortable now?" He went right back into hypnosis. I continued, "When you know you have wiped out every sense of guilt you had and have recognized that you had a right to be born free of responsibility for your mother's trouble your 'yes' finger will lift."

The finger lifted. He then turned on and off his angina pain four times on his own initiative and was delighted with his accomplishment. As we prepared to leave the plane he said, "You know, I feel much better about my man in Denver. By dividing his work he will be much more productive and he will probably live a lot longer. I am going to present this idea to him instead of making him feel he is being demoted."

This man wrote me a thank-you letter several weeks later and reported that all had gone well and he had been surprisingly free of discomfort.

Sterility, Dysmenorrhea, Failed Analgesia in Labor, Habitual Abortion, Premature Labor, Toxemia, Frigidity

Cases relating to this class of problems have been discussed elsewhere (Cheek 1968). They are mentioned to alert the investigator to the fact that problems seeming to originate later in life may have their preparation at birth with a long intervening latent period. It would be logical to speculate that some genitourinary system problems in men, particularly premature ejaculation and impotence might have similar origins. My experience as an obstetrician has been restricted in dealing with men. I found, however, that males who believed they had caused great distress to their mother during birth were overly apprehensive when their wife approached the time of labor. It was urgently necessary to check their guilt feelings and their identifications of their wife with their mother.

Obstetrical and gynecological problems including leukorrhea, recurrent vaginitis, failure to tolerate contraceptive pills, severe acne and repeated postcoital cystitis can frequently be traced to a sense of feeling unwanted as a female at the time of birth. It does not matter how much love and acceptance is shown later. The child will imprint on such remarks as "We wanted a boy this time" or "We did not select a name for a girl." They distrust subsequent shows of appreciation and always have trouble accepting compliments graciously.

The Executive Syndrome or the Hyperachiever

Hypnotized people often feel subjectively that their drive stems from a feeling of not amounting to much at birth or feeling that they must prove their worth to a parent who was either unconscious or seemed disinterested in them. One such was a physician in my section of an American Society of Clinical Hypnosis workshop at an annual convention. As I was working with another physician in a demonstration of age-regression this doctor asked if a tremendous need to succeed could be traced to attitudes at birth. His pendulum swings indicated this to be a fact. He went into hypnosis and I quote his words: "During the session I was hypnotized and regressed back to the time of birth. I could see very vividly the conditions that existed at that time. I was in the bedroom of my grandmother's house, my mother was lying there on the bed, the doctor was standing on the right side of the bed and the nurse at the foot of the bed, to the left hand side. She was holding me in some towels and rubbing me briskly while the doctor was wiping his hands and putting some things away. As she worked with me the doctor remarked, 'Don't waste too much time, I don't think he is worth saving.' I was a seven and one-half month premie, weighing 3½ pounds, delivered at home."

In a letter the doctor explained that he had run his father's ranch at age 16. At 30 he had expanded operations into 5 counties. He decided to become a physician at 40 and obtained his degree at 44, practiced as a family doctor but this was not enough. He built and organized one of the most popular ski resorts in Utah. The doctor added in his letter, "You have asked if the hypnosis has made any difference in the way that I have been living. The answer is unequivocally 'yes.' I find myself with a better understanding of why I do things. However, I have to fight to keep myself from getting too involved."

Discussion

The purpose of this report is not to itemize personal experience or to classify disease entities according to their relation to birth experience. I want only to suggest therapeutic possibilities. It is my custom now after earlier approaches via the "twenty question" route to explore birth memory and the subjective feelings of patients immediately when I start therapy. The reasoning here is two-fold. Experience has shown that many hours can be wasted by letting patients climb around the branches of memory and getting nowhere at the top of the tree of life. I now feel that it is possible to trust the subjective reports about birth memory if physiological and ideomotor responses appear before the subject is able to know and talk about the memory at a higher level of thought association.

A second value is discovery that attack on a primary conditioning process may allow rapid dissipation of unfavorable responses that occurred with the initial experience. Approaching from the top of the tree is not as satisfactory. By that later time there have developed more rigidly fixed patterns of disturbed behavior.

Imprinting
This is a term coined by Konrad Lorenz (1935) for a short term learning process that does not fade with the passage of time. Lorenz observed it first with greylag geese. Spalding (1873) had earlier studied it with chickens. Spalding further noted that a biological survival behavior pattern of wanting to be close to the first observed moving object could be reversed into fear and evasive action at the sight of the first moving object if the chicks were kept hooded for four days after hatching. Generally speaking imprinting occurs as a feature of survival in lower animals and it occurs in close proximity to hatching for birds and birth for mammals.

It is clear to me that the term imprinting may also be applied to any response that becomes fixed by the emotional or physiological stress with which it first appears. I have witnessed this with a German shepherd dog that showed an immediate and inappropriate response to bumping a lamp with his tail as I was playing with him. As a six-months-old puppy he had bumped that same lamp while I was playing with him. The shade had fallen onto a radiator. The valve of the steam radiator fell off permitting a cloud of steam under pressure to escape. The puppy had jumped across the room under a card table and stood there trembling. Two years later, and now a champion show dog weighing 96 pounds, he jumped across the room, knocked over the card table as he tried to hide and stood trembling as he awaited the expected explosion from the radiator.

It is no new thought that permanent behavior characteristics could be shaped by birth trauma and later by emotionally loaded experiences. It has not been easy, however, to uncover such experiences. They have either been approached from a talking level of awareness or the stress of the real event has been so great that the patient has unconsciously repressed the information. It is naive to think that experiences occurring before the beginnings of conscious memory and those associated with traumatic or drug-induced unconsciousness could be uncovered with techniques primarily using conversational levels of thought. Erickson (1937) was able to do it, but it took many hours of work and many repetitions of the total review by the hypnotized subject.

The secret to obtaining birth memories and those of unconscious states in very brief spans of therapy time lies in using ideomotor responses. There are two benefits in having the subject repeatedly review the event at an ideomotor level of awareness before attempting to obtain a verbal report. The first involves the apparent fact that each repetition at a deeper-than-verbal level of awareness accumulates more and more information as the stress of the experience is lessened. Repetition seems to raise the horizon of experience from the moment of its occurrence as a revivification to higher zones of thought that have developed later in life and therefore permit placing it into more distant perspective. The real event can be exposed to forces of conscious reason and reassessed. This corrective process obviously does not occur when a primal experience is reactivated unconsciously at a time of stress.

Bernard Levinson has reported an excellent example of this phenomenon (1965) with a patient who continued a reactive depression caused by overhearing her surgeon say he thought her lesion could be cancerous. The anxiety was initiated while she was unconscious in the operating room. It was not relieved by explanation later that the lesion was benign. Only when her conscious memory could be applied during an age-regression to the real event could she make the necessary correction of her disturbed behavior. My experiences with the imprintings of careless conversation in the operating room have repeatedly substantiated this observation. It is painfully clear that misunderstandings of events at birth can also shape a lifetime of disturbed behavior which cannot change until the therapist is able to help the patient expose the understood or misunderstood impressions to the light of mature reason and judgment.

BIBLIOGRAPHY

Cheek, D. B. Unconscious perceptions of meaningful sounds during surgical anesthesia as revealed under hypnosis. *American Journal of Clinical Hypnosis* 1 (1959):103-113.

Cheek, D. B. and L. M. LeCron. *Clinical Hypnotherapy.* New York: Grune and Stratton, 1968.

Erickson, M. H. Development of apparent unconsciousness during hypnotic reliving of a traumatic experience. *Archives of Neurology and Psychiatry* 38 (1937):1282-1288.

LeCron, L. M. A hypnotic technique for uncovering unconscious mate-rial. *Journal of Clinical and Experimental Hypnosis* 2 (1954):1-3.

Levinson, B. States of awareness under general anesthesia, a case report. *Medical Proceedings* 11 (1965):243-245.

Lorenz, K. Imprinting. *Journal of Ornithology,* 83 (1935):137.

Spalding, D. A. On instinct. *Macmillan's Magazine* (Feb. 1873), 287, 289. (Quotations from James, W. *Principles of Psychology.* New York: Holt, 1890.)

Short-term Hypnotherapy for Frigidity Using Exploration of Early Life Attitudes

Summary—Experience with 255 women with sexual problems has shown the importance of early life feelings of acceptance and love in the development of healthy responsiveness. Women incapable of forming strong attachments to men require extended therapy beyond the scope of this study. Results with therapy comprising an average of two hours are given with the most recent 100 women. Steps of therapy were suggested by results of hypnotic age-regression studies of normal women capable of multiple orgasms during intercourse. A detailed account is given of one successful therapeutic session involving the combination of ideomotor questioning with light hypnosis. Use was made of ideas offered by the patient.

Suggestion permits a hypnotized individual to remember sensations and eventually to reproduce physiological adaptive responses. These responses may be strengthened by repetition. Results with behavior modification using hypnosis appear to improve when patients are oriented first to formative experiences before attempting correction of maladaptation derived from these primal events. The alternative of working back from later toward earlier experience often leads to frustration.

Combination of light hypnosis with use of unconscious, symbol movements or ideomotor responses allows rapid access to significant information and rapid, productive rehearsal with frigidity problems or "sexual dysfunction" within the time limitations of three office visits, comprising two hours. The methods involved have been considered at length in publications by LeCron (1954, 1961) and one by Cheek and LeCron (1968).

Presented to the 18th Annual Scientific Meeting of the American Society of Clinical Hypnosis, Seattle, 1975. Reprinted with permission from *American Journal of Clinical Hypnosis* 19 (1976):20-27.

Adequate levels of hypnosis can be achieved with 100% of women who are willing for change and are subconsciously motivated toward continued improvement. Some women may consciously express a wish to improve their sexual feelings, may rid themselves of sexual inhibitions but quit therapy or continue to remain frigid with a current sexual partner. They may appear to be treatment failures at the conclusion of therapy but suddenly find themselves responsive several months later. Some may find during therapy that they have been cohabiting with the wrong man because they have never dared commit themselves to the right one.

Failures, resistances and obscure successes occur with any problem that brings a patient to a doctor. The treatment of frigidity is no exception.

What Normal Women Have Taught Us During Age-regression

The plan of therapy used by the author has been learned from women, capable of multiple orgasms, during hypnotic age-regression studies of their sexual development. All of these women reported a sense of total acceptance by their parents from their moment of birth. With this beginning they recognized that orgasm frequently occurred under circumstances that were associated with further show of loving attention. This included nursing, being gently bathed and having diapers changed.

They all seemed to have escaped punitive action when they were exploring their genitalia with their fingers or rubbing against various objects in autoerotic maneuvers. Some thought they had experienced orgasms in dreams as early as 6 years of age and all knew they had before the age of 10. Through their dreams they learned that thoughts could lead to orgasm after the initial conditioning for such feelings in an environment of love and acceptance.

From the teachings of these fortunate women the following flow plan of therapy evolved:

1. Hypnosis was explained to the patients as a means of understanding unconscious sexual attitudes and of improving self confidence.
2. The sequential steps of early learning about orgasm were outlined to them.
3. They were shown about the effort effect of Coué with a demonstration of postural suggestion and this was followed with an introduction to use of the Chevreul pendulum for discovering information that was not known to them consciously.
4. Fascination with these ideomotor responses permitted easy introduction into a light state of hypnosis without confronting the patient with a formal induction.
5. At this point it could be learned if there were any fundamental difficulties between the patients and their sexual partner by orienting them to the moment of first meeting, getting their "sixth sense" subconscious reaction. The time orientation then shifted to recent feelings about the sexual partner.

6. Birth experience and later sexual feelings were next explored and sexual feelings reinforced.

Author's Classification of Frigidity

In the beginning of this study an effort was made to divide women into classes depending on their reports during the initial office visit. Continued experience, however, has shown that there is little prognostic value in this division with the possible exception of women who have been orgasmic in the past and are no longer responsive (A-3). Perhaps others working in this area will show whether or not this classification is worth continuing. It seemed at first probable that women who had experienced some form of orgasmic response would be fundamentally different from those who had never had an orgasm with masturbation, in dreams or in any sexual encounter. This division had no subgroups. The women who had experienced some form of orgasm formed Class A.

Class A: Women Who Have Experienced Orgasm

A-1—Women who have had orgasms in sleep, with petting or with masturbation but have never had an orgasm with a male sexual partner during intercourse.

A-2—Women who have experienced orgasm of some sort with their current sexual partner. This could be orgasm with clitoral stimulation, oral sex, or it could be the supposedly ultimate, the "vaginal orgasm." The standing in this group was expressed as a percentage of orgasms relative to the number of encounters.

A-3—Women who have experienced orgasm with another partner in the past or have done so in the past with their current partner but no longer are responding this way.

Some women fall into this group because of a misunderstanding associated with a gynecological operation of some sort. These may be helped over their problem easily providing the trouble leading to surgery was not caused by conflict with the sexual partner.

Women in Class A-3 usually have very good reasons for restraining their sexual feelings. Guilt, fear of pregnancy and resentment toward the partner are the salient factors. Sometimes it is possible to diminish resentment by helping the patient realize that she has been weighing some past injury too heavily or has been identifying the partner unfairly with some previous male, a father, brother or former sexual partner. Most commonly the Class A-3 women have recognized that they are with the wrong man. They may profit from extended psychotherapy that does not fall within the scope of therapy for frigidity. Most of the treatment failures belong in this group.

Class B: Women Who Have Never Had Any Kind of Orgasm

This is not a firm group. Many women who think they have never had an orgasm will find they have had subliminal ones during sex play, petting or in sexual dreams. Some will remember a feeling like an orgasm while being nursed, being bathed or being leaned against by an appreciative puppy dog or a purring kitten. These feelings were stopped when masturbatory experiments drew expressions of disgust, shame or anger from a parent.

Individuals in this group may be very easy or very difficult to help toward better sexual gratification. The case to be presented was one of the easy ones. The helpful factor was her security in the rediscovered love of her first husband. All the good qualities had been there before she married him the first time. Her frigidity had weakened the bond as the children were born. He had assumed that she was rejecting him.

Case Example With Class B Patient: No Conscious Memory of Orgasm

Diana M, a 28-year-old para 3 gravida 3, Caucasian woman, referred by a gynecologist for her sexual problem. She had just remarried her first husband and wanted to make the marriage work this time with agreement at all levels of communication. She said she had never had an orgasm with dreams, masturbation or intercourse. She had never tried to masturbate. She belonged in Class B. Initial estimate of her prognosis with hypnotherapy was gloomy because of her age, multiple marriage difficulties and 11 year history of total frigidity.

Background History

Diana was the first of five children, an unplanned pregnancy when her mother was 20 years old. There were some problems that grew worse as other children arrived. Mother became involved in an affair and the marriage broke up when Diana was 8 years old, a critical time for her. She loved her father very much and felt it as a personal rejection when her father moved out of the home. She resented the new stepfather who moved in almost at once.

At 14 Diana took up Catholicism. At 17 she became pregnant after unprotected intercourse with her boy friend, Ron, whom she married in a reproduction of her mother's plight when Diana was conceived. After birth of their third child the marriage broke up. She married quickly again but it was a bad union that lasted only 2 years.

She began dating Ron again and had just remarried her first husband at the time of her first consultation. She said that she had always enjoyed sex with him but had never had an orgasm at any time in her life.

First Interview and Introduction to Hypnosis

One hour had been reserved for the patient but brief appointments for two other patients permitted 2 hours total time for the therapy to continue while I was out of the consultation room.

The explanation about hypnosis so interested the patient that she was in a light state even before she was given a test of postural suggestion with her arms extended and one arm supporting an imaginary heavy weight. Her trance deepened and she appeared delighted on discovering that the heavy arm floated up toward the ceiling when the weight was replaced by "big balloons."

Finger signals were assigned on her right hand for "yes," "no" and "I don't want to answer." Her compliance with the suggestions was checked by asking her to think the word "yes" and finding that the assigned finger rose in the typical intermittent way. Questions and directions then began as follows:

Q. "Does the inner part of your mind know that you can have orgasms with intercourse just as well as or even better than other normal women?" (The phrasing was aimed at showing the patient my unspoken belief that she was a normal woman, capable of normal sexual responses about which I had spoken during my introduction regarding the values of hypnosis. She had already demonstrated that she could make a heavy arm feel light and that it could actually move upward against the pull of gravity without any sense of effort on her part.)

A. (There was no effort made to speak but she appeared amused as she felt her "yes" finger lifting.)

Q. "Go a little deeper now and let the deep part of your mind orient back in time to the very first breath you are taking at the moment you are born. When you are there your 'yes' finger will lift. Your 'no' finger will lift each time you are hearing someone talking in that room where you are born. When you are warm and comfortable again in the nursery your 'I don't want to answer' finger will lift. Don't try to remember anything consciously. This is a long time before conscious memory begins." (Her respiratory rate had increased followed by the lifting of her "yes" finger before I had finished my directions to her, showing that she was not threatened by her memories of birth.) I continued. "Go over that entire experience quickly several times so that I can ask you some questions. Is your mother awake at the time you are born?"

A. (finger signal) "No."

Q. "Does that little baby Diana feel welcome as a girl when she is born?"

A. (finger signal) "Yes."

Q. "Let a thought come to you. How does that baby know she is welcome? When you know your 'yes' finger will lift. As it lifts let that thought come up to where you can talk about it."

A. (The "yes" finger lifted quickly. Five seconds later she began to speak.) "I just know she wanted a girl—even if she *didn't* nurse me." (This addition at the end of her response called for some clarification.)

Q. "Does it make a difference to this baby that she is not nursed?"
A. (verbalized) "No," an answer contradicted by her unconscious gesture with her "yes" finger.
Q. "What is important about nursing?"
A. (The level of hypnosis decreased at this moment as the patient spoke.) "There is a feeling of love that goes with nursing at a mother's breast—I missed that." This apparent biologic need for nursing, not recognized by her more conscious level of awareness reflected by the verbal answer but indicated by the ideomotor level of thought association, demands more attention by obstetricians and pediatricians who believe breast feeding is not necessary. Denial of breast feeding has appeared too often in the age-regression evaluations of patients with peptic ulcer, gall bladder disease and colitis (Cheek 1975).
Q. "Now orient back to your birth again. When you are there your 'yes' finger will lift. (The finger lifted in 4 seconds, a very rapid response.) "Come up from there to the first moment when you are having some feeling that you would later recognize as a climax or like a climax. When you are feeling that subconsciously your 'no' finger will lift. When it lifts, look around in your mind's eye and tell me what allows you to have that feeling." The wording of this direction expresses the therapist's total expectation of a positive response, an important lesson learned from the author's experience with anesthesia research (Cheek 1959) and the search of significant dreams with obstetrical patients (Cheek 1965).
A. Her "yes" finger lifted to indicate the reorientation and lifted again to indicate something to report. She shifted into conversation saying, "My mother is cuddling me and showing that she loves me."
Q. "Come up now to a later experience. When you are there your 'no' finger will lift. Tell me what is happening."
A. "My daddy is chucking me under the chin and smiling at me."
Q. "So you can see as an adult woman that pleasurable sexual feelings can be started by stimuli that are not primarily sexual, your mother cuddling you and your daddy showing that he loves you and thinks you are cute. Come up from those early lessons telling you that you are sexually normal to the first moment when something makes you feel you cannot have those feelings. When you are there at the first important moment your 'yes' finger will lift and you can tell me what is happening."
A. (After a lag of 10 seconds before lifting the finger) "I'm playing with myself. Mother comes in and says, 'Diana! Don't *do* that!' She looks very angry."
Q. "Come up to the next important thing that relates to your sexual feelings."
A. "I have lots of dreams that feel good.—Lots of dreams but I can't let anything happen. I always stop."
It was next pointed out to the patient while she was still oriented to the early months of her life that exploration of genital sensations by a baby is normal, that all babies are well equipped for sexual orgasm from the moment they are born. This ability continues until someone with authority makes them feel self-conscious or guilty over a process of learning that

must have been started by the Creator. If mammals did not enjoy sexual intercourse their species would die out. If they did not know that genital stimulation felt good they would be galloping around all their lives and there would be no babies. If breast stimulation did not feel good mother mammals would not nurse their young and their babies would die.

Q. "Now go over one of those dreams that felt good but this time go over it as it should have been, experiencing the feelings you would have had normally if your mother had not made you feel guilty when she saw you playing with yourself. As you start the dream your 'yes' finger will lift and *each* time you are reaching a subconscious climax your 'no' finger will lift. Do *not* try to feel it consciously because you are not conscious when you are dreaming. First, you must know these feelings subconsciously before you can feel them consciously. Remember that all mammals have sexual dreams. It must be the will of God that this occur to further the knowledge learned by actual physical contact with the genital organs." (The patient indicated three subconscious orgasms but did not show any change in respiration or pulsations of her neck vessels.)

The next step was to ask the patient to carry the knowledge about the importance of dreams a little further. She was told that sexually normal women have told us they have experienced small orgasms as children while just holding hands with little boys they like, something "very much like what you felt when your daddy chucked you under your chin" (a thought added to reinforce her recognition that she had been "normal" before her mother scolded her about the auto-erotic normal explorations). She was asked to hallucinate an experience holding hands and that she would feel a climax each time she squeezed his hand. Her 'no' finger was to lift each time she was feeling his pleasurable sensation which the little boy would know nothing about. Almost immediate responses were given and now the patient was showing slight quickening of her respiration as her 'no' finger lifted each time. The hour was drawing to a close. She was progressing so fast that I felt it might be appropriate to move directly to an attack on the problem of frigidity in relation to her husband. It was already clear that the bond between them was very good.

Q. "Would it be all right for you to really feel what a climax can be like for you and your husband if I go out of the room to examine some patients?"

A. (finger signal) "Yes."

Q. "Other normal women who have never been made to feel guilty about their sexual feelings have told me that when they have felt a warmth of love between themselves and their husband that they have had orgasms being kissed on their lips, caressed around their breasts and kissed on their neck. They have had orgasms just as they feel his penis entering their vagina, again as they move their hips from side to side bringing his penis in contact with the very sensitive nerves on each side of the vagina inside. They say they have felt a build up to a climax as they rapidly contract and relax their vaginal muscles around the whole length of the firm penis 10 or 12 times and that this can be repeated. Each climax becomes stronger because a woman is able to have an orgasm repeatedly without having to wait the way a man has to wait. The strongest of all can be when you feel him swelling inside you at the moment he is reaching his climax. You can even come again just by contracting your muscles around him inside after he has ejaculated. Please orient your memory now back to some time that could have been perfect for you and your husband had you known then what you are learning today and as it would have been if you had never had any fears or guilt feelings given you by your mother. Let your body feel all the sensations from the top of your head down to your heels. I am going out to examine some patients and I will not need this room. First, go over, the experience having just your fingers telling you how much you are feeling, then as you keep going over it you will start to feel it physically at a conscious level. When your inner mind knows that you can select what kind of climax you can have and how many you want to have, when you know that you are really satisfied your right arm will begin to lift up as though you had those balloons attached to it. When that occurs please let yourself come out of hypnosis and open the door so I know you are through."

It only took about five minutes after I left the room before the door opened. Ten minutes after that I found her back in her chair in a deep trance. I asked, "Does the inner part of your mind feel that you are as normal sexually as I do?" To this her finger answered "Yes." She was awakened and two more appointments were made in case she later wanted to be seen.

The interview was on Thursday. The following Monday the patient called to say she did not need to come back. She and her husband had gone to Carmel that week end. It had been a wonderful experience for them both and she had just received some roses and a note from her husband saying "To my new Diana."

Summation of Author's Total Experience, 255 Cases of Frigidity

Since incorporating use of ideomotor signalling methods in the treatment of female sexual dysfunction I have worked with 255 women. There was inadequate follow up in 124 of these and there were 18 who dropped out before completion of treatment. I felt that the only good thing that could be said about this total group was that 96% of the women had learned how to induce their own hypnosis.

A much better estimate of results could be obtained on consideration of the most recent 100 cases after I had better criteria for acceptance into the treatment regimen. It was soon evident that some sociological division had to be made in selection. This depended not on ability to pay but on the ability to form some meaningful relationship with a man. It is not easy to decide who should be excluded in this area but a rough rule of thumb was to exclude those who were floating without attachment and those who were unmarried and had a history of multiple tenuous attachments. These women had needs for psychotherapy but it seemed to me that their needs related to problems of self image of another sort requiring longer range therapy before much could be done about the sexual problem bringing them to my office.

Author's Estimate of Results 100 Cases

	Number Responding	Percent
1. Some improvement with current partner	60	60
2. No change in sexual performance	40	40
3. Dropped out before completion of therapy	0	0
4. Made worse by therapy	0	0
Change of Sexual Status	**Number of total**	
1. Shift from "no orgasm" (Class B) to A-2	16	22
2. Shift from Class A-1 to A-2 (all Catholic)	4	4
3. Shift from "past orgasmic but no longer" (Class A-3 to orgasmic A-2)	2	9
4. Subjectively satisfactory improvement in orgasmic Class A-2 group	38	65
	60	100

In an attempt to justify this apparent "placebo effect percentage" it must be said that all of the women were able to use self-hypnosis. All have derived personal benefit in other areas through their being able to correct unfavorable attitudes toward their parents and themselves. Approximately 86% have corrected one or more gynecological problems having to do with hypersensitivity of the urogenital tract. These include dysmenorrhea, recurrent cystitis, vulvo-vaginitis and Herpes genitalis ulcers. It appears that women asking for help with frigidity may sometimes be willing to accept a little help with something of benefit to them when they may not be ready for the goal they have consciously set for themselves.

Discussion

Those who are not familiar with ideomotor questioning techniques may find themselves as suspicious of information offered by hypnotized subjects as they are when such information is offered during ordinary conversational hypnosis. All who are experienced in the use of hypnosis have recognized the willingness of good subjects to comply with expressed or implied wishes of the therapist at the level of nearly conscious ideation involved in conversational communication.

It has not been the author's experience that this type of willingness extends to the level of ideation reflected by ideomotor responses. A feature of utmost importance has been repeatedly demonstrated. Very significant experiences responsible for continued patterns of behavior are stored at a level of awareness that can be reached and reflected by ideomotor responses. The usual steps of recall are from most recent events toward earlier ones that set the stage for the ones first recalled. If allowed to continue the investigation may lead to strong resistances on nearing a primal event of a threatening nature.

The chance of this occurring is greatly diminished if the search starts with birth with the onus softened by a dissociated, retrospective view as from the time of interview. The knowledge of language can then be used to describe events occurring before there was such knowledge. Furthermore, it is much easier to evaluate the significance of experiences the patient discovers are related to the problem requiring investigation. The thread of pertinence remains intact with the talking part of the patient tied to the time of interview while the much deeper zone reflected by ideomotor activity is studying evidence.

Dangers of Embarrassment and Patient Dependency

Occasionally a relatively uninhibited woman will show visible signs of reaching an orgasm while rehearsing pleasurable sexual possibilities. It should be stressed here that hypnotized subjects using ideomotor methods are always aware of their surroundings. It is their right to feel as much as they wish. It is easy to know whether or not they may be embarrassed by their awakening to the concept that thoughts can evoke physiological responses. This is the goal of therapy for frigidity. If the patient seems embarrassed I ask for a finger signal in answer to whether or not the patient would progress more rapidly with me out of the room. Some patients (as the one presented here) do very well when left alone. Others, however, need personal guidance and will feel rejected if the therapist leaves them. My advice here, as with all other types of doctor-patient relationships, is to decide whether or not you feel comfortable in the situation. If you are troubled your patient will feel troubled, whether or not you are using hypnosis.

There is no danger of a patient becoming seriously dependent upon the therapist during treatment for a sexual problem unless the patient has very tenuous attachment to her sexual partner, and the therapist falls into the trap of presuming that the close relationship of therapy is a license to forget the needs and goals of the patient. Difficulties in this area do not occur when the therapist constantly involves the patient with thoughts relating to her husband or sexual partner.

Conclusion

The author does not wish to convey the idea that the methods presented are more successful than others involving other modalities. He is a gynecologist with limited time for hypnotherapy. The methods described have proven of value with treatment of various gynecological difficulties; included among them are the very important problems of women who are unhappy with their sexual inhibitions.

BIBLIOGRAPHY

Cheek, D. B. Unconscious perception of meaningful sounds during surgical anesthesia as revealed under hypnosis. *American Journal of Clinical Hypnosis* 1 (1959):101-113.

———. Some newer understandings of dreams in relation to threatened abortion and premature labor. *Pacific Medicine and Surgery* (Formerly *Western Journal of Surgery, Obstetrics and Gynecology*) 73 (1965):379-384.

———. Significance of dreams in initiating premature labor. *American Journal of Clinical Hypnosis* 12 (1969):5-15.

———. Maladjustment patterns apparently related to imprinting at birth. *American Journal of Clinical Hypnosis* 18 (1975):75-82.

Cheek, D. B. and L. M. LeCron. *Clinical Hypnotherapy.* New York: Grune and Stratton, 1968.

LeCron, L. M. A hypnotic technique for uncovering unconscious material. *Journal of Clinical and Experimental Hypnosis* 2 (1954):1-3.

———. *Techniques of Hypnotherapy.* New York: Julian Press, 1961.

PART FIVE

SOCIAL-COMMUNITY CONTEXT: CULTURE, ORGANIZATIONS AND SCHOOLS

BENJAMIN R. TONG

26

On the Confusion of Psychopathology With Culture: Iatrogenesis in the Treatment of Chinese Americans

Benjamin Tong is trained in theater arts, Chinese health and healing practices and Taoist disciplines. He has pursued graduate work in sociology and holds a Ph.D. in professional (clinical and community) psychology. At this writing, he is a Professor at the Graduate School of Psychology at the Wright Institute, Berkeley, California, where he serves as instructor and clinical supervisor. In addition to qualitative research activities (as Research Associate at the University of California's Berkeley Institute for the Study of Social Change), Tong teaches Asian-American Studies and counseling at San Francisco State University. His current interests include cross-cultural issues in psychotherapy, long-term consequences of the Japanese-American concentration camps, Southern-Chinese and Scandinavian folk cultures, adult development, aging, stress disorders and organizational problems in modern corporate structures.

When not practicing psychotherapy, studying ancient esoteric Chinese art or acting/writing, Benjamin Tong continues his research of more than a decade on the impact of racist stereotypes characterized by mystifying *positive* qualities. Dr. Tong's work moves naturally from identifying iatrogens to eliciting their demise. Ever change-oriented, he has been innovative in counseling, research, restructured (for greater validity) school texts and generally expanded community awareness. Blending a style of spontaneous explosion and careful patience, Dr. Tong is a strong example of one who fights iatrogens with both data base and personal forcefulness. My thanks to him for writing the following chapter specifically for this handbook.   **R.F.M.**

Some twenty years ago, Vita Sommers, an American psychoanalyst, reported treating "an American-born Chinese" who suffered from massive self-hatred, low self-esteem and identity confusion.

> Ever since Chune can remember, he had to work for "White" people. . . . All his life he felt that white people were "superior" to Chinese. . . . In spite of many critical feelings toward Americans, *he wished he could be an American.* He felt deeply ashamed of being Chinese. When *I reflected that it must have been confusing for him to have lived in two entirely different cultures,* Chune

The author gratefully acknowledges the assistance of Frank Abe, Joseph Lam and Rena MacDavid in the preparation of this chapter. © 1981 by Benjamin R. Tong.

felt grateful that I could understand him, for he finds it difficult to adjust to either one. He feels different among Americans and equally different among Chinese.[1]

The twenty-nine-year-old patient, furthermore, could not relate to women apart from momentary identification with symbols of white masculinity.

To him, all Americans appeared manly, husky and superior. Also, his poor English bothered him. *He resented the fact that "even though I was born here, people call me Chinese."* With a good deal of feeling, he often commented, "I wish I were white." Being white meant to him feeling accepted, secure, justified in being self-assertive; whereas being Chinese was identical with submission, discrimination and rejection. . . .
    During his Army service he had dated white girls only. This was the only time in his life that he was aggressive, that he didn't feel inferior. In fact, he felt very proud of himself because he was the youngest first sergeant in a mixed Army unit. He had more than 100 men under his command and was chosen out of 1200. He believed that it must have been his military uniform which gave him an appearance of manliness and importance, and a feeling of success. He wondered, "How come that I feel so utterly unmanly now? *Do I have two personalities?"*[2]

The proper treatment for all these complaints, curiously enough, was to urge the patient to accept the view of himself, "an American-born Chinese," as a perpetual alien in his own home country. "His better acceptance of his Oriental background was most vividly expressed in his marriage to a Chinese girl, . . . and in the opening of his studio called Oriental Design."[3] That is to say, the solution to being treated like a foreigner was to learn to love the problem.

We have here a situation, not altogether uncommon in America, that can be quite accurately diagnosed as iatrogenic: self-contempt and mystification promoted as health in a white supremacist society. In response to the patient's misguided concern that he might become an American—which in fact he already was—the therapist reinforced the racist notion that those who are not white cannot claim America as home. The prevailing "social reality," according to Sommers, is that

. . . there can never be a complete solution to their problem. They can never slough off the signs of their origin, the racial characteristics (nonwhiteness) which set them apart from the members of the Western world (i.e., white people), with whom they so desperately sought to identify.[4]

For this kind of pathology to go unquestioned, both therapist and client had to act in collusion, specifically in line with the assumption that *Chinese America as a way of life does not exist.* The same ideological tenet obtained when *Japanese* bombers attacked Pearl Harbor on December 7, 1941, and *Japanese Americans* were held responsible. The white racist lumping of Nikkei[5] with America's Asian wartime enemy quickly led to the brutal incarceration of 110,000 Americans of Japanese descent in ten American concentration camps.[6]

For yellow America, one has to be either "Asian," meaning eternal foreigner, or "American," meaning bogus white. There are no other viable options for sense of self. This is what Jeffery Chan and Frank Chin have referred to as the Concept of the Dual Personality.

> The so-called "blending of East and West" divides the Chinese American into two incompatible segments: (1) the foreigner whose status is dependent on his ability to be accepted by the white natives; and (2) the handicapped native who is taught that identification with foreignness is the only way to "justify" his difference in skin color.... The handicapped native is neither black nor white in a black and white world. In his native American culture, he has no recognized style of manhood.... In his use of language, voice inflection, accent, walk, manner of dress and combing his hair, the handicapped native steeps himself in self-contempt for being "quick to learn ... and imitative." At worst, he's a counterfeit begging currency. At best he's an "Americanized Chinese," someone who's been given a treatment to make him less foreign.[7]

Furthermore, regardless of option selected within this "either/or" syndrome, the yellow American is to exhibit behavior that can be readily appreciated as passive, ingratiating, reticent, non-complaining and self-denying, a profile reminiscent of earlier black stereotypes of groveling servitude and the image of constricted womanhood that concerns contemporary feminists. In the best-seller, *What Really Happened to the Class of '65?* (Medved and Wallechinsky 1976), the lone Chinese American in a predominantly white high school class gave open testimony to the warped sensibility of the "handicapped native" who runs full throttle to earn white acceptance.

> I don't think I ever went through a period of real rebellion against my parents. They never forced me to be Oriental—I just was. Socially, it was ... I don't know. Instead of being Chinese, I could have had a broken nose, or a gimp leg, it could have been anything. I mean, in high school I might as well have been crippled!...
> I (tried to) ... test myself and prove to the world that I could do all things that a blond and blue-eyed girl could do.... I had to really be a sort of super-person in order to do this—you know, super nice and super bright and super everything.

This kind of persona is not limited to individual instances of alienated yellow behavior. A case in point would be the marked contrast in the response of the American-Jewish community to the recent motion picture, *Wholly Moses!,* and that of Chinese America to the making and showing of the forty-ninth Charlie Chan movie, not to mention the Peter Sellers comedic version of Fu Manchu and the reappearance of the "Kung Fu" television series.

Five Othodox Jewish groups representing over two thousand rabbis and a million Orthodox Jews denounced *Wholly Moses!* as the "most vicious attack ever upon the Jewish religion in the history of the American movie industry."[8] When the "Kung Fu" series first appeared in the early 1970s, objections to the maligning of yellow history and culture were barely audible. Nearly a decade later, with racist stereotypes returning in full force in the mass media, most of Chinese America remains silent as before.[9] By comparison, it is well established in the conventional wisdom that a white man made up in charcoal playing any kind of black commits commercial and artistic, if not actual, suicide.

How are we to interpret the pervasive yellow response of relative silence? Beginning with Chinese Americans themselves, most concerned with explanation would reach, almost reflexively, for the conceptual handle of "culture." Psychologist Derald Sue (Sue and Wagner 1973, 144), for one, attributes "obedient, conservative, conforming and inhibited" yellow behavior to "Asian cultural values, emphasizing restraint of strong feelings," while whites are more likely to display "spontaneity, assertiveness. ..." Historian S. W. Kung (1962, 69), in his comments on an earlier generation, concluded that "their timidity, unaggressiveness and lack of protest provoked ... attacks, simply because such characteristics were interpreted by (white) Westerners as signs of weakness. Finally, sociologist Rose Hum Lee (1960, 140) made the same confirmation: " ... the behavior pattern of the (early Chinese-American) settlers was largely unsuitable for a highly competitive, masculine-oriented (white EuroAmerican) culture."

Such observations by Chinese-American intellectuals were commonplace at a time, notably the 1950s and 1960s, when Sommers and other white academists were actively legitimizing the phenomenon of long-suffering, inert handicapped natives.[10] In the late '60s and early '70s, civil rights activism and the rise of racial minority "consciousness" triggered a debate around the question of "mental illness" versus "culture": That is to say, is timid and docile behavior indicative of psychopathology *or* are Americans of Asian descent so inclined by reason of cultural predisposition?

Those who articulated the position of self-contemptuous constriction euphemized as culture took up arms around the work of psychologists Stanley Sue, Derald Sue and their colleagues. Fundamental to their perspective is the assumption that Chinese America as a unique, vital, self-generating way of life does not exist. We are either sinological museum pieces or foreigners living only to be white.

> The *Chinese individual in America* is in a position of conflict between the pulls of both his cultural background and the *Western values* he is exposed to in school and by the mass media. *American* values emphasizing spontaneity, assertiveness, and independence are often at odds with many *Chinese values*. As *Chinese people* progressively adopt more of the values and standards of the *larger community* as their own, the transition is not always smooth. Indeed, culture conflict seems to be an intimate part of the Asian-American experience.[11]

Words like "American, Western," and "larger community" give dominion to whites. They affirm the white supremacist edict that America belongs to our citizenry of European ancestry, while the rest of us exist and have our being on these shores of our homeland as a matter of white privilege.[12] The Sues perceive no Chinese-American history, culture or sensibility other than what whites have created for us. We are to believe that

Chinese Americans did nothing for themselves, among themselves or by themselves, apart from that which whites have validated.

According to the Sues' version of yellow history, the clinical profile of a good deal of Chinese-American behavior—"blunted affect, dependency, inferiority feelings, ruminations, somatic complaints and lack of social skills (Sue and Sue 1971, 46)"—is traceable to the legacy of their "sojourner" forebearers, an essentially reclusive, "un-acculturable" lot.

> Most Chinese who immigrated to the United States did so with the express purpose of going back to China after making their "fortune" in America. This was less true for the Japanese. As a result, identity and adherence to Asian values were important to the Chinese.... The Chinese tended to enter occupations in urban settings and congregate in areas where communities acted as buffers to what was viewed as a hostile society. Acculturation was therefore, strongly discouraged among the Chinese (Sue and Kirk 1973, 143).

This argument bears critical examination. Chinese Americans today exhibit disturbed behavior by virtue of the fact that their predecessors had never intended to settle in America. Refusing to "adopt the ways of the new Western world," they clung to "their ethnic identities and homeland ties," in contrast to the early Japanese who were "much more focused toward making a new home" in the Old West. Since "many more of the early Japanese immigrants brought their families," their progeny, it follows, were ultimately "more comfortable in Western culture" (Sue and Frank 1973, 143-144).

That the articles from which these citations were drawn contained not a single piece of historical documentation merely gives emphasis to the depth of racist ignorance in this point of view. First of all, abundant evidence points to early yellow behavior as anything but that of temporary visitors huddled up in cocoon-like withdrawal from the rest of American society.

> They married women of their choice (or tried to), started businesses, sent for families (when they could), even developed whole towns of their own. Would the whites have demanded that 'The Chinese Must Go!' (even before the coming of the yellows) and mounted one piece of exclusionary legislation after another if the Chinamans were going to leave after completion of their extraordinary projects? No, the Chinese came to stay.[13]

By eliminating key events in the history of white behavior, the Sues, whether or not they intend to, wind up defending the workings as well as the consequences of institutional racism. It was a "difference" in international relations that resulted in "many more of the early Japanese immigrants" bringing over families: The Chinamans[14] were systematically blocked from sending for spouses by order of the infamous Chinese Exclusion Acts. A series of congressional decrees (1882-1943), singling out the Chinese by name, broke up thousands of Cantonese wage-laborer families. If "differential acculturation" is apparent (i.e., if more Japanese Americans than Chinese Americans seem to be devoted to white values), the contrast might well be explained in terms of differences in collective experience.

Herded into urban stockades upon completion of their work on farm and railroad projects, and in mining locations, the Chinamans not only kept alive their pagan heritage but gave it new form. True to "folk" Cantonese cultural tradition, which prizes daring, cunning and total assertion of the self to fanatical extremes,[15] the trapped Chinamans—acting very much like permanent residents—attempted to buy up whole orchards, smuggle Chinese women into the country and continually sue in the courts for guarantee or restoration of rights.[16]

Furthermore, Chinamans hardly lived out their rugged lives around deep yearnings for white acceptance ("acculturation"). Refusing Christian conversion—it was not uncommon for whites to stone them from the steps of churches[17]—they fought for survival on their own terms and forged new meanings to what I have termed the "jawk jierh-si hah" tradition.

> Locked out of legitimate economic enterprise by white law, the Chinamans invented *fake Chinese culture* to survive. The men picked up, scraped up, whatever they could get their hands on and pushed it on whites as the essence of a sophisticated Cathay running clear back to neolithic Shang. *That* was the stuff of abalone shells becoming sacred religious artifact, "beggar's chicken" becoming gourmet fantasy, and garbage becoming "chop suey." All this, along with lies about underground tunnels, opium dens and dancing girls, was *heritage*—a legacy and history school books will not acknowledge and surviving Chinamans will not tell, at least not readily. Tourism emerged as a distinct if humiliating tradition in the culture of Chinese America. . . .
>
> An acknowledgement of Chinese American language, culture and sensibility begins with legitimation of expressions like *jawk jierh*. To the (real) Chinese in places like Hong Kong, the term simply means "to catch a pig," literally and finally. To Chinese Americans, *jawk jierh* is the act of cheating, deceiving, outwitting or exploiting another. No one uses the expression in that way except Chinese Americans, including Chinese Americans who would deny the existence of Chinese America. It expresses—all at the same time—the anger, the ingenuity, and the audacity of the old Chinamans. Every successful con number that was run on a "look-see man" was a cathartic act of revenge. Revenge by Chinamans who remembered, as subsequent generations have not, the indignities they endured when white corporate giants like (Charles) Crocker and their Chinese merchant accomplices shanghaied them into pig pens (barracoons) on American ships and transported the newly "contracted" coolies of the late 1860's across the Pacific, to resolve the problem of unmanly white laborers who fled from the awesome task of building a railroad line through solid granite.[18]

Returning to the central issue of "mental illness" versus "culture," we can say, on the strength of well-established though not properly legitimized history, that the position of the Sues and their associates leaves much to be desired. As for whether timid and docile behavior is indicative of psychopathology, the Sues, voicing concern over "adjustment" problems, insist that *mental health means being comfortable with white values and being accepted by whites. Those of us who resist "adopting Western culture" become prime candidates for emotional disturbance.* To cite their comparative studies again, "Japanese Americans appear better adjusted than their Chinese counterparts. . . . this may represent some form of differential acculturation in which Japanese Americans may be more comfortable in Western culture" (Sue and Frank 1973, 144). "Cultural factors," moreover, "often impede the process of psychotherapy" should "repressive, emotionally withdrawn, verbally inhibited" yellows be referred for "treatment." The Sues report that their white "colleagues often have remarked that (Asian-American clients)... are difficult to deal with therapeutically" (Sue and Sue 1974, 424, 426). In short, not being like "Caucasians who behave in a more spontaneous and assertive manner" makes for "cultural factors inhibiting self-referral," which in turn leaves the poor yellow increasingly mired in his disturbed condition.

The situation, however, is not really serious: "If Asian Americans face oppression as a minority group, we would find some expression of this, perhaps in the form of high rates of psychopathology. But this is not the case." For the Sues, racist oppression is narrowly understood to involve only "racism in housing, employment and interpersonal relationships (Sue, Sue and Sue 1975, 907, 909)." "Current stereotypes of Chinese and Japanese," being "exceedingly favorable," mean "a greater willingness of white Americans to view Asians in a positive fashion. They also reflect the achievement of Chinese and Japanese (Sue, Sue and Sue 1975, 909; Sue and Kitano, 1973, 96)."

"But even more striking evidence of success" is "the reduction of social distance between Asians and whites" by reason of whites "allowing" their "model minority" to "intermarry and to form intimate relationships with the dominant group;... hence, the minority group is accepted by the dominant one (Sue, Sue and Sue 1975, 907)." It is difficult to find a more classical affirmation of the colonized mind than this, save perhaps for Frantz Fanon's description of black women dying for the love of the white colonist:

> The great dream that haunts every one of them is to be the bride of a white man.... One could say that all their efforts are directed to this end.... Their need to gesticulate... their calculated, theatrical, revolting attitudes, are just so many effects of the same mania for grandeur. They must have white men, completely white and nothing else will do. Almost all of them spend their entire lives waiting for this stroke of luck.... [19]

In short, while the Sues do not feel entirely at ease with such "side effects" of "positive stereotypes" as non-assertiveness, verbal inhibition and social reticence (Sue and Kitano 1973, 96), they are fully convinced that Chinese-American behavior in its general contemporary cast *is* representative of "culture" and, for the most part, is *not* psychopathological. In his most recent major article, Stanley Sue (1977, 388) recommends the corrective of training Asian Americans "to become more assertive and to intervene in social systems" on their own behalf. Since "Asian culture de-emphasizes assertiveness, does this mean that Asian Americans will lose some of their cultural heritage? I do not believe so since... Asian American culture is bicultural." Again, the assumption here is that "assertiveness" is somehow not indigenous to yellow culture and experience. "Bicultural," moreover, is the latest in a series of fashionable euphemisms for the "either/or" bind of the dual personality. The term also implies that to the extent yellows have indeed been assertive in recent years (e.g., in civil rights activity), it was the result of "increased exposure and contact with Western (i.e., white) society (Sue 1977, 385)."

My own point of view, contrary to the Sues, is that a critical understanding of Chinese America as a psychohistorical phenomenon without precedent will lead to an appreciation of the *real* substance of our Cantonese-American heritage as well as the debilitating nature of the so-called "positive," essentially racist, stereotype passing for yellow sensibility of long standing. An accurate assessment of the latter is not possible without, first of all, an intelligent grasp of the former.

I attempted to demonstrate earlier that the stereotype of the meek and mild perpetual alien is held in place by the assumption that Chinese America does not exist. Peter Bourne puts this racist perspective in a nutshell: "Content in the past to adapt by isolation and avoiding any attempt to become assimilated, many Chinese (Americans) are now willing and eager to become absorbed into the mainstream of American life."[20] We were once social recluses but now we crawl out of our voluntary hideouts and make a mad dash to embrace whiteness. *That,* presumably, is the whole of Chinese American history.

A more useful conceptualization beyond that of the racist "either/or" is hinted at in the work of Daphne Phillips (1975, 218), who, in studying the migration of Italians to rural Australia, observed that

> Rather than simply exchanging their original culture for that of the host society, migrants may actually begin with a culture slightly different from that of the majority of their compatriots; may hesitate between competing versions of the host culture; and may find that their life situation leads them into developing a new culture, different alike from that of their origin, that of their hosts, and that to which they aspire.

I have suggested elsewhere, in like manner, that a more valid frame of reference would be one that involves what I term a *three-dimensional view.*

> Put simply, this involves considering (1) that which was *transplanted* from the Old World and left unchanged; ... (2) that which was brought over and, in the process of interacting with an American social and political reality, *transformed;* ... and (3) that which was *created* on these shores through appropriation from other ethnic groups ... (Tong 1977, 4).

Chinese-American English emerged, for example, as a distinctive social dialect with multiple regional variations, as a result of business and social transactions. Linguistic historian J. L. Dillard (1973, 171-172) discovered that Chinaman "Pidgin" was the *lingua franca* whenever white railroad foremen, court reporters, cowboys, sightseers and businessmen interacted with yellows. "There is ... reason to believe that the average resident of the West in the times around Gold Rush days found Pidgin either very useful or absolutely necessary," particularly when Chinamans refused to talk business unless their own tongue was used. It was from this universe of discourse that expressions like "longtime no see" and "hep sabby" crept into the national vernacular.

At the same time, words from transplanted Chinese language in time took on transformed meanings. We have seen that *jawk jierh* simply means, literally, "to catch a pig" to Chinese, while the very same phrase translates as "cheat" or "deceive" in Chinese-American language. Similarly, the telephone to the Chinese is *dien wah,* "electronic voice," but to Chinese Americans, particularly those of Cantonese lineage, the indispensable voice box is *hom sien,* "screaming wire." Even subtler distinctions of an intragroup nature have been unearthed in recent work by Lorraine Dong and Marlon Hom (1980).

It would be simplistic, then, if not ludicrous, to view Chinese-American culture and sensibility, as the Sues and other scholars do, simply as an instance of static "traditional" clan village attitudes and norms. It is certainly *much more* than that. On the other hand, it is also *no less* than a certain degree of transplanted, unchanged world views, values, and practices. By "traditional Chinese ways," however, I am *not* talking about that complex of conventional culture which virtually every writer on Chinese America has argued to be the whole of our social world.[21]

My position differs from theirs in that I do not hold to a unidimensional perspective of transplanted Cantonese culture. We can take a critical cue from Karen Horney, the eminent neopsychoanalyst (1885-1952) who wrote of *competing versions of the same culture* in her seminal works on neurotic conflict. Inherent in white Christian middle-class American values are two contradictory interpretations of Protestantism: The Protestant Principle preaches relating to others in a spirit of self-giving concern but the so-called "Protestant Ethic" sanctions ferocious, dehumanizing competition.[22] A common expression that captures the alienating quality of the opposing imperatives is "There's Sunday going-to-church behavior and then there's Monday morning back-to-the-rat-race behavior!"

In a similar fashion, there is more than one version of transplanted Cantonese/Chinese-American culture. (Figure 1 provides a schematic summary.) Derived from othodox Confucianist values, and later blended with the requirements of what Chin and Chan (1972) have termed white "racist love," the "Conventional" version was reinforced in pre-socialist China by a medieval social and political order that mandated the peasantry to practise "filial piety," unconditional obedience and emotional restraint. The ideal Conventional Self came into the fullness of being through a near-fanatical loyalty to family, clan and emperor, without regard for personal wishes or priorities.

Sinologists are in general agreement that the ruling groups of ancient China—the monarchy and the scholar-official administrative class—exploited Confucian philosophy as a potent device for controlling a numerically overwhelming peasantry. Balaz (1964, 18) has observed that

The scholar-officials and their state found in Confucianist doctrine an ideology that suited them perfectly. . . . in Han times, shortly after the formation of the empire, it became a state doctrine. The virtues preached by Confucianism were exactly suited to the new hierarchical state: respect, humility, docility, obedience, submission, and subordination to elders and betters.

Figure 1: Competing Versions of Transplanted Chinese-American Culture

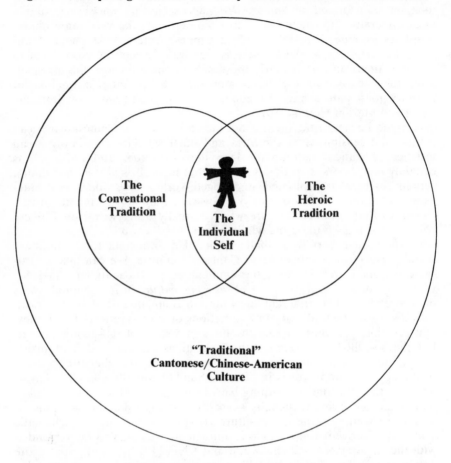

The Conventional Tradition

The Heroic Tradition

The Individual Self

"Traditional" Cantonese/Chinese-American Culture

The Conventional sensibility is predominant at this point in the Chinese-American experience, enforced quite thoroughly by institutional racism (most especially mass media and official histories), lingering but firmly transplanted Confucianist values, Christian eugenics and the crass tourist culture that emerged some seventy years ago in response to racist insulation in ghettoes.[23] The unchallenged convictions of the Sues and others is testament to the effectiveness of these vehicles that have perpetuated the mystification for nearly five decades.

The picture is not complete, however, if we wish to account for Cantonese and Cantonese-American behavior that is clearly aggressive, daring, individualistic and volatile. The first Chinamans hailed from a world where mild disagreements led to internecine war, total self-sufficiency was prized above all else and spontaneous alliances carried a quality of fraternal loyalty that even the Confucianists could not help but envy (Hsiao 1961; Teng and Fairbank 1966; Tong 1978; Wakeman 1974).

Coexistent with the Conventional Tradition was the "Heroic," which exalted a time-honored Cantonese sense of self: the fierce, arrogant, independent individual beholden to no one and loyal only to those deemed worthy of undying respect, on that individual's terms. The enduring role models for this sensibility are to be found in myth and legend surrounding such "folk" heroes as Ngok Fei, the warrior-general; Fah Muk Lon, the woman warrior; and the brothers of the Peach Garden—most especially Kwan Kung, the most popular deity of the people, god of war, plunder, loyalty, righteousness, high executioners, literature, actors, the Buddha who defends the realm to the Buddhists, the official high king of military pacification to the Taoists, the official equal of Confucious by Manchurian decree, the embodiment of revenge (Bush 1977; Hsia 1968; Stover 1974; Wakeman 1972; Wilhelm 1962; Wright 1960).

In his otherwise strangely ambivalent work, *My Country and My People,* Lin Yutang (1935, 18) observed, as so many others have, that "South in Kwantung, one meets ... a different people, ... (it is a world) where people eat like men and work like men, enterprising, carefree, spendthrift, pugnacious, adventurous, progressive and quick-tempered, where beneath the Chinese culture a snake-eating aborigines tradition persists ... Since the Heroic Tradition has not been written about in any extensive fashion, a detailed discussion appears in order.

For countless "tradition-oriented" Americans of Cantonese descent, the cosmos consists essentially of *numerous realms of being* or ontological dimensions, each of which exerts an active, ongoing influence on the others. Between "this life" and the "next"—not to mention the past, the present and the future—there is a vitally profound continuity. In medieval China, both the powerful and the common experienced a universe with "many layers of heaven and many layers of hell."[24] *Within* each of these intersecting spheres of influence, moreover, inhabitants confronted their own special set of internal conflicts and issues.

In a universe of multiple dimensions in perpetual contention with one another—where differences in power distribution and evolutionary status were enormous[25]—*the metaphor for life was war.* On earth alone, whole nations as well as individuals and groups acted as sovereign predators who, despite social contracts designed to regulate human conduct, continually bumped up against each other, took from one another, and sustained what Christopher Lasch (1978) would call a "war of all against all."

Thus, the heart of Cantonese "folk" mythic vision congealed around the image of the *hero* or *warrior* as representative of the self's highest possibilities. Everything a Cantonese does is tantamount to an act of war. To be sure, this is not as barbaric a phenomenon as it may sound to Western ears, because it does not mean murderous violence in every instance; it is not amoral, for the highest moral law—the only moral law—is that one must keep his word; and it is not to be equated with the deranged narcissistic individualism diagnosed by writers like Lasch because the individual *is* preoccupied with loyalty and *does* form (frequently spontaneous) alliances.

One is born and one dies in war. One never wins the war but that is life. The only genuine source of dignity and self-respect resides in the achievement of a warrior's autonomy. Patterns of everyday culture, it followed, gave expression to such concerns as strategy, tactics, alliances, power and loyalty. History and its lessons became particularly important for an existence of perpetual contention. As Han Suyin (1972, 25) wrote of the young Mao Tse-tung,

> Chinese fiction is fictionalized history, with no attempt to disguise the fact. Tales of strategy and tactics, of how battles are won and political schemes concocted, are the backbone of the romances which Mao and millions of other Chinese little boys loved and continue to love.

Every resource of culture was material for waging war. J. W. Freiberg (1977), for one, has made a compelling case for the indispensable role of Taoist principles in Mao's tactical maneuvers during the Chinese Revolution. Transactions between ontological spheres, even of the most mundane sort, took on the qualities of military-like negotiation. For example, whenever Tsao Shen, the Kitchen God, ascends to Heaven (usually before the start of the Lunar New Year) to give his annual report on a family, members of the household mount a festival in his honor, complete with offerings of sweet dishes at the altar. This is done in order to urge the deity to render a favorable account of the family's behavior for the past year (Day 1975, 32; Lee 1965, 64).

Describing Sun Tze's classic, *The Art of War,* Han Suyin observed:

> The influence of Sun Tze's classic book *The Art of War,* written two thousand years before, extends throughout Chinese history, and also influenced Mao's generation. The book is regarded as a treatise not only on the conduct of war but also on the conduct of all affairs where rivalry occurs, negotiations with an enemy or a potential enemy, tactics and strategy in war or in peace. Chinese encyclopedias contain extensive sections devoted to the literature of war. *The concept of war and peace as alternate facets of the same application of power is as old as Chinese history.*[26]

Cantonese popular culture was heavily influenced by Buddhist and Taoist elements, particularly those engrained in the image of the hero, the ideal role model of humanness as exemplified in the person of *the wandering monk.* Skilled in the healing, fighting, and scholarly arts, this member of all communities along the Road of Life exhibited what C. T. Hsia (1968, 18) has termed an "amoral autonomy." He was loyal to no man and acknowledged no established authority or principles. Ultimately, he trusted only his own basic intuitive sense of what was right. Donald Munro (1969, 139) argues, quite rightly, that, more than anything else, the Taoists played a central role in dispelling the claim of all apriori powers over the individual, beginning with the state.

> The repudiation of the idea that the human social order has some basis in nature led the Taoists beyond a doctrine of innate equality to a denial of any inequalities among men as adults. It enabled them to dispense with the notions of merit, social rank, and privilege—in short, to dispense with the trappings of the Confucian aristocracy of merit. . . .

Little wonder, then, that cultural vehicles for transmitting the Heroic Tradition were perpetually "folk" or subterranean. Popular novels like *The Romance of the Three Kingdoms* and *Water Margin* periodically received the stamp of Imperial censorship. Especially suggestive of a dangerous anarchism was the hero who had "no nerves." Robert Ruhlmann (1960, 164) summed it up best:

> Neither good news nor bad news affects his composure; he displays neither hatreds nor affections. He has infinite patience. He can prepare and wait twenty years to take revenge, and, in the meantime, he smiles and talks courteously to the man on whom he intends to wreak vengeance. Knowingly, he watches and interprets others' actions, but seldom reveals his own feelings. Life-long concentration helps him to hide his quick and intense sensitivity under a mask of relaxed self-confidence.

Here, then, was the Heroic Tradition of everyday Cantonese and Cantonese-American folk, complete with a vision of *ideal* self-hood (heroic character), conduct (heroic behavior), and even community (spontaneous alliances with a rudimentary egalitarianism). As Hsia (1968, 86-87) puts it, this code requires a hero to be honorable but

> The concept of honor is not defined in the traditional Confucian manner. Filial piety is indeed stressed (in *Water Margin*) . . . But the code departs from Confucian teaching in its observance of the other basic human ties. It pays little attention to the conjugal relationship . . . and it exalts the ideal of friendship to the point of usurping the language of brotherhood. This ideal not only endorses the Confucian saying invoked in the book, "Within the four seas all men are brothers," but encourages the practice of knight-errantry insofar as it is preferable to execute justice by one's own hand rather than through the official channels. . . .
>
> Moreover, friendship is not lightly bestowed, despite the injunction that all men are brothers. The existence of an unwritten code implies that members of the heroic community are able to spot one another by unmistakable signs of behavior.

When the Sues declare that contemporary Chinese-American stereotyped behavior is traceable to a legacy of non-assertive, reclusive, "unassimiable" forebears, they defend the mystification of white supremacist institutions that euphemize psychopathology as culture. Convinced that he or she is descended from a race of pathologically inhibited compliant nobodies, the average Chinese American walks about in a fog of self-contempt, looking to other groups, very often in desperation, for a more viable sense of self. Sommers' twenty-nine-year-old yellow male patient, so indistinguishable from many of his breed, represents the final "success" of deformed history. In his own agonizing search for the collective roots of his personal makeup, James Baldwin (1963, 10) wrote: " . . . the past is all that makes the present coherent, and . . . that past will remain horrible for exactly as long as we refuse to assess it honestly."

Timid and docile behavior *is* indicative of emotional disorder.[27] If Chinese Americans seem to be that way by virtue of cultural "background," it is the case *only* to extent that white racism, in combination with our heritage of Confucian repression, made it so. The early Chinamans *consistently* shaped themselves and justified their acts according to the fundamental vision of the Heroic Tradition. Their stupendous feats of daring and courage, however, remain buried beneath a gargantuan mound of white movies, popular fiction, newspaper cartoons, dissertations, political tracts, religious meeting minutes and now psychological studies, that teach us to look upon ourselves as perpetual aliens living only for white acceptance.

It is intriguing to note, on the other hand, that the latest waves of Cantonese newcomers are "bringing back" the once-popular practice of displaying statues of Kwan Kung and Tsao Shen (who is also the god of collective anarchy) in prominent places like store windows, living rooms and restaurant kitchens. Five movie theaters in San Francisco's Chinatown alone flash, around the clock, all manner of mass-produced "heroic" films involving themes of fanatical loyalty and murderous revenge. Popular "ethnic" literature streams into the ghetto with a steady supply of kung fu warriors, cunning sages, strategy-wise generals and wily serpent women. The martial arts schools are experiencing increased enrolment. And everywhere one turns, young and old alike can be heard recounting folklore and legend with heroic themes.

All this is somehow reminiscent of the spirit in which the Chinamans of old took on an Old West that was up for grabs to adventurers who dared stake a claim on whole chunks of American soil. I am reminded of the alarmist words of a white journalist (Powderly 1901, 7) at the turn of the century:

> Chinese laborers cross our borderline between the United States and Canada disguised as clergymen, as nuns, as Quakers and as Indians; they come over the line by rail, boxed in barrels, covered top and bottom by potatoes; they come over sandwiched between bales of hay; they come in freight cars buried under corn, wheat and oats....[61]

FOOTNOTES

[1] Sommers, "Identity conflict," 638. Emphasis supplied.

[2] Ibid. Emphasis supplied.

[3] Ibid., 640.

[4] Ibid., 644. Italics in the original.

[5] Of recent coinage, this is the proper designation for Japanese Americans.

[6] A number of works have appeared since the "Relocation Experience" to document and explain the event. For my money, the single most impressive treatise to date is Michi Weglyn's *Years of Infamy: The Untold Story of America's Concentration Camps.* New York: William Morrow, 1976.

[7] Chin and Chan, "Racist love," 72. Emphasis in the original.

[8] "Orthodox Jews Denounce 'Moses'" *San Francisco Examiner* (7 July 1980). The protesting Jewish groups "called on major presidential candidates and their parties to declare opposition to what they called blasphemy and mockery under the guise of humor..." This savage mockery of our God, our Bible, including the Ten Commandments, and our prophet and

teacher Moses is comparable to events that occurred in Nazi Germany and Soviet Russia."

[9] The exception to this general silence has been groups like the Coalition of Asians to Nix Charlie Chan which, in a coast-to-coast effort, organized demonstrations in front of movie theaters that featured *Charlie Chan and the Curse of the Dragon Queen*. This effort, involving only a few hundred people, along with general debunking by most movie reviewers, resulted in a quick closing of the film following a one-week initial run (*East/West* 25 February 1981). The few Asian-American voices that protested the "Kung Fu" television series, back in the early 1970s, were generally uninformed, their main concern being that a white actor, David Carradine, had been selected to play the lead role of a Shaolin monk, instead of a yellow. The one exception was playwright/critic Frank Chin who wrote what was very likely the only historically-informed critique published by the major media (Chin 1974).

[10] *See also* Sommers, "Experiment in group psychotherapy" and "Impact of dual-cultural membership on identity." Psychoanalytic anthropologist Warner Muensterberger (in Rohein 1951, 54) ran around the "Chinese quarters" in San Francisco and New York and documented the "fact" of stereotyped behavior by alluding to the explanation that "the male heroes of many Chinese folk tales are not strong or dominant characters. They are artists and scholars ... Very often these men do not show an immediate interest in profane matters." Anthropologists Abel and Hsu ("Aspects of personality"), concluded from their Rorschach studies of China-born and American-born Chinese Americans

that yellow females were apparently more open and expressive than their relatively more polite and suppressive male counterparts. This was because the former "were able to move more freely and be more easily accepted in (white) American society and by (white) American suitors. ..." (cited from subsequent conclusions in Abel, *Psychological Testing*, 60). Why this was so, Abel and Hsu did not say. Lee ("Chinese boys and girls," 32), had the impression, from observing patterns of adolescent behavior among Chinese Americans in the San Francisco Bay area, that conflict between foreign-born parents and native-born offspring can result in reinforcement of behavior reminiscent of the stereotype of passivity. "Overanxiety" in the older generation can lead to "constant and insistent ordering and forbidding." In their psychoanalytic interpretation of essays written by forty foreign-born Chinese students at a midwestern university, Scofield and Sun ("Differential effect upon personality," 221), were even more direct and ominous: Severe child-rearing practices have led to the consequence of "schizothemic" personalities who "tend to be more withdrawn, suspicious, shy, emotionally immature, sensitive and introverted. ..."

[11] Sue and Sue, "Counseling Chinese Americans," 638. Emphasis supplied.

[12] Up to the present day, psychological research on Chinese-American "ethnic identity" continues to be grounded in this racist either/or mentality. A case in point is the dissertation questionnaire of a Chinese-American doctoral candidate currently completing her work at a major university. Phyllis S. Lee, in her "Youth Opinion Survey," uses such questions as the

following, to inquire of opinions according to a "agree/disagree" (Likert) scale:

I rate the opinions of my American friends higher than those of my Chinese friends.

It is proper for Chinese people to be quiet, polite and well-behaved, especially around Americans.

It is more appropriate for us to follow the ideas of Confucius than the ideas of the Western world.

If I had to choose to be more Chinese or American, I would choose to be more American.

13 *See also* Tong, "Living death defended," 187. In their pioneering oral history research on various segments of the San Francisco Chinatown population of the early 1970s, Victor and Bret Nee (*Longtime Californ'*, 19-20), discovered that many, if not most, of the so-called "sojourners" (and later on, their sons who followed them to the New World) had very little inclination to return home to their clan villages in Canton. Sandmeyer (*Anti-Chinese Movement in California*, 97-98), in his timely and still accurate work on the anti-Chinese movement, documented in detail the rural settlement patterns of the early Chinamans. Self-contained Chinatowns were literally all over the Old West in the nineteenth century.

14 Contrary to popular understanding, *Chinaman* (pl., *Chinamans* not *Chinamen* as Maxine Hong Kingston would propose), is not a derogatory term for Chinese Americans. The earliest immigrants insisted that they be identified as such (Jacobs and Landau 1971, 126); it was white journalistic writings that eventually made the word synonymous with *yellow nigger.*

15 *See,* for example, vivid descriptions by such noted sinologists as Vogel, *Canton under Communism,* 19-20;

Wakeman, *Strangers at the Gate;* and Teng and Fairbank, *China's Response to the West,* 35-36.

16 *See,* for example, Chinn et al., *A History of the Chinese in California;* Low, "Laws under which we have lived"; and Yu, "Chinese in American courts."

17 Walker (*San Francisco's Literary Frontier* and *Ambrose Bierce*), described Bierce's bitter pro-Chinaman attacks on whites who expressed their "Christian hatred" in this and other forms.

18 Tong, "Living death defended," 190. Italics in the original. I have taken the liberty here to correct my previous use of *Chinamen* by substituting *Chinamans* where appropriate. *See also* my subsequent essay "Warriors and victims." *Si hah* means "give it a try."

19 Fanon (*Black Skin, White Masks,* 57) is actually citing from case study work by one Abdoulaye Sadji.

20 Bourne, "Chinese student," 276-77. This is identical with Sue, "Psychological theory and implications."

21 In addition to the Sues and their associates, others such as the following have also advanced the notions of Asian Americans being the product of a Confucian social universe that stressed little other than clannishness, patriarchal loyalty, hard work and passive demeanor: Abbott, *Harmony and Individualism;* Barth, *Bitter Strength;* Hsu, *Challenge of the American Dream;* Lyman, *Chinese Americans;* Sollenberger, "Chinese-American child-rearing practices"; Sung, *Mountain of Gold;* Toupin, "Counseling Asians"; Weiss, "Selective acculturation and the dating process" and *Valley City;* and Yuan, "Voluntary segregation." It should be emphasized that while the content of their views plays into the devices of those institutions that perpetuate white supremacy, I am

not suggesting that these writers are intentionally racist. I suspect gross ignorance of the breadth, depth and complexity of the yellow experience would be a more accurate diagnosis.

[22] Horney, *The Neurotic Personality of Our Time.* Max Weber, *Protestant Ethic,* is to be credited, I believe, with the original coinage of the concept, the Protestant Ethic.

[23] *See* Tong ("Warriors and victims"), for a detailed discussion in addition to Tong ("Living death defended").

[24] A classic expression translated into English by Sifu Kwong Gate Chan of the Tao Institute of San Francisco, personal communication, 1980.

[25] These dimensions number in the thousands and include worlds for weak ("yin"), "attached" ghosts longing to return to terra firma, warrior spirits of previously fierce humans, departed spirits of various animals, highly evolved "immortals," etc. *See,* for example, Thompson, *Chinese Religion;* Wolf, *Religion and Ritual;* and Bodde, *China's Cultural Tradition.*

[26] Han, *The Morning Deluge,* 47. Emphasis supplied.

[27] A recurring diagnostic impression has been "mixed characterological disorder," consisting of variously blended combinations of such syndromes as: social phobia, schizoid personality disorder, avoidant personality disorder, dependent personality disorder. *Diagnostic Statistic Manual (SDM-III).* Washington, D.C.: American Psychiatric Association, 1980.

BIBLIOGRAPHY

Abel, T. M. *Psychological Testing in Cultural Contexts.* New Haven, Conn.: College and University Press, 1973.

Abel, T. M. and F. L. K. Hsu. Some aspects of personality of Chinese as revealed by the Rorschach Test. *Rorschach Res. Exch. & J. Projective Techn.* 13 (1949):285-301.

Abbott, K. A. *Harmony and Individualism: Changing Chinese psychosocial functioning in Taipei and San Francisco.* Taipei: Orient Culture Service, 1970.

Balaz, E. *Chinese Civilization and Bureaucracy: Variations on a theme.* Translated by H. M. Wright and edited by A. F. Wright. New Haven: Yale University Press, 1964.

Baldwin, J. *Notes of a Native Son.* New York: Dial, 1973.

Barth, G. *Bitter Strength: A history of the Chinese in the United States, 1850-1870.* Cambridge: Harvard University Press, 1964.

Bodde, D. *China's Cultural Tradition: What and Whither?* New York: Holt, Rinehart & Winston, 1962.

Bourne, P. G. The Chinese student: Acculturation and mental illness. *Psychiatry* 38 (1975):269-277.

Bush, R. C. *Religion in China.* Niles, Ill.: Argus Communications, 1977.

Chin, F. "Kung Fu" is unfair to Chinese. *New York Times,* 24 March 1974.

Chin, F. and J. P. Chan. Racist love. In *Seeing through Shuck,* edited by R. Kostelanetz. New York: Ballantine, 1972.

Chinn, T. W., P. Choy and M. H. Lai. *A History of the Chinese in California.* San Francisco: Chinese Historical Society, 1969.

Day, C. B. *Popular Religion in pre-Communist China.* San Francisco: Chinese Materials Center, 1975.

Dillard, J. L. *Black English: Its history and usage in the United States.* New York: Vintage, 1973.

Dong, L. and M. K. Hom. Chinatown

Chinese: the San Francisco dialect. *Amerasia J.* 7, no. 1 (1980):1-29.

Fanon, F. *Black Skin, White Masks.* Translated by C. L. Markmann. New York: Grove Press, 1967.

Freiberg, J. W. The dialectic in China: Maoist and Daoist. *Bulletin of Concerned Asian Scholars* 9, no. 1 (1977):2-19.

Han, S. *The Morning Deluge: Mao Tsetung and the Chinese Revolution, 1893-1954.* Boston: Little, Brown and Co., 1972.

Horney, K. *The Neurotic Personality of our Time.* New York: Norton, 1937.

Hsia, C. T. *The Classic Chinese Novel: A critical introduction.* New York: Columbia University Press, 1968.

Hsiao, K. C. *Rural China: Imperial control in the nineteenth century.* Seattle: University of Washington Press, 1961.

Hsu, F. L. K. *The Challenge of the American Dream: The Chinese in the United States.* Belmont: Calif.: Wadsworth, 1971.

Jacobs, P. and S. Landau. *To serve the Devil.* Vol. 2 of *Colonials and sojourners.* New York: Vintage, 1971.

Kung, S. W. *Chinese in American Life: Some aspects of their history, status, problems and contributions.* Seattle: University of Washington Press, 1962.

Lasch, C. *The Culture of Narcissism: American life in an age of diminishing expectations.* New York: Norton, 1978.

Lee, C. *Chinatown, U. S. A.* Garden City, N.Y.: Doubleday, 1965.

Lee, P. S. *Youth Opinion Survey: Part I.* 1980. Mimeo.

Lee, R. H. Delinquent, neglected, and dependent Chinese boys and girls of the San Francisco Bay Region. *J. Soc. Psych.* 36 (1952):15-34.

——. *The Chinese in the United States of America.* Chicago: Oxford University Press, 1960.

Lin, Y. T. *My Country and my People.* New York: John Day, 1935.

Low, H. W. Laws under which we have lived. *Bulletin of the Chinese Historical Society of America* 9, no. 3 (1974):1-5.

Lyman, S. M. *Chinese Americans.* New York: Random House, 1974.

Medved, M. and D. Wallechinsky. *What Really Happened to the Class of '65?* New York: Ballantine, 1976.

Muensterberger, W. Orality and dependence: Characteristics of southern Chinese. In *Psychoanalysis and the social sciences,* edited by G. Rohein. New York: International Universities Press, 1951.

Munro, D. J. *The Concept of Man in Early China.* Palo Alto, Calif.: Stanford University Press, 1969.

Nee, V. G. and B. D. Nee. *Longtime Californ': A documentary study of an American Chinatown.* New York: Pantheon, 1973.

Phillips, D. The effect of immigration on the family: The case of Italians in rural Australia. *Brit. J. Sociol.* 26, no. 2 (1975):218-226.

Powderly, T. V. Exclude anarchist and Chinaman. *Collier's Weekly* 28 (14 December 1901):7.

Ruhlmann, R. Traditional heroes in Chinese fiction. In *The Confucian Persuasion,* edited by A. F. Wright. Palo Alto, Calif.: Stanford University Press, 1960.

Sandmeyer, E. C. *The anti-Chinese Movement in California.* 1939. Champaign-Urbana: University of Illinois Press, 1973.

Scofield, A. and C. W. Sun. A comparative study of the differential effect upon personality of Chinese and American training practice. *J. Soc. Psych.* 52 (1960):221-224.

Sollenberger, R. T. Chinese-American child-rearing practices and juvenile delinquency. *J. Soc. Psych.* 74 (1968):13-23.

Sommers, V. S. An experiment in group psychotherapy with members of minority groups. *Intl. J. Grp. Psychoth.* 3 (1963).

———. Identity conflict and acculturation problems in Oriental-Americans. *Am. J. Orthopsychiat.* 30 (1960):637-644.

———. The impact of dual-cultural membership on identity. *Psychiatry* 27 (1964):332-344.

Stover, L. E. *The Cultural Ecology of Chinese Civilization: Peasants and elites in the last of the agrarian states.* New York: New American Library, 1974.

Sue, D. Ethnic identity: The impact of two cultures on the psychological development of Asians in America. In *Asian-Americans: Psychological perspectives,* edited by S. Sue and N. N. Wagner. Ben Lomond, Calif.: Science & Behavior Books, 1973.

Sue, D. and A. Frank. A typological approach to the psychological study of Chinese and Japanese American college males. *J. Soc. Issues* 29, no. 2 (1973):129-148.

Sue, D. and S. Sue. Chinese-American personality and mental health. *Amerasia J.* 1, no. 2 (1971):36-49.

Sue, D. W. and B. A. Kirk. Differential characteristics of Japanese-American and Chinese-American college students. *J. Couns. Psych.* 20, no. 2 (1973):142-148.

———. Psychological characteristics of Chinese-American students. *J. Couns. Psych.* 19, no. 6 (1972):471-478.

Sue, D. W. and S. Sue. Counseling Chinese-Americans. *Pers. & Guid. J.* 50, no. 8 (1972):637-644.

Sue, S. Psychological theory and implications for Asian Americans. *Pers. & Guid. J.* 55 (1977):381-389.

Sue, S. and H. H. L. Kitano. Stereotypes as a measure of success. *J. Soc. Issues* 29, no. 2 (1973):83-98.

Sue, S. and D. W. Sue. MMPI comparisons between Asian-American and non-Asian students utilizing a student health psychiatric clinic. *J. Couns. Psych.* 21, no. 5 (1974):423-427.

Sue, S., D. W. Sue and D. W. Sue. Asian Americans as a minority group. *Am. Psychologist* 30 (1975):906-910.

Sung, B. L. *Mountain of Gold: The story of the Chinese in America.* New York: Macmillan, 1967.

Teng, S. Y. and J. K. Fairbank, eds. *China's Response to the West: A documentary survey, 1839-1923.* New York: Atheneum, 1966.

Thompson, L. G. *Chinese Religion: An introduction.* Belmont, Calif.: Wadsworth, 1969.

Tong, B. R. A living death defended as the legacy of a superior culture. *Amerasia J.* 2, no. 2 (1974):178-202.

———. Asian American culture and mental health: A few critical notes. *Newsletter of the Association of Asian American Psychologists* 3, no. 4 (1977):3-7.

———. Warriors and victims: Chinese American sensibility and learning styles. In *Extracting learning styles from social/cultural diversity: A study of five American minorities,* edited by L. Morris, G. Sather and S. Schull. Norman: Southwest Teacher Corps Network, University of Oklahoma, 1978.

Toupin, E. S. W. A. Counseling Asians: Psychotherapy in the context of racism and Asian-American history. *Am. J. Orthopsychiat.* 50, no. 1 (1980):76-86.

Vogel, E. F. *Canton under Communism: Programs and politics in a provincial capital, 1949-1968.* New York: Harper Row, 1971.

Wakeman, F. *Strangers at the Gate: Social Disorder in south China, 1839-1861.* Berkeley: University of California Press, 1974.

———. The secret societies of Kwangtung, 1800-1856. In *Popular movements and secret societies in China, 1840-1950,* edited by J. Chesneaux. Palo Alto, Calif.: Stanford University Press, 1972.

Walker, F. *Ambrose Bierce, the Wicked-*

est Man in San Francisco. San Francisco: Colt Press, 1948.

——. *San Francisco's Literary Frontier.* New York: Alfred A. Knopf, 1939.

Weber, M. *The Protestant Ethic and the Spirit of Capitalism.* 1904. Translated by T. Parsons. New York: Scribner, 1958.

Weiss, M. S. Selective acculturation and the dating process: The pattern of Chinese-Caucasian inter-racial dating. *J. Marriage & the Family* 32 (1970):273-278.

——. *Valley City: A Chinese community in America.* Cambridge, Mass.: Schenkman, 1974.

Wilhelm, H. From myth to myth: The case of Yüeh Fei's biography. In *Confucian personalities,* edited by A. F. Wright and D. Twitchett. Palo Alto, Calif.: Stanford University Press, 1962.

Wolf, A. P., ed. *Religion and Ritual in Chinese Society.* Palo Alto, Calif.: Stanford University Press, 1974.

Wright, A. F. *The Confucian Persuasion.* Palo Alto, Calif.: Stanford University Press, 1960.

Yang, C. K. *Religion in Chinese Society: A study of contemporary social functions of religion and some of their historical factors.* Berkeley: University of California Press, 1967.

Yu, C. Y. The Chinese in American courts. *Bulletin of Concerned Asian Scholars* 4, no. 3 (1972):22-30.

Yuan, D. Y. Voluntary Segregation: A study of New York Chinatown. In *Minority responses: Comparative views of reactions to subordination,* edited by M. Kurokawa. New York: Random House, 1970. Orig. pub. in *Phylon,* 1963.

D'ARCY J. HELMER

27

Iatrogenic Intraorganizational Processes as One Mediator of Burnout

A community psychologist and consultant, D'Arcy Helmer has been well grounded in the full variety of organizational structures available to modern bureaucracies. He has just completed a study of burnout among nurses in two differently structured systems. With this theme in mind, I located my favorite passage from the business meeting minutes of a campus in which burnout was common-place.

> Dean Z presented Motion 138 as follows: that the No Smoking regulation be modified so that smoking be allowed in administrators offices . . . The motion was seconded but did not pass. (Two voted in favor and six opposed.) Dean Z then announced he would veto the Campus Executive Committee action, authorizing smoking in the administrative offices.
>
> —February 14, 1975

In this innovation in creative democracy was born the idea for passing a law by vetoing its legislative failure. Neither on that campus nor in one of Helmer's nursing units did the decision-making process fail to make its iatrogenic impact: only when those most directly affected by significant decisions make those decisions can we foresee noniatrogenic consequence. Our thanks to Helmer for a personality so relentlessly positive that burnout flees on sight. **R.F.M.**

Research examining the effects of burning-out/burnt-out helpers on their clients is to my knowledge nonexistent; perhaps, in part, because of the difficulties inherent in collecting *sensitive information* (e.g., defense mechanisms). Iatrogenic behavior refers to incidents where helpers create more problems for clients during the process of *helping*. The purpose of this chapter is to explore the possibility that *entrenched burnout* (long-term burnout: several weeks, months) can lead to iatrogenic behavior, and to point to intraorganizational processes as one potential encourager/discourager of iatrogenic behavior. Of course, focusing on intraorganizational processes is not to naively disregard the importance of personal factors, interorganizational factors, societal factors or the interactions between the four sets of previously mentioned factors as potential contributors to iatrogenic behavior. Rather, the focus on intraorganizational processes is because of their predominance in the organizational situations under consideration. The data base for this chapter is a recent study (Helmer 1980) which examined burnout, job stress and job satisfaction in two public health nursing organizations located in different regions.

The literature on burnout sprouts a myriad of burnout definitions. Reviewing some of these definitions will suffice to indicate the breadth of different burnout conceptualizations and may suggest some precipitating processes involved in iatrogenic behavior. One group defines burnout as involving increased feelings of emotional exhaustion, the development of negative attitudes toward clients and the tendency to evaluate oneself negatively (Pines and Maslach 1978; Maslach 1978; Maslach and Jackson 1978). Freudenberger (1977) defines burnout as a set of symptoms: cynicism, negativism, inflexible and almost rigid thought patterns, a closed mind about change and innovation, a paranoia of peers and administrators, a condescending attitude, lack of communication with colleagues, withdrawal, developing a sense of helplessness and hopelessness about clients and speaking of clients in negative terms. Cherniss, Egnatios, Wacker and O'Dowd (1980) define burnout as an increased tendency to view clients as objects rather than people; a decline in hope, idealism and optimism; and increasing departmentalization and withdrawal from work. Mitchell (1977) conceptualizes burnout as occurring in three consecutive stages: physical fatigue, psychological fatigue and spiritual fatigue. For Kahn (1978), burnout is a syndrome of inappropriate attitudes toward clients and toward oneself. Howard, Cunningham and Rechnitzer (1978) claim that burnout is a condition that grows out of extreme job pressure, and that burnouts may still enjoy their work because the job satisfaction that is attained from living at an accelerated pace moderates the stressful aspects of this accelerated pace. The assumption is that contextual factors do not inhibit or *shut down* the experience of job satisfaction. Kemp (1977) defines burnout as an addiction to one's own biochemistry, specifically to a high level of adrenalin production. Vash (1980) conceptualizes burnout as a number of burnout styles resulting from extreme job pressure: dropping out completely; dropping out to another location; staying and showing little concern for organizational goals and those people in it; complaining about physical symptoms; having no principles and adopting the principles of a supervisor; and the person who goes by the book. Public health nurses have their conceptualization of burnout too. As one nurse declared "There are several kinds of burnout occurring: The hell with it, I will do what I can; There is an easier way of making a living; and I will take an early retirement." The predominating thread which permeates most burnout definitions is the loss of motivation to continue in the work (loss of morale); thus, a broad definition of burnout may be a loss of motivation to continue in the work.

Collectively, these definitions suggest that burnout is a process rather than a static state. It may be reasonable to assume that the more *entrenched* (long-term) the burnout process becomes, the greater the potential for iatrogenic behavior occurring. Perhaps, it is reasonable to assume that the loss of personal respect is a necessary precipitant of iatrogenic behavior. How we think/feel about ourselves is probably positively related to how we think/feel/interact with others (Buber 1958; Rogers 1959; Fromm 1939; Gergen 1971). Burnout suggests a synthesis of the constructs job satisfaction, morale, self-perception and job stress.

Burnout might be conceptualized as a process where the continual thwarting of premium personal/professional values results in a loss of self-respect (negative shift in self-perception), in the context of stress coming from any or all of personal factors, intraorganizational factors, interorganizational factors and societal factors.

I will now turn to the public health nurse data which suggests a positive relationship between the prolongation of burnout/low morale and iatrogenic behavior. Induction is necessary because of the difficulties involved in gathering self-report information (e.g., defense mechanisms) from potential iatrogenics.

Sample one consists of ten nurses who were randomly selected from a public health unit of sixty nurses. Each nurse in sample one was interviewed. Ninety percent of the nurses indicated that they have experienced burnout.

People who burn out have negative images of themselves which probably affect the quality of the care/service that they offer. I suspect that some burnouts are just there for the paycheck.

I accompanied a burnt-out nurse who left a mother feeling inadequate about her childcare when her childcare was quite good. I think burnout really affects the quality of the care. In problem family situations, a burnt-out nurse may set off a crisis, thus making the situation worse, feeding a negative attitude about public health nurses.

Burnout is occurring in isolated cases. Nurses burn out because of unrealistic expectations of what the job should be offering them and their lack of awareness with regard to bureaucracies. Those who overextend themselves have poor self images, are out to prove something to themselves in the work environment and tend to have a depressive orientation. Overextension and subsequent burnout is going to lower your efficiency as a helper.

With regard to the effects of burnout on clients, I think it depends on whether the helper internalizes or projects her emotional/physical drain. I tend to drive myself to continue to give, rather than having a negative impact on clients.

Burnout occurs because the nurse's values/expectations are incongruent with organizational values and she refuses to change. I have six months to go before I quit, and my husband (a student) and baby are the only reasons I am working.

If you overextend yourself you get sick. People who burn out do not invest in themselves; their work efficiency is low; and they may create worse problems for their clients.

Low morale is a function of personal/professional expectations that I bring to the work. Burnout occurs in phases. Depending on where you bring the burnout process to a halt determines how burnout affects you and your clients. If you halt the burnout process in its early stages there may be little or no affect on you or your clients. If the burnout process develops, work efficiency may be considerably impaired, nurse-client trust/rapport may be negatively influenced, community attitudes toward public health nurses may be negatively affected ("she does not care") and clients may shut you out completely.

If burnout occurs as a short phase, even if you open up a can of worms with a problem family, you can follow-up fast. However, if burnout is long term, the helper may create more problems for the client and the health and social service system.

A number of things positively relate to the loss of morale. These are personal and professional life, self-esteem and work efficiency.

I have days when I know I should not be working; my efficiency is low and I do not put effort into my work, though I still do the work because I think I should. With respect to lowered efficiency, problem families have so many problems that they probably do not even notice that I am any different and bright individuals probably wonder what is wrong with me.

Sample two consists of ten nurses who were randomly selected from a public health unit of fifty nurses. Each nurse in sample two was interviewed. Accordingly ninety percent of the nurses in this sample said: "I have come to expect less of myself because of the work situation." Eighty percent said: "The administrative way of handling things is the key to the loss of personal respect." Ninety percent of the individuals in sample two said: "Morale at the unit is low." Fifty percent said: "I have experienced a loss of morale since I started the work." Fifty percent reported a loss of motivation to continue in the work which suggests, according to the broad definition of burnout mentioned previously, at least fifty percent of sample two have experienced/are experiencing burnout.

I have experienced a loss of morale since I started the work because the administrative policies have inhibited me from doing what I consider to be my professional role.

Low morale is a function of the person's expectancies that they bring to the work not being fulfilled. Young nurses are hardest hit because of the way the administration loads demands on them.

I feel worn out and totally frustrated with the work situation. I get up in the morning and wonder how I am going to get through another boring day. The whole day is meaningless for me.

Low morale comes from within the nurse: a general life situation, self-fulfilling prophecy and a tendency to focus on the negatives and not positives in the work.

My efficiency has been lowered because of the frustration I experience and verbalize at the unit. Because of my high profile, the administration squashes me at any opportunity which does not leave me feeling very good.

Low morale is a problem and has become progressively worse since a major change in senior management.

Low morale is a function of not having a permanent supervisor on our team. Supervisors are key people with regard to morale at the unit. If we get a permanent supervisor who can stay healthy, we will stay healthy.

It is interesting to speculate why individuals in sample one when asked about low morale responded utilizing the term *burnout,* yet individuals in sample two did not utilize the term in response to low morale questions. Perhaps, burnout rates and durations are greater in sample two, relative to sample one, and this data suggests the utilization of defense mechanisms. Lack of reference to *burnout* by individuals in sample two may be a function of defense because a poor intraorganizational environment which is not supportive of helper well-being may influence the nurses to believe, as a survival mechanism, that their well-being and the quality of service they provide is not substantially affected in a deleterious way.

Interestingly, individuals in samples one and two differ markedly with regard to their perceptions of what factors cause burnout or low morale. Individuals in sample one perceived burnout to be caused predominantly by "personal factors," and second, by "person/situation factors." Factors mentioned were: seeing the negative effects of mistakes, compensation for the lack of gratification in personal life, unrealistic expectations of what the job should be offering, a lack of awareness with regard to bureaucracies, a function of me, and no win situations and personal biography. Other factors were: personal values/expectations incongruent with organizational values/expectations, lack of challenge and boredom with the work and driving themselves into the work instead of taking time to invest in themselves.

In contrast with the individuals in sample one, nurses in sample two perceived low morale to be caused predominantly by "intraorganizational factors," and second, by "personal factors." These factors were: a major change in senior management, not having a permanent supervisor on the team, administrative policies, the work situation, frustrations experienced at the unit, a self-fulfilling prophecy from within the nurse and a tendency to focus on negatives not positives.

Perhaps it is reasonable to assume that some perceived causes of burnout or low morale (e.g., intraorganizational factors) are related positively to iatrogenic behavior for some individuals. The bridge I want to build here is between iatrogenic behavior and how intraorganizational processes can encourage/discourage iatrogenic behavior. This is not to suggest naively that iatrogenic behavior occurs only as a result of intraorganizational processes, rather intraorganizational processes may be mediating iatrogenic behavior more so than other factors in the organizational situations under consideration: personal factors, interorganizational factors, societal factors and their interactions.

Intraorganizational processes for sample one probably tend to discourage the development of iatrogenic behavior. Ninety percent of the nurses in sample one indicated that the resources for coping with job stress on both a formal and informal basis are superb. "The work environment is super; good staff-management relations; good supervisory support; an open-door directorship; and a terrific collegial support system." All individuals in sample one thought "The communication between the decision-makers and the front line workers is good. The efforts made by the management to keep the nurses informed of decision-making processes are good." "I think there has been an improvement in communication during the last few years. Specifically, the management has persisted with regular meetings for communication purposes (e.g., providing information on decisions and the rationale for these decisions)." Processes occurring in the work groups are relevant as intraorganizational processes. "Our group philosophy is that primary needs of group members should be met before any individual can be effective in community work. If you go into the community when your needs are not fulfilled, you may do more damage than good." This information indicates concern for helper well-being. Nurse participation in decision-making processes is actively sought. "Although the director has the final say, she seeks advice from supervisors who relay information on decisions-in-process to the nurses, and the director asks for our input." "Front-line workers can participate with the administration in decision-making processes in several ways: planning committees, record committees, co-ordinators meetings and in meetings with supervisors." All nurses in sample one said that "...working in public health allows the expression of personal/professional values that are important in the context of a job." Although these processes are likely to discourage *entrenched burnout* and iatrogenic behavior, the health unit's progressive philosophy might encourage burnout and in some cases iatrogenic behavior.

Part of what may encourage burnout and possibly iatrogenic behavior was cited by one nurse:

> High personal expectations in a progressive environment can cause difficulties. My expectations and experience make me vulnerable because the administration is so progressive and asks me about taking on new obligations. When I am not reinforced for saying no to the administration, I end up draining myself.

To summarize, burnout occurring for nurses in sample one is probably encouraged by the unit's *progressive orientation* toward health care combined with *high personal expectations.* Once the individual is entrenched in the burnout process, perhaps then the unit's progressiveness and time pressures in the work encourage iatrogenic behavior. In contrast, burnout and iatrogenic behavior are likely discouraged because of the concern for staff well-being, excellent support systems, good communication processes and staff involvement in the decision-making processes.

> The reason why burnout rates are not high, at the unit, is because of the excellent support systems. Different groups offer different levels of caring about helpers, though these differentials in caring may not affect the well-being of helpers because of the excellent management and collegial support systems.

Individuals in sample two experienced different interorganizational processes which may encourage burnout and iatrogenic behavior. According to all the nurses in sample two (100 percent), "The lack of a formal support system contributes to poor working conditions." Good communication processes, a component of a *healthy* support system, are almost nonexistent. "Communication between the staff and management is poor. Furthermore, the communication between the staff and the region (Medical Officer of Health and the board) is poor to nonexistent," according to all the nurses in sample two.

> Even with the support of the supervisor, the Medical Officer of Health has the final say and often does not communicate with the nurses about the decision. It seems like decisions are made magically without input from the

nurses. The director does not communicate with the nurses because of her heavy workload. Communicating with the hierarchy is problematic because we have to go through the nurse-management committee. Rapport between the nurses and management is poor; consequently, it is difficult to keep up with changes in policy.

This data suggests that management's orientation toward the staff does not facilitate staff well-being.

Ninety percent of the nurses said the administration gave out few positive reactions and were quick to give out negative ones if an incident occurred. All individuals in sample two said: "The administration functions autocratically." Ninety percent of nurses in sample two said, "No input is sought from the nurses for policy-making decisions, individual preferences for participation in programs, assessing visiting priorities in the community, new programming or the reorganization of existing programming."

According to all the individuals in sample two: "A number of administrative expectations make the working conditions poor." These expectations were: rules about how the work was to be done and not to be done, thus, you were not utilizing your knowledge; nurses were expected to be good at all work obligations, consequently individual strengths and weaknesses were not recognized; monthly visiting quotas; setting priorities; and carrying out obligations that were in conflict with, and sometimes went against, community needs." Most staff nurses responded to the work situation in similar ways. Ninety percent of the nurses ignored the administration. When they could not ignore the administration, they were frustrated and angry. One individual, or ten percent of sample two, ignored the administration. All nurses stated that when the "administration is confronted on any issue, nothing changes." Intraorganizational processes have an impact on the facilitation/inhibition of personal/professional values in the context of a job. Ninety percent of the nurses in sample two thought their value expression was inhibited due to lack of time and the way in which the administration structured the job. Ten percent of the nurses, or one individual, thought that the job allowed for the expression of personal/professional values in the context of a job. According to ninety percent of the nurses, their values/principles had shifted since their student days, because they expected less of themselves "due to frustration with the work situation."

Clearly, individuals in sample two inhabit an intraorganizational environment which is not constructive to the facilitation of their well-being. One assertion, which stems from the data, is that a poor intraorganizational environment encourages *entrenched burnout* and iatrogenic behavior.

My message is one which expresses concern for the well-being of helpers in human service organizations and how the level of *helper well-being* has direct impact on the well-being of community members. Demand for health and social service work likely will continue to escalate in the 1980s which means the workload demands and associated pressures likely will increase demands on helping resources. To facilitate the well-being of helpers in organizational settings and to minimize the development of iatrogenics, it may be worthwhile giving consideration to intraorganizational processes. Intraorganizational processes deserve the attention and corresponding action of those individuals holding the "political purse strings" in the health and social service system because the well-being of directors, supervisors and primary helpers has important implications for the levels of burnout and iatrogenic behavior occurring; and ultimately for the well-being of community members.

BIBLIOGRAPHY

Buber, M. *I and Thou*. New York: Charles Scribers and Sons, 1955.

Cherniss, C., E. Egnatios, S. Wacker and B. O'Dowd. The professional mystique and burnout in public sector professionals. In *Social Policy*. New York: Praeger, 1981.

Freudenberger, H. J. Burn-out: Occupational hazard of the child care worker. *Child Care Quarterly* 6 (1977):90-99.

Fromm, E. *Escape From Freedom*. New York: Rinehart, 1939.

Gergen, K. *The Concept of Self*. New York: Holt, Rinehart & Winston, 1971.

Helmer, D. J. Burnout, Job Stress, and Job Satisfaction in Public Health Nursing. Master's thesis, Wilfrid Laurier University, Waterloo, Ontario, 1980.

Howard, J., D. Cunningham and P. Rechnitzer. *Rusting Out, Burning Out, Bowing Out*. Toronto: *Financial Post*, 1978.

Kahn, R. Job burnout: prevention and remedies. *Public Welfare* 36 (1978):60-63.

Kemp, B. J. Personal communication with Carol Vash, 1977. In *The*

Burnt-Out Administrator. New York: Springer Pub. Co., 1980.

Maslach, C. The client role in staff burnout. *Journal of Social Issues* 34 (1978):111-124.

Maslach, C. and S. E. Jackson. *The Measurement of Burnout*. Berkeley: University of California, 1978.

Mitchell, M. D. Consultant burnout. In *The Annual Handbook for Group Facilitators 1977*, edited by J. Jones and J. Pfieffer, 143-146. San Diego, Calif.: University Associates, 1977.

Pines, A. and C. Maslach. Characteristics of staff burnout in mental health settings. *Hospital and Community Psychiatry* 29 (1978):233-237.

Rogers, C. A. A theory of therapy, personality and interpersonal relationships, as developed in the client centered framework. In *Psychology: a study of a science*. Vol. 3, edited by S. Kotch. New York: McGraw-Hill, 1959.

Vash, C. *The Burnt-Out Administrator*. New York: Springer Pub. Co., 1980.

ROBERT F. MORGAN

28

Community Dispersion or Problem Resolution?: Plight of the Community Residential Appendicitis Patients

The following has been attributed to Petronius Arbiter, 210 B.C.: "We trained hard. . . . . but it seemed that every time we were beginning to form up into teams we would be reorganized . . . I was to learn later in life that we tend to meet any new situation by reorganizing; and a wonderful method it can be for creating the illusion of progress while producing confusion, inefficiency, and demoralization" (Gee 1976). A modern bumper sticker says it more succinctly: "Confusion is its own reward." **R.F.M.**

Maybe it was the right decision for the wrong reasons.

Whatever the rationale, Governor Reagan of California and others launched the new wave of institutional economy back in the 1970s by closing down the large treatment institutions or trimming their budgets as much as possible. The subsequent savings were supposed to follow the clients into the community, but by the time several layers of government had been navigated there wasn't much left. As part of this wave, all across North America, institutional (costly) services gave way to community based care. In some places, the care was excellent; in others, it was nonexistent (Morgan 1981; Morgan and Wilson 1983).

The concept of least restrictive care within one's own community is both valid and important. As the years rolled by, more good than harm was done in following its path. On the way, some important cautions had to be heeded:

Were there some expensive services needed for a fairly small group of clients which could *not* be reproduced in every community? Was there a role for the diminished institutions in moving from custodial/iatrogenic care to innovative/model-change agent? In the push for community dispersal of clients classified as retarded or disordered, was the responsibility of returning them to normal (or superior) functioning being lost in the push for new geography? Had the defeatism of the old institution traveled along with the exodus to the community, leading to steady-state placement expectations? To what extent was community placement being used as a political or economic scam to mask substantially reduced funding for crucial services?

Here is a hypothetical case. Suppose appendicitis were considered to be an incurable condition. While many at one time died of it, modern medicine developed a powerful blend of chemotherapy maintenance and humanistic milieu to allow appendicitis patients to keep their inflamed appendix with dignity. Across the continent, specialized appendicitis wards sprang up in every major, most medium and a few minor hospitals. Appendicitis (much like mental retardation) was erroneously considered something with which one had to learn to live. Then the appendicitis patients organized; Community Residential Appendicitis Patients, Inc. was formed. Soon residential patients were moving into co-operative housing in the neighborhood community, still buttressed by drugs killing pain and reducing inflammation. As part of the new self-help consciousness, special personalized rigs and pulleys were provided so residential appendicitis patients could enjoy sex without putting strain on the abdomen. Annual conventions and competitions became part of the social fabric of the new common (but proud) identity of the appendicitis handicapped; university programs evolved from the disorder and theses were written tracing its history; a specialized magazine with centerfold was circulated to the new group; one female member became a horizontal starlet, pulleys and all. But in the midst of the growing social identity nexus, a lone institution announced this simple cure: "Let's take *out* the appendix!"

By all means: least restrictive community care. The least restrictive return to the community is to leave behind the disability. That will take much work, substantial resources and, minimally, a desire to do so.

BIBLIOGRAPHY

Gee, D. G. Petronius Arbiter. Unpublished paper. Ottawa, Ontario, 1976.

Morgan, R. F. *Interventions in Applied Gerontology*. Dubuque, Iowa: Kendall/Hunt, 1981.

Morgan, R. F. and J. Wilson. *Growing Younger*. New York: Stein and Day, 1983.

GEOFFREY NELSON

29

Community Psychology and the Schools: From Iatrogenic Illness to Prevention

Geoff Nelson is one of the leaders and key historians of the community psychology movement in Canada. His active and varied exchange/consultation/prevention programs within community school systems have gone far to set successful examples for a professional milieu which only recently has begun to develop its applied capabilities. Once a clinical psychologist, Nelson now co-ordinates the field-based practica for graduate training in social-community psychology at Wilfrid Laurier University, and personally participates in an innovative school exchange program which shares career roles with a nonacademic school psychologist administrator. Nelson typifies a fresh generation of competent clinicians who shift ever more of their productive time from treatment to prevention, from disease model to health model. The following comprehensive chapter specifically was developed for this handbook to delineate the present *state of the art,* based on the key premise that prevention may be conceptualized as iatrogenics inside out. This last chapter perhaps best describes where we stand now and where we must go next.   **R.F.M.**

Introduction

Iatrogenic illness, as we have read throughout this book, is a term that has been coined to describe the phenomenon of a client seeking the help of a professional to remedy a problem, but the *helping* response of the professional creates a new problem for the client over and above the one for which the client sought help. That is, as a result of the professional intervention, the client is worse off than before. Popular clichés are used to describe this phenomenon. "The cure was worse than the illness." "The operation was a success but the patient died." For the most part, the term *iatrogenic illness* has been used in the context of a medical, defect-rehabilitation model in which the problems of a client are treated by a professional helper. The etymology of the word *iatrogenic* is found in two Greek words: *iatros,* the physician or healer, and *genesis,* creation or origination.

I would like to thank Jim Dudeck, Bruce Tefft and Richard Walsh for their helpful comments on an earlier draft. I would also like to thank Helen Macnaughton for typing this chapter.

Thus, *iatrogenic illness* is a somewhat paradoxical term meaning illness that is created by the healer.

Moving beyond the doctor-patient relationship, one can view a style of service delivery, an organization, or a society as healers, or conversely, as sources of iatrogenic illness. Thus, social institutions that are designed to help people may, in fact, exacerbate the problems of individuals or create new problems. Viewed this way, the concept of iatrogenic illness can be useful in the context of prevention, as well as treatment. In the public health model of primary prevention (Caplan 1964), one must first determine harmful environmental influences and then remove them or build adaptive host resistances to decrease the incidence (number of new cases) of a problem in a given population. In this model, harmful environmental influences can be regarded as sources of iatrogenic illness. In this respect, prevention is the antithesis to iatrogenic illness.

A Conceptual Framework For Examining Iatrogenic Illness and Prevention

In this chapter, I shall examine the concepts of iatrogenic illness and prevention in the context of one of society's major institutions, the schools. Before beginning this review, however, I shall outline a conceptual framework for examining iatrogenic illness and prevention in the context of the schools. The field of community psychology has been very much concerned with preventive intervention in the schools. As consultants engaged in changing school environments to prevent problems, community psychologists have used different conceptual models to guide their efforts. Currently, there are three major concepts that are seen to be important for various types of intervention in the schools: the ecological perspective, empowerment and multiple levels of analysis.

The Ecological Perspective
The ecological perspective, which is borrowed from biology, emphasizes the interaction between persons and their environments. According to this perspective, problems arise when resources are not appropriately matched with human needs. Therefore, to prevent problems, one must determine adaptive *fits* or *matches* between persons and their environments.

The ecological perspective in community psychology, which has been advanced primarily by James Kelly, emphasizes that the relationships between persons and various aspects of their environments are complex and continually changing. Trickett, Kelly and Todd (1972) have argued that the rational, problem-solving model of prevention developed in public health has been oversimplified in its application to mental health problems. One cannot simply try to identify *the* cause of a problem and then remove it. In the mental health field, there are often many interacting causes of a mental health problem and many equally viable methods of treating or preventing the problem. While there are certainly general factors that uniformly have either a positive or negative influence on everyone's mental health, it is also often the case that different factors affect different individuals in different ways. People who experience stressful life events can grow from their experiences as well as suffer. Also, the potential destructive influence of a stressful life event can be magnified by the presence of other stressors or nullified by the coping skills of the individual or the presence of social and economic supports and resources (see Dohrenwend & Dohrewend 1974).

Trickett, Kelly and Todd (1972) have outlined four general ecological principles for preventive interventions in the schools.

The principle of interdependence—According to this principle, the various subunits in an ecological system are interrelated. Thus, changing one part of the system will result in changes in other parts of the system. The implication of this principle is that it is necessary to have a thorough understanding of the system before attempting to change it. This should include an historical understanding of the setting. Too often psychologists intervene prematurely or without sufficient knowledge of the potential outcomes of the intervention. Such interventions often end up creating new problems or recreating past problems, as Sarason (1971, 1972) has pointed out so well. Thus, the principle of interdependence suggests that it is important to anticipate side effects of one's intervention so as not to create iatrogenic illness.

The principle of cycling of resources—This principle refers to how resources are defined, distributed and used in a system. Knowing what resources are available and how those in a setting view these resources and use them is important for any prevention program. Matching resources to identified needs is essential for preventive interventions. Conversely, when resources are needed, but are unavailable, socially induced iatrogenic illness may result.

The principle of adaptation—This principle emphasizes that environments make demands on people to which they must adapt. As was mentioned previously, adaptation is viewed as a function of both the person and the environment. Those espousing an ecological perspective do not view differences in adaptation between people as defects judged against a single standard. To the contrary, they acknowledge and value diversity in persons and their environments (Gordon & Shipman 1979; Rappaport 1977). Thus, differences can be viewed as adaptive or maladaptive depending upon the situational context and the values of the observer. Therefore, iatrogenic illness may develop as a result of labeling a behavior pattern as *maladaptive* or an individual as *dysfunctional.*

The principle of dynamic equilibrium and succession—This principle emphasizes that persons and environments are constantly changing. Furthermore, the notion of succession suggest that preventive interventions cannot merely solve current problems but that they must enable individuals and their communities to meet the future demands of a changing environment. Thus, preventive interventions require a long-term time perspective according to this principle.

The ecological perspective is currently the dominant paradigm for community psychology (Holahan & Spearly 1980; Rappaport 1977). Furthermore, the ecological principles described by Trickett, Kelly and Todd (1972) can be used for the design and evaluation of preventive interventions in the schools. Failure to take these principles into account in planning change may unintentionally lead to iatrogenic illness.

Empowerment

Another important concept for examining prevention and iatrogenic illness in the schools is that of *empowerment*. In his review of Western medicine, Illich (1976) argues that modern health systems are a major source of iatrogenic illness. In spite of technological advances in the treatment of diseases, iatrogenesis is built into modern medical systems, according to Illich. He explains this paradox by asserting that the public has become increasingly dependent on professional experts and less responsible for their own health. In this way, the medical professions have become more powerful, and the domain of health has become medicalized so that more and more conditions are seen to be indicative of illness requiring professional intervention. As a consequence, citizens feel less power, control and responsibility over their own lives.

The national community mental health program in the United States provides a good illustration of Illich's arguments. As considerable sums of federal money have gone into training mental health professionals and providing nation-wide community mental health services, more disorders of mental health are being *discovered*. The current psychiatric classification system (DSM-III) has cast a broad net over a variety of behavior patterns that are now considered to be abnormal (e.g., shyness in childhood). While mental health professionals have profited considerably (in terms of money, power, status, etc.) from this movement, there is no evidence that this expensive national program has improved the mental health of the public (Chu & Trotter 1972). To the contrary, the mental health system can be viewed as an agency of social control of *deviants,* who lack personal, political and economic power.

The remedy for iatrogenic illness, according to Illich, is to restore " . . . those conditions that endow individuals, families and neighborhoods with control over their own internal states and over their milieu" (1976, 121). Similarly, Rappaport (1981) refers to attempts to help people control their own lives as *empowerment*. This concept of empowerment has become a focal point for community psychology. The growth of self-help programs and natural support systems has been seen as important for the promotion of mental health and the prevention of problems (Gottlieb 1979). Moreover, consultation theorists, operating from the diverse models of community mental health (Caplan 1970), organization development (Schmuck & Runkel 1977) and social action (Alinsky 1946), all seek to empower their clients, be they individuals, organizations or communities. These theorists all emphasize that a consultant is a facilitator who helps people to solve their own problems, rather than an expert who tries to solve people's problems for them. Furthermore, a successful consultative intervention is deemed to be one which leaves the client and setting with skills, programs or power that persist after the consultant has left the scene. In summary, empowerment is an important concept for preventive interventions as an antidote to iatrogenic illness.

Multiple Levels of Analysis

A final important conceptual consideration is that iatrogenic illness and preventive interventions can be examined from several levels of analysis. Illich (1976) has examined iatrogenic illness in terms of clinical, social and cultural levels of analysis. Similarly, community psychologists have conceptualized their interventions in terms of different levels of analysis (Rappaport 1977). Mental health consultation focuses on the individual and small group levels of analysis, as does the medical model. However, the mental health model seeks to help natural caregivers help their clients, while the medical model emphasizes a direct treatment approach. Organization development is concerned with creating new programs or changing existing programs to better meet the needs of both clients and staff. Finally, social action seeks to redistribute resources and power within a community through organization of the poor and powerless.

The essential elements of these models of consultation are presented in table 1. The models differ from one another in terms of the temporal point of intervention. Primary prevention stops problems before they get started. Secondary prevention involves detection and effective treatment of a problem in its early stages. Tertiary prevention emphasizes treatment and rehabilitation to reduce the negative effects of an established problem.

In summary, the concepts of the ecological perspective, empowerment and multiple levels of analysis have been outlined as a framework for examining iatrogenic illness and preventive interventions in the schools. In the next section, research on interventions in the schools will be reviewed. Following the models presented in table 1, the review will consider separately interventions within different levels of analysis: individual-small group, program-organizational and social-community.

Levels of Analysis and Intervention in the Schools

Individual-Small Group Level

For the most part, psychology and other helping professions have focused their attention and efforts on exceptional children in the schools. Children who do not function well academically or emotionally are assessed to determine what personal or small group characteristics may be responsible for their problems. Either internal factors (e.g., genetic, organic or intrapsychic) or small group factors (e.g., family, peer group, teacher-child relationship) are seen to be the cause of the child's behavioral or learning problems. Intervention strategies are usually aimed at modifying the behavior of the individual or the small group so that the exceptional child becomes more *normal* and fits into the existing school system.

Table 1: Models of School Intervention

	Medical Model	Community Mental Health Model	Organization Development Model	Social Action Model
Level of Analysis	Individual-small group	Individual-small group	Program-organizational	Social-community
Target Population	Children who are referred for help	Problem children in the school	Entire class-rooms or schools	Groups of community citizens
Inter-vention Goals	Alleviation and cure of individual problems	Improving the functioning of children by improving the skills of caregivers (i.e., parents, teachers, non-professionals)	Improving organ-izational climate and morale by improving com-munication, decision-making processes and individual competencies	Development of community competencies and control through re-distribution of power and resources
Level of Prevention	Tertiary	Secondary	Primary	Primary
Roles and Methods of the Consultant	Diagnosis, therapy, referral	Early identi-fication, mental health consultation, supervision, program plan-ning and evaluation	Organizational diagnosis and group process facilitation, program plan-ning and evaluation	Systems critic, advo-cate, policy analyst and researcher

Behavior problems of children in the schools—There is a large body of research indicating that a significant percentage of children experience school adaptation problems. Based on a review of twenty-seven studies, Glidewell and Swallow (1969) estimated that approximately 30 percent of all elementary school children suffer school adaptation problems, while 10 percent require immediate help because of the severity of their problems. Moreover, rates of maladaptation have been estimated as high as 70 percent in one inner-city school system in Chicago (Kellam, Branch, Agrawal & Ensminger 1975).

Furthermore, it has been shown that the need for mental health and special educational services far exceeds their availability. It has been estimated that less than 30 percent of school-aged children receive the help they need (Joint Commission on Mental Health of Children 1970). Similarly, studies reviewed by Trickett, Kelly and Todd (1972) showed that professional mental health services both in and outside the school are insufficient to deal with the problems of high school students. Manpower studies have consistently found that there are simply not enough applied psychologists in either Canada (Arthur 1971) or the United States (Albee

1959) to treat all children in schools who need help, nor will there be enough in the future.

Thus, substantial numbers of children in our public schools have significant problems in adaptation and do not receive professional help for these problems. What are the consequences of this neglect? Many studies have found that there are normal *behavior problems* of childhood (see Clarizio & McCoy 1976). That is, many children display certain behavioral problems that are specific to a developmental phase and which are outgrown in time (e.g., fears, temper tantrums). On the other hand, many studies which have identified children displaying deviant behavior in their early years of school have shown that sizeable percentages of these children (roughly 30 percent) continue to have significant problems during their adolescent and adult life (Gersten, Langner, Eisenberg, Simcha-Fagan & McCarthy, 1976; Robins 1966). Antisocial behavior (Gersten et al. 1976; Loeber 1982; Robins 1979) and, to a lesser extent, social isolation (Combs & Slaby 1977; Rinn and Markle 1979) appear to be particularly significant risk factors for adult mental health problems. Also, children who have multiple problems and severe problems appear to have the greatest difficulty later in life (Clarizio & McCoy 1976).

Finally, research has underscored the importance of the child's immediate environment in the maintenance and, sometimes, the development of behavioral problems (Hetherington & Martin 1979). While there are often various intrapersonal causes of children's learning or emotional difficulties, the child's significant others (parents, teachers, etc.) can usually help or exacerbate the problem through their reactions. For example, in the case of antisocial behavior in children, Patterson's (1976) research has shown how the social environment can increase or decrease this behavior depending upon the contingencies of reinforcement and punishment. He uses the term *coercive interactions* to describe and to explain the manner in which antisocial behavior in children and parental and/or teacher management styles are mutually maintained in dysfunctional family and/or school systems.

The medical model — Historically, helping professionals in the schools have worked within a medical model framework. Within this model, school psychologists have typically assumed three general roles: diagnostician, therapist and referral agent. If a child is experiencing behavioral and/or learning problems in school, the first step in the medical model is to obtain an accurate diagnosis of the problem. Then the child can receive appropriate treatment or be referred elsewhere for such treatment (e.g., a special class or an agency which can provide specialized help). On the surface, this seems to be a sensible approach and undoubtedly it is worthwhile in many cases. However, even if this model is properly applied, it has serious shortcomings as a general approach to remedying children's school adaptation difficulties. In a recent article, Albee (1980) argued that in promoting an ideology of "blaming the victim" (Ryan 1971), the medical model is *evil:* a source of iatrogenic illness. Theorists who view a child's family, peer group or culture as primarily responsible for the child's lack of success in school are usually considered to be more liberal in their views than those who espouse an organic perspective. However, Ryan (1971) argues that in ignoring the larger social-political context of children who fail in school, such theorists continue to perpetuate the victim blaming ideology. To determine if, in fact, the medical model is a source of iatrogenic illness as Albee has claimed, it is necessary to examine the consequences of this model for the practice of psychology in the schools.

The practice of the medical model in the schools does not adequately take into account the previously outlined ecological principles for the design of preventive programs. First, the medical model ignores the principle of interdependence by attempting to remove problems from their natural context. One-to-one therapy or remedial help on a once-a-week basis in the guidance or resource office, or in the more remote mental health clinic, is used to *fix* the dysfunctional child. Unfortunately, as was discussed in the previous section, the parent and teacher can play a pivotal role in the child's maladaptation. Thus, many school psychologists and special educators have had the experience of moving a *problem* child from his regular class to a special class, only to find that a new *problem* child often pops up in the same regular class. Failing to deal with the contribution of the teacher or the classroom system to behavioral deviance can perpetuate the creation of special education candidates.

This leads into another problem regarding the principle of adaptation. Failure to adapt to the classroom or school is viewed as the child's problem within a medical model framework. Thus, diagnosis tends to focus on characteristics of the child (e.g., dull, normal intelligence, hyperactive, etc.), rather than on the child in relation to his/her environmental context. While proper diagnosis leads to a cure of the child's problems in school adaptation in some cases, many writers have pointed out that there are also negative aspects to the labeling process. Goldstein, Arkell, Ashcroft, Hurley and Lilly (1975) have summarized several of the main arguments against labeling practices in the schools. First, there is the problem of overgeneralization. Diagnostic labels are often inferred from one behavior rather than several different aspects of functioning. Judged against one single standard, children given the same label are expected to be very similar. In reality, however, there is considerable behavioral and intellectual diversity within such categories, and labeled children can also share much in common with nonlabeled *normal* children. Thus, for example, the term *the six-hour retarded child* has been coined to refer to the child who has scored very low on an intelligence (IQ) test at school, but who is very socially competent and adapts well outside the school environment. A related concern is that labels become reified in such a way that teachers come to believe that *behavioral disorders* and *mental retardation* really exist (Szasz 1961), when in fact, labels are merely concepts or metaphors that are used to describe various aspects of an individual's functioning. An unfortunate consequence of this type of thinking is that teachers may come to interpret other aspects of the child's behavior in terms of the label and to find pathology simply because they have been cued to look for it. While the evidence is far from clear, there is some indication that labeling can create a self-fulfilling prophecy and stigmatize the child (Hobbs 1975). The classic study by Rosenthal and Jacobson (1968) demonstrated that labels can affect teachers' expectancies and behavior toward children in such a way as to modify the child's behavior to conform with the label. While the results of this study have been criticized, Seaver (1973) has recently documented the effects of teacher expectancies on children's academic performance.

Another negative aspect of labeling is that most professional diagnostic systems are pathology-oriented. Elaborate methods of describing and defining children's weaknesses have been devised, while little attention has been paid to assessing children's strengths and competencies or characteristics of environments that foster competence or incompetence (Cowen 1977). These labels smack of *name calling* and often serve the purpose of blaming the child for his problems, rather than examining the child in the context of the teacher-student relationship, the school, the community, etc. Such labels often imply pathological and unalterable dead-end states, thus instilling a defeatist philosophy (Morgan 1978) and removing responsibility for education from the teacher and the school. Indeed, IQ, achievement and psychiatric assessment methods are so broad-band (general) and have such low-fidelity (predictive utility) that they seldom provide teachers with useful information for educational programing. More often, such assessments are used to segregate special education students, who are frequently poor or minority group students, from the regular stream of education. Once in the special education track, it is difficult to get out of it.

With regard to the principle of cycling resources, the evidence reviewed earlier indicates that professional resources are not plentiful enough to meet the needs of all children requiring help. Any school psychologist who has had to cope with the overwhelming caseload demands of serving several schools; who has felt the frustration of referring a family to another agency for help only to encounter a waiting list of several months; or who has seen the family drop out of therapy for whatever reason will recognize the truth in this statement. With this myopic view of appropriate resources, many children must go without the help they need.

Finally, with regard to the principle of succession, the medical model emphasis on *curing* the child seems inappropriate. Many exceptional children require continuous input and environmental support to insure their adaptation to school. Traditional therapies that remove the child from his natural context are often not sufficient to create meaningful and long-lasting improvement for the child. In his review of the literature, Levitt (1971) argued that there is no solid evidence to support the effectiveness of traditional therapies delivered by child guidance clinic professionals for emotionally troubled youngsters.

In terms of the concept of empowerment, the medical model emphasizes that there are clear differences in status and power between professionals and their clients. Rather than focusing on collaboration and mutual problem-solving, the professional functions as an expert who diagnoses the problem and makes recommendations. Thus, parents and teachers are taught to rely on the judgments of professionals, to whom they send their hyperactive or learning disabled children for brain scans, intellectual assessments, play therapy, etc. The nature of this professional assessment and intervention process encourages parents and teachers to seek magic solutions.

In summary, the evidence presented in this section shows that the medical model does not take into account ecological principles, nor does it emphasize the concept of empowerment. In failing to do so, the medical model has many shortcomings as a style of service delivery for the schools. The question remains as to whether the medical model is a source of iatrogenic illness, as Albee (1980) has claimed. Without a doubt, the medical model approach helps some children. On the other hand, professionally delivered, person-centered interventions do not always help children, nor are there enough professionals to meet the needs of all children with problems.

If the medical model is the exclusive approach to school intervention and there are no other attempts to change the social and organizational conditions that may give rise to children's behavior problems, then the model is a source of iatrogenic illness. Labeling a behavior pattern as a problem without providing a program to deal with that problem is a serious disservice to the client. This process draws attention to the negative or problematic aspects of the child and can lead to a self-fulfilling prophecy that the child will always be a problem. If such self-fulfilling prophecies occur, and there is some evidence that they do (Hobbs 1975), then the medical model style of service delivery is a source of iatrogenic illness.

The community mental health model—A viable alternative to the medical model with prospects for prevention is the community mental health model. While this model is similar to the medical model in its focus on the exceptional individual or the individual in the context of small groups (e.g., the family, peers, teacher-student, etc.), it differs in several important respects. Rather than blaming the child, this model adheres to the principle of interdependence by looking at the interaction between the child and his significant others as the root of many childhood problems. Thus, the intervenor works in an indirect consultative or mental health *quarterback* role to improve the skills of mediators (parents, teachers, nonprofessional helpers, etc.) to help the child, rather than directly intervening in a therapeutic role, as in the medical model. That is, the professional consultant attempts to empower the consultees to better deal with their problems.

Also, rather than passively waiting for cases to be referred, the community mental health consultant often actively seeks to identify *high risk* children early. Thus, the community mental health model is often aimed at secondary prevention, early detection of problems and prevention ("nipping the problem in the bud"), whereas the medical model focuses on tertiary prevention, rehabilitation of well-established problems. This future-oriented, preventive focus acknowledges the principle of succession.

In their review article on intervention programs in elementary schools, Levine and Graziano (1972) point out that many of the *innovative* roles and activities of psychologists working within the community mental health model can be traced back to the work of psychologists at the turn of the century. For example, Lightner Witmer established the first psychoeducational clinic in North America in Pennsylvania in 1896. In Witmer's clinic, psychologists functioned primarily as consultants and had a strong intervention orientation. These pioneers were concerned with developing a range of special services geared to the needs of children.

Present day community mental health consultants have engaged in a variety of activities in schools (Bardon 1976; Gallessich 1974). While psychodiagnostics has not been eliminated, it certainly has been deemphasized. When assessments are done, the utility of the information for instructional programing has been stressed. Variously referred to as psychoeducational, problem-solving or behavioral assessment (Berger 1979; Brooks 1979; Ross 1980), this approach focuses more on behaviors and learning styles than on traits and on strengths as well as weaknesses. Thus, this approach to assessment is essentially idiographic (situation specific) as opposed to nomothetic (general). It is concerned with tailor-making an intervention to meet the needs of the individual child, rather than with affixing the global, trait labels that are characteristic of medical model practice. Finally, assessment focuses on the role of the environment, as well as the child's personal characteristics, in shaping the child's adaptation. Consistent with the principle of adaptation then, the aim of diagnosis in the community mental health model is to find the appropriate niche for the child in his school environment.

In the community mental health model, the intervenor follows the general principle of consultation to teach others to do rather than doing oneself. Thus, the consultant works through other professionals or nonprofessionals who are significantly related to the child to effect change in the child. Much has been written about theories and methods of consultation (Altrocchi 1972; Caplan 1970; Goodstein 1978; O'Neill & Trickett 1982). These writers have consistently emphasized the need for the consultant to develop a trusting, collaborative relationship with the consultee. Caution has also been raised about being clear about issues and potential pitfalls involved in different phases of the consultative intervention (Cherniss 1976). Successful consultative programs to the schools have noted the importance of informal and formal aspects of the working relationship between the consultant and consultee and have recommended practical guidelines for the practice of mental health consultation in the schools (Allen, Chinsky, Larcen, Lochman & Selinger 1976; Mannarino & Durlak 1980). Finally, research on many different types of consultative interventions with different types of organizations has generally indicated the positive effects of consultation on the consultee, client or the system (Mannino & Shore 1975).

In the school setting, many consultation programs have been aimed at improving the child management styles of teachers and/or parents in order to change children's maladaptive behavior. Behavior modification and communication-relationship approaches have been the most widely used models for teacher and parent training in child management. In the area of teacher training, a considerable amount of research has demonstrated the effectiveness of training teachers to use behavior modification techniques to improve the problem behavior of elementary school children (O'Leary & O'Leary 1976). Such consultative programs have been delivered on both an individual basis and in a small group workshop format. A noteworthy example of the group workshop approach is one of the programs described by Allen et al. (1976) in the multifaceted preventive program they developed for one school. They found that teachers trained in behavior modification skills successfully improved the on-task work behavior of targeted disruptive children in their classrooms, whereas the behaviors of disruptive children of untrained teachers did not improve. Furthermore, the newly acquired skills of trained teachers generalized to nontargeted children. Another study has shown that teachers who have been trained in a behavior modification approach to child management can successfully train other teachers so they have a significant impact on their students (Jones, Fremouw & Carples 1977). Moreover, serving as a trainer of new teachers resulted in further decreases in the disruptive behavior of their own students. This is an excellent example of the principle of cycling resources. Similarly, in the area of parent training, both behavior modification and relationship-communication approaches to child management have been taught to parents in either a group or individual format and have been found to improve the problem behavior of maladapting children (Bernal, Kinnert & Schultz 1980; Reisinger, Ora & Frangia 1976; Tavormina 1974).

Other school intervention programs have used nonprofessionals as companions and change agents for young children experiencing school adaptation problems, while mental health professionals have functioned in the roles of trainer, supervisor and program evaluator. Working within an early detection and secondary prevention model, these programs have used mass screening and assertive case-finding procedures to identify children's problems early on. These programs have varied widely in terms of the nonprofessional helpers used, the training and supervision they receive, and the target population with whom they work (Zax & Specter 1974). Overall, research has not only clearly indicated the effectiveness of these nonprofessional helpers (Karlsruher 1974), but it has also shown that they are at least as effective and are sometimes more effective than professionals (Durlak 1979). These findings underscore attention to the principle of cycling resources.

Secondary prevention programs have successfully used retired people, alienated high school students, university students and mothers to geometrically expand helping resources to children. Thus, many more needy children can be reached using this approach than can be reached from a service delivery system based on the medical model. Nonprofessionals are usually selected on the basis of their interpersonal skills, motivation and enthusiasm, which is usually assessed through an interview or some type of role-play in a group interaction (Dooley 1980). Programs often differ widely in the amount of training and supervision that is provided. Some programs provide minimal training based on the belief that nonprofessionals have natural helping skills that might be lost if the nonprofessional were molded into a professional helping style. Other programs provide very specific and intensive training in helping skills, such as behavior modification (Balch & Solomon 1976).

The Primary Mental Health Project developed by Emory Cowen and his colleagues (Cowen, Trost, Lorion, Dorr, Izzo & Isaacson 1975) has been a model of research and program development using nonprofessionals as companions for maladapting primary grade children that has been widely disseminated and adopted across North America (Cowen, Davidson & Gesten 1980). Their evaluations have shown that mother aides are successful in improving the behavior of shy/anxious children, but less successful with antisocial children (Cowen, Gesten & Wilson 1979). While the natural helping characteristics of mother aides (i.e., warmth, acceptance, etc.) may be appropriate for shy/anxious children, they have found that training either mothers (Cowen, Orgel, Gesten & Wilson 1979) or alienated high school students (Tefft & Kloba 1981) in a more behavioral, action-oriented approach is necessary to improve the behavior of antisocial children.

Other programs have demonstrated the effectiveness of nonprofessionals training maladapting children in social skills on a small group basis (Bry & George 1980; Durlak 1977; Kirschenbaum, De Voge, Marsh & Steffen 1980). Moreover, two recent studies have shown the superiority of a behavior modification as opposed to relationship approach to social skills training for young children (Durlak 1980; LaGreca & Santogrossi 1980). While there is scanty evidence regarding the importance of supervision, one study has found that supervised university students were significantly more effective than unsupervised university students acting as companions to maladapting elementary school children (Karlsruher 1976).

In terms of the ecological principles, the community mental health model is an improvement over the medical model, but it is also not without problems. Regarding the principle of interdependence, the interaction of the student with his/her peers, teachers and parents is emphasized. However, the larger social context of the child's behavior is ignored. Many children with academic and social behavior problems live in poverty, and more fundamental social changes may be needed to address these difficulties. Furthermore, the context of the mediators, parents and teachers is often ignored. Many parents and teachers may have the skills needed to help children, but they may be under such stress themselves or be so lacking in support that they cannot effectively put their skills into action.

The community mental health model has an expanded view of helping resources. With professional psychologists working as consultants, program supervisors and evaluators, while teachers, parents, peers and nonprofessionals do the front-line intervention work, many needy children can be reached. While there is a positive cycling of resources in this model, there remains a focus on labeling problem children and removing them from normal activities for special help. Identifying children thought to be *at risk* for future problems may have the same negative consequences as the medical model practice of diagnosing pathology. Furthermore, with large-scale screenings, many more children than usual will be labeled, and there will be a considerable error rate in such screenings since many children do outgrow early problems. On the other hand, if screening is not done, many children whose problems persist would not be identified and helped early. This is certainly not an easy dilemma to resolve, but it may be better to identify the needs of *all* children rather than classifying children as *adapting* or *maladapting.*

In terms of the principle of succession, the research reviewed suggests that programs produce positive changes in children with behavioral problems and that these changes endure for at least follow-up periods of up to one year. Further research is needed to determine the long-term secondary preventive effects of these programs and the most appropriate match between types of children and the characteristics of helpers and intervention strategies.

With regard to the concept of empowerment, the community mental health model empowers natural custodians to help children, rather than empowering children to help themselves. Thus, as in the medical model, there remains a difference in power between the helper and the helpee. The problem that can arise with this approach is that the consultees may learn new and better ways to control their clients, rather than helping the clients to realize their own goals. Winnett and Winkler (1972) noted this potential for abuse in their review of teaching behavior modification techniques to teachers. They found that teachers were often using these techniques to render their students "still, quiet, and docile."

In summary, while the community mental health model is an improvement on the medical model in some respects, it also shares some of the same problems. The community mental health model extends the reach of the professional, thus, there is the potential for more people to be helped but also for more people to be harmed. Illich (1976) refers to the identification of *high-risk* populations and prevention programs as "medical imperialism." Professionals are essentially marketing their product in attempting to persuade others that they need parent or teacher effectiveness programs or that children who are acting up or who are not interacting socially much in the early grades need social skills training. In this approach, the professional, not the consumer, ascertains the need. In this way, iatrogenic illness may result from the dependence of a large clientele ("everybody needs therapy") on professionals, which undermines the clients' sense of self-efficacy.

Program-Organizational Level

Traditionally, psychology as a discipline has emphasized the study of the individual. Consequently, most psychologists' involvement with the schools to date has focused on the individual or small group level of analysis (Levine & Levine 1970). Even the more innovative secondary prevention programs described in the previous section maintain a person-centered as opposed to systems-centred focus. Using Ryan's (1971) concept of exceptionalism versus universalism, most school psychology programs, as well as those of other helping services, attempt to improve the behavior of exceptional children. An alternative is to focus on the school or classroom as an organization to meet the needs of all children (a universal focus). Attempting to change the school as a system to reduce the problems and promote the adaptation of the entire student population represents a move into the arena of primary prevention.

While this is a praiseworthy goal, it is easier said than done. As Sarason (1971) has pointed out, professional psychologists know little about the culture of the school and the processes by which organizational change is accomplished. While sociologists have studied the characteristics of schools as organizations for some time, theory and research on how the school as an organization relates to the needs of students for socialization, academic learning, and psychological well-being is in its early stages of development. Short on such theory and blinded by the traditional focus on the individual, psychologists and other helping professionals who try to effect programmatic changes in the schools often "re-invent the wheel" or create innovation without real change. Without an understanding of the processes by which new programs are created, implemented and maintained, psychologists run the risk that their organizational level interventions will fail (Sarason 1972).

Moos (1973) has described several different ways of conceptualizing human environments. In this section, I will review each of these approaches and illustrate them with research on the schools. Assessment methods and intervention programs derived from each approach will be described. Moreoever, research will be examined to determine characteristics of school environments that are related to either the social or academic growth of students or to student problems in those areas. That is, the review will focus on environmental variables that can potentially prevent problems and promote growth and those variables which may be sources of organizational-induced iatrogenic illness.

Physical-architectural environment—The first method of assessment stems from the field of environmental psychology and focuses on the physical and architectural design of the environment. Trickett, Kelly and Todd (1972) have reviewed several studies which have related the architectural design of the schools to student and faculty interaction rates. For example, one study (Myrick & Marx 1968) found that the separation of vocational and academic classes into separate wings of a high school (for the sake of cutting down noise) actually led to decreased interaction between vocational and more academically-oriented students. Another study (Snyder 1967) found less formal interaction and cohesion when an old high school in a single building was closed and faculty and students moved into a more spacious campus with several small buildings. In terms of the ecological principle of succession, these studies demonstrate that it is important to examine potential negative side effects of interventions that are designed to *improve* the physical environment.

Gump (1980) has recently reviewed the literature on the correlates of traditional enclosed classrooms versus classrooms with an open-space design. Open-space classes are associated with greater physical mobility and social interaction than enclosed classes which are more likely to promote in-seat, on-task behavior. Interestingly, students from higher socioeconomic status (SES) backgrounds show relatively high self-esteem and liking for school in open classrooms, while lower SES students show somewhat lower self-esteem and poorer achievement in such classrooms compared with their peers in traditional classrooms. In a similar vein, O'Neill (1976) found that elementary school girls high in divergent thinking ability had higher self-esteem in open-space classrooms than in traditional classrooms. The self-esteem of girls high in convergent thinking ability was not affected by the type of classroom. Finally, those girls who were low in both divergent and convergent thinking ability had lower self-esteem in open-space classrooms than in traditional classrooms.

The results of this research point to the need for educators and psychologists to consider the *fit* between the student and the environment in planning the architecture of schools. Educational reforms, such as the open-space classroom, that are broadly implemented before they are adequately researched can end up creating as many problems as they solve. Thus, it is important for planners to recognize the ecological principle of adaptation that different types of physical and architectural variables of a setting affect students in various ways.

Behavior settings— A second method of assessment is the behavior settings approach that has been developed by Barker (1968) and his colleagues. The two major components of a behavior setting are a standing or routine pattern of behavior and the physical and temporal aspects of the environment. In a behavior setting, there are certain implicit *rules of the game* for conduct that are demanded by the environment. To a large extent, behavior is dependent on the setting and is independent of the particular persons in the setting. For example, a classroom math lesson or recess on the playground are different behavior settings. In traditional classrooms, there are roughly twenty-five to thirty students, a teacher, desks, various academic materials, etc., and the norms for behavior are quiet seat work, small group work, etc. The playground is a more unstructured environment with a large, open area, some recreational materials (e.g., balls, jungle gyms, etc.), a large number of children and usually only one or two adult supervisors. The norms for behavior are running, playing and other physical activity. These two contrasting behavior settings are associated with different types of behavior, independent of the specific children, teachers or schools in question. For example, Moos (1973) has reviewed evidence that children show much more aggressive behavior in unstructured situations, such as recess, than in structured situations, such as the classroom.

Two areas of research in the schools that have used the behavior settings approach in considering both physical and human components of environments are research on school size and population turnover. Based on their research in high schools, Barker and Gump (1964) have advanced the theory of undermanning. Basically this theory asserts that as the size of an organization increases, there are more individuals available for each behavior setting in the organization. The result of this situation is that students in small schools will experience more invitations and pressure to become involved in and take responsibility for manning different behavior settings (e.g., extracurricular activities) than students in large schools. Thus, students in small schools should experience more activity, involvement and growth, while students in large schools should be less involved and feel more alienated.

The research by Barker and Gump (1964) clearly supports this theory. While there were somewhat more varied activities and classes available in larger schools, students in smaller schools were actually involved in a wider range of activities. Students in smaller schools felt more responsible and were more satisfied with the growth they experienced in meeting challenges, while students in larger schools expressed more vicarious satisfactions (e.g., being in a school with a winning basketball team). Furthermore, academically marginal students in small schools felt more needed and were better integrated than students in larger schools. Gump (1980) reviewed several recent studies of these big school versus small school differences and found that all of these studies have convincingly replicated the initial findings of Barker and Gump (1964).

Kelly (1969, 1979) and his colleagues have studied high school behavior settings in terms of population turnover (proportions of faculty or students entering or leaving the school each year). Schools with high turnover rates were termed fluid environments, while schools with low turnover rates were termed constant environments. Observations revealed that fluid environments were characterized by a high degree of activity, social interaction between groups and individuals, diversity in dress and conduct, etc., while constant environments were more quiet with little permeability of established social groups and a strong emphasis on conformity and privacy. These differences held across a wide variety of behavior settings (e.g., hallways, cafeteria, principal's office, etc.).

Thus, while the physical aspects of the two settings were quite similar, the norms for behavior were significantly influenced by the rate of population turnover. Consistent with the person-environment interaction view of adaptation, Kelly predicted that students with coping styles characterized by exploratory behavior (a preference for experiencing novelty) would adapt better in fluid environments, while those with a low preference for exploration would adapt better in constant environments. This hypothesis was confirmed as students with a high preference for exploration were more likely to be labeled deviant by a faculty in constant environments rather than in fluid environments. However, a recent publication based on this longitudinal research (Edwards & Kelly 1980) has provided only minimal support for the previously mentioned person-environment interaction hypothesis.

Researchers using the behavior settings approach to the assessment of school environments have not discussed the implications of this approach for intervention. However, the research on school size certainly suggests that smaller schools involve a greater cycling of resources than do larger schools. Students are seen as resources which are crucial to the functioning of a smaller school which leads to a greater degree of student involvement. The smaller school as a social unit may be one that empowers students to take more responsibility for their environment, while the larger school, in reducing many students to a spectator role, may be a source of alienation and iatrogenic illness. In terms of Kelly's research on population turnover, the importance of the fit between the person and the environment is again underscored. For some students, a fluid environment may be their best niche, while others may adapt better in a constant environment. Educators and psychologists can potentially prevent problems by finding a positive match between students and school environments. On the other hand, trying to fit all students into the same type of environment may result in the development of iatrogenic illness in some students.

Peer-induced climates—A third approach to environmental assessment involves describing the personal and behavioral characteristics of the inhabitants of the environment (e.g., age, educational level, social skills, social class, etc.). According to this approach, the quality of the environment depends, to a degree, on the types of people who live in that environment. Thus, the environment can be described in terms of the average characteristics of *individual* members. This approach is well illustrated by a recent longitudinal study by Rutter, Maugham, Mortimore and Ouston (1979) of twelve inner city secondary schools in London, England. The primary objective of this study was to identify various aspects of school atmosphere and to determine if these factors were associated with rates of delinquency, school behavioral problems, academic achievement and school attendance over the three-year period in which the students were in secondary school. In an attempt to determine if school atmosphere factors were causally related to the aforementioned outcome variables, the authors measured the following factors prior to the students' entry into secondary school: the students' verbal aptitude, parental occupation and ratings of the students' behavior by their primary school teacher.

The authors were concerned with how the aggregate pre-test data (prior to entering secondary school) for the twelve different schools were related to the outcome variables (assessed during the last year of secondary school). They referred to the composition of the student body upon entering secondary school as the "balance of intake." That is, some schools may have a high percentage of students with low verbal aptitude or a high percentage of students with poor social behavior compared with other schools. In fact, the authors found that several aspects of the balance of intake were significantly related to attendance, achievement and delinquency. For example, schools with relatively higher percentages of students with higher verbal aptitude and higher SES had better rates of attendance than schools with higher percentages of students who were of lower verbal aptitude and lower SES. However, the balance of intake factors were not significantly related to the overall school atmosphere scores. The importance of this finding will be apparent later, when I return to a discussion of this study.

Along the same line, research reviewed by Trickett, Kelly and Todd (1972) has shown that working class students in predominantly middle class SES schools tend to go to university at relatively high rates, whereas middle class students in predominantly working class schools tend to go to university at relatively low rates. Thus, characteristics of the total student body tend to influence the academic and social functioning of individual students.

In terms of interventions based on this approach, psychologists have been involved in designing curricula aimed at promoting the intellectual and social growth of students (Zax & Specter 1974). While the focus is on changing the behavior of individuals, the intervention is aimed at the total population of the classroom or school, not at a select few individuals.

One approach that has received much recent attention seeks to promote the social competence of students. Such interventions seek to develop those skills in children which will hopefully help the children to cope with future interpersonal conflict and life crises in a constructive fashion. This focus on social competence stands in sharp contrast to the traditional emphasis on pathology. Developing social competence in all school children may be a method of primary prevention of school maladaptation.

The first decision point in designing a program to promote social competencies is to decide what competencies will be taught. Unfortunately, while there has been considerable work in defining and classifying pathology, there has been far less research on determining what behaviors are necessary for successful adaptation to different environments. Jahoda (1958) first attempted to grapple with characteristics of positive mental health and outlined several broad traits that she felt were important. Subsequently, behavior-oriented psychologists have emphasized that social skills are generally situation-specific (Van Hasselt, Hersen, Whitehill & Bellack 1979). That is, a social behavior that is adaptive in one situation may not be adaptive in another situation (i.e., the ecological view of adaptation). On the other hand, cognitive-oriented psychologists have argued there are general cognitive problem-solving strategies that are adaptive across many situations (Spivack, Platt & Shure 1976).

Considering the many diverse theoretical views of social competence, it is not surprising that a variety of different methods have been used to assess social competence (e.g., self-report questionnaires, teacher rating scales, sociometric or peer ratings, role-play tests, naturalistic observation and structured problem-solving tests). Asher, Oden and Gottman (1977) have identified several social skills for children that are related to being liked and having friends in school including: responding positively to others, communicating accurately, being very good at something and having skills in initiating a relationship. Moreover, measures of social competence in children have been shown to be inversely related to measures of behavioral maladaptation in school (Gesten 1976; Spivack, Platt & Shure 1976) and to be independent of IQ (Spivack et al. 1976).

The social problem-solving approach to primary prevention has been pioneered by Spivack and Shure (1974). They describe the development of different measures of social problem-solving and they report the results of three programs aimed at teaching such skills to poor inner city preschool children. With an emphasis on teaching ways of thinking rather than *appropriate behaviors,* these programs aim to teach children to think of the consequences of various actions, to understand cause-effect relations, to be able to generate behavioral alternatives to dealing with a problem situation, etc.

In their first study, inner city preschool children were randomly assigned to one of three groups: treatment, attention-placebo and a no treatment control group. Children in the treatment group received daily instruction (five to twenty minute sessions per day) in social problem-solving from university students, while children in the attention-placebo condition played games with the university students for an equivalent amount of time. The results showed that the treatment group improved significantly more than the other two groups on measures of social problem-solving *and* behavioral adaptation, as rated by their preschool teachers who did not know the children's status in the experimental conditions. In the second study, four teachers were trained in the use of the social problem-solving curriculum and then implemented the program with half of their students. Once again, the results showed that the treated children improved significantly more than control children both on measures of problem-solving and teacher ratings of classroom behavioral adaptation.

In the final study, twenty preschool classes in nine inner city schools were randomly assigned to treatment and control groups. The teachers implemented the social problem-solving curriculum over a ten-week period. Again, their results showed that treated children, including those classified as either impulsive or inhibited, improved significantly more. Overall, 36 percent of the trained group were rated as adjusted at pretest, while 71 percent were rated as adjusted at post-test. For the control, 47 percent were rated as adjusted at pretest, while 54 percent were rated as adjusted at post-test. Since both training and the ratings of behavioral adaptation were done by the teachers, there is a possibility of rater bias in the results. However, evidence that such bias was not operating is provided in ratings done by the children's kindergarten teachers, who were unaware of the children's participation in the project. These results indicated that the post-test differences between groups persisted six months after the conclusion of the program.

Independent investigations of the effects of social problem-solving curricula with third and fourth grade children have confirmed Spivack and Shure's (1974) findings that training leads to the acquisition of problem-solving skills (Allen, Chinsky, Larcen, Lochman & Selinger 1976; Weissberg, Gesten, Rapkin, Cowen, Davidson, Flores de Apodaca & McKim 1981). However, these independent investigations have not consistently replicated Spivack and Shure's (1974) findings that problem-solving skill acquisition is associated with improved behavioral adaptation in the classroom (Gesten & Weissberg 1979). Furthermore, there is a need for long-term follow-up of the effects of social problem-solving curricula on children's adaptation.

The work on social skills and social problem-solving training in the classroom is a good illustration of the ecological perspective. In teaching such skills in the classroom, the natural context of the child is emphasized. Thus, the principles of interdependence and adaptation are acknowledged in that student's try out these new skills in conflict situations with each other. Furthermore, resources are cycled so that students who have acquired these skills can be effective in helping other students. Finally, in terms of the principle of succession, the problem-solving framework is one which can be used to deal with future problems of various types.

Organizational structure—A fourth method of conceptualizing school environments is concerned with dimensions of organizational structure, such as decision-making processes, authority and span of control of those in various roles, formal and informal channels of communication, etc. Sarason (1971) and Trickett, Kelly and Todd (1972) have examined the roles of personnel in schools in terms of the potential for organizational innovation and change. Beginning with the role of students, Trickett et al. emphasize that the school is the milieu in which students must accomplish various developmental tasks. For example, high school students struggle with becoming independent, developing opposite sex relationships and deciding on career and vocational plans. They feel that the peer group is an especially potent influence in adolescent development because students are united by the fact that they *must* attend school, but have little power or control over how the school is run.

Within the classroom, the teacher is boss and the teacher may, and many often do, unilaterally make decisions about the constitution of the classroom (e.g., rules for behavior, instructional material to be used, etc.). Teachers often attempt to establish their authority to obtain classroom control and order early in the term. Once classroom order is established, the second priority for the teacher is to teach students the *facts* and to insure that they get the *right* answers, not on helping students to learn how to think (Holt 1964). Students are seldom consulted as to what they would like to learn or the standards for conduct within the classroom that they feel are fair.

Lest the reader think that I am villainizing teachers, the role of the teacher in the classroom vis-à-vis students is determined to a large extent by factors outside of the classroom, as the principle of interdependence would suggest. Establishing tight classroom control is often seen as indicative of a teacher's competence to the principal, other teachers and parents. Also, teachers are under pressure to see that their students attain a certain level of academic achievement within the year's time that the teacher instructs those children. Working alone with a group of at least twenty-five children, all with diverse needs and personalities, for several hours a day, day in and day out, is a difficult job for anyone. Sarason (1971) points out that under these pressures, many teachers experience feelings of inadequacy because they cannot meet the needs of all of their students. Also, teachers who have been teaching for several years often lose their initial enthusiasm, experiencing the effects of routine and boredom in their jobs.

Unfortunately, the school organization can often be a negative influence on teachers that can create iatrogenic illness. First of all, Sarason (1971) has argued that in their teacher training, teachers are usually poorly prepared for life in the classroom. Training tends to be predominantly academic rather than practical in nature, with questionable relevance to managing and teaching a large group of children for a sustained length of time. The situation is even worse in our universities with most university professors having had absolutely *no* preparation for classroom teaching. Thus, just as prospective parents who face the task of child raising without any preparation or education often end up parenting as they were parented, the new teacher often falls back on the experiences of how he/she was taught or on his/her instincts.

Once teachers have started their careers, there is little opportunity for support or continued professional development. Sarason (1971) has argued that "teaching is a lonely profession" even though teachers are surrounded by others all day. In school organizations, there is a low degree of interdependence among teachers, with each teacher operating in his/her own little island. Thus, opportunities for support and sharing of information and feelings among teachers regarding teaching styles, classroom management techniques, etc., is lacking. Furthermore, many teachers feel that they have little power in the system and are seldom consulted about policy changes by the upper echelons of the administration. Not surprisingly, since teachers are often treated as children, they, in turn, often treat their students in the same manner. Sarason (1971) argues that in order for teachers to continue *to give* to their students at a high level requires that they experience *getting* at a high level. Unfortunately, the structure of most professional development programs for teachers consists of isolated one-shot workshops in which some outside expert comes in and makes a presentation to a group of teachers. Sometimes teachers may gain valuable ideas and practical suggestions from these workshops that they can incorporate into their classroom teaching, but more often than not the professional development day is a day of relaxation away from the students. Thus, professional development programs are often wanting because there is no plan or continuity which is needed for teacher growth. Also, these programs are usually held out of the context of the specific schools in which teachers work, so there is no opportunity for organization development.

Turning to the principal, both Sarason (1971) and Trickett et al. (1972) emphasize the importance of the principal's sanction and support for innovation. Trickett et al. (1972) reviewed evidence suggesting that teacher morale and effort are related to a principal's support for innovation within the school. Furthermore, there is some evidence to suggest that the principal's role is more crucial in lower than in higher SES schools.

Being responsible for the management of the school, the principal must mediate between upper level administrators, teachers, students and parents. In higher SES schools, the principal's role may be more of business-like caretaker function, whereas in lower SES schools principals may need to be more skilled in conflict resolution, problem-solving and program planning given the many crises and problems faced by these schools.

Sarason (1971) argues that, like teachers, principals are not well prepared for their jobs. Sarason states that good principals know how to use their power to manipulate *the system* to the advantage of their school. While many good teachers are selected to be principals, being a good teacher does not mean that the individual will have the requisite political and managerial skills for functioning as an educational leader.

Similar leadership skills are required of school superintendents and upper-level administrators. These administrators play key roles in the formation of educational policy and procedure. As is the case with principals, research has shown that the sanction and support of school administrators is crucial for successful organization development and innovation (Fullan, Miles & Taylor 1980).

The role of the school psychologist and other special educators is also shaped by his/her training, interests and skills, and the receptivity of school administrators, principals and teachers to various intervention strategies. Some psychologists are comfortable primarily with testing and thus, school personnel come to expect this and use the school psychologist solely for this purpose. Other psychologists are interested in a broader range of intervention strategies, such as classroom consultation, in-service training, program planning and evaluation, etc. (Bardon 1979; Gallessich 1974). However, some school personnel (from teachers to upper-level administrators and heads of special services) are not interested in these activities and, in some cases, will actively resist their implementation. Headway and change can be made in such circumstances when the psychologist receives strong support from within his/her department, but progress is usually slow. Unlike principals and teachers, school consultants must rely solely on expert and referent power (their professional skills and personal qualities) to effect change (Martin 1978). They are essentially guests in the school. Sarason (1971) has discussed some of the reasons for conflict between special services personnel and school personnel. Thus, like the teacher, the students and others in the school system, the school consultant can feel frustrated that he/she is not being allowed to function in the manner desired because of various organizational constraints.

In terms of interventions based on this organizational structure approach, some psychologists in the schools have turned their attention to interventions aimed at organization development (Medway 1975). Richard Schmuck has been the pioneer in developing and evaluating programs to create organizational change both for the classroom and the total school. Schmuck (1968) has reported the results of two projects aimed specifically at improving group processes and atmosphere at the classroom level. The first study examined the effects of a teacher-development project involving three groups of teachers: a laboratory group ($n = 20$), a seminar group ($n = 20$) and a control group ($n = 10$). The laboratory group received four weeks of intensive training during the summer and follow up bimonthly discussion groups in the fall after their classes had started. The program included sensitivity training, didactic instruction on classroom group processes, problem-solving, analyzing data from their own classrooms, discussing and sharing ideas used by other teachers and role playing. The seminar group did not participate in the summer program, but held weekly seminar meetings during the fall. Their program was similar in format to that of the laboratory group with the exception that it did not include sensitivity training or role playing. The control group received no training.

The dependent measures included self-report questionnaires filled out by students regarding classroom group processes; attitudes toward self, peers, teacher and the school; and observations and diaries kept by the teachers. The data were collected at the beginning of the year, mid-year and at the end of the year. Overall, the results showed that with respect to classroom group processes, the laboratory group was superior, followed by the seminar group, while the control group performed the most poorly. The laboratory trained group tried more innovative plans to improve classroom group processes and achieved better communication than teachers from the other two groups. Similarly, the students of laboratory trained teachers improved significantly more than the students of teachers in the other two groups with respect to perceived influence on the classroom and perceived friendship status within the classroom. Finally, the laboratory trained teachers experienced significantly more feelings of *esprit de corps* in terms of frequent contacts and telephoning one another about professional matters than seminar trained teachers.

A second project described by Schmuck (1968) was aimed at providing support and professional growth for teachers. Six highly trained mental health professionals (two psychiatrists, two clinical psychologists and two social workers) with a psychodynamic orientation worked with forty upper-elementary school teachers in small groups for one-half day per week for fifteen weeks. There was also a control group of twenty teachers. Measures similar to those used in the previous project were collected prior to the beginning of the project in September and after the project had ended in May. The group passed through several phases during the project. Initially, many of the teachers were quite negative and blamed parents, students and administrators for classroom problems. Next, the teachers began to ask the consultants for answers and solutions and, finally, teachers began disclosing their own fears and doubts and turning to one another for support and practical suggestions. The results showed that teachers who received consultation improved significantly more than control teachers on measures of self-concept as a teacher and ways of defining and handling problems in the classroom. However, the program had no significant effect on the students of the project teachers. Unlike the previous project, this project was aimed almost exclusively at dealing with teachers' affect rather than dealing with both teachers' affect and behavior in the classroom via role playing and sensitivity training.

The final project done by Schmuck and his colleagues (Schmuck, Runkel & Langmeyer 1969) involved working with the entire faculty in August prior to the beginning of the school year. The first two days consisted of group exercises and small group discussions aimed at improving the communication skills of the faculty (e.g., self-disclosure, listening, etc.). With this foundation of the importance of effective interpersonal communication, the next four days were spent on organizational problem-solving. First, three general problem areas were identified by the faculty. Next, the faculty formed three groups to tackle each of these problems. Each group was coached in using a problem-solving model which consisted of diagnosing the roots of the problem, brainstorming for solutions, designing a concrete plan of action and implementing the plan with the entire faculty.

In the fall, the project leaders held individual interviews with each faculty member with a focus on unresolved problems. In December, a one and one-half day workshop was held to work on communication between teachers and administrators, and in February a one and one-half day workshop was held to follow up on progress in the three problem areas. The researchers reported both qualitative and quantitative data pertaining to the effects of the project.

Beginning with the qualitative data, nineteen of the fifty-four teachers reported in their fall interviews that they were applying techniques that they had learned in the laboratory to their classes. More of the decision-making power in the school was shifted from administrators to an advisory committee. At the end of the year there was only 3 percent turnover in the faculty, compared with 10 to 16 percent in other junior high schools in the same district. The project leaders were asked to run the laboratory again the following August. First the principal and then six teachers attended workshops run by the National Training Laboratory (NTL), the pioneer group in organization development which was started in 1947 by the well-known applied social psychologist Kurt Lewin and his colleagues. Finally, a new position, consultant on interpersonal relations, was created at the school and, subsequently, several other junior high schools in the area created similar positions.

Turning to the quantitative data, the researchers collected questionnaire data from the teachers early and late in the school year. Furthermore, the same data were collected from six control junior high schools. The results showed that the experimental school improved significantly more than the control schools on several measures. First, teachers in the experimental school reported significantly better feelings about the principal than control teachers. They felt that the principal was easier to get along with, made better decisions, helped facilitate problem-solving in meetings and treated teachers more as professionals. Secondly, experimental teachers reported significantly better feelings about staff meetings than control teachers. Teachers felt they could be more open and deal with problems more completely and they reported more commitment to and satisfaction with the outcome of faculty meetings. Finally, there were significantly more innovations in the experimental school than in the control schools in terms of curriculum changes, new forms of organization and new methods of problem-solving.

Since the initial work, Schmuck and Runkel (1977) and their colleagues have successfully expanded their efforts to working with entire school divisions. In one division, a *cadre* of people within a system were trained in organization development skills (Schmuck 1982). This internal consultation group carries on organizational renewal activities with minimal outside assistance and has been quite successful.

While the work of Schmuck and his colleagues is the most outstanding and best-known application of organization development to the schools, this area of intervention is expanding. In a recent comprehensive review of theory, research and practice of organization development in the schools, Fullan, Miles and Taylor (1980) found numerous studies of such interventions in the schools even though the first applications began as recently as the mid-1960s. While they noted wide diversity in applications of organization development to the schools, Fullan et al. (1980, 135) felt that most of these efforts are captured by the following definition:

> Organization development in school districts is a coherent, systematically-planned, sustained effort at system self-study and improvement, focusing explicitly on change in formal and informal procedures, processes, norms or structures, using behavioral science concepts. The goals of organization development include improving both the quality of life of individuals as well as organizational functioning and performance with a direct or indirect focus on educational issues.

In their review, the authors found that a consistent finding in the literature is that the initial entry and organizational readiness is crucial for the ultimate success of the intervention. Given favorable entry conditions, several well-controlled evaluations have shown that organization development interventions can significantly improve school decision-making processes, teacher morale and, importantly, classroom climate and student morale for follow-up periods of up to one year. The authors conclude that organization development is a useful intervention strategy for school improvement.

The organization development approach clearly follows ecological principles. Communication between administration, teachers and students and the well-being of each of these groups is seen as vital for the functioning of the total school, thus acknowledging the principle of interdependence. Resources are cycled in this approach with everyone being regarded as a potential resource. Matching up the needs of individuals with that of the system is seen as essential for enhancing adaptation. Finally, the research suggests that these interventions can be largely self-sustaining and able to effectively deal with future problems (the principle of succession), if an internal cadre of consultants is formal and trained. In summary, the organization development approach is one that strives to empower the school organization to solve its own problems.

Social climate—Another approach to conceptualizing human environments focuses on social climate. Since the early study by Lewin, Lippitt and White (1939) on the effects of various leadership styles on classroom functioning, there has been a great deal of research on correlates of the social climate of the classroom. In their review of research on classroom group processes, Schmuck and Schmuck (1975) have found that cohesiveness, friendship patterns, communication patterns, group attractiveness and a variety of other variables derived from social psychological theory and research have been shown to be related to measures of self-concept, liking of school, social competence, etc. Trickett and Moos (1973) have developed a standardized questionnaire to measure various aspects of the social climate of high school and junior high school classrooms. Various subscales are used to measure three main dimensions of classroom atmosphere: relationship, personal development and system maintenance and change dimensions.

In an initial study using this scale, Trickett and Moos (1974) found that various aspects of classroom atmosphere were differentially related to various aspects of satisfaction and mood. For example, classroom competition was inversely correlated with satisfaction with school but directly correlated with satisfaction with the amount of material learned. In general, various aspects of the relationship dimension of classroom atmosphere (involvement, affiliation, teacher support) were positively correlated with student satisfaction with the teacher and other students and feelings of security and interest. Another study (Moos & Moos 1978) found these relationship factors to be positively correlated with students' grades. On the other hand, teacher control was found to be negatively correlated with both grades and absenteeism. Similarly, Moos (1978) found that teacher control-oriented classrooms were associated with student dissatisfaction and unhappy moods. Students reported the highest level of satisfaction and the happiest moods in structured affiliation-oriented classrooms and supportive competition-oriented classrooms. Using observational measures, Kaye, Trickett and Quinlan (1976) found that high-support classes, as measured by the Moos' scale, were characterized by more frequent teacher praise and use of student ideas than low-support classrooms. Similarly, high-control classrooms were characterized by less teacher praise and student-talk initiations than low-control classrooms.

In general then, classrooms providing support and structure are associated with more positive social-emotional outcomes in students than classrooms emphasizing teacher control and task orientation. However, some studies have also suggested the importance of person-environment interactions in this area of research. For example, Harpin and Sandler (1979) examined the role of a personality variable (internal versus external locus of control) and an environmental variable (high- versus low-control classrooms) in the social and academic adaptation of junior high school students. They found that internal boys had higher grades in low-control than in high-control classrooms, but external boys showed more behavioral maladaptation in low-control than in high-control classrooms.

One major longitudinal study introduced earlier (Rutter et al. 1979) has attempted to measure aspects of the atmosphere of the total school and to relate them to measures of students' academic, behavioral and social adaptation. The researchers measured these factors through observations, interviews with staff and questionnaries for students. The results showed that these measures of school atmosphere and the *balance of intake* factors were strongly related to the four outcome measures: delinquency rates, behavioral adaptation, academic achievement and school attendance. Furthermore, the school atmosphere and balance of intake factors were relatively independent of one another.

Several aspects of school atmosphere were either positively or negatively related to the outcome variables. Students adapted better to schools with a strong academic emphasis. Indexes of academic emphasis were the total amount of time spent teaching, departmental or group curriculum planning, assigning homework and displaying students' work on the walls. Also important were teachers' actions during class lessons. Starting class on time, spending lengthy time on the lesson and spending time working with the whole group was associated with good outcomes. High levels of teacher praise were associated with positive student behavior, while frequent disciplinary interventions and use of corporal punishment were associated with behavioral problems. Other factors that were associated with positive outcomes are as follows: good care and condition of the school, schools in which students felt they could approach teachers with a problem, schools which encouraged student responsibility and participation, schools with low teacher turnover rates, schools where teachers were involved in curriculum planning and schools with experienced teachers. The researchers selected the thirty-nine school atmosphere items which were significantly associated with one or more of the outcome variables and ranked each of the schools on these factors. They then totaled these rank scores to produce one score for each school. The overall school atmosphere score was found to be significantly and highly correlated with each of the outcome variables: behavior ($r = .92$), achievement ($r = .76$), attendance ($r = .65$) and delinquency ($r = .68$). Thus, research has clearly shown that various aspects of classroom and school atmosphere are related to students' academic and behavioral adaptation to school.

In terms of intervention, there has been a great deal of research examining the effects of group process techniques designed to alter the social climate of the classroom. One approach has been to develop a co-operative and supportive atmosphere by increasing student interdependence in the classroom. Small groups of students are given structured academic tasks which require co-operation, and the groups are rewarded for the achievement of the group, not the individual. This type of intervention has been implemented by many investigators using different techniques, but the results across studies are very consistent. Compared with approaches which emphasize competition or individualized instruction, the co-operation approach produces superior academic achievement. Moreover, students exposed to the co-operative approach show increased self-esteem, capacity to take the role of others, liking and willingness to learn from others, decreased racial prejudice, etc. (Gump 1980; Johnson, Maruyama, Johnson, Nelson & Skon 1981; Slavin & DeVries 1979). Thus, many benefits can accrue from this emphasis on teamwork.

In terms of ecological principles, interdependence between students is the key to a co-operative classroom atmosphere. Cycling of resources occurs with teamwork and peer tutoring. Research has shown that adaptation of the student is a function of the interaction between student characteristics and the climate of the classroom.

Applied behavior analysis—The applied behavior analysis approach describes the environment in terms of contingencies of reinforcement and punishment. Derived from operant conditioning, this method has had widespread use in research on classroom management. Research on classrooms (O'Leary & O'Leary 1976) has consistently shown that teacher praise and other positive consequences for appropriate academic and social behavior in children results in increased frequency of those behaviors. On the other hand, criticism and reprimands for inappropriate behavior often leads to increased frequency of those behaviors. On a larger scale, the results of the Rutter et al. (1979) study are consistent with these findings. Thus, teacher attention, whether positive or negative, is usually a potent source of reinforcement for students' classroom behavior. The expression "spare the rod and spoil the child" definitely does not stand up to behavior modification research on classroom and family management. Unfortunately, research indicates that rates of teacher praise for appropriate student behavior is low (O'Leary & O'Leary 1976; Rutter et al. 1979). More frequently, teachers attend to students when they are not working or are misbehaving.

There has been a great deal of research on behavior modification interventions in the classroom. Much of this research has focused on training teachers to modify the behavior of a target child who was selected because he/she displayed some type of problem in the classroom. However, in some programs, teachers have used behavior modification strategies (e.g., contingent use of teacher attention, token economy) to improve the behavior of all students in a classroom (O'Leary & O'Leary 1976). Other studies have shown that group contingencies for the behavior of an entire class are at least as effective as individual contingencies in improving students' academic and social behavior in the classroom (Hayes 1976; Litow & Pumroy 1975).

An excellent example of the application of the behavior modification approach to management of the classroom as a whole is a recent large-scale study by Greenwood, Hops, Walker, Guild, Stokes, Young, Keleman and Willardson (1979). A total of fifty primary grade classes (grades one to three) were randomly assigned to an experimental program or a control condition. A group of consultants (resource teachers and guidance counselors) were trained to implement the program. Teachers were then trained by the consultants over six two-hour meetings in a standardized classroom management program that included instruction in the contingent use of teacher attention, behavioral assessment, posting rules for classroom behavior, consequences for group behavior, etc. Consultants then followed up with a total of seventeen visits to each classroom to facilitate implementation of the program. The results showed significant increases in teachers' use of praise, significant increases in appropriate social and academic behaviors for the students and slightly better achievement for experimental than control classrooms. Moreover, the students, teachers and consultants were highly satisfied with the program, so much so that the majority of the teachers continued to use all aspects of the program during the next school year.

This approach emphasizes the interdependence of teacher and student behavior and uses contingency management to improve student adaptation. Resources are cycled in that students learn to reinforce themselves and other students. In line with the principle of succession, students learn new skills that hopefully become self-reinforcing so that these skills will prove useful in future situations.

Summary—The research reviewed in this section has shown that several different conceptual approaches to describing and intervening at the programorganizational level in schools can improve the organizational structure of classrooms and schools, the competence and coping skills of teachers and students and person-environment matching for enhanced school adaptation. That organizational intervention in the schools is fertile ground for primary prevention is further underscored by its consistency with the ecological principles outlined earlier. In its focus on the classroom or school as a system, organization development recognizes the principle of interdependence. Thus, improvement in faculty group functioning can lead to improvements in classroom functioning which, in turn, can have beneficial outcomes for individual teachers and students. Secondly, with its emphasis on the need for school and classroom systems to solve their own problems, such interventions use the principle of cycling of resources in a positive way. That is, everyone in the system is a potential helper and helpee. This orientation then emphasizes the need for mutual help and resource exchange (Nelson, Bennett, Dudeck & Mason 1982). Regarding the principle of adaptation, organizational interventions have been shown to be sensitive to the need for determining adaptive person-environment fits. Finally, the organizational interventions described are consistent with the principle of succession in their emphasis on promoting competence and problem-solving skills within students, teachers, classrooms and schools to anticipate and positively cope with future environmental changes and problems.

Furthermore, the ultimate goal of the organizational level interventions reviewed is to empower the organization and the people in it to solve their own problems. Thus, preventive interventions at this level are an antidote to organizationally-induced iatrogenic illness.

There are also limitations to organizational interventions in the schools. Many school problems that administrators, teachers and students experience arise outside of the school. Thus, there is a need to examine the school in its larger social and community context. The underlying values of organizational interventions are such that the structure of society is unquestioned. The focus is on dysfunctional institutions, rather than underlying social structures. Institutions, such as schools, are seen to be in need of reform. The means and ends of achieving reform emphasize co-operation, consensus and democracy.

In focusing on the school as a closed system, organizational interventions ignore the interdependence of schools with larger social structures. Organizational level analysis is an important but incomplete representation of schooling. Failure to incorporate an analysis of social structure can lead to interventions that produce a new set of problems. For example, teaching students how to co-operate may be dysfunctional if the economic environment which they enter upon graduation is one that emphasizes competition for scarce jobs.

Social-Community Level

Schooling takes place in a social and community context. In this section, I will discuss how the larger social context influences schooling and possible preventive interventions at this level of analysis.

Socioeconomic status and school adaptation—In assessing school problems at the social-community level, an important relationship to consider is that between SES and school adaptation. Research in Canada (Martell 1974) and the United States (Coleman et al. 1966; Jencks 1972) has consistently shown students' educational achievement to be positively related to their family's SES. Jencks (1972) reported that using a combined index of father's occupation and income, the correlation between SES and educational achievement has consistently been found to be about .55 throughout the first half of the twentieth century. Similarly, low SES children are more prone to social and emotional problems at school, early school dropout and problems with the law and criminal justice system than high SES children (Joint Commission on Mental Health of Children 1970). Likewise, research has consistently shown SES to be inversely related to the incidence of social and emotional problems for adults (e.g., Dohrenwend & Dohrenwend 1969). Thus, it is clear that children's problems in school adaptation are significantly related to their family's SES.

While there is little disagreement about the empirical relationship between poverty and school adaptation, there is considerable disagreement and controversy in both the helping professions and the public about the *interpretation* of this relationship. That is, the theoretical explanations that have been invoked to explain this relationship reflect diverse values and belief systems about the nature of man, such as conservative versus liberal ideologies, the heredity versus environment debate, etc. This controversy is not simply an abstract philosophical debate. Quite to the contrary, the theoretical view to which one adheres on this issue has profound consequences for policies and interventions regarding schooling which ultimately have an impact on families and children. In this section, I will present the major explanations for the SES-school adaptation relationship.

Ryan (1971) and Dokecki, Strain, Bernal, Brown and Robinson (1975) have both presented excellent reviews of the major explanations of the SES-school adaptation relationship. These explanations can be covered under three general categories. The first explanation is the racial and genetic inferiority hypothesis. Basically this hypothesis asserts that lower-class students adapt poorly to school because they have poor genetic potential for learning. There is a natural selection process operating in society based on the notion of survival of the fittest, such that the strong naturally rise to the top of the SES ladder while the genetically weak and inferior drift to the bottom of the ladder. What is the evidence in support of this hypothesis? The evidence is far from clear and has been subject to widely different interpretations and conclusions. Much of the controversy has focused on the heritability of IQ scores. Researchers and the public tend to look for evidence to support their ideology. Thus, conservatives seek to find evidence for the genetic influences on IQ, where liberals look for environmental influences.

While it is well beyond the scope of this chapter of review the IQ controversy, several important points must be briefly noted. The first point concerns the measurement of intelligence. One misconception about IQ tests that most researchers do agree on is that IQ tests do *not* measure genetic potential and capacity; they measure learning. This learning may reflect genetic and environmental influences, but the IQ test score should be treated as a broad-band index of learning and not as a reification of something called intelligence. Secondly, the learning content sampled on IQ tests consists mainly of verbal and arithmetic skills, skills in logical reasoning, etc., which are learned in school and reflect middle-class culture. Attainment of these skills is important for adaptation and survival in school and middle-class life, but it may be irrelevant for survival and adaptation to nonwhite, lower-class environments. Skills for adaptation in these latter environments are simply not sampled on IQ tests.

Given this qualification about traditional measures of intelligence, research regarding the heritability of IQ scores has been of sufficiently poor quality that it is subject to widely divergent conclusions. Jensen (1969) has argued that 80 percent of the variance in IQ scores can be accounted for by genes, while Jencks (1972) has argued that the figure is more in the neighborhood of 45 percent. On the other hand, in a thorough methodological critique and review of studies purporting to demonstrate genetic influences on IQ, Kamin (1974, 176) came to the following conclusion:

> Where the data are at best ambiguous, and where environment is clearly shown to have an effect, the assumption of genetic determination of I.Q. variation in any degree is unwarranted. The prudent conclusion seems clear. There are no data sufficient for us to reject the hypothesis that differences in the way people answer the questions asked by testers are determined by their palpably different life experiences.

Indeed, some of the strongest evidence for the genetic influences on IQ is provided in the studies by Sir Cyril Burt, whose data have been recently shown to be fraudulent (McAskie 1978).

A second hypothesis regarding the SES-school adaptation relationship focuses on cultural deprivation and the culture of poverty. According to this view, poor families have a deviant set of values that are passed on from generation to generation which impede the poor from striving for success and pulling themselves up by their bootstraps into the mainstream of society. According to this view, poor children do not adapt well to school because they are unmotivated and have been deprived of middle-class experiences. Thus, as Ryan (1971) notes, poor children are not innately inferior but functionally inferior because of poor home upbringing.

There are several problems with this viewpoint. First of all, this view stresses that there is only one standard of adaptation, that based on middle-class values and competencies. When individuals from poor families or different cultures do not attain the standard, the failure to adapt is seen to be the problem of the individual, not of the standard. Thus, differences are seen as deficits, and the strengths of the individual or the culture are ignored. Poor children are seen as poorly prepared for the middle-class orientation of the school, according to this view. The school is never seen as being poorly prepared to deal with the different culture of the children. Thus, the cultural deprivation hypothesis is antithetical to the ecological view of adaptation. A second problem is that empirical evidence challenges the belief that poor people are poorly motivated for educational success. Research has shown that poor and working class families have high aspirations for their children and place considerable emphasis on having them succeed in school (Ryan 1971; Sennett & Cobb 1973).

A final problem with this viewpoint is that poor children's frustration with school, their lack of motivation and the external locus of control and apathy of poor families is not considered in its social and community context. The fact that there may be institutional constraints on the aspirations of poor people (i.e., striving is punished and not reinforced) is ignored. Thus, this viewpoint fails to understand the behavior of the poor in terms of its larger social and community context.

The final hypothesis regarding the SES-school adaptation relationship focuses on society and its institutions. According to this viewpoint, the educational system is a reflection of society (Hyman 1979). On the surface, Canadian and American societies are based on the noble values of freedom, justice, equality of opportunity, democracy, etc. However these values are merely symbolic platitudes that serve to obscure the fact that there is tremendous social and economic inequality in society according to Edelman (1977). The majority of the wealth and means of production in Canada and the U.S. is concentrated in the hands of a small, corporate ruling class. This elite class is concerned with promoting their economic self-interests and maintaining the present social class structure that is based on social and economic inequality. While Marx argued that economic oppression would serve to unite the working class who would then revolt and overthrow the corporate elite, his prediction has not been born out in Canada and the U.S. Some have argued that this is because the working class and middle class enjoy a relatively high standard of living (i.e., they have been bought off).

Others, such as Apple (1980) and Sennett and Cobb (1973), have argued that this materialist view that the relative economic affluence of the working class is the cause of the perpetuation of the class system in North America is oversimplified. They have presented a social psychological model of class that places a heavy emphasis on the role of the educational system in this process. According to their view, the educational system mirrors society in its emphasis on competition and survival of the fittest. The function of schooling then is to serve corporate interests by maintaining the class structure. Hence, schools are "rigged" to maintain a class structure that separates *winners* from *losers*. This is achieved through an emphasis on competition, streaming into different academic tracks, promotion versus nonpromotion policies, grading practices and standardized testing programs that define students' performance in terms of a normal distribution curve, grouping and ranking practices, the informal groups and cliques that develop among students, etc.

A key element in Sennett and Cobb's (1973) model is the influences of schooling in socializing children. Children are taught to accept the authority of people of a higher educational and social class level (i.e., their teachers) as legitimate. These authority figures then have the right to judge them (through grading and promotion decisions, etc.). These agents of socialization instill a myth of opportunity. That is, if one works hard and excels, then one will be rewarded by moving up the SES ladder. Thus, education is the great equalizer. Therefore, a child's sense of self-worth is contingent upon his/her ability to prove himself/herself. If the child fails to achieve, according to the judgment of school authorities, then that child can only blame himself/herself, not the system.

In this manner, schools by and large maintain children within their parents' SES level and create acquiescence in children in accepting the legitimacy of the school system. The myth that education gives all students an equal chance to succeed is a lie. Since schools emphasize middle-class values and competencies, middle-class children enter school with a great edge over lower-class children. These differences are then reinforced in school and the differences in achievement and adaptation widen as children progress through the grades. When poor children fail to learn school content at the same rate as their middle-class peers, they receive negative feedback from their teachers and begin to react with disruptive behavior and injured self-esteem. Rather than viewing such behavior as stemming from poor family functioning or inadequate social skills, as the typical school consultant would, Sennett and Cobb (1973) view this behavior as rebellion against an unjust class system. This rebellion is often suppressed as children accept their teachers' judgments that they must be placed in a lower stream or special class. However, there are hidden injuries of such practices on the dignity and self-esteem of these children, according to Sennett and Cobb (1973).

Kohl (1967) who taught poor black children at the elementary level in Harlem described the reaction of his students when he explained to them how standardized tests and the resultant bell-shaped curve of test scores would determine their academic placement for the next year. When presented with the *rules of the game* in such an honest and straightforward manner, these young children reacted with outrage. The class then decided that they wanted to practice doing these tests so they could do their best, and they ended up scoring fairly highly for students in that ghetto school. While the notion of practicing clearly violated the rules for standardized testing, it is obvious that middle-class children receive practice on similar tasks at home that typically give them the edge over lower-class students in testing situations.

In their interviews with working-class men, Sennett and Cobb (1973) found that these men who had not attained a high level of education made considerable sacrifices so that their children could gain the education that they did not obtain. When the children of these men did not show great interest or inclination to school and academics, these men felt betrayed and their dignity was further injured. Attempting to gain dignity by vicariously living through their children was not successful.

In summary, different explanations for the fact that poor children tend not to adapt well to school have been presented and discussed. In the next sections, I will discuss the implications of these hypotheses for action consequences.

Victim blaming interventions—The racial and genetic inferiority and cultural deprivation hypotheses regarding the SES-school adaptation relationship share the ideology of *blaming the victim*. That is, the individual child is held responsible for his or her failure to adapt to school, whether the causal factor for this failure is seen to be organic-constitutional (within the child) or familial-cultural (within the child's immediate environment). Ryan (1971) has argued that whereas the racial and genetic inferiority hypothesis was the commonplace explanation for the SES-school adaptation relationship in the past, the cultural deprivation hypothesis is currently in ascendency. For example, this viewpoint is underscored in Jencks' (1972, 141) influential report in the U.S.:

> ... Cultural attitudes, values and taste for schooling play an even larger role than aptitude and money. Even if a middle-class child does not enjoy school, he evidently assumes that he will have to stay in school for a long time. Children with working-class parents or lower-class parents evidently assume that if they dislike school they can and should drop out. As we shall see, students who plan to drop out usually assume they will have to take low-status jobs. But such jobs evidently seem more acceptable to working-class students than to most upper-middle-class children. This suggests that if we want to equalize the educational attainment of children from different economic backgrounds, we will probably have to change not only their test scores and financial resources, but also their attitudes and values.

A similar ideology is reflected in the Hall-Dennis Report in Ontario, Canada which was written around the same time as Jenck's report in the U.S. (see Martell 1974).

The consequence of these two *victim blaming* hypotheses for school intervention practice within a medical model framework. Earlier I criticized the medical model, assuming that its intentions for helping are benevolent, but arguing that its practices are inadequate and ineffective. I will outline here the concerns of critics who have challenged the supposed benevolence of helping professionals working within a medical model framework (Edelman 1977). These critics argue that it is necessary to examine the social, political and historical context of medical model diagnostics and therapy in order to understand the latent as well as the manifest functions of such practice. While the manifest function of the medical model is to cure problems, the latent function, it is argued, is justification and maintenance of social and economic inequality. That is, the medical model is based on the conservative philosophy that individuals are responsible for their problems and must change to adapt to social conditions. Thus, maintenance of the status quo and survival of the fittest are key themes.

Within this framework, individual differences involving poor intellectual, academic or behavioral functioning are labeled defects. Several writers (Blanton 1975; Hobbs 1975; Levine & Levine 1970; Rhodes & Sager 1975) have studied such labeling practices for school children from a historical perspective. They have shown that in the past the labeling of school adaptation problems has led to the separation and exclusion of *problem children* from the mainstream of education. Rather than providing effective treatment that would enable the student to return to his/her normal environment, these alternative residential and institutional programs often had negative effects on their clients (Hobbs 1975). The development of these medical model practices were closely tied with the philosophy of Social Darwinism and the eugenics movement shortly after the turn of the century. That is, the growth of the helping professions was associated with the perceived need to protect society from the unfit. The problems of poor, immigrant children were believed to be caused by their racial and genetic inferiority, and the helping professions became society's agents to control these subgroups.

Under the guise of science, I.Q. tests (Kamin 1974) and achievement tests (Levine 1976) were used by psychologists to justify policies of exclusion and institutionalization, compulsory sterilization of the mentally retarded, immigration quotas for persons of certain nationalities, etc. The feeble-minded, lazy, insane and incorrigible now became the mentally retarded, the slow learner, the mentally ill and the delinquent with the advent of these new professions. While the scientific weaknesses of psychological and psychiatric diagnostic methods are manifold, it is only recently that these limitations have been strongly acknowledged (Phillips, Draguns & Bartlett 1975). As psychiatry, psychology and social work became established as professions, they became firmly entrenched in the medical model and began to concentrate their efforts on *treatable* middle-class problems to the neglect of the often more needy lower-class children. Such classic studies as that conducted by Hollingshead and Redlich (1958) have shown that lower-class children who need the most help usually get the least help or help of the poorest quality. Even recent studies, such as the Nader report on the supposedly *progressive* national community mental health centers program in the U.S. (Chu & Trotter 1974), have shown a perpetuation of the two-class system of care (one for the affluent and one for the poor) and a solidification of medical model practice under the guise of *community mental health*. "Old wine in new bottles" is the phrase that aptly describes this movement that has furthered professional self-interests without significantly changing the nation's mental health. Similar differences in funding for education exist between middle-class and poor communities. Thus, the best teachers usually end up teaching in middle-class schools. The stressors on teachers working in ghetto schools have been well described by teachers who have taught in tough inner city schools in Boston (Kozol 1967), New York (Kohl 1967) and Toronto (McLaren 1980).

In its emphasis on genetic inheritance, the racial and genetic inferiority hypothesis inspires a fatalistic attitude. Medical model practices derived from this hypothesis have ranged from actively destructive policies (e.g., compulsory sterilization) to policies of benign neglect. However, medical model and, to some extent, community mental health policies based on the cultural deprivation and culture of poverty hypothesis have been even more insidious. The action implication from this hypothesis is to modify the values and enhance the competence of poor children, and, if possible, their parents, to more of a middle-class orientation.

The major policy initiative based on this line of thinking has been preschool education programs for poor children. In the U.S., the nation-wide Head Start program, which has been so popular and resilient that it has escaped even the tight, budget-cutting administrations of Nixon, Ford and Reagan, has been the premier example of this paradigm. Rappaport (1977) thoroughly reviewed the research on these preschool intervention programs and found that controlled studies showed academic and intellectual gains for children who participated in the program relative to control children who did not participate in the program. However, while these gains were evident when the Head Start children first entered elementary school, they gradually vanished as the children moved through the elementary grades. Rappaport (1977) argued that these gains were lost because such programs are based on the faulty premise of the paradigm that these children needed to be culturally and academically enriched. In Rappaport's (1977) estimation, the school institutions need to be changed as well as the children in order for such gains to be maintained.

Similar criticisms can be leveled at primary and secondary prevention programs aimed at developing the social skills of elementary school children. From a radical viewpoint, such programs establish compliance, deference to authority and appropriate middle-class etiquette that obscures class conflict and social and economic inequality. This viewpoint is well stated by Martell (1974, 16) in the following passage:

> The essence of the approach is contained in what might be termed a policy of "state therapy," in which the velvet glove of the government psychologist and social worker provides a cover for the older iron fist of the police and the army. At its centre lie the ideas you find in Hall-Dennis: that this is a society without classes, without inherent conflict of interest between the ruled and the rulers, a society in which individual growth can flourish, provided there is sufficient "communication" between the corporations, the government, and the people. The solution to any problem lies in our capacity to talk about it, openly and warmly. For each of us, personal happiness lies just around the corner. And it's up to each of us, as individuals, to make that potential happiness come true, with a little help from our shrink or our social worker.

In summary, the medical model practices that stem from the victim blaming hypotheses, whether they emphasize organic or cultural factors to explain the SES-school adaptation relationship, are pathogenic. Thus, such policies that are institutionalized at the social and community level of analysis are a source of iatrogenic illness.

Social action interventions—The third hypothesis implicates social and community systemic factors in poor children's difficulties in adapting to school. According to this view, problems arise in poor communities because people lack money and power, or, to use Ryan's (1971) terms, *loot and clout*. Thus, interventions stemming from this hypothesis follow a social action model, which attempts to change the system and the rules of the game, rather than trying to modify individuals to adapt to the system.

The social action model emphasizes the need for community citizens to organize themselves and participate in the planning, policy-shaping and decision-making of social and community affairs that affect their lives (Altshuler 1970; Head 1971; Weissman 1970). Under the rubric of "maximum feasible participation" (Moynihan 1969), the U.S. federal government built the concept of social action into the large-scale social programs of the Kennedy-Johnson era to combat juvenile delinquency, poverty and other massive social problems in the ghettos of American cities. The ideal of these programs was to transform the alienation, frustration, apathy and despair of disenfranchised minority groups, especially blacks, into productive self-help efforts by giving them a voice in the political processes from which they had long been excluded.

Social action is viewed by community psychologists as a way of changing social and community systems (Klein 1968). Viewing a community as a system of interdependent people who contribute to the fulfillment of each others' needs (i.e., the ecological principle of interdependence), Bloom (1971) argues that a community in which diverse factions are organized to plan for the future will develop a sense of power and control over the events which shape their community. The development of this internal locus of control will, in turn, enhance citizens' feelings of self-esteem (i.e., the ecological principle of adaptation). Similarly, Kelly (1971, 130) believes that "community development becomes a preventive intervention when aroused and motivated community groups work together to effectively plan for future unknown events" (i.e., the principle of succession).

The role of the community psychologist in social action can be characterized as that of collaborator and participant-conceptualizer. In this role, the psychologist works directly with citizens to help them to better solve their problems. Working at the *grass roots* level, the psychologist is an advocate for and is accountable to the community (Rappaport & O'Connor 1972) in working toward the goal of social and community change that will result in a more equitable distribution of power and resources (i.e., the principle of cycling resources) (Bloom 1971).

Kellam and Schiff and their colleagues (Kellam, Branch, Agrawal & Grabill 1972; Schiff 1972) have presented a good example of the social action approach to community psychology and the schools. Kellam and Schiff are two psychiatrists who attempted to develop a community mental health center in Woodlawn, a predominantly black community in Chicago. They began by making the tactical error of selecting a physical site for the program without first obtaining the support and sanction of the community. This action prompted The Woodlawn Organization (TWO), an organization of community citizens which had developed with the consultation of the well-known community organizer Saul Alinsky, to intervene. As a result of this intervention, the mental health program established a community advisory board composed of existing leaders in the community who were empowered to represent different citizen groups on the board. Thus, the operation of the mental health program was controlled by the community and not by professionals from the university. As Schiff (1972, 240) states: "the basic facts are that the board really runs this program because nothing is really done apart from the board and the board's consent."

The community advisory board decided they wanted the mental health program to have a preventive focus on the adaptation of first grade children in the public schools. Over the next several years, the community and the mental health professionals engaged in a joint partnership in research and program development to improve the mental health of children in the early elementary grades. Schiff has provided a description of the natural history of the program, the obstacles they encountered and the way in which they coped with such problems and the results of their evaluations of the program. Some of the positive results of this collaborative intervention were: a positive impact of the early intervention program on the psychosocial and educational adaptation of children who participated in the program relative to control children, improved teacher attitudes toward children, increased parental involvement in their children's schooling and expansion of the program.

Kurtz and Schrumpf (1978) describe the organization of an alternative education program. Recognizing that many alternative school programs become *dumping grounds* for low-status students, the authors outlined several steps in program planning and implementation to insure the stability and meaning of alternative programming. The first step is a recognition of the beliefs and values suggesting the necessity of an alternative program. In their program, a group of alienated, rebellious, bored students whose needs were not being met by the regular school system were identified. Kurtz and Schrumpf emphasized the need for an appropriate student-school environment match to facilitate the adaptation of this group of students. Thus, an alternative program that emphasized varied learning styles, respect for individual differences and an appreciation for the worth of each student was conceived as necessary to meet the needs of these students. At this stage, the parents and students were consolidated to solicit support from all levels of the school division.

The second step involved establishment of a district policy which recognizes the need for alternative programs. Thus, organizational sanction and support in the form of board policy, adopted in writing, was obtained to serve as guidelines for developing the program. The third step was the building of an alternative program. An important aspect of their program was that the students and their parents were active collaborators in the development of program goals, rules and procedures. In their program, staff and students had equal say in decision-making, with all decisions requiring an 80 percent majority vote and with no one having veto power. In designing the program, staff and students emphasized that the program needed to differ in both style and content from the regular school. The authors stressed the importance of maintaining the integrity of the program by insuring that it differed from the regular school. If these differences were diminished because the program would be seen by some as too unconventional then it would run the risk of being co-opted and end up resembling the program it was intended to replace.

Once the program had been developed, the final step was to maintain it. The authors discussed the importance of working closely with the regular school, with the alternative school teachers moving towards tenure, to insure institutionalization of the alternative program. Also, the need for accountability through program evaluation documenting the positive impact of the program on students was stressed.

An example of a social action program aimed at school change in a Canadian community is provided by O'Neill and Loomes (1982). The authors describe how they helped to organize a parent group to obtain more educational resources for children with learning problems. Through organization and social action, this group was able to change the school system to better meet the needs of learning disabled children. In summary, the programs described by Kellam et al. (1972) and Schiff (1972), Kurtz and Schrumpf (1978), and O'Neill and Loomes (1982) are excellent examples of community control in the creation of new resources to meet the educational and social needs of children.

While social action programs at the community level are important, they also have built-in limitations. Many problems arise outside of the community context. Social and economic inequality is imbedded within the fabric of American and Canadian society and it is difficult to attack at the community level. Furthermore, in the realm of human services, such as the schools, there is a trend toward increasing centralization and bureaucratization in policy-making, such that local communities and school boards have diminished authority in governing their own affairs. As Weissman (1970, 145) notes: the "neighborhood council can't by itself create more jobs, stop wars, raise wages or build new housing." In analyzing the problems of the War on Poverty programs in the U.S., Rein (1970, 160) argues that many of the causes of local problems are external to the community.

> The fundamental problem is evidently not the manner in which institutions function, but their inability to function at all. The employment services do not have jobs to offer, the schools cannot pay enough good teachers, the housing authorities cannot build decent cheap homes in attractive neighborhoods. The services themselves are as impoverished as those who use them. The Community Action Programs can only encourage agencies to make more imagina-

tive use of what they have. However worthwhile, the improvement is bound to be marginal. Anything more must depend on a large-scale redistribution of resources.

In this vein, some analysts have argued that the entire human services enterprise is pathogenic. The growth of the welfare state in Canada and the U.S. has certainly benefited a large segment of the middle class who earn their living as well-paid human service professionals (Levine & Levine 1970; Platt 1977), but it may serve to oppress the poor whose needs are supposedly served by these programs. Piven and Cloward (1971) have analyzed the functions of public welfare in the U.S. during this century. Their basic argument is that human service programs have periodically expanded or contracted to serve the purpose of defusing social unrest and suppressing potential turmoil and rebellion by the poor and enforcing a work ethic. In their historical analysis, they found that during periods of economic affluence, welfare and human service programs were contracted, while such programs were expanded during periods of economic hard times (e.g., the Roosevelt New Deal programs during the great depression) and social unrest (e.g., the Kennedy-Johnson programs during the turbulent 1960s following massive black migration to the ghettos of the major cities of the North). Viewed in this way, human-service programs may be considered as a sort of novacaine to dull the pains of a life of poverty, rather than as a means of eliminating the causes of social problems: poverty and oppression.

Another piece of research in support of Piven and Cloward's (1971) analysis is a study by Brenner (1973) in which it was found that the rates of admission to New York state mental hospitals since the turn of the century are highly positively correlated with New York's unemployment rates. In other words, a healthy economy supports healthy individuals. Rather than funneling public money into highly fragmented human-service programs that are of dubious value in ameliorating the social problems associated with poverty, an alternative is to bypaes the middlemen and middlewomen (the helping professionals and their service programs) and to funnel that money directly into the pockets of poor people. It seems eminently sensible that people are poor because they lack money, not because they lack services. A number of suggestions for social and economic reforms at reducing income inequality in Canada have been made by Adams, Cameron, Hill and Penz (1971), including: centralized collective bargaining, manpower training programs, a guaranteed annual income program, tax and transfer reforms, etc. The role of the psychologist in this paradigm is one of systems critic and policy-analyst and researcher. For example, research on the impact of guaranteed annual income experiments on the psychosocial well-being of poor families may demonstrate the primary preventive potential of such interventions.

Summary—The action consequences of different explanations for the SES-school adaptation relationship have been discussed in the previous sections. Interventions based on victim blaming ideologies are pathogenic and contributing to iatrogenic illness at the social and community levels of analysis. In contrast, the social action model has potential for primary prevention with its emphasis on empowering citizens to change social and community structures.

In terms of ecological principles, the social action model stresses the interdependence of the school and community and the need for schools to be responsive to the needs of local communities. In terms of cycling of resources, the redistribution of power and resources is seen as necessary for all community residents to have control over their lives. To promote positive adaptation, the social action model emphasizes changing social systems to adapt to the needs of people, rather than encouraging people to adapt to an unjust system. Finally, through community organization, the social action model strives to empower community groups to meet future challenges without external assistance.

Conclusion

To date, the bulk of research and practice in the schools by psychologists and special educators has fallen under the medical model and the community mental health model, with a focus on programing for exceptional children. Given the arguments and research reviewed in this chapter, continuation of school intervention predominantly within this person-centered framework will only further serve to create iatrogenic illness. Alternatively, promising strategies for preventive intervention in the schools have been reviewed. These programs have been guided by ecological principles and have focused on several different levels of analysis. Given that primary prevention is a desirable direction to pursue, I will conclude by outlining some of the sources of opposition to primary prevention.

Reasons against pursuing primary prevention programs have been presented both by its proponents (Zax & Specter 1974) and its antagonists (Lamb & Zusman 1979). One of the most frequent criticisms of primary prevention is that there is not sufficient knowledge to establish prevention programs. For example, Kessler and Albee (1975) argue that compared to the field of primary prevention, the field of psychotherapy appears to be a robust science. However, one must bear in mind that psychiatrists, clinical psychologists and social workers have been researching the effects of psychotherapy for some time. When psychotherapy was in its infant stages of development thirty years ago, similar criticisms were made about the lack of any solid evidence for its effectiveness (Eysenck 1952). Given the research on psychotherapy that has occurred since that time, no one would raise such a criticism today. Because the field of primary prevention is young and requires a long-term time perspective, convincing longitudinal studies are needed before the promise of primary prevention can be realized. However, the research reviewed in this chapter certainly suggests that primary prevention programs in the schools are feasible. Moreover, contrary to Lamb and Zusman's (1979) assertion that there is no evidence that competency promoting interventions prevent emotional disorders, the research on problem-solving interventions for elementary school children reviewed in an earlier section of this chapter has demonstrated primary preventive effects, at least in the short-run.

Another reason for opposing a primary prevention orientation involves questions about the etiology of emotional problems. Lamb and Zusman (1979) argue that there is no sound evidence for a cause and effect relationship between social conditions and mental illness, but there is evidence that most major mental illness is genetically determined and thus, not preventable. Without repeating the nature-nurture controversy that was previously discussed in the context of IQ scores, suffice it to say that while there is evidence for genetic factors in the development of emotional problems, the evidence is far from clear that emotional problems are wholly determined by genetic factors. Regarding the cause-effect relationship between social conditions and emotional problems, there is some evidence for the social causation of mental health problems (Nelson, Potasznik and Bennet 1983). Furthermore, there is strong correlational evidence that the two are related, and to experimentally manipulate social conditions to examine changes in rates of emotional problems is tantamount to conducting a primary prevention program. While such a large scale primary prevention program has not as yet been attempted, the evidence from Rutter et al.'s (1979) longitudinal, quasi-experimental study certainly suggests that some secondary schools prevent problems while others create them.

Another concern about the primary prevention orientation is that its concepts and definitions are fuzzy (Lamb & Zusman 1977). One of the proponents of primary prevention (Cowen 1977) has acknowledged this weakness and has argued that the field needs to advance in baby steps (i.e., specific, concrete programs with clear goals and measurable outcomes) rather than ponderous giant steps.

Shifting from an exclusively clinical-service orientation to a primary-prevention orientation is viewed with skepticism, because critics argue that such a shift would result in poorer treatment for the impoverished and those with serious problems in adaptation. Furthermore, it is argued that such an orientation would be very costly because of the enormity of the need. These are important reasons for opposing primary-prevention programs. To be sure, some balance needs to be struck between primary-prevention programs and direct-service programs (Nelson, Bennett, Dudeck & Mason 1982). However, most human services, including schools, invest *all* their resources in direct service and none in primary prevention. Indeed, one of the reasons for a shift to a primary-prevention orientation is that direct service based on the medical model has proved so inadequate, and yet it is very costly! It is a fact in the public health field that no dread disease of mankind has ever been eradicated through treatment or tertiary prevention efforts.

If existing financial resources were redistributed so that much of the direct service delivery in schools was conducted by trained and supervised nonprofessionals, following the community mental health model, this would release enough resources to permit experimenting with primary prevention programs. The initial costs of such programs may be high, but if they are effective and worthwhile, then they will ultimately reduce service costs. Because primary prevention is future-oriented and nonpalpable, it is difficult to convince people of the need for it. Society and human services tend to focus on crisis management, so that it is usually "the squeaky wheel that gets the oil." This is certainly a difficult trend to reverse. However, if the public can be shown that their tax dollars are being taken by the government and funneled into ineffective programs, they will demand greater accountability and demonstration of program effectiveness through evaluation research to justify expenditures. From this viewpoint, experimentation on primary preventive alternative programs is certainly worth trying.

Another source of opposition to primary prevention lies in the threat it poses to professionals. The role of the professional vis-à-vis the politics of social change is often debated when the shift to a primary-prevention orientation is discussed. For example, Lamb and Zusman (1979) argue that neither are mental health professionals sufficiently trained for, nor is it their place to enter the political arena to work for social change to overcome poverty, unemployment or discrimination. What the authors fail to discuss is the evidence of the political activity of professionals when it comes to protection of their vested self-interests. For example, Chu and Trotter (1974) described how the American Medical Association (AMA) lobbied in the U.S. Congress against aspects of the community mental health centers' legislation that threatened the interests of psychiatrists. Similarly, psychiatrists lobby against including psychologists in government health care reimbursement programs, while Ph.D. level psychologists similarly seek to exclude M.A. level psychologists. However, these mental health professionals do stand united on one issue: their opposition to nonprofessional service providers.

Simply stated, even if they wanted to, professionals and academics cannot assume a stance that is apolitical or value-neutral. Because we all live in the context of small groups, organizations, communities and society at large, we cannot help but become involved in the politics of decisions that affect our lives. Given the models presented in this chapter, the question that professionals in the educational system must ask of themselves concerns their values and ideology. Once these values are acknowledged, then the corresponding model and methods of intervention can be followed. Political skills are just as important in maintaining the status quo as they are in changing it.

Lamb and Zusman (1979) make a good point in arguing that mental health professionals are predominantly trained in clinical methods and are, thus, poorly qualified to initiate the social, community and organizational change that is required for primary-prevention programs. They are correct in this observation and this is certainly another trend that needs to be reversed. Training for community psychology needs to be different from that for clinical psychology. Given its focus on multiple levels of analysis of human problems, community psychology needs to incorporate inter-disciplinary viewpoints and content into its training programs.

Finally, the last major source of opposition to primary prevention programs is that of organizational, social and community resistances. Zax and Specter (1974) argue that in a capitalist society there may be a social need for winners and losers, and that the collaborative community interventions needed for primary prevention may go against the grain of the North American ethic of competition, rugged individualism and privacy. Their observation is an important one with which community psychologists in the schools and other settings must grapple, for these resistances may be the pathogenic forces that create iatrogenic illness at multiple levels of analysis. There are no pat answers to dealing with these resistances to primary prevention, but it is clear that community psychologists need to develop political sensitivities and skills as well as conceptual and methodological skills. We need to develop primary-prevention programs that can be shown to be effective through evaluation research, but also need to understand the processes by which effective programs are created and implemented in natural settings. Sound prevention programs are the antidotes to clinical, organizational and social iatrogenesis. Our work is cut out for us, so may the force be with us.

BIBLIOGRAPHY

Adams, I., N. Cameron, B. Hill & P. Penz. *The Real Poverty Report.* Edmonton: Hurtig Ltd., 1971.

Albee, G. W. *Mental Health Manpower Trends.* New York: Basic Books, 1959.

———. A competency model to replace the defect model. In *Primary Prevention of Psychopathology.* Vol. 4, *Promoting Competence and Coping During Adulthood,* edited by L. Bond and J. Rosen. Hanover, N.H.: The University Press of New England, 1980.

Alinsky, S. D. *Reveille for Radicals.* New York: Random House, 1946.

Allen, G. J., J. M. Chinsky, S. W. Larcen, J. E. Lochman & H. V. Selinger. *Community Psychology and the Schools: A Behaviorally Oriented Multi-level Preventive Approach.* New York: John Wiley & Sons, 1976.

Altrocchi, J. Mental health consultation. In *Handbook of Community Mental Health,* edited by S. E. Golann and C. Eisdorfer. New York: Appleton-Century-Crofts, 1972.

Altshuler, A. *Community Control: The Black Demand for Participation in Large American Cities.* Pegasus, N.Y.: Western Publishing, 1970.

Apple, M. W. Analyzing determinations: Understanding and evaluating the production of social outcomes in schools. *Curriculum Inquiry* 10 (1980):55-76.

Arthur, A. Z. Applied training programmes of psychology in Canada: A survey. *Canadian Psychologist* 12 (1971):46-65.

Asher, S. R., S. Oden & J. Gottman. Children's friendships in school settings. In *Current Topics in Early Childhood Education.* Vol. 1, edited by L. Katz. Hillsdale, N.J.: Lawrence Erlbaum Associates, 1977.

Balch, P. & R. Solomon. The training of paraprofessionals as behavior modifiers: A review. *American Journal of Community Psychology* 4 (1976):167-179.

Bardon, J. I. The state of the art (and science) of school psychology. *American Psychologist* 31 (1976):785-791.

———. Educational development as school psychology. *Professional Psychology* 10 (1979):224-233.

Barker, R. G. *Ecological Psychology.* Stanford: Stanford University Press, 1968.

Barker, R. G. & P. V. Gump. *Big School, Small School.* Stanford: Stanford University Press, 1964.

Bernal, M. E., M. D. Kinnert & L. A. Schultz. Outcome evaluation of behavioral parent training and client-centered parent counseling for children with conduct problems. *Journal of Applied Behavior Analysis* 13 (1980):677-691.

Berger, N. S. Beyond testing: A decision-making system for providing school psychological consultation. *Professional Psychology* 10 (1979):273-277.

Blanton, R. L. Historical perspectives on classification of mental retardation. In *Issues in the Classification of Children.* Vol. 1, edited by N. Hobbs. San Francisco: Jossey-Bass, 1975.

Bloom, B. L. Strategies for the prevention of mental disorders. In *Issues in Community Psychology and Preventive Mental Health,* edited by G. Rosenblum. New York: Behavioral Publications, 1971.

———. Prevention of mental disorders: Recent advances in theory and practice. *Community Mental Health Journal* 15 (1979):179-191.

Brenner, M. H. *Mental Illness and the Economy.* Cambridge: Harvard University Press, 1973.

Brooks, R. Psychoeducational assessment: A broader perspective. *Professional Psychology* 10 (1979):708-722.

Bry, B. H. & F. E. George. The preventive effects of early intervention on the attendance and grades of urban adolescents. *Professional Psychology* 11 (1980):252-260.

Caplan, G. *Principles of Preventive Psychiatry.* New York: Basic Books, 1964.

———. *The Theory and Practice of Mental Health Consultation.* New York: Basic Books, 1970.

Cherniss, C. Preentry issues in consultation. *American Journal of Community Psychology* 4 (1976):13-24.

Chu, F. D. & S. Trotter. *The madness establishment: Ralph Nader's study group report on the National Institute of Mental Health.* New York: Grossman, 1974.

Clarizio, H. F. & G. F. McCoy. *Behavior Disorders in Children.* 2d ed. New York: Thomas Crowell Co., 1976.

Coleman, J. S. et al. *Equality of educational opportunity.* Washington, D.C.: U.S. Government Printing Office, 1966.

Combs, M. L. & D. A. Slaby. Social skills training with children. In *Advances in clinical child psychology.* Vol. 1, edited by B. B. Lahey & A. E. Kazdin. New York: Plenum Press, 1977.

Cowen, E. L. Baby-steps toward primary prevention. *American Journal of Community Psychology* 5 (1977):1-22.

———. The wooing of primary prevention. *American Journal of Community Psychology* 8 (1980):258-284.

Cowen, E. L., E. R. Davison & E. L. Gesten. Program dissemination and the modification of delivery practices in school mental health. *Professional Psychology* 11 (1980):36-47.

Cowen, E. L., E. L. Gesten & A. B. Wilson. The Primary Mental Health Project (PMHP): Evaluation of current program effectiveness. *American Journal of Community Psychology* 7 (1979):293-303.

Cowen, E. L., A. R. Orgel, E. L. Gesten & A. B. Wilson. The evaluation of an intervention program for young school children with acting-out problems. *Journal of Abnormal Child Psychology* 7 (1979):381-396.

Cowen, E. L., M. A. Trost, R. P. Lorion, D. Dorr, L. D. Izzo & R. V. Isaacson. *New Ways in School Mental Health: Early Detection and Prevention of School Maladaptation.* New York: Human Sciences Press, 1975.

Dohrenwend, B. P. & B. S. Dohrenwend. *Social Status and Psychological Disorder: A Causal Inquiry.* New York: Wiley, 1969.

Dohrenwend, B. S. & B. P. Dohrenwend, eds. *Stressful Life Events: Their Nature and Effects.* New York: John Wiley & Sons, 1974.

Dokecki, P. R., B. A. Strain, J. J. Bernal, C. S. Brown & M. E. Robinson. Low-income and minority groups. In *Issues in the Classification of Children.* Vol. 1, edited by N. Hobbs. San Francisco: Jossey-Bass, 1975.

Dooley, D. Screening of paratherapists: Empirical status & research directions. *Professional Psychology* 11 (1980):242-251.

Durlak, J. A. Description and evaluation of a behaviorally oriented school-based preventive mental health program. *Journal of Consulting & Clinical Psychology* 45 (1977):27-33.

———. Comparative effectiveness of paraprofessional and professional helpers. *Psychological Bulletin* 86 (1979):80-92.

———. Comparative effectiveness of behavioral and relationship group treatment in the secondary prevention of school maladjustment. *American Journal of Community Psychology* 8 (1980):327-330.

Edelman, M. *Political Language: Words That Succeed and Policies That Fail.* New York: Academic Press, 1977.

Edwards, D. W. & J. G. Kelly. Coping & adaptation: A longitudinal study. *American Journal of Community Psychology* 8 (1980):203-215.

Eysenck, H. J. The effects of psychotherapy: An evaluation. *Journal of Consulting Psychology* 16 (1952):319-327.

Fullan, M., M. B. Miles & G. Taylor. Organization development in schools: The state of the art. *Review of Educational Research* 50 (1980):121-183.

Gallessich, J. Training the school psychologist for consultation. *Journal of School Psychology* 12 (1974):138-149.

Gersten, J. C., T. S. Langner, J. G. Eisenberg, O. Simcha-Fagan & E. D. McCarthy. Stability and change in types of behavioral disturbance of children and adolescents. *Journal of Abnormal Child Psychology* 4 (1976):111-127.

Gesten, E. L. A health resources inventory: The development of a measure of the personal and social competence of primary grade children. *Journal of Consulting & Clinical Psychology* 44 (1976):775-786.

Gesten, E. L. & R. Weissberg. Social problem-solving training and prevention: Some good news and some bad news. Paper presented at the annual meeting of the American Psychological Association, New York City, 1979.

Glidewell, J. C. & C. S. Swallow. *The Prevalence of Maladjustment in Elementary Schools: A report prepared for the Joint Commission on the Mental Health of Children.* Chicago: University of Chicago Press, 1969.

Goldstein, H., C. Arkell, S. C. Ashcroft, O. L. Hurley & M. S. Lilly. Schools. In *Issues in the Classification of Children.* Vol. 2, edited by N. Hobbs. San Francisco: Jossey-Bass, 1975.

Goodstein, L. D. *Consulting with Human Service Systems.* Reading, Mass.: Addison-Wesley, 1978.

Goodstein, L. D. & I. Sandler. Using psychology to promote human welfare: A conceptual analysis of the role of community psychology.

American Psychologist 33 (1978):882-892.

Gordon, E. W. & S. Shipman. Human diversity, pedagogy, and educational equity. *American Psychologist* 34 (1979):1030-1036.

Gottlieb, B. H. The primary group as supportive milieu: Applications to community psychology. *American Journal of Community Psychology* 7 (1979):469-480.

Greenwood, C. R., H. Hops, H. M. Walker, J. J. Guild, J. Stokes, K. R. Young, K. S. Keleman & M. Willardson. Standardized classroom management program: Social validation & replication studies in Utah and Oregon. *Journal of Applied Behavior Analysis* 12 (1979):235-253.

Gump, P. V. The school as a social situation. In *Annual Review of Psychology* 31 (1980), edited by M. R. Rosenzweig and L. W. Porter, 553-582.

Harpin, P. M. & I. N. Sandler. Interaction of sex, locus of control, and teacher control: Toward a student-classroom match. *American Journal of Community Psychology* 7 (1979):621-632.

Hayes, L. A. The use of group contingencies for behavioral control: A review. *Psychological Bulletin* 83 (1976):628-648.

Head, W. The ideology and practice of citizen participation. In *Citizen Participation: Canada,* edited by J. Draper. Toronto: New Press, 1971.

Hetherington, E. M. & B. Martin. Family interaction. In *Psychopathological Disorders of Childhood.* 2d ed., edited by H. D. Quay and J. S. Werry. New York: John Wiley & Sons, 1979.

Hobbs, N. *The Futures of Children: Categories, Labels, and Their Consequences.* San Francisco: Jossey-Bass, 1975.

Holahan, C. J. & J. L. Spearly. Coping & ecology: An integrative model for community psychology. *American Journal of Community Psychology* 8 (1980):671-685.

Hollingshead, A. B. & F. C. Redlich. *Social Class and Mental Illness.* New York: Wiley, 1958.

Holt, J. *How Children Fail.* New York: Dell, 1964.

Hyman, I. A. Psychology, education, and schooling: Social policy implications in the lives of children and youth. *American Psychologist* 34 (1979):1024-1029.

Illich, I. *Medical Nemesis: The Expropriation of Health.* New York: Bantam Books, 1976.

Jahoda, M. *Current Concepts of Positive Mental Health.* New York: Basic Books, 1958.

Jencks, C. *Inequality: A Reassessment of the Effect of Family and Schooling in America.* New York: Harper & Row, 1972.

Jensen, A. R. How much can we boost I.Q. and scholastic achievement? *Harvard Educational Review* 39 (1969):1-123.

Johnson, D. W., G. Maruyama, R. Johnson, D. Nelson & L. Skon. The effects of cooperative, competitive, and individualistic goal structures on achievement: A meta-analysis. *Psychological Bulletin* 89 (1981):47-62.

Joint Commission on Mental Health of Children. *Crises in Child Mental Health: Challenge for the 1970's.* New York: Harper & Row, 1970.

Jones, F. H., W. Fremouw & S. Carples. Pyramid training of elementary school teachers to use a classroom management "skill package." *Journal of Applied Behavior Analysis* 10 (1977):239-253.

Kamin, L. J. *The Science and Politics of I.Q.* New York: Lawrence Erlbaum Associates, 1974.

Karlsruher, A. E. The nonprofessional as a psychotherapeutic agent: A review of the empirical evidence pertaining to his effectiveness. *American Journal of Community Psychology* 2 (1974):61-77.

——. The influence of supervision and facilitative conditions on the psychotherapeutic effectiveness of nonprofessional and professional therapists. *American Journal of Community Psychology* 4 (1976):145-154.

Kaye, S., E. Trickett & D. Quinlan. Alternative methods for environmental assessment: An example. *American Journal of Community Psychology* 4 (1976):367-377.

Kellam, S. G., J. D. Branch, M. S. Agrawal & M. E. Ensminger. *Mental Health and Going to School: The Woodlawn Program of Assessment, Early Intervention, and Evaluation.* Chicago: University of Chicago Press, 1975.

Kellam, S. G., J. D. Branch, K. C. Agrawal & M. E. Grabill. Woodlawn Mental Health Center: An evolving strategy for planning in community mental health. In *Handbook of Community Mental Health,* edited by S. E. Golann & C. Eisdorfer. New York: Appleton-Century-Crofts, 1972.

Kelly, J. G. Towards an ecological conception of preventive intervention. In *Research Contributions from Psychology to Community Mental Health,* edited by J. W. Carter. New York: Behavioral Publications, 1969.

——. The quest for valid preventive interventions. In *Issues in Community Psychology and Preventive Mental Health,* edited by G. Rosenblum. New York: Behavioral Publications, 1971.

Kelly, J. G., ed. *The High School: Students & Social Context in Two Mid-Western Communities.* Hillside, N.J.: Lawrence Erlbaum, 1979.

Kessler, M. & G. W. Albee. Primary Prevention. In *Annual Review of Psychology* 26 (1975), edited by M. R. Rosenzweig & L. W. Porter, 557-591.

Kirschenbaum, D. S., J. B. DeVoge, M.

E. Marsh & J. J. Steffen. Multimodal evaluation of therapy versus consultation components in a large inner-city early intervention program. *American Journal of Community Psychology* 8 (1980):587-601.

Klein, D. C. *Community Dynamics and Mental Health.* New York: Wiley, 1968.

Kohl, H. *Thirty-Six Children.* New York: New American Library, 1967.

Kozol, J. *Death at an Early Age: The Destruction of the Hearts and Minds of Negro Children in the Boston Public Schools.* New York: Bantam Books, 1967.

Kurtz, D. & F. Schrumpf, Organizing alternative education. Prepared as a reference paper for educators who are interested in alternative education options in public schools, 1978.

La Greca, A. M. & D. A. Santogrossi. Social skills training with elementary school students: A behavioral group approach. *Journal of Consulting and Clinical Psychology* 48 (1980):220-227.

Lamb, H. R. & J. Zusman. Primary prevention in perspective. *American Journal of Psychiatry* 136 (1979):12-17.

Levine, M. The academic achievement test: Its historical context and social functions. *American Psychologist* 31 (1976):228-238.

Levine, M. & A. M. Graziano. Intervention programs in elementary schools. In *Handbook of Community Mental Health,* edited by S. E. Golann and C. Eisdorfer. New York: Appleton-Century-Crofts, 1972.

Levine, M. & A. Levine. *A Social History of Helping Services.* New York: Appleton-Century-Crofts, 1970.

Levitt, E. E. Research on psychotherapy with children. In *Handbook of Psychotherapy & Behavior Change:*

An Empirical Analysis, edited by A. E. Bergin and S. L. Garfield. New York: John Wiley & Sons, 1971.

Lewin, K., R. Lippitt & R. White. Patterns of aggressive behavior in experimentally created "social climates." *Journal of Social Psychology* 10 (1939):271-299.

Litow, L. & D. K. Pumroy. A brief review of classroom group-oriented contingencies. *Journal of Applied Behavior Analysis* 8 (1975):341-347.

Loeber, R. The stability of antisocial and delinquent child behavior: A review. *Child Development* 53 (1982):1431-1446.

McKaskie, M. Carelessness or fraud in Sir Cyril Burt's kinship data? A critique of Jensen's analysis. *American Psychologist* 33 (1978):496-498.

McLaren, P. *Cries from the Corridor: The New Suburban Ghettos.* Toronto: Methuen, 1980.

Mannarino, A. P. & J. A. Durlak. Implementation and evaluation of service programs in community settings. *Professional Psychology* 11 (1980):220-227.

Mannino, F. V. & M. F. Shore. The effects of consultation: A review of the empirical studies. *American Journal of Community Psychology* 3 (1975):1-22.

Martell, G., ed. *The Politics of the Canadian Public School.* Toronto: J. Lorimer & Co., 1974.

Martin, R. Expert and referent power: A framework for understanding and maximizing consultation effectiveness. *Journal of School Psychology* 16 (1978):49-55.

Medway, F. J. A social psychological approach to internally based change in the schools. *Journal of School Psychology* 13 (1975):19-27.

Moos, R. H. Conceptualizations of human environments. *American Psychologist* 28 (1973):652-665.

——. A typology of junior high and high school classrooms. *American Educational Research Journal* 15 (1978):53-66.

Moos, R. H. & B. Moos. Classroom social climate and student absences and grades. *Journal of Educational Psychology* 70 (1978):263-269.

Morgan, R. F. The iatrogenic psychology of practitioners' defeatism and other assertions of the null hypothesis. *Psychological Reports* 43 (1978):963-977.

Moynihan, D. P. *Maximum Feasible Misunderstanding: Community Action in the War on Poverty.* New York: Free Press, 1969.

Myrick, R. & B. S. Marx. An exploratory study of the relationship between high school building design and student learning. Washington, D.C.: U.S. Department of Health, Education and Welfare, 1968.

Nelson, G., E. M. Bennett, J. Dudeck & R. V. Mason. Resource exchange: A case study. *Canadian Journal of Community Mental Health* 1, no. 2 (1982):55-63.

Nelson, G., H. Potasznik & E. M. Bennett. Primary Prevention: Another perspective. *Canadian Journal of Community Mental Health* 2 (1983).

O'Leary, S. G. & K. D. O'Leary. Behavior modification in the school. In *Handbook of Behavior Modification and Behavior Therapy,* edited by H. Leitenberg. Englewood Cliffs, N.J.: Prentice-Hall, 1976.

O'Neill, P. Educating divergent thinkers: An ecological investigation. *American Journal of Community Psychology* 4 (1976):99-107.

O'Neill, P. & P. R. Loomes. Building a community group to improve local schools. In *Psychological Consultation in Educational Settings,* edited by J. L. Alpert. San Francisco: Jossey-Bass, 1982.

O'Neill, P. & E. J. Trickett. *Community Consultation.* San Francisco: Jossey-Bass, 1982.

Patterson, G. R. The aggressive child:

Victim and architect of a coercive system. In *Behavior Modification and Families*, edited by L. A. Hamerlynck, L. C. Handy & E. J. Mash. New York: Brunner/Mazel, 1976.

Patterson, G. R. & M. J. Fleischman. Maintenance of treatment effects: Some considerations concerning family systems & follow-up data. *Behavior Therapy* 10 (1979):168-185.

Phillips, L., J. G. Draguns & D. P. Bartlett. Classification of behavior disorders. In *Issues in the Classification of Children*. Vol. 1, edited by N. Hobbs. San Francisco: Jossey-Bass, 1975.

Piven, F. F. & R. A. Cloward. *Regulating the Poor: The Functions of Public Welfare*. New York: Vintage Books, 1971.

Platt, A. M. *The Child Savers: The Invention of Delinquency*. Chicago: University of Chicago Press, 1977.

Rappaport, J. *Community Psychology: Values, Research & Action*. New York: Holt, Rinehart & Winston, 1977.

Rappaport, J. & R. D. O'Connor. Advocacy and accountability in consultation to the poor. *Mental Hygiene* 56 (1972):39-47.

Rein, M. *Social Policy*. New York: Random House, 1970.

Reisinger, J. J., J. P. Ora & G. W. Frangia. Parents as change agents for their children: A review. *Journal of Community Psychology* 4 (1976):103-123.

Rhodes, W. C. & M. Sager. Community perspectives. In *Issues in the Classification of Children*. Vol. 1, edited by N. Hobbs. San Francisco: Jossey-Bass, 1975.

Rinn, R. C. & A. Markle. Modification of skill deficits in children. In *Research and Practice in Social Skills Training*, edited by A. S. Bellack & M. Hersen. New York: Plenum Press, 1979.

Robins, L. N. *Deviant Children Grow Up: A Sociological and Psychiatric Study of Sociopathic Personality*. Baltimore: Williams & Wilkins, 1966.

——. Follow-up studies. In *Psychopathological Disorders in Children*. 2d ed., edited by H. C. Quay and J. S. Werry. New York: John Wiley & Sons, 1979.

Rosenthal, R. & L. Jacobson. *Pygmalion in the Classroom: Teacher Expectation and Pupil's Intellectual Development*. New York: Holt, Rinehart & Winston, 1968.

Ross, A. O. *Psychological Disorders of Children: A Behavioral Approach to Theory, Research, and Therapy*. 2d ed. New York: McGraw-Hill, 1980.

Rutter, M., B. Maughan, P. Mortimore & J. Ouston. *Fifteen Thousand Hours: Secondary Schools and Their Effects on Children*. Cambridge, Mass.: Harvard University Press, 1979.

Ryan, W. *Blaming the Victim*. New York: Vintage Books, 1971.

Sarason, S. B. *The Culture of the School and the Problem of Change*. Boston: Allyn & Bacon, 1971.

——. *The Creation of Settings and the Future Societies*. San Francisco: Jossey-Bass, 1972.

Schiff, S. K. Free inquiry and the enduring commitment: The Woodlawn Mental Health Center 1963-1970. In *Handbook of Community Mental Health*, edited by S. E. Golann and C. Eisdorfer. New York: Appleton-Century-Crofts, 1972.

Schmuck, R. A. Helping teachers improve classroom group processes. *Journal of Applied Behavioral Science* 4 (1968):401-435.

——. Developing an organizational team within a school district. In *Psychological consultation in education settings*, edited by J. L. Alpert. San Francisco: Jossey-Bass, 1982.

Schmuck, R. A., P. J. Runkel et al. *The Second Handbook of Organization*

Development in Schools. Palo Alto, Calif.: Mayfield, 1977.

Schmuck, R. A., P. J. Runkel & D. Langmeyer. Improving organizational problem-solving in a school faculty. *Journal of Applied Behavioral Science* 5 (1969):455-482.

Schmuck, R. A. & P. A. Schmuck. *Group Processes in the Classroom.* Dubuque, Iowa: W. C. Brown Co., 1975.

Seaver, W. J. Effects of naturally induced teacher expectancies. *Journal of Personality and Social Psychology* 28 (1973):333-342.

Sennett, R. & J. Cobb. *The Hidden Injuries of Class.* New York: A. A. Knopf, Inc., 1973.

Slavin, R. E. & D. L. DeVries. Learning in teams. In *Educational Environments and Effects: Evaluation, Policy, and Productivity,* edited by H. J. Walberg. Berkeley: McCuthchan, 1979.

Snyder, E. E. The differential effects of innovation on the student social structure of a high school. *Sociology Quarterly* 8 (1967):103-110.

Spivack, G. & M. B. Shure. *Social Adjustment of Young Children: A Cognitive Approach to Solving Real-Life Problems.* San Francisco: Jossey-Bass, 1974.

Spivack, G., J. J. Platt & M. B. Shure. *The Problem Solving Approach to Adjustment: A Guide to Research and Intervention.* San Francisco: Jossey-Bass, 1976.

Szasz, T. *The Myth of Mental Illness.* New York: Delta, 1961.

Tavormina, J. B. Basic models of parent counseling: A review. *Psychological Bulletin* 81 (1974):827-835.

Tefft, B. M. & J. Kloba. Underachieving high school students as mental health aides with maladapting primary grade children. *American Journal of Community Psychology.* In press.

Trickett, E. J., J. G. Kelly & D. M. Todd. The social environment of the high school: Guidelines for individual change & organizational redevelopment. In *Handbook of Community Mental Health,* edited by S. E. Golann & C. Eisdorfer. New York: Appleton-Century-Crofts, 1972.

Trickett, E. J. & R. Moos. The social environments of junior high and high school classrooms. *Journal of Educational Psychology* 65 (1973):93-102.

——. Personal correlates of contrasting environments: Student satisfaction in high school classrooms. *American Journal of Community Psychology* 2 (1974):1-12.

Van Hasselt, V. B., M. Hersen, M. B. Whitehill & A. S. Bellack. Social skill assessment and training for children: An evaluative review. *Behavior Research and Therapy* 17 (1979):413-437.

Weissberg, R. P., E. L. Gesten, B. D. Rapkin, E. L. Cowen, I. Davidson, R. Flores de Apodaca & B. J. Mckim. Evaluation of a social-problem-solving training program for suburban inner-city third grade children. *Journal of Consulting & Clinical Psychology* 49 (1981):251-261.

Weissman, H. *Community Councils and Community Control: The Workings of Democratic Mythology.* Pittsburg: University of Pittsburg Press, 1970.

Winnett, R. A. & R. C. Winkler. Current behavior modification in the classroom: Be still, be quiet, be docile. *Journal of Applied Behavior Analysis* 5 (1972):499-504.

Zax, M. & G. A. Specter. *An Introduction to Community Psychology.* New York: John Wiley & Sons, 1974.

Robert F. Morgan

Afterthought

In this handbook, the full spectrum of professional/scientist/practitioner self-criticism has been sampled. A mix of conceptual, case history and research-oriented chapters presents a reasonable state-of-the-art for the 1980s, following in the footsteps of such key earlier, albeit more specialized, works as Ivan Illich's *Medical Nemesis: The Expropriation of Health* (1976), Robert Mendelsohn's *Confessions of a Medical Heretic* (1969) and *Male Practice: How Doctors Manipulate Women* (1981), the courageous *New England Journal of Medicine* with contributors of the quality of Knight Steel, Nathan Couch et al. and the many earlier works of Breggin, Cheek, Friedberg, Rogers, Rosenthal, Szasz, Tong and all the other contributors to this handbook.

Traditionally, the author has the last word. However, in this book, I would like to share it with some of my distinguished colleagues who have contributed much in our field but who, for one reason or another, were unable to participate in this project. I would like to mention their names and share excerpts from some of their letters of regret.

Weston La Barre, James B. Duke Professor of Anthropology Emeritus, is anthropology's most creative and unpredictable genius; a distinguished master of a dazzling variety of important but articulate works on understanding our species. He is one of the few people I have encountered who can be simultaneously outrageous and erudite. He has the potential (in his "last" book?) to not only unearth and counter iatrogenesis but to explain its roots logically within the human condition. While unable to contribute, he writes:

> Much enjoyed, profited from your feisty, independent-minded paper on iatrogenic pathology in *Psychological Reports* which I had otherwise not seen. I admire because I would like to aim at iconoclastic escape myself from contemporary folklores and the garbage lazy minds believe.
>
> Do you know my newest book? I should warn you, you might end up not even believing the Tooth Fairy: *The Ghost Dance: Origins of Religion* ... Come to think of it, this is my next-to-the-last book.
>
> It was good of you to send me your offprint. You were right in knowing that I would relish it!

Dr. Guy Lefrancois, Honorary Professor, Department of Educational Psychology, University of Alberta, is one of the most effective authors in the textbook area for behavioral science. True to his style, his letter was my all-time favorite:

> I thank you for your invitation to contribute to your proposed book on iatrogenic behavior. Regretably, I must plead overwork, overcommitment,

lack of time, ignorance, stupidity, insanity, iatrogenic interference, and most especially, a vicious editor. Being both lazy and a chickenshit, I must unhappily decline.

Dr. J. Fred Little, Director of Continuing Education at Wilfred Laurier University, is a philosophy professor and administrator, effective at both. Despite this, he has so far retained his capacity for critical thinking and, even, fresh ideas. Instead of replying in a letter, he sent the following message using a bureaucratic memorandum form which I think, independent of content, symbolically belongs in any handbook purporting to cover iatrogenesis.

> The concept of the iatrogenic is an intriguing one. My most grievous complaint is vs. those philosophers who, ostensibly in the interest of legitimizing their trade, trivialize the business of philosophy by reducing it to logico-linguistics and, in the process, put forth such null-hypotheses as "There is no truth independent of the per-con/ceiver," and "There are no moral facts." etc. But a dissertation on such topics would be much more conceptually than behaviourally oriented, and devoid of the kind of data that sprinkle your sample article. Finally, even if such an approach were acceptable, I don't foresee any opportunity to pull my thoughts together into publishable form within the next couple of months.

Dr. Thomas Pettigrew, Professor of Social Psychology, University of California at Santa Cruz, has probably done at least as much effective combat with iatrogenesis as any other living social psychologist. While unable to contribute, he deserves a salute and thanks for his support.

Dr. Hans Toch, State University of New York at Albany, is a brilliantly creative social psychologist and expert on legal and criminal behavior. His textbooks *Legal and Criminal Psychology* (1961) and the *Psychology of Social Movements* (1966) have become classics; *Violent Men* (1980) has just been revised and re-released; and recent books *Psychology of Crime and Criminal Justice* (1979) and *Therapeutic Communities in Corrections* (1980) are contributing within the criminal justice area. With a background including social perception research and the analysis of unusual communications (e.g., United Nations *crackpot* mail), this professor of criminal justice writes:

> Your book sounds great, but I'm way overcommitted as is, trying to extricate myself from promises unwarily made months ago. If it were physically possible I'd do it, but the result would be self-administered iatrogenics problems, or whatever.

So as not to totally miss the important impact Toch would add to our handbook, the following excerpt is presented from a paper delivered at the 15th InterAgency Workshop of the Sam Houston University Criminal Justice Center, Huntsville, Texas, in May 1980. I very much enjoy his stylistic blend of Mark Twain, Saul Alinsky, Burt Reynolds, Ricardo Montalban, Herve Villechaise and Kurt Lewin; hopefully it comes through in this excerpt chosen as yet another point of view from which to observe the situations described by Max in chapter 15.

Liberating Prison Guards

If Commissioner Estelle and Professor Beto are laying in wait expecting me to say something outrageous so they can lynch me, let me disabuse them of this fond hope—I shall confine myself to the most insipid, noncontroversial statements possible. For openers, I shall assert that prison management is too important to be left to prison managers. What I mean is that we shall have more effective prisons when we involve our rank and file staff in policy making, and only at that stage.

In goods-producing industries all over the world, we have experienced what polysyllabic academics call the "post-industrial revolution." This revolution highlights the alienation of younger, better educated, more sophisticated workers, who are disgusted with the authoritarian structure (the boredom, the contempt for initiative and ingenuity), that is embodied in the assembly line and in the classic management model in which work is designed and planned in offices, and is executed by presumably mindless slobs in the shop and on the tier. This disgust and alienation shows up in a variety of ways, including the sort of job action we experienced in New York prisons. Manifestations of alienation that may be familiar to you are astronomical turnover, abuse of sick time and disability benefits, a veritable delight in filing grievances, contempt for supervisors and union officials and a heck of a lot of grousing.

The most fashionable response to the alienation problem has been the Quality of Work Life movement, which has spread over the globe like wildfire. These programs provide workers with opportunities to participate in planning their jobs —in studying them, thinking about them, and suggesting new ways of organizing work. In American automobile factories—when we had American automobile factories—workers planned new plants and assembly line operations, designed technical innovations (such as ways of improving quality control and safety), organized themselves into teams, designed training modalities and generally concerned themselves with improvements in work conditions.

I find it ironic that the revolution I refer to has so far bypassed the correctional officer. By this I mean that the solution has bypassed the officer—the problem has hit him with a vengeance.

I don't wish to be misunderstood: some of my friends are correctional administrators, and I know they are doing good work. I know this because I meet them in scenic places, at lavish and sumptuous gatherings where correctional policy matters are thoughtfully discussed. It is possible that correctional officers quietly attend such conclaves and if I have yet to be introduced to one, it may be my own fault.

Why do I say that it is ironic that prisons have failed to involve correctional officers in policy planning? Among the many reasons are that unlike the executives of automobile factories, who have rarely dirtied their manicured hands, correctional executives often are rank and file correctional workers whose singular abilities have brought them recognition and promotion. One would expect such persons to resonate to the plight of their erstwhile peers.

Unlike assembly line workers, guards have a complex job in which much discretion is exercised. The guts of the guards' job does not lend itself to the sort of subdivision into time and motion units that can be planned and monitored.

I defy anyone except a correctional officer to tell me what a good correctional officer is supposed to do, and how quality work among officers is recognized and rewarded. I have the impression that we come down like tons of brick on the officer who makes mistakes (provided we catch him) but we ignore quality performance. This is diametrically opposed to the dictates of applied learning theory.

Officers have watched from the sidelines while we attempted experiments in inmate democracy and have expanded opportunities for inmates; it is not unreasonable for guards to suggest that system benefits can be secured only by felons.

Despite the myth of powerful custody forces, guards are low on the staff pecking order. Civilians rarely respect guard views or listen to their assessment of, and advice about, inmates. Guards escort inmates to their encounters with other staff, and sit waiting for them. Guards are inmate baby sitters, while others classify, teach and counsel inmates, and make decisions about them. I could go on with this roster, but I don't wish to outlast my welcome. Let me turn to other matters.

Let me make a second quietly noncontroversial statement, which is that officer alienation is unrecognized because it is obfuscated by everyone in the corrections business. To expand this theme would take all day, but I can illustrate some of what I mean.

I see an incestuous conspiracy to redefine serious officer morale problems as *stress.* Being stressed suggests that one is nutty without the stigma of being nutty, because it implies that someone else is responsible for one's nuttiness and is willing to pay for it, and one usually only pretends to be nuts anyway, to get fringe benefits. There is a prestige bonus for the guards, because we inherited the stress fad from policemen, such as Boston's finest. Managers like stress, because it sounds like the godgiven consequence of running an organization, and it is therefore less troubling than the idea that workers are acutely unhappy with their job conditions and your outdated management style. It is easy to deal with stress. Stressed workers can be bought off, and can be subjected to canned *stress reduction* programs by nonintrusive (though expensive) consultants. Lastly, stress is very fashionable; to have stressed workers brings correctional managers in line with the concerns of federal agencies.

What the facts really boil down to is that some guards like to spend time away from their jobs, because their jobs are not challenging, rewarding or satisfying. As an example, in one of our upstate New York facilities an officer was hit by an inmate. He was not hit hard, but the experience was understandably unpleasant. The officer took several days of workmen's compensation leave, but for once he was unlucky, because he won a publicized victory pushing an occupied bed down 600 feet of street. He won the race but lost his pay. Curiously enough, the officer had a medical certificate. It diagnosed him as a case of "contusion of the mandible."[1] The mandible is the jaw. A contusion is tissue injury without laceration. The diagnosis was a lingua-in-mandible diagnosis, but so are others.

I think undesirable inmate trends take excessive blame for trends in officer discontent. No doubt there are more inmates today than in whatever good old days one wishes to refer to, and inmate populations probably contain more volatile and un3avory mixes. No doubt a time existed—though not in my memory —when inmates were obsequious and ingratiating, and when they never talked back. Gangs may be as new as some of my colleagues maintain. There may be more craziness among inmates, more violence, self-righteousness, militance, dumbness, rebelliousness and ornariness.

However much change we wish to talk about though, the point that offends me is the claim that observed decrements in guard morale are a corollary of such change. The claim exonerates supervisors, of course, and it places working conditions beyond the control of managers. Social scientists are happy with the scheme, because they always see guards through the eyes of inmates. And everyone really wins, because if we have more and worse inmates, we need more and better guards.

The last resort of the ignoble is the argument that officers are alienated because the guards we have are the wrong guards, insufficiently educated and cosmopolitan, too backwoodsey, too white and prejudiced, too untrained. It is probably a truism that any organization can hypothetically improve its manpower pool, but it is equally a truism that any person can do a better job under more favorable conditions. No organization can succeed with a staff it holds in contempt. A staff one gives up on is a staff that gives up. This means that fewer people stay, those who stay show up as infrequently as they can, do a sloppy job and grouse. In other words, the prophecy becomes self-fulfilling. I quarrel with some widespread assumptions, such as the importance that is attached to formal education. We should clearly value expertise in an officer, but I see no evidence that an officer can acquire expertise by reading my books or listening to me. I suspect the officer's capacity to solve problems, to make wise decisions, to interact sensitively with others, to influence and lead are capabilities that can all be developed and refined.

But I suspect this can best be done more directly, such as in work-related training modules designed (with expert consultation) by officers themselves. I doubt whether officers would end up with Sociology 101 or Human Relations II, but it is possible.

It occurs to me that my having mentioned the New York officer strike carries the implication that any managers who do not follow my advice must alert the National Guard. I don't think this necessarily follows. My point is that the time for work enrichment is ripe, not that officers are pounding on our doors demanding job expansion. What the officers are doing is complaining about the definition of their jobs. *Corrections Magazine* reports, for example, that "many (officers) resent what they believe is their too limited role as jailers of American convicts as well as the lack of encouragement from administration to work more actively with inmates." There is also resentment over what they see as the gap between themselves and the treatment *staff.* An eloquent officer is quoted as asking, "How in the world can you feel worthwhile if you're just opening and closing doors?"[2] The prescription implications are clear. *Corrections Magazine* writes that "some officers believe that they and their colleagues often have been an unused resource within the prisons. They insist that they should have had a part in staffing the raft of new programs that have been brought into institutions in recent years."

The custody-treatment distinction that bothers academics who have never seen a prison is not troublesome for guards. One officer asked *Corrections Magazine,* "Why can't the guard be in the helping profession and still make sure that nobody runs away?"[3] Where roles have been expanded, officers seem appreciative. The guards interviewed at the Vienna Correctional Center to a man report they wouldn't trade their new jobs for their old ones.[4] Officers in a Maryland program who work as rehabilitators have done what few civilians can do: they have reduced inmate recidivism rates.[5]

My point is not a reproach. I am not suggesting that we have been blind to the issue of officer role expansion. The old con of yesteryear was well matched with the old keeper. Chain gangs needed no officer-counselors; classical management was congruent with stone age service modalities. Officer role expansion would even have proved premature in the treatment honeymoon days, in which traditional mental health disciplines tried their hands at inmate rehabilitation, and failed. Enlightened mental healthnicks and modern managers are compatible with sophisticated guards. And, as Fogel notes, so is a due process climate, which means due process for inmates and staff, as opposed to just for inmates.[6]

If pluralistic ignorance exists among guards, as it does among inmates[7] and delinquents,[8] the officer subculture becomes imaginary. In other words, the brave can afford to be braver than they suspect, because concensus on such premises as "never talk to a con" or "never rat to a sergeant" is falsely assumed, and no guard group really cares whether Officer Jones lets a depressed inmate show him pictures of his unfaithful wife, or runs a counseling group in the protective segregation gallery.

The converse of the pluralistic ignorance coin is that the brave enjoy unsuspected support in the shape of fellow progressives they did not know existed. This means idealists cannot only come out of the closet, but can share change-relevant concerns with fellow-idealists, who are similarly liberated. This is the sort of arrangement we call a *support system,* as opposed to groups we disapprove of, which we call *subcultures.*

Support systems make the difference between Kamikaze missions and reform efforts, because they insure that when the risk-takers charge up the hill there is someone behind them, which is not only comforting but auspicious. It is the ingredient that ultimately differentiates between John Brown's raid and Bunker Hill, or their equivalents.

Liberating efforts to me does not mean liberating individual prison guards. I have no interest in raising hopes that merely initiate a respite from routine, but that ultimately spawn disillusionment. At my advanced age, time starts to count, and dramatic gestures—such as one-shot reforms—become uncomfortable luxuries. Once my colleagues and I throw our ball, I want the virtual assurance that there is a team out there to carry it. Enlightened administrators matter, and so does our enlightened union leadership. What matters most though, is the availability of a substantial number of enlightened officers. I am here to assure you that we have such officers, that I have talked with them, and that given half a chance, they are ready to be a potent and effective resource for meaningful correctional reform.

FOOTNOTES

[1] Alan Fram. Correctional officer a loser after being hailed a winner. *Albany Times Union,* May 6, 1980.

[2] Edgar May. Prison Guards in America: The Inside Story. *Corrections Magazine* 2, 3ff (December 1976): 47.

[3] Ibid., 48

[4] Ibid., 42

[5] Richard J. Ward and David Vandergoot. Correctional officers with case loads. *Offender Rehabilitation* 2 (1977):31-38.

[6] David Fogel. We are the living proof. *The Justice Model for Corrections.* Cincinnati, Ohio: W.H. Anderson, 1975.

[7] Stanton Wheeler. Roles conflict in correctional institutes. In *The Prison: Studies in Institutional Organization and Change,* edited by D.R. Cressey. New York: Holt, Rinehart and Winston, 1961.

[8] David Matza. *Delinquency and Drift.* New York: Wiley, 1964.

I was gratified to see that even those not joining us in this specific effort were still in support of our goals, not afraid of losing (pseudo) scientific objectivity by using scholarly tools in the service of useful social/professional change. Such support is still of great value, yet one can remember well when it was even in shorter supply. It was in some large part due to the efforts of Dr. Martin Luther King Jr. and his associate, Dr. Robert L. Green, that the public cooperation between academic scientists and activists became as acceptable as it is today. His 1967 speech to the American Psychological Association in Washington, DC was such a watershed, I believe, for psychology. In memory of this, I would like to continue with a satirical piece written by myself in 1966 for Drs. King and Green.

IF YOU WERE A SOCIAL SCIENTIST, WOULD YOU LET YOUR SISTER MARRY AN ACTIVIST?

Why did you let them meet in the first place?

Social science has traditionally confined itself to dispassionate *objective* dissection of its subject matter. When individual scholars joined a South American tribe, enrolled in a vegetarian cult, dyed their skin black and toured Georgia, it was all quite proper. The intended products preserved the chastity of science, being mainly categorical description and safely abstracted theory. It was understood that at no time was the serious social scientist to become emotionally involved in the culture under the microscope. *Value judgments* by the investigator were dutifully dissipated, displaced or denied. With this important understanding, volumes of valuable descriptive material drawn from our rich human environment were skillfully collected and filed through the years.

Of course, recent decades have brought acknowledgment that even incorruptible social scientists have emotions, ethics, personal values, even socially useful ideas. We had assumed until recently, however, that these mundane biases would always be set aside for the more profound concerns of professional activity. You can understand then how legitimate it was for us to smile upon the forthright approach of many scholars to the new wave civil rights and similar activist groups so often in the news these days. You are undoubtedly aware that we felt the intentions were honorable all around.

What was our horror when we realized the social scientists were BECOMING INVOLVED! Who ever thought that our ever increasing body of facts would be *used?*

What are the implications of such hanky-panky?

Frankly, (let us be blunt) we are afraid of pregnancy. The intercourse of ideas has in the past often led to profound social change. Now the maternity seems to lie with our supposedly detached investigators . . . isn't one of the most sacred charges of science to keep the investigator as much as possible from influencing the events he observes? And as this disturbing affair has progressed to intimate contacts, we must in good faith pose this fundamental question: What about the baby?

It's not that there is any objection, beyond the principle of the thing, to *individual* social scientists marrying into movements they identify with human freedom, progress and dignity. Despite the poor example set, this remains their own responsibility. It is the product disturbed and aroused society. Nor can we condemn society's attitude here. If nothing was done about it . . . who knows . . . our grandchildren might all be mongrels: half knowledge and half purpose.

It has been said by liberals and egg-heads that such mixed marriages both activate the scientist and educate the activist. It has been said by liberals and egg-heads that such mixed marriages make activists responsible and scientists respectable (or was it the other way around?). We are also told that the offspring resulting from these erotic affairs often grow up to be an improvement on either parent . . . some become projects or organizations capable of accomplishing socially important goals (literacy training for a million disadvantaged illiterates; job placement for thousands of previously unemployable adolescents; educational headstarts for children raised in sterile surroundings; hope and productive involvement in our society for millions of presently disillusioned and restless Americans).

But this misses the point. We must all remember our *place.* Activists must continue their rapid social movement without common direction; scientists must maintain their common direction without social movement. Remember, it was Ben Franklin who said to his companions, "Let's hang together lest we hang separately," which will give you a good idea of the shady kind of company liberals like Franklin hung around with.

Ramifications: some of my best friends are behaviorists.

Many feel the dangers of discipline mixing are overstressed. It is true that most activists themselves oppose intermarriage with social scientists (do blackbirds mate with robins? They do?). And among the social scientists, only a very few (admittedly distinguished) have sincerely advocated coupling their skills to activists' implementation of social change. The majority of these educated defectors from the status quo call themselves *behavioral scientists* or even *behaviorists*.

Please don't misunderstand my intentions here. Some of my best friends are behavioral scientists. Of course, the ones we feel the most comfortable with are those securely embedded in today's responsible patterns of society. If they rock the boat at all, it's one under sail in their own bathtub.

The problem is that behavioral scientists intend to move from their *observations* of behavior to its *prediction.* The insidious consequences are obvious to anyone who remembers Lamont Cranston or Bert Parks: prediction leads to control.

Do we dare allow the potential manipulators of human nature to be influenced by activists (or vice versa)? Wouldn't this be like sending our West Point cadets to Hanoi and Peking for their training? (Let them wait until *after* they graduate.)

Luckily, most behavioral scientists are not so inclined. Even the most dynamic and persuasive activist leaders often speak to campus groups with rare subsequent effect on the activity of liberal professors beyond several stale observations to a somnolent freshman class the next day.

And when the professors, in their turn, lecture to activist groups, the audience receives facts, hope, sincerity, cheer, even entertainment. Yet look closely and notice that no specific approaches to constructive action change hands.

Temporarily, then, the danger is minimal. But the coast is far from clear. Behavioral scientists and activists are being brought together *publicly* in at least one conference this year. Naturally, past history is most likely to repeat itself: while no one leaves any pragmatically wiser, than when he came, all leave radiating infectious cheer and satisfaction, a debt discharged.

On the other hand, any conference such as this risks the unscheduled eroticisms mentioned earlier: a mass orgy of ideas.

Such interplay of concepts will inevitably lead to the baby-making mentioned already. You can imagine what sort of husband and father an activist would be. If you can't, let's take a second and see.

First of all, despite the inferiority complex common to social scientists, activists do not have greater skill and endurance or longer prefaces than their scientific counterparts (when it comes to making speeches). But in those speeches, they never tire of telling the public to stop spinning prayer wheels and start taking their lives in their own hands. They tell us our collective thirst after first must discriminate between ginger ale and blood.

This kind of exhortation rarely reaches the social scientist "where he lives." When activists sing "We shall not be moved," they sing the theme song of the status quo scholar . . . the educated-insulated reflection of a constipated mind.

Then why do I get the strong feeling that we are beginning to move at last?

Hopefully, our handbook has begun a network of communication through which fresh ideas can be generated and improved. Certainly, the comments from readers, members of the helping professions or not, are very welcome.

We will also, of course, be reviewed by academic critics. Some will say too much has been said and others too little. No handbook in this area will be totally inclusive and, even with our wide sampling, there will undoubtedly be serious areas of omission. While it is healthy for we as critics to be criticized, one hopes the biases of the reviewers will be stated as explicitly as ours have been.

Behavior Today (December 11, 1978) announced the following:

> Dr. Joan Rogers and researchers at the University of Hawaii's Medical School reported that hamster eggs can be fertilized by human sperm in a laboratory dish, once the eggs have undergone special preparation.

Based on hypothetical iatrogenics, offspring from such a union might most readily be found among: politicians, professional helpers, academic administrators, rugs, or reviewers of scholarly books.

A pleasant exception to this *reviewer stereotype* were the tough but articulate students in one of my psychology classes who critiqued the first draft of this manuscript. While nearly all suggested changes, most (though of often shaky income) vowed to buy the book. Florida-born psychology major Denise Harrison said:

> ...the chapters flowed nicely into an ordered sequence. It is quite obvious that a lot of work and research went in to perfecting the book...By reading between the lines, I came to a conclusion that absolutely astonished me. The authors of the book genuinely care more about people than preserving the *good name* of their professions. I thought it was just great when the authors pointed out that therapists are not almighty and that in many cases they should question their approach to therapy.

Alberta-born, Waterloo County Board of Education teacher, Arline Crockford exemplified student reaction to the manuscript with her extensive list of grammatical/typographical, format and conceptual changes (most incorporated) followed by:

> According to the text, the manuscript is intended for "professional, classroom and enlightened consumer use." It would definitely be suitable for the classroom—indeed, how refreshing it would be to have a text containing scholarly works (e.g., those by Carl Rogers, Michael Miller, etc.) interspersed with easy-to-read works (such as Peter Breggin's), and the satirical, often humourous contributions by others (e.g., the Corn Soup Principle, as well as many of the editor's articles). Furthermore, the manuscript not only contains chapters by many well-known scholars, but it also includes works from a variety of disciplines (physical science, mental health, psychiatry) and chapters putting forth differing points of view....
>
> The manuscript can also be rated highly from a professional standpoint. The scholarly nature of the book as a whole, combined with the reputations of the contributors, leaves little doubt as to the book's value to the field. The more humourous articles keep the reader's interest up by providing him/her with a "change-of-pace." (If I ever see patients leaving a counselling service with balloons tied to their ears, I will know that at least one counsellor was so impressed with the book that he/she is taking everything in it literally!)
>
> As a teacher [for eighteen years], I was able to relate to many of the articles. For example, the Corn Soup Principle—just as you can have corn

soup with no corn, or psychotherapists with no therapy, so you can have teachers who do not teach. Also Helmer's work dealing with nurse burnout was quite applicable to teaching (and no doubt many other professions). Chapters twelve and twenty-nine were, of course, most directly applicable to the field of teaching.

Responding for a moment to Dr. Nelson's article (chapter 29), which I read not as a student but as a professional, I found that while I was reading it I was evaluating my own performance, and the overall situation in the school, in terms of what Dr. Nelson had written. That the article would prompt me to undertake such an evaluation, and that such an evaluation would prove to be beneficial in terms of Dr. Nelson's assertions, is tribute indeed to the article's content....

To conclude, I would like to refer to the passage stating that it is hoped this book "informs, educates, stimulates, amuses or exposes that which we need to improve our services." I have certainly been informed, educated, stimulated, amused and have had weaknesses in my profession exposed. I am looking forward to reading the published version.

Amid the bouquets and bandaids, came some genuine premeditated contributions. Three anecdotes were supplied by Ottawa-born Corporal John Whetstone, Royal Canadian Mounted Police, also a psychology major.

A man was attempting to fix the flat tire on his car on a deserted road running parallel to a fence of an asylum for the mentally insane. When he took off the wheel nuts, they accidentally rolled down a drain pipe. The man started cursing, wondering out loud what he could do. Eventually he sat down on the grass and began to cry. An inmate who had quietly observed the situation walked over to the fence and volunteered: "Why don't you take one lug nut of each of the other wheels and use them to hold the spare tire on." The man totally astounded, stated: "Why that's brilliant, what are you doing in there." The inmate replied: "Just because I'm crazy, doesn't mean I'm stupid."

● ● ●

In 1947, millions of soldiers were rushing home from war. Many travelled via the country's railways, thereby conquesting terminals as they attempted to obtain tickets, catch trains or meet friends and loved-ones. In one station, in the midst of this confusion, sat a bewildered and frightened woman named Elsa. She would periodically look up at a stranger and babble some incoherent sounds, and consequently was ignored. Eventually Elsa began to cry and thus drew the attention of an officer of the law. When he tried to intervene, Elsa continued to babble and cry. The officer, not being able to understand the girl, started to become irritated with her. Elsa sensing anger became frightened and started crying hysterically. The policeman deduced she was insane and decided to escort her to the local sanitarium.

Elsa was initially diagnosed as a psychotic and over a period of time given a variety of drugs to help control her, and return her to reality. The drugs calmed her but she continued to cry, talk incoherently, and became depressed. A new doctor recommended that ECT would cure the depression and subsequently Elsa was given shock treatments. She reacted by initially becoming increasingly upset and then withdrew totally into herself. She was rediagnosed as catatonic.

As the years passed she was subjected to various other psychotherapies without success. The doctors, in frustration classified her as an extreme form of dementia and consigned Elsa to a ward for incurable and chronic patients.

In 1970, a new attendant was assigned to Elsa's ward. One day he heard her babbling and slowly walked over to listen. He smiled and began to babble back to her. After a moment Elsa opened her eyes, looked up at the smiling face, and then jumped to her feet, grabbed the attendant and began to hug him.

A group of doctors standing nearby rushed over and separated the two. One demanded, "What is going on here? What do you mean by babbling at this patient and exciting her?" The attendant completely nonplussed replied, "Sir, we weren't babbling, we were speaking Polish."

A story, yes, alas a true story, for it happened in Kingston, Ontario.

●   ●   ●

To Max (whose story reminds me of this one):

Once upon a time there was a King who was loved by all his subjects but one, an evil witch. The King had one strange habit: he would only drink gooseberry wine. Every year all the people of the kingdom gathered to watch the King sample the best of the lands' gooseberry wines and enjoy a feast. On this day, as tradition dictated, the citizenry drank nothing but water.

The witch on the day of the gathering cast a spell over all the water wells, causing anyone drinking the water to become psychotic.

The morning after the feast, the people woke up to bid farewell to their King. When the King spoke the people began to wonder how he had changed. Soon they formed groups to discuss the King's affliction and to plot his overthrow. The King was mystified, the witch elated.

The King realizing some treachery had befallen upon his subjects, found the witch and wrung out the secret of the poisoning of the wells.

The following day just as the people marched to the King's castle to depose him, the King drank of the well water. The citizens realizing the King was normal again cheered and laughed. Of course, they all lived happily ever after (except the witch).

This is a fairy tale. In reality, people are far more absurd in what they expect.

The closing remark I have saved for West German-born, registered nurse and psychology/sociology major, Hildegard Heutzenroeder. Faithfully critiquing this manuscript, she warned of a new and specialized psychosurgery which potentially could be aimed directly at the contributors to this handbook: "the *Optoectomy* which severs the cord connecting the eyeballs to the rectum, thus eliminating a certain negative outlook on life." May we all enjoy life to its fullest, cords and balls intact. Cheers. **R.F.M.**

Adapted from the movie *Serpico*

Name Index

Subject Index